THE WAY

EDWARD R.D. GOLDSMITH
1928–2009

Environmental campaigner, philosopher, and systems theorist, Edward Goldsmith co-wrote *A Blueprint for Survival* in 1972, which inspired the formation of political parties around the world focusing on Green issues and the transition to a more sustainable society. *The Case Against the Global Economy*, which he co-edited with Jerry Mander in 1996, became an influential work contributing to the growing movement against globalisation. Goldsmith was a lifelong advocate of indigenous peoples and of the importance and relevance of their traditional ways of life, being a founding member of the charity Survival International. In 1969, he established *The Ecologist* as the premier journal for ecological and environmental thinking. He was a recipient of the Honorary Right Livelihood Award and of the *Chevalier de la Legion d'Honneur*.

www.edwardgoldsmith.org

'This is a way of seeing the world, a subjective and emotional way, not just an objective and rational one. It involves seeing the world with wonder, with awe, and with humility, as something to feel part of—to love and to cherish rather than to exploit.'

THE WAY
AN ECOLOGICAL WORLDVIEW

·SPECIAL EDITION·
EDWARD GOLDSMITH

VELTUNE PUBLISHING

This edition first published by
Veltune Publishing Ltd.
Maidenhead, United Kingdom
8th November 2014

The Way—An Ecological Worldview
Special Edition
by Edward Goldsmith

Paperback ISBN 978-0-9576315-0-2

Philosophy—Epistemology—Systems theory—
Cybernetics—Evolutionary theory—Human ecology—
Anthropology—Sociology—Economics

Typographic design and layout
Text in 11 on 12.5 pt Monotype Dante
Titling in Garamond Premier Pro Subhead

First proof, v3.1, November 2014

Earlier versions of this book were published in the United Kingdom
by Rider, an imprint of Century House (first edition, 1992),
and by Themis, an imprint of Green Books (second edition, 1996);
and in the United States by Shambala Publications (first edition, 1993),
and by the University of Georgia Press (second edition, 1998);
all under the title,

The Way—An Ecological World-view.

CONTENTS

INTRODUCTION

MODERN SOCIETY is rapidly destroying the natural world on which it depends for its survival. Everywhere on our planet the picture is the same. Forests are being cut down, wetlands drained, coral reefs grubbed up, agricultural lands eroded, salinised, desertified, or simply paved over. Pollution is now generalised—our groundwater, streams, rivers, estuaries, seas, and oceans; the air we breathe, the food we eat—all are affected. Just about every living creature on earth now contains in its body traces of agricultural and industrial chemicals—many of which are known or suspected carcinogens and mutagens.

As a result of our activities, it is probable that species are being made extinct at least one hundred to a thousand times faster than the natural rate, with only a fraction of these being known to science.[1] The earth's magnetic field is being changed, with no one knows what possible consequences. The ozone layer that protects humans and other living things from ultraviolet radiation has already been severely depleted; and our very climate is being so transformed and destabilised that within a few decades we will probably experience climatic conditions in which no human has ever lived before.

By destroying the natural world in this way, we are making our planet progressively less habitable, and if current trends persist, it may very soon cease to be capable of supporting complex forms of life. This may sound far-fetched—unfortunately, it is only too realistic. Over the course of thirty years, my colleagues and I documented the trends and the likely outcome *ad nauseam* in *The Ecologist*.

Why, we might ask, are we doing this? The answer is that our society is committed to *economic development* or 'progress'—an undertaking that by its very nature must systematically increase the impact of our economic activities on an environment ever less capable of sustaining it and ever more deeply degraded by it.

An idea of the gross mismatch between the impact of human activities and the environment's capacity to sustain them is provided by the fact that at the turn of the twenty-first century we had coöpted for our own use and for our various economic activities some forty per cent of the biosphere's terrestrial net primary production (NPP).[2] What is more, if economic activities continue to expand at this rate, within no more than a few decades we would be coöpting one hundred per cent of NPP —which, of course, is not remotely conceivable.

All this has been of little, if any, concern to our political leaders. They continue to go about their normal business as if the problem did not exist. Thus, although 170 scientists sitting on the Inter-Governmental Panel on Climate Change (IPCC), set up by the United Nations, warned them that carbon dioxide emissions must be reduced by sixty to eighty per cent immediately in order to stabilise climate, the British government began work on the largest road-building plan in the country's history and talked happily of doubling its road capacity by the end of the twentieth century.[3] The then incumbent American administration openly admitted that, whatever the climatic consequences, it planned to go on increasing carbon emissions into the foreseeable future, refusing to set either targets or deadlines for their reduction.[4] Since then, our politicians have shown at least some willingness to recognise the problem—however, their total failure to reach agreement on any serious policy only ensures that carbon emissions will continue to rise well into the future.

Corporate interests are, if anything, even less concerned. The oil industry has been very active in lobbying governments to prevent them from taking any measures that, in the interests of reducing carbon emissions, might lead to a reduction in oil consumption with a consequent dip in sales.

In general, the main constraint on governmental action to tackle the serious environmental problems that face us is the lobbying campaigns of these very powerful industrial groups intent on defending their petty short-term interests, come what may.

More surprising, however, has been the almost total indifference with which the scientific world has viewed these critical problems. Its acknowledged role is to provide governments and society at large with knowledge that serves the public interest and maximises the general welfare. But how can it achieve this task if it systematically ignores the fatal process that is rendering our planet ever less habitable and that, if unchecked, must inevitably lead to the extinction of our species along with countless others? Our scientists bring to mind those Australian Aborigines, who, when they first sighted Captain Cook's impressive ship sailing up the Australian coast north of Botany Bay, went about their normal activities as if this strange monster were simply not there.[5] Perhaps they hoped— consciously or unconsciously—that by ignoring it to the point of not recognising its very existence they might induce this aberration to go away and leave them alone.

The parallel is more than superficial. In both cases, a life-threatening challenge is systematically ignored because its occurrence is irreconcilable with the prevailing *worldview*, which would be totally discredited were the challenge shown to be real. The American anthropologist A.F.C. Wallace shows convincingly that tribal peoples will go to any lengths to preserve their cognitive structure or 'mazeway', as he refers to it (chapter 66). A scientist will go to equal lengths to do so—as Thomas Kuhn, Michael Polanyi, Gunther Stent, and other enlightened philosophers of science have shown (chapter 12).

The underlying worldview that scientists share with almost everybody else with influence in our society, I refer to in this book as the worldview of *modernism*, which is faithfully reflected in the reductionist paradigms of science and economics.

One of the two most fundamental tenets of the worldview of modernism and its derivative paradigms is that all benefits (and therefore our welfare and our wealth) are *artificially* manufactured (chapter 39)—the product of science, technology, and industry, and of the economic development that these make possible. Thus, health is seen as something that is dispensed in hospitals—or at least by the medical profession—with the aid of the latest technological devices and pharmaceutical preparations. Education is seen as a commodity that can be acquired in schools and universities. Law and order, rather than being natural features of human society, are seen instead as provided by a police force in conjunction with law courts and a prison system. Even society is seen as artificial, brought into being by the 'social contract'. Not surprisingly, a country's wealth is measured by its per capita Gross National Product (GNP), which provides a rough measure of its ability to provide its citizens with all such manufactured commodities—a principle faithfully reflected in modern economics. The inestimable benefits provided by the normal functioning of the biosphere—such as a favourable and stable climate, fertile soil, and fresh water, without which life on this planet would not be possible—are totally ignored and assigned no value of any kind. It follows that to be deprived of these 'non-benefits' cannot constitute a cost, and the natural systems that provide them can therefore be destroyed with economic impunity.

The second fundamental tenet of the worldview of modernism follows quite logically from the first—it is that to maximise all benefits (and hence our welfare and our wealth) we must maximise economic development or 'progress', which is, above all, the systematic replacement of the *biosphere* or real world (the source of natural benefits) by the *technosphere* or surrogate world (the source of artificial benefits). To question the efficacy of this fatal process, or to suggest that it might not be entirely beneficial, is to blaspheme against the holy writ of what is in effect the religion of the modern world. No true believer will accept that the terrible social and environmental destruction we are witnessing today is the inevitable product of this sacred process. Instead, it will be imputed

to deficiencies or difficulties in its implementation—government interference, corruption among local officials, or freak conditions that are
unlikely to recur.

In this way, the worldview of modernism and its specialised paradigms prevent us from understanding our relationship with the world
we live in and of adapting to it so as to maximise our welfare and our
real wealth. Instead, it serves primarily to rationalise economic development or 'progress'—the very activity that is leading to the destruction of
the natural world, with consequences that are only too evident to all
(chapter 65).

How, we might ask, is it possible for our 'objective' scientists to behave
in so unobjective a manner? The answer is that science is not objective—a
fact that has been well established by Michael Polanyi, Thomas Kuhn,
and other philosophers of science (chapter 15). One reason why scientists
accept the reductionist paradigm of science and hence the worldview of
modernism is that these particular 'ways of seeing' rationalise the policies
that have given rise to the modern world in which they, and indeed most
of us, have been brought up. It is very difficult for people to avoid regarding the world they live in—the only one they have ever known—as being
the normal condition of human life on this planet. Just as an abandoned
child who sleeps in the sewers of an urban slum and lives off petty crime
and prostitution regards their own lot as totally normal, so scientists regard it as normal that our rivers have been transformed into sewers; that
our drinking water is contaminated with human excrement, pesticide residues, nitrates, radionuclides, and heavy metals; that our agricultural land
is eroding faster than soil can possibly form by natural processes; that our
natural forests are being systematically replaced with ecologically vulnerable and soil-destroying monocultures of fast-growing exotics; that our
cities are increasingly ugly, chaotic, and polluted; and that our children
spend most of their spare time being entertained by violent and sadistic
imagery on the screen. All this, and much else that is totally aberrant and
destructive, most mainstream scientists will take to be normal.

This general human tendency to regard the only world we know as
normal is reflected in just about all the disciplines that are taught in
schools and universities. Thus, the modern discipline of economics is
based on the assumption that the destructive economic system that operates today is normal; the discipline of sociology on the assumption that
the modern atomised and crime-ridden society is normal; political science
on the assumption that the elected dictatorships that govern modern
nation states are normal; and agricultural science on the assumption that
large-scale, mechanised, chemical-based agriculture (that is rapidly trans-

forming much of our arable land into desert) is normal. It simply does not occur to many academics that what they take to be normal *is highly atypical of humanity's total experience on this planet—necessarily short-lived and wholly aberrant.* They are like biologists who have only seen cancerous tissue and understandably mistake it for a healthy organism.

Another reason why the scientific community still accepts the reductionist paradigm of science is that, though it paints the most misleading picture of reality, it is nevertheless very coherent and self-consistent. This must be so, for scientific theories are not adopted by mainstream science because they have been proved to be true by experimentation in controlled laboratory conditions, or even as a result of simulation on a mathematical model, but because, above all, they happen to fit in particularly well with the prevailing paradigm of science. Those theories that do not conform, what is more, are systematically contorted into a shape that enables them to do so.

During the twentieth century, the behaviourists made psychology conform to the reductionist paradigm of science. The neo-Darwinists and, even more so, the sociobiologists did the same for biology. Modern sociology has also become mechanistic and reductionistic, and the development of the new ecology in the 1940s and '50s has engendered a 'Newtonian' ecology, which rather than provide the theoretical foundations for the environmental movement of today (as most environmentalists firmly believe) serves instead to further rationalise and hence legitimise the very process of economic development or 'progress' that is the principal, if not the only, cause of the environmental degradation that they seek so ardently to bring to an end (chapters 1, 22, and 38).

In this way, all academic knowledge has been forced, Procrustean-like, into the reductionist paradigm of science; stretched or shrunk to fit an atomised and mechanistic vision of the world in which people are no more than machines and their needs purely material and technological —precisely those that the state and the industrial system are capable of satisfying. At the same time, any social and ecological problem that might arise is interpreted in such a way as to appear amenable to a technological solution—the only one that our modern industrial society can provide. It is all very neat and logical, but it is a pure figment of the scientists' imagination.

Another reason why our scientists are still wedded to the paradigm of reductionist science is that it is capable of perpetuating itself, however wide the gap may be between the world it depicts and the world as it really is. For if knowledge is only accepted to the extent that it fits the paradigm, any knowledge that does not fit, however true and important it might be, is by the same token ruthlessly rejected (chapter 12). This disposes of all theories based on the assumption that the world is orderly and purposive rather than random and blind (chapters 26 and 27); organised rather than atomised (chapter 40); cooperative rather than purely competitive (chapters 44 and 45); dynamic, creative, and intelligent rather than passive and robotic (chapters 28, 29, and 32); self-regulating rather than managed by some external agent (chapters 20 and 23); tending to maintain its stability or homeostasis rather than geared to perpetual change in an undefined direction (chapter 19)—in other words, all theories based on the assumption that the world is *alive* rather than dead and machine-like.

In terms of this false paradigm, we can never correctly interpret the problems that threaten our survival, nor can we, on the basis of the world-view of modernism, justify the policies needed to bring to an end the destruction of the planet and the disintegration of society in order to develop a sustainable and fulfilling way of life. In these conditions, a *holistic* and *ecological* worldview—in the light of which all this becomes possible— must be a most urgent requirement.

I have tried in this book to state clearly the basic principles underlying such a worldview. These principles are all closely interrelated, forming a broad and self-consistent model of our relationship with the world in which we live.

I had worked at the book, on and off, for several decades before it underwent a considerable change. It was always clear to me that the inspiration must come from the worldview of traditional or *vernacular* societies —in particular, from the earth-centred worldview of the earliest period when people everywhere really knew how to live in harmony with the natural world. Interestingly, I have often been criticised on this score. However, it has always seemed to me as presumptuous to postulate an ideal worldview, as it is to postulate an ideal society, for which there is no precedent in the human experience on this planet, and whose biological, social, and ecological viability has never been demonstrated. If Karl Marx made that mistake, so too do today's adepts of economic development or 'progress', who seek to create an artificial technological world without asking themselves whether we are capable of adapting to it (chapter 48) or whether the biosphere is capable of sustaining it for more than a few decades.

What struck me later on was that the main features of the worldview of early traditional societies were everywhere basically the same. They emphasised two fundamental principles that necessarily underlie an ecological or biospheric worldview.

The first is that the living world or biosphere is the basic source of all real benefits and hence of all true wealth (chapter 39) but will only afford us these benefits if we preserve its critical order (chapters 41 and 61).

From this fundamental first principle naturally follows the second, which is that the overriding goal of the behaviour pattern of an ecological society must be to preserve the critical order of the natural world (or *cosmos*) that encompasses it.

A cursory study of the worldview of traditional and, in particular, *chthonic* or 'earth-centred' peoples shows that many societies actually had a word for such a behaviour pattern—*ṛta* to the Hindus in Vedic times; *aša (asha)* to the ancient Persians; *ma'at* to the ancient Egyptians; *dharma*, also to the Hindus and later taken up by the Buddhists; and *dào (tao)* to the Chinese (chapter 61). These terms can often refer to the critical order of the cosmos, but they are generally used to denote that path or 'way' that must be taken in order to preserve its critical order. If many other societies do not have a specific term for it, the concept of the Way is nevertheless built into their worldview (chapters 62 and 63).

Explicit or implicit adherence to the Way is critical. It is only by following it that a society can subordinate the petty, short-term political and economic considerations (which at present alone preoccupy us) to fundamental social, ecological, and moral imperatives—the basic condition for survival on this beleaguered planet. Hence the title of this book.

NOTE ON THE TEXT

The task of trying to formulate the underlying principles of a coherent and self-consistent worldview has been more difficult than I originally thought, because it has meant describing each one in terms of all the others and hence in terms of the whole. Its structure is thus circular—there is no obvious place to begin, and the book can only really be understood by someone who has already read it. It is therefore recommended that the reader gains some familiarity with its contents and the basic thread of its ideas first and then reads it again to better focus on the deeper discussion that ties the various parts together.

To assist the diligent reader, a bracketed chapter reference has been placed after each principle that needs to be seen in a wider context, while a substantially enlarged and revised glossary of key terms and concepts is provided at the end of the book. Some of the terms that require clarification in this way have been *italicised* where they first appear in the text. The glossary also serves as a useful synopsis, distilling many of the key concepts that form the basis of discussion. Some further explanatory notes are provided at the beginning of each index.

The purpose of this 'special edition' has been to improve the reading of the text and to render it more accessible to a wider audience. Chapter headings have been rephrased and the order of the chapters reärranged to provide a more logical progression of ideas. In addition, the text has been rendered more accessible by simple changes to the language. Other than this, the content remains much as it was in the second edition, with the exception of chapter 37 (which has been substantially rewritten to aid clarity) and a few short passages here and there that illustrate, expand on, update, or qualify certain critical points. Finally, all the many quotations cited in the book have been newly copy-edited and referenced, with errata corrected as necessary. It should also be noted that the *emphasis* in quotations has, in most cases, been added.

ACKNOWLEDGEMENTS

Like all syntheses of this sort, the book cannot be regarded as the work of a single person. I owe much to many people. I started the work that led to its writing in the 1950s. For a long time I worked in isolation. One of the first people I discussed it with was Ion Gresser of the *Institut du Cancer* at Villejuif near Paris. Another was Joël de Rosnay, who, in the early 1960s, introduced me to the General System Theory of Ludwig von Bertalanffy, which has coloured all my thinking ever since. I am very grateful to Armand Petitjean, Alain Hervé, Jacques Grinevald, and Richard Willson, with whom I have had endless discussions on the various subjects dealt with in this book. I am also particularly indebted to that remarkable man James Lovelock, who was my neighbour in Cornwall for many years, and whose Gaia thesis I regard as vital to the development of an ecological worldview.

I am likewise indebted to Eugene Odum, one of the few academic ecologists whose work has not been distorted to fit the paradigm of mechanistic science. His writings have been an important part of my education. The history of ecological thought I learned primarily from Donald Worster, from his seminal book *Nature's Economy* (1977).

I would like to mention my friend Helena Norberg-Hodge, whose worldview just about coincides with my own. I am further indebted to Robert Mann, Grover Foley, and Andrew McFarlane for the many evenings we have spent together discussing these issues in Auckland, New Zealand; to Rajni Kothari, Ashis Nandy, Vandana Shiva, and their colleagues at the Centre for the Study of Developing Societies in Delhi; to Paul Blau and my other friends of Ecoropa, with whom I have had many enlightening discussions; and to that scientific arch-heretic Rupert Sheldrake.

I am also indebted to Satish Kumar, who introduced a new dimension into my life in 1974 by arranging for me to spend four months with the Gandhi Peace Foundation in New Delhi. It was as a result of my stay there that I realised the incalculable relevance of the thought of Mahatma Gandhi to the development of an ecological worldview. It was also then that I met most of my Indian friends, from whom I have learned so much. I must thank, too, Sunderlal Bahuguna and Mohamed Idris, who—along with Richard St Barbe Baker ('the Man of the Trees') —are among the most inspiring people I have met.

I am particularly indebted to Krishna Chaitanya, possibly the greatest polymath of all time, who is not only one of India's leading art critics but has written an eight-volume history of Malayālam literature and a ten-volume history of world literature and has still found time to write a remarkable five-volume synthesis of the physical and social sciences, of which I have made shameless use. Krishna Chaitanya is also the author of many erudite studies of India's cultural heritage. It is from him that I learned of the Vedic principle of *ṛta* (the Way)—the behaviour pattern adhered to by early Indian society to maintain the critical order of the cosmos.

I must also acknowledge the encouragement I have received from my very close colleagues Peter Bunyard and Nicholas Hildyard, with whom I worked for many years. Nicholas, by taking over the task of running *The Ecologist* with its associated activities, provided me with the leisure to write this book. I must thank Arne Næss, who, after reading a summary of this book in *The Ecologist*, urged me to complete it and get it published. I also thank my very close friend John Aspinall for having so enriched my life during all the years I was writing this work; my brother, Jimmy, for his great support; and my wife, Katherine, for her support—also for putting up over the years with the antisocial lifestyle that is the lot of a writer committed to a long-term project of this sort.

I must also thank Brian Goodwin, Donald Hughes, Jerry Ravetz, Wolfgang Sachs, Giuseppe Sermonti, Denys Trussell, and again Jacques Grinevald, Nicholas Hildyard, James Lovelock, Arne Næss, and Donald Worster, all of whom kindly consented to read the original manuscript of this book, pointing out errors and making other valuable comments.

Finally, I must thank Tessa Strickland, my original editor, for her enthusiasm—without her, *The Way* (1992) would never have been published in the first place—and again Denys Trussell, who helped me to finish it; Mike Kirkwood, my very patient copy editor; Annie Ouvry, who typed it over and over again; Hilary Datchens, Lynda Wright, and Simone Hawkins, who over the years managed to type a mountain of notes and various drafts.

PART I

THE NATURE OF ECOLOGY

1

ECOLOGY IS HOLISTIC

To say. . . that a man is made up of certain chemical elements is a satisfactory description only for those who intend to use him as fertiliser.
Herbert J. Muller

If the organism is a . . . system with an organisation above the chemical level, then it is clear that it requires investigation at *all levels*, and the investigation of one level (*e.g.* the chemical) cannot replace that of higher levels.
J.H. Woodger

All particulars become meaningless if we lose sight of the pattern which they jointly constitute.
Michael Polanyi

We have to start with a concept of the whole organism as the fundamental entity in biology and then understand how this generates parts that conform to its intrinsic order—resulting in a harmoniously integrated, though complex, organism.
Brian Goodwin

E COLOGY EMERGED as an academic discipline towards the end of the nineteenth century, largely in response to the realisation that biological organisms and populations were not arranged randomly but, on the contrary, were organised to form 'communities' or 'associations' whose structure and function could not be understood by examining their parts in isolation. The early academic ecologists had been so impressed by this that they compared the ecological community to a biological organism. In the first American book on animal ecology, published in 1913, C.C. Adams insisted that

> the interactions among members of an [ecological] association are to be compared to the similar relations existing between the different cells, organs, or activities of a single individual . . . The physiological needs and states of an association have as real existence in individual animals as have similar needs in the cell or cells which compose the animal body.[1]

This view of the ecological community became so well established that Daniel Simberloff refers to it as 'ecology's first paradigm'.[2] In 1953, F.S. Bodenheimer noted that the concept of the community as an organism is stressed in nearly every textbook of ecology and, '. . . backed by established authority, is generally regarded, if not as a fact, then at least as a scientific hypothesis not less firmly founded than the theory of transformation [i.e. evolution]'.[3] It was this concept above all that distinguished ecology from biology proper.

However, this *holism* of the early ecologists was irreconcilable with the underlying paradigm of reductionist science, in terms of which the world is seen as random, atomised, and mechanistic. Unfortunately, it is the latter view of the world that is alone capable of generating the science-based manufactured goods required to satisfy commercial ends (pesticides, antibiotics, and genetically engineered microörganisms, for instance). The holistic approach, on the other hand, does not yield the kind of information required for these purposes. As the biochemist N.W. Pirie notes,

> Those who are obsessed by the interactions of everything with everything else . . . are of necessity diffuse. Practical conclusions are not drawn from the holistic contemplation of totality.[4]

For that reason alone, ecology had to be transformed—but there are other reasons too. Ecology had to become respectable if it was to be taught in universities, and this meant making it conform to the paradigm of reductionist science. This process started in the 1940s.

The American scholar of science and religion Ian Barbour defines reductionism as 'the attributing of reality exclusively to the smallest constituents of the world, and the tendency to interpret higher levels of organisation in terms of lower levels.'[5] The justification for this is the dogma that only discrete particle-like entities are real—larger more 'diffuse' natural systems being no more than 'abstractions' that can only be studied in terms of their 'real' particle-like constituents.

Because it is physics that deals with the smallest constituents of the world (those at the lowest level of organisation), it is considered to be the only real science—'aristoscience' as the Australian philosopher John Passmore calls it.[6] The New Zealander Lord Rutherford—one of the fathers of nuclear physics—went so far as to say that 'science is either physics or stamp collecting.'[7]

The gratuitous assumption that all knowledge about the world we live in can be reduced to the language of physics is still largely unquestioned in scientific circles, and scientific progress consists largely in the achievement of this task. The Nobel Laureate Francis Crick, co-discoverer of the genetic code, states the reductionist credo very explicitly. 'Eventually,' he writes, 'one may hope to have the whole of biology "explained" in terms of the level below it, and so on right down to the atomic level . . .'[8] It is becoming quite clear, however, that the enterprise Crick proposes will never be realised, nor can it be without reference to the higher levels of organisation. Nevertheless, the basic philosophy of reductionism has survived relatively unscathed, and it has led to the most obscurantist trends in the disciplines dealing with life processes at the higher levels of organisation.

As Alexandre Koyré, perhaps the foremost Newtonian scholar, points out,

> the unholy alliance of Newton and Locke produced an atomic psychology, which explained (or explained away) mind as a mosaic of 'sensations' and 'ideas' linked together by laws of association (attraction)—we have had, too, atomic sociology, which reduced society to a cluster of human atoms, complete and self-contained each in itself and only mutually attracting and repelling each other.[9]

Koyré disowns these products of physics envy in the name of Newton himself, assuring us that he is 'by no means responsible for these and other monstra engendered by the overextension—or aping—of his method'.

The reductionist and mechanistic ecology that came into being in the 1940s is another such monster. One of its main architects was the Oxford ecologist Arthur Tansley. He denied the basic holistic principle that the whole is more than the sum of its parts and hence that it is not amenable to study by the reductionist method of science. 'These "wholes"', he wrote, 'are, in analysis, nothing but the synthesised actions of the components in associations.' A mature science, in his view, must isolate 'the basic units of nature' and must 'split up the story' into its individual parts.

> It must approach nature as a composite of strictly physical entities organised into a mechanical system. The scientist who knows all the properties of all the parts studied separately can accurately predict their combined result.[10]

The reductionist approach to ecology, however, is usually traced to the earlier writings of the botanist Henry Gleason, whose famous article 'The Individualistic Concept of the Plant Association'[11] was first published in 1926 and presented and discussed at the International Botanical Congress that year. Gleason's main argument was that only the individual is real. Larger associations—such as ecological communities or human communities—he saw as abstract entities that only exist in the mind of the beholder. An association has no real identity of its own—it merely represents 'the coincidence of certain plant individuals and is not an organic entity of itself'.[12] For only the components are easily measurable, and only they can be isolated and studied with precision in controlled laboratory conditions. It is these assumptions that still underlie 'analytical' or 'reductionist' science.

Initially, Gleason's thesis was very badly received. As he later recalled, 'to ecologists I was anathema. . . . For ten years, or thereabout, I was an ecological outlaw,'[13] for his thesis simply did not fit in with the ecological paradigm of the times. However, as the latter was transformed so as to make it conform with the reductionist paradigm of science and hence with the worldview of modernism, so Gleason's ideas became increasingly acceptable until they eventually became an integral part of accepted biological wisdom. Robert McIntosh refers to them as 'a viable and even expanding tenet of current ecological thought,'[14] while P.A. Colinvaux, in a well-known textbook of ecology, goes so far as to describe the holistic view of the community as a 'heresy'.[15] Other modern ecologists go further and actually claim that their own work has provided incontestable proof of the validity of Gleason's philosophy. J.T. Curtis, for instance, tells us that the entire evidence of [my own plant ecology] study in Wisconsin can be taken as conclusive proof of Gleason's individualistic hypothesis of community organisation . . .[16]

The American ecologist R.H. Whittaker regards his own 'gradient analysis' as providing similar evidence.[17]

How, we might ask, can they possibly make such claims? The answer is that science provides a means of collating data but not of *interpreting* them—hence, data are simply interpreted in terms of a scientist's own particular conceptual framework or paradigm. Thus, if Curtis and Whittaker believe that the biosphere is 'atomised' and 'random', they will probably interpret the results of their experiments in such a way as to rationalise their reductionist beliefs (chapter 12).

The truth is that small systems are not more 'real' but merely *simpler* than larger systems. It is for that reason alone that they can be studied by physicists in terms of the limited methodology of science.

Natural systems, however—especially those at the higher levels of organisation, such as societies, ecosystems, and the biosphere itself—are incomparably more complex than the relatively simple entities that physicists study. As Wolfgang Köhler notes,

> If organisms were more similar to the systems which physics investigates, a great many methods of the physicists could be introduced in our science without much change. But, in actual fact, the similarity is not very great. One of the greatest advantages which makes the physicist's work so much easier is the simplicity of his systems . . . An amœba is a more complicated system than all systems of the inanimate world.[18]

Living systems display all sorts of qualities that inanimate things do not display, or do so only in an embryonic or latent way—qualities that become very much more developed as we move up from simple forms of life to more complex ones, such as humans. The important point is that these qualities are not apparent from a study of the system's constituent parts but only once we see the system as a whole—hence, something may appear to be acting independently when seen from below, only to be found to be acting as part of a wider coordinated strategy when seen from above.

Thus, the coordination of the behaviour of the parts by the whole (chapter 43) is only apparent once we have identified the way in which the larger whole is organised. That living systems cooperate not just with each other but with the whole (*i.e.* that they seek to maintain it—

chapter 46) is also only evident if we look at them within the context of the larger whole.

Ludwig von Bertalanffy notes that the essential difference between events 'so ordered as to maintain the system and those running wild to destroy it' is fundamentally obscured by considering biology and indeed sociology in physical terms.[19] 'What does "health" or "norm" mean in contrast to "disease" and "pathology"?' he asks, 'Nothing, so far as the laws of physics and chemistry are concerned . . . But without these and similar notions, there would be no science of medicine and indeed of biology.' Nor, we may add, would it be possible to establish the essential distinction between evolutionary and anti-evolutionary processes (see chapter 65).

Nor can reductionist science help us understand the problems caused by the degradation and disintegration of a larger system, such as an eco-system or the biosphere itself, whose vital features it continues to deny, and whose very existence as a total living entity it continues to question (chapter 35). Passmore feels that it is precisely because of this insistence in trying to understand the world in terms of physics that scientists have been so unsuccessful in understanding the real problems that face us today.

> If we are still ignorant about most of the phenomena we encounter in our daily life—whether it be human nutrition or the life history of animals—this ignorance can in part be set down to the aristoscientific emphasis on a very different kind of knowledge.[20]

Eugene Odum, though he admits the successes of the reductionist approach, considers that

> cell-level science will contribute very little to the wellbeing or survival of human civilisation if we understand the higher levels of organisation so inadequately that we can find no solutions to population overgrowth, social disorder, pollution, and other forms of societal and environmental cancer.[21]

It is probably by seeking to understand the simple in terms of the complex, rather than the complex in terms of the simple, that we can best understand the true nature of our relationship with the world of living things. Alfred North Whitehead intimated this when he suggested that the concept of organism should be extended downward to include the particle (chapter 6). W.H. Thorpe was more explicit, 'We have to work back into the physical sciences', he wrote, 'equipped with the concept of organism derived from the biological sciences.'[22] Better still, he might have said, from the self-regulating ecosystem or from the biosphere itself. This would reveal structures and functions that, though clearly visible at the higher levels of organisation, are but embryonic at the lower levels. It would reveal, too, that these structures and functions, rather than being independent, are in effect the *differentiated* parts of larger natural systems and life processes, indeed, of the biosphere as a whole, to whose regulatory needs they are subjected and to whose stability they must necessarily contribute (chapters 43 and 46).

2

ECOLOGY STUDIES THE PURPOSE
INHERENT IN LIVING THINGS

The attitude of biologists to teleology [purpose] is like that of the pious towards a source of temptation which they are unsure of their ability to resist.
Sir Peter Medawar

Teleology is like the kind of woman people do not want to be seen with in the street yet are prepared to tender their love to in secret.
Ernst Wilhelm von Brücke

Still, all the while like warp and woof, mechanism and teleology are interwoven together, and we must not cleave to the one nor despise the other, for their union is rooted in the very nature of totality.
D'Arcy Thompson

Teleological explanations in academe are a sin against the holy spirit of scientific rationality—they deny the objectivity of nature.
James Lovelock

The Gaia hypothesis . . . is an alternative to that pessimistic view which sees nature as a primitive force to be subdued and conquered [and that] equally depressing picture of our planet as a demented spaceship forever travelling driverless and purposeless around an inner circle of the Sun.
James Lovelock

THE TELEOLOGICAL EXPLANATION of a life process centres on
its purpose, function, or goal—Aristotle's 'final cause'—rather than
on its antecedent or 'initial' cause, which alone is accepted by the scientific
community. Teleology, the neurophysiologist and Nobel laureate Ragnar
Granit tells us, is required to answer the question of *why* things happen,
which we must know if we are to understand *how* things happen.[1]

This must be true of any entity or process. Thus, Robert Fuller and
Peter Putnam tell us that

> a skilled electronics engineer is often unable to derive the function of a
> rather simple electronic circuit, despite a complete knowledge of the net-
> work and the properties of its elementary units. On the other hand, if
> one has a guiding idea as to the overall function of the circuit, then it is
> possible to examine the component parts and see just what role they play
> in this function . . .[2]

Granit also notes how this is true in determining how the eye adapts to
light and darkness.

> . . . when rods and cones were discovered in the vertebrate retina, had
> it not become evident that rods dominated in retinas of night animals
> and cones in those of daylight animals . . . , this discovery would have
> remained an observation of but limited consequence. Instead, under-
> standing of its meaning ('why') made it a cornerstone in a large body of
> biological research dealing with the adaptation of the eye to light and
> darkness, rod vision and cone vision, and the rod-free central fovea of the
> human retina.[3]

In the same way, it is by establishing what is the goal of any organism or
natural system that we are in a position to ask how it sets out to achieve
it. This is often referred to as the *cybernetic* method.

It is by using this method that James Lovelock developed his famous
Gaia thesis. To examine the earth cybernetically, he writes, is to ask the
question

> 'What is the function of each gas in the air or of each component of the
> sea?' Outside the context of Gaia, such a question would be taken as cir-
> cular and illogical, but from within, it is no more illogical than asking
> 'What is the function of the hæmoglobin or of the insulin in the blood?'
> We have postulated a cybernetic system—therefore, it is reasonable to
> question the function of the component parts.[4]

Lovelock starts off by pointing to the extraordinary constancy of the chemical composition of the biosphere—the oxygen and carbon dioxide content of the atmosphere, for instance, and the salt content of the sea. He then searches for processes that could assure this constancy. Ralph Gerard notes how the physiologist proceeds in precisely the same way.

> The physiologist's whole life is concerned with problems of organic purpose, though he rarely likes to say it, particularly in public. We see purposeful behaviour all through the body—it is the only way it makes sense to us. And then we look for the mechanisms to account for it.[5]

In terms of the reductionist paradigm of science, this teleological method of building up knowledge is totally illegitimate. To accuse a scientist of using a teleological argument is to accuse them of being unscientific, indeed, of being a veritable charlatan. Very few scientists would be willing to take that risk. Even Lovelock did not originally admit that his argument is teleological. The Daisy World model, which he developed with Andrew Watson, is primarily designed to show that cybernetic processes need not be teleological. However, it is but a rudimentary and indeed hypothetical cybernetic process, and it would prove very much more difficult to build a realistic model to demonstrate that the dynamic, sequential, and creative cybernetic strategies of complex forms of life in the real world are non-teleological (chapters 28, 22, and 29).

Mainstream scientists will go to the most extraordinary lengths to make it appear that the statements they make are non-teleological. One ruse is to deny the purposiveness of life processes altogether and to argue that nature only *appears* purposeful. Julian Huxley tells us that,

> at first sight, the biological sector seems full of purpose. Organisms are built *as if* purposefully designed, and work *as if* in purposeful pursuit of a conscious aim. But the truth lies in those two words 'as if'. As the genius of Charles Darwin showed, the purpose *is only an apparent one*.[6]

George Gaylord Simpson elaborates further,

> No conscious seizing of opportunities is here meant [by the use of the word purpose], nor even an unconscious sensing of an outcome. The word is only a convenient label for these tendencies in evolution—that what *can* happen usually does happen; changes occur as they may and not as would be hypothetically best; and the course of evolution follows opportunity rather than plan.[7]

The opposite is true. The 'seizing of opportunities' is itself a teleological concept. An adaptive individual does not seize any opportunity to bring about a random change—it seizes the one that suits its purposes; the one that it judges to be 'hypothetically best' for itself and for the larger system of which it is part.

More devious expedients are resorted to in order to make it appear that scientists can avoid arguing teleologically. Thus, Peter Calow notes how throughout the modern biological literature we find

> a great array of teleological jargon bearing witness, as it were, to the *homeorhetic* tendency of living systems. Biologists are always talking of one thing occurring 'for the purpose of something' or 'in order that something might happen' or 'serving the function of something' and so on.[8]

However, some philosophers still go to great lengths to show that these statements can be translated into a non-teleological form. This often leads them 'into a morass of circumlocutions'.[9] Thus, biologists, as Colin Pittendrigh notes, have been prepared to say 'a turtle came ashore *and* laid its eggs,' but not that 'it came ashore *to* lay its eggs.'[10]

Calow also shows how it is possible to translate teleological propositions into non-teleological language.[11] Thus, the teleological statement 'the function of the vertebrate heart is to pump blood,' can be translated into non-teleological language simply by saying that 'the heart is a necessary condition for the circulation of blood in vertebrates.'

Another device resorted to by mainstream scientists is to provide a purely mechanistic explanation of purpose. The inspiration came from the machine with *feedback*. These machines are programmed in such a way that they seek to achieve a goal. They avoid teleology in the sense that they are not seen as tending towards Aristotle's 'final cause'—hence, their behaviour is not seen as requiring some sort of supernatural explanation. The principle involved is also reconcilable with causality, reductionism, statistical method, and, of course, a mechanistic view of the world (*mechanomorphism*).

As Henri Atlan puts it, 'this new type of goal directedness is acceptable in that it is not derived from theological idealism but from neo-mechanism,' and hence from a scientifically acceptable rather than a scientifically unacceptable *metaphysics*.[12] It became known as *teleonomy*— a term first used by Colin Pittendrigh and later taken up by many other leading biologists.

The acceptance of 'teleonomy' enables us to ask the question 'why' rather than 'how', but only within a limited sphere—that of the functioning of a machine. It may indeed tell us what is the *immediate* goal of a natural process, but it tells us nothing of the *ultimate* goal to which its achievement contributes. It even implies that there is no such ultimate goal. More recently, the development of molecular biology, epitomised by the decoding of the genetic code by Francis Crick and his colleague James Watson, has further increased the credibility of the notion of teleonomy. Living things, molecular biologists maintain, give the *impression* of seeking to achieve a goal or final cause, but this is only because they have been genetically programmed to move in this direction. Instead of taking the form of a computer program, the *deus ex machina* is now a genetic program.

However, no life process can be understood simply in terms of the information with which it has been programmed, *for it is also coordinated by the larger system of which it is part*—the life processes that provide it with the environment with which it is constantly interacting and from which it derives much of the information required for its development (chapter 21). Thus, a developing embryo acquires information during the entire embryological process—first from the cytoplasm, then from the womb, and later, once it is born, from the family, community, and ecosystem of which it is part.

It is one of the main attractions of Darwinism for scientists that it appears to be non-teleological—but that is an illusion. Competition, for example, implies competition *for* something. Since competition, for Darwinists, is intimately linked with the notion of the 'survival of the fittest', it means competition for survival. But why should living things want to survive? We assume that they do—but this is a gratuitous assumption. Stones do not want to survive particularly—at least they make no visible effort to do so. Lamp bulbs, nylon stockings, and many other consumer products are designed specifically not to survive, since it is 'economic' to build into them 'planned obsolescence'.

Another key Darwinian concept, natural selection, is equally teleological—a point made by P.P. Grassé. There cannot be selection without purpose ('intention'), he notes, yet 'by making selection the driving force of evolution of the fittest, they [the neo-Darwinists] confer an inherent purpose to all living things, a purpose that becomes the supreme law of the individual, the population, [and] the species.'[13]

In reality, the concept of selection is of use to neo-Darwinists because it provides a means of delegating surreptitiously and, it is hoped, imperceptibly to a vague and undefined 'environment' the teleological functions that organisms alone are capable of fulfilling adaptively. In this way, the organism's behaviour can be made out to be blind and random. It is a desperately feeble subterfuge, especially as this very environment that has been endowed with selective purpose must itself be made up of other living organisms (chapter 43).

Ecology has to be teleological, for purposiveness is possibly the most essential feature of the behaviour of living things (chapter 27). It is only in terms of a teleological ecology that we can understand the role of living things within the wider context of the biosphere—in particular, their fundamentally whole-maintaining character (chapter 46), which above all makes possible the order, integrity, and stability of the living world.

3

ECOLOGY STUDIES LIVING THINGS
IN THEIR NATURAL CONTEXT

If the brain is interactive and dependent on context (context which is, more-over, ever changing and often unrecognised by experimenters) . . . then trying to strip away context and trying to avoid interactive effects can be trivialising and self-defeating.

Keith Oatley

Whereas the laboratory method's power lies precisely in its isolation of the phenomenon to be studied, ecological science is, on principle, anti-isolationist. It is the science of totalities. As such, it is anti-scientific—as science, at present, is usually conceived and practised.

Lynn White, Jr.

S CIENTIFIC METHOD INVOLVES studying the behaviour of living things in 'controlled laboratory conditions'—which means isolating them from the larger systems of which they are part. The information thus gained would be less questionable if these larger systems were no more than random arrangements—but they are not. Living things are the differentiated parts of the natural systems that make up the biosphere, and the biosphere has a critical structure that enables it to maintain its stability in the face of environmental challenges (chapter 41) and to provide each of its subsystems with an optimum environment (chapter 48).

This principle has obvious implications. A natural system behaves very differently within its natural environment from the way it behaves once subjected to an artificial environment that bears little relationship to that in which it evolved, and hence one removed from the natural systems of which it is a differentiated part. This is true at all levels of organisation within the biosphere.

Thus, at a molecular level, a hæmoglobin molecule in solution has a different affinity for oxygen than when it is inside a red blood cell. A cell that has been removed from an egg at an early stage in its development, as the German embryologist Hans Driesch showed, can develop into a whole organism instead of developing into a differentiated part of an organism.[1] As Michael Apter has pointed out so eloquently, the behaviour of a cell depends on its position in a total pattern, which means that 'cell interaction is . . . of crucial importance,'[2] an embarrassing fact that cannot be explained in terms of reductionist science. This is true not just of isolated cells but also of tissues—that is why grafting and budding and modern tissue culture in general are at all practicable.

Paul Weiss, though himself a laboratory biologist, notes that

> Biochemists, by and large, study organic chemical interactions (*e.g.* enzyme reactions) in physically orderless or deliberately disordered states (test tube solutions or tissue pulp). This is a technical necessity, and a lot can be learned through these methods. But they fall far short of reproducing the way things happen in the living system—they can show at best what *might* happen but not what actually does happen in the organised state; for in an organism, chemical reactions occur, in the first place, not ubiquitously and indiscriminately (as in a mixture) but rather in critical patterns of localisation and segregation, and second, without the pampering and nursing care of a learned experimenter.[3]

The same is true of the behaviour of organisms. As Eugene Odum notes, many insects are destructive pests in an agricultural habitat but not in their natural habitat, where parasites, competitors, predators, or natural chemical inhibitors keep them under control.[4]

The more the environment of living things differs from that in which they evolved, the more their behaviour is likely to become maladjusted, unadaptive, and, as a result, disruptive to the larger systems of which they are part (chapter 48). Thus, until recently, it was generally assumed that baboons were individualistic, competitive, and aggressive creatures—a notion based on a study conducted by the former chief scientist to the British government Lord Zuckerman of baboons in the London Zoo.[5] When the baboons were actually studied in the wild, however, they were found, on the contrary, to be orderly, cooperative, and peaceful.[6] It then became clear that Zuckerman's baboons were *äsocialised* and delinquent —their behaviour resembling that of some of the äsocialised and delinquent inhabitants of our rundown inner cities (chapters 45, 47, and 51).

In the same way, the responses to the sight of a piece of cheese of a laboratory animal confined in a box or cage are likely to provide very little valid information as to the normal behaviour of the members of its species towards the food on which they normally feed, because such animals have not been adapted by their evolution or upbringing to living in boxes or cages, nor to dealing with isolated pieces of cheese. They have not, in fact, been biologically, socially, or cognitively adjusted to dealing with such an artificial situation (chapters 50, 51, 52). In addition, living things do not react blindly to stimuli. They seek to make sense of them (chapter 31), and as the Gestalt psychologist Keith Oatley notes, 'that sense will include the whole context in which the material is presented.'[7] But how can they make sense of something when its context has been systematically removed—when a 'context-free situation' has been created to satisfy the exigencies of scientific method?

Experiments carried out in the impoverished environment of a laboratory, as Krishna Chaitanya notes, are biased 'against cognition and intelligence'.[8] They have been set up in such a way as to lend credence to the myth that living things simply react blindly and robotically to specific stimuli. This is even more the case if the animals have actually been brought up in the aberrant conditions of a laboratory where their cognitive faculties have been stunted.

Living things studied in isolation from the natural systems within which they developed as individuals and as a species are little more than freaks, their behaviour providing little valid information about their normal whole-maintaining behaviour within the biosphere. The study of the behaviour of living things is of value to the extent that it be allowed to occur in conditions resembling as much as possible those in which they evolved and grew up.

4

ECOLOGY EXPLAINS THINGS IN TERMS OF
THEIR ROLE WITHIN THE BIOSPHERE

Claude Bernard was right! The microbe is nothing, the environmental conditions [*le terrain*] everything.
Louis Pasteur

At the present day, the whole subject of causation is in a chaotic state. Men of science . . . who use the notion, appear to be too busy amassing facts to trouble themselves much about what they mean by it; and philosophers . . . seem, for the most part—from the time of Hume onward—to entertain beliefs on this subject which are very difficult to harmonise with the use of the notion in biological science.
J.H. Woodger

The meaning of any natural thing or event cannot be fully grasped or explained scientifically until we discover its relations to the other components of the orderly flow of process we call our cosmos.
C. Judson Herrick

M AINSTREAM SCIENCE sees an event in the real world as the product of a 'cause'. A cause is another discrete event that has been observed empirically by the process of *induction* to precede it in time, on the basis of which it is assumed that it will always have the same effect.

This principle of explanation fits in perfectly with the paradigm of science. It is reductionistic—the cause being a discrete, isolated event (chapter 3); mechanistic, since the cause is a switch that triggers off a specific effect; predictable, since switches are not creative or intelligent (chapters 29 and 32); compatible with the notion of randomness and blindness (chapter 26), since the causal process occurs in isolation from all other processes; and non-teleological (chapter 2), since the cause must necessarily precede the effect.

However, it provides a very misleading picture of events in the real world, for a life process (contrary to the impression conveyed by neo-Darwinism) does not occur in a void but as an integral part of a much wider process—the evolution of the biosphere itself. As such, it is subject to the regulation of the biosphere as a whole—a total, integrated system or *continuum* existing in both space and time (chapters 36 and 49). Such regulation of the part by the whole can be termed holistic causation or, as it has also been referred to, 'emergent' or 'downward' causation.

A life process also evolves for a purpose, that of fulfilling a specific function within the wider biosphere of which it is part. In doing so, it contributes to the maintenance of the critical order and hence the stability of the biosphere. It is this very role or purpose within the biosphere that must be taken to be its cause—that is if the term 'cause' is to be of any use in the understanding of life processes.

What is more, the same cause will not always trigger off the same effect, for if a living thing cannot achieve its goal in the normal way, it will seek to do so in a different way—for life processes display *equifinality*, the ability to reach the same endstate from a variety of different starting points. For this reason alone, the scientific principle of causality must be rejected, for how can we explain a life process in terms of a single causal event if it can achieve its goal even when the event does not occur (chapter 21).

If a normal whole-maintaining (or *homeotelic*) process cannot be explained in terms of discrete, isolated causes, nor can a whole-disrupting (or *heterotelic*) process that prevents natural systems from achieving the goal they were designed to achieve (see chapters 46 and 47). The reason is that such a heterotelic event can trigger off a veritable chain reaction of ever more disruptive events. That event which is taken to constitute a cause may thus be but one of a very long series of events, each one of which can be regarded as constituting a cause. Consider the following passage from the writings of George Perkins Marsh, a nineteenth century American diplomat and one of the most important precursors of today's ecology movement.

> The aquatic larvæ of some insects constitute, at certain seasons, a large part of the food of fresh-water fish, while other larvæ, in their turn, prey upon the spawn and even the young of their persecutors. The larvæ of the mosquito and the gnat are the favourite food of the trout in the wooded regions where those insects abound. Earlier in the year, the trout feeds on the larvæ of the Mayfly, which is itself very destructive to the spawn of the salmon, and hence, by a sort of house-that-Jack-built, the destruction of the mosquito that feeds the trout, that preys on the Mayfly, that destroys the eggs, that hatch the salmon, that pampers the epicure may occasion a scarcity of this latter fish in waters where he would otherwise be abundant. Thus, all nature is linked together by invisible bonds, and every organic creature, however low, however feeble, however dependent, is necessary to the well-being of some other among the myriad forms of life with which the Creator has peopled the Earth.[1]

What, then, is the cause of the epicures' frustration? Why have they been deprived of their smoked salmon? The obvious answer is that the mayfly has eaten the salmon's eggs. But is that a sufficient cause? Obviously not, since mayflies would not have been a problem if there had been enough trout around to eat them. The absence of the appropriate number of trout is thus another cause of this sad event. But it is not a sufficient cause either, since if there had been enough mosquito larvæ around for the trout to eat, they would not have left the area. Hence, the absence of mosquitoes can also be regarded as a cause, though still not a sufficient cause, for if people had not killed the mosquitoes there would still have been plenty of larvæ. Clearly, we must consider the problem in greater depth. To begin with, it would appear that the people in the area once used to put up with the mosquitoes—why, then, do they not do so now? Perhaps people had recently moved into the area who were particularly sensitive to mosquito bites. Perhaps, too, they had been persuaded by a chemical company to get rid of the mosquitoes—which they would otherwise have tolerated—by spraying them with an insecticide that the corporation happened to manufacture. But why should people be foolish enough to poison their environment with carcinogenic pesticides? Why, too, should chemical companies be allowed to manufacture them? To answer these questions would mean describing the dynamics of our industrial society and how it actually came into being.

Of course, in such a society, it is politically and commercially expedient to take only the most immediate cause as determinant and ignore all the others. This appears to justify the most superficial treatment possible, accommodating rather than changing the aberrant social and economic structures on which we have become dependent for the satisfaction of our short-term interests. If the cause of crop damage is seen to be a specific pest, this justifies waging chemical warfare against it (which suits the pesticide manufacturers). If the cause of an infectious disease is taken to be a specific microbe, this justifies the use of antibiotics to eliminate it (which suits the pharmaceutical industry). The adoption of these solutions, moreover, stimulates other commercial activities, such as transport, banking, and retailing, all of which provide jobs, contribute to the tax revenue of the state, and (temporarily at least) improve our material welfare.

Unfortunately, technological expedients only solve technological problems. They cannot reverse the disruption of natural systems. By alleviating the symptoms, they merely render the problems more tolerable *and thus serve only to perpetuate them.*

René Dubos, the Franco-American microbiologist and father of what might be referred to as the 'ecology of health', pointed out that microbes are not solely in themselves the cause of infectious diseases.[2] Human beings will always be inhabited by vast populations of microbes—indeed, according to the American microbiologist Lynn Margulis, known for her work on microbial ecology and the Gaia thesis, we harbour in our bodies as many microbial cells (prokaryotes) as animal cells (eukaryotes), most of them playing an essential role in our metabolism.[3] Dubos traces the source of many diseases to a breakdown in the critical balance between the individual and their 'endogenous' microbial populations brought on by a range of possible factors, such as old age, malnutrition, exposure to low-level radiation or chemical pollutants, or to a virus that disrupts the immune system.[4]

Louis Pasteur, who was the first to incriminate the microörganism as the sole instigator of infectious disease, eventually saw the error of his ways.[5] W.R. Day, an authority on plant diseases, also saw very clearly that simply blaming the parasite leads to the neglect of fundamental causes.[6] An infectious disease may be caused by a subtle combination of factors that reduces the resistance of an organism, making it vulnerable to an attack that under normal conditions it would repel with ease. Since the late 1980s, for example, there has been widespread deaths of dolphins and seals reported in and around the North Atlantic and North Sea, pointing to their contamination by low levels of all sorts of heavy metals, chemicals, and radionuclides that combine to reduce the effectiveness of the immune system of sea mammals against the viruses that have been officially implicated.[7] The truth is that highly-polluted seas have simply ceased to provide a healthy habitat for these animals and many other complex forms of life.

The same is probably true of the degradation of forests in Europe and on the East Coast of North America, where trees have died in increasing numbers. The often designated killer is 'acid rain' containing high levels of sulphuric acid, created when sulphur dioxide emissions from power stations and factories combine with the moisture in the atmosphere. But trees are ill and dying in areas where there is little or no sulphur dioxide pollution. It is more likely that a subtle combination of pollutants of all sorts—in the air, in the rainfall, and in the soil itself—is responsible, leaving us to face the depressing fact that our industrial society is giving rise to conditions that are ever less capable of sustaining complex forms of life like large trees. Such conditions are the opposite to those that obtain in a mature or climax ecosystem, where everything conspires to reduce the incidence of such problems to a minimum.

It is impossible to understand the daunting problems that confront us today in terms of the narrow scientific concept of causality. They should be examined, instead, within their total biospheric context. In this way it would become clear that these problems cannot be solved by technological means but only by correcting the social and ecological maladjustments of which they are but the symptoms. It would also be clearer that this must mean bringing about the most fundamental changes to our society and economy and to their relationship with our increasingly degraded biosphere, so that the restoration and preservation of its critical order, on which our survival necessarily depends, becomes our overriding goal (chapters 61 and 64).

5

ECOLOGY SEEKS TO DESCRIBE
THE ORDER OF NATURE

There is no law except the law that there is no law.
John Archibald Wheeler

All things under Providence are regulated and measured by the Eternal Law, but those of the individual (who participates in this Law) by the Natural Law. Not that these two are different laws but only the universal and the particular aspects of one and the same Law.
St Thomas Aquinas

For gods and men alike, there are certain destined bounds which normally and rightly circumscribe their power. It is just possible to exceed them—but only at the cost of provoking an instant *nemesis*.
F.M. Cornford

Almost everywhere in the world, man has been disregarding the Divine Law and the Laws of Nature to his own undoing. In his pride, he has rampaged over the stage of the earth, forgetting that he is only one of the players put there to play his part in harmony and oneness with all living things.
Richard St Barbe Baker

The basic laws of nature have not been repealed.
Eugene Odum

To STUDY THE STRUCTURE and function of the biosphere and its constituent natural systems is to seek out their pattern. The general features of this pattern are relatively inelastic, which is another way of saying that they are subject to controls or constraints[1]—in this case, that particular set of innate constraints required to ensure that their behaviour will serve to maintain the stability of the biosphere. It is these constraints that we must refer to as 'the laws of nature' or biospheric laws. These laws are not absolute, as were those that Pierre-Simon Laplace and Julien La Mettrie saw as applying to the mechanistic world that they depicted (chapter 13). Biospheric laws can be violated, *but only at a cost*—that of reducing stability, both directly at a specific level of organisation and indirectly at other levels within the wider organised structure (or *holarchy*) of the biosphere (chapters 42 and 43).

Adherence to a specific set of laws is required to maintain the order, and hence the stability, of a natural system—if these laws are disregarded, the degradation and eventual demise of the system will follow. As we move from one level of organisation to the next up the holarchy of the biosphere, so new sets of laws come into operation (so-called 'emergent laws'). These laws do not supersede those that are operating at lower levels but complement them.

Thus, if a man is to remain healthy, his behaviour must be subject to a set of physical, chemical, biological, psychological, social, and ecological constraints. Among other things, he must breathe fresh air, drink clean water, feed himself properly, and live in an environment that has not diverged too drastically from that to which he has been adapted by his evolution and upbringing (chapter 50). He is of course able to violate these laws, but he will pay the penalty, for his health must suffer as a result. As a member of a larger natural system (the family), he must behave in a husbandly way towards his wife and in a fatherly way towards his children, or his family will simply disintegrate. The family, in turn, is part of a community, and the community is part of a wider society contained within one of the ecosystems that constitute our biosphere. If the latter is to maintain its stability, all the individual living things that compose it must follow a highly organised set of laws that together constitute the laws of nature. It is the failure of modern society to observe the constraints necessary for maintaining the integrity and stability of the various social and ecological systems of which it is part that is giving rise to their disintegration and destabilisation, of which the increased incidence of discontinuities, such as wars, massacres, droughts, floods, famines, epidemics, and climatic changes, are but the symptoms (chapter 64).

Unfortunately, the very principle of biospheric law is incompatible with the reductionist thesis that is essential to modern science, according to which natural systems are no more than the sum of their constituent parts and thus have no identity, no integrity, and no stability. It is incompatible, too, with the notion of randomness or blindness—also critical to modern science—in terms of which life processes are no more than accidental, chance happenings (chapter 26). It is incompatible with the notion of causality. Thus, Robert Boyle objected to the notion of 'laws' because, for him (as for all other reductionist scientists), events cannot be 'caused' by laws, only by antecedent events. When an arrow is shot from a bow, he insisted, 'none will say that it moves by a law but by an external impulse.'[2] It is also incompatible with the empiricist thesis that only observable events are real—all theoretical explanations of life processes being largely ignored.

Since laws cannot be totally denied, scientists have demoted them to the status of 'statistical regularities'. This means that there is no reason why any laws should apply to the world we live in, other than that they have, on the whole, been observed to do so. This statistical view of the world provides a means of reconciling the embarrassing evidence for an orderly world (and hence one governed by laws) with the reductionist paradigm of science (chapter 40).

However, even this concession to reality is regarded as unacceptable by Ilya Prigogine, the Belgian Chemist and Nobel Laureate who became an intellectual cult figure in France, Belgium, and elsewhere. Prigogine considers that the only universal laws are those of classical thermodynamics (appendix 1). However, they only apply to those things that are near 'thermodynamic equilibrium' and are thereby in a state of 'homogeneity' (*i.e.* to a world in which all energy is in its final degraded or homogeneous state, and all matter, by inference, is in a state of disorder or randomness—the 'primeval soup'). Since living things do not fall within this category, the laws of classical thermodynamics cannot apply to them, and since there are no other laws, it must follow that the behaviour of living things is not subjected to any laws at all.[3]

This sounds very much like the worst sort of mediæval casuistry, yet Prigogine assures us that it is the only view that a scientist can possibly adopt—for it is the only one that is reconcilable with statistical theory. When the Newtonian paradigm was in fashion, he admits, there were indeed laws. However, it was by specifically rejecting the notion that nature is governed by laws that it became possible to free science from the 'Newtonian Myth' (appendix 1).[4]

The French philosopher and social theorist Edgar Morin seems also to have accepted the Prigogine mythology in its entirety. In response to René Thom's criticism that they had invented a new 'popular epistemology', Morin retorted that the only popular epistemology we find reference to today is that of 'the laws of nature, society, and history'.[5] In other words, only the stupid and the uneducated still believe that the natural world is governed by laws. Modern science has abolished them all and has thereby liberated humanity so that it is free to create its own laws and to determine the course of its own evolution and hence its own destiny. This is exactly the message required to rationalise our competitive and individualistic modern society—the global free-for-all that is leading to the disintegration of our societies and the destruction of our planet to satisfy short-term economic and political interests.

In terms of the worldview of ecology, the opposite is true. The main feature of the biosphere is its incredible order (chapter 40). This order is critical, and it can only be maintained if all life processes within the biosphere are subject to laws or constraints, which are at once self-imposed (chapter 46) as well as further determined by the larger systems of which they are part and that make up the holarchy of the biosphere (chapter 43). These constraints, what is more, are not of a random nature—they are precisely those that must lead living things to contribute to the maintenance of the biosphere's critical order (chapter 61) and that thereby cause them to behave in accordance with its fundamental needs (chapter 46). Significantly, traditional people have always recognised an organised set or 'holarchy' of laws governing at once their own behaviour and that of society, the natural world, and the all-encompassing cosmos itself —laws that it is their moral duty to observe as rigorously as possible (chapter 61).

6

ECOLOGY IS A UNIFIED ORGANISATION OF
KNOWLEDGE

What we find among the Zuñi [of New Mexico] is a veritable arrangement of the universe. All beings and facts in nature, 'the sun, moon, and stars, the sky, earth, and sea—in all their phenomena and elements—and all inanimate objects, as well as plants, animals, and men', are classed, labelled, and assigned to fixed places in a unique and integrated 'system' in which all the parts are coordinated and subordinated one to another by 'degrees of resemblance'.

Émile Durkheim and *Marcel Mauss*

Each profession makes progress, but it is progress in its own groove. Now, to be mentally in a groove is to live in contemplating a given set of abstractions. The groove prevents straying across country, and the abstraction abstracts from something to which no further attention is paid. But there is no groove of abstractions which is adequate for the comprehension of human life. Thus, in the modern world, the celibacy of the mediæval learned class has been replaced by a celibacy of the intellect, which is divorced from the concrete contemplation of the complete facts.

A.N. Whitehead

Normal science [is] a strenuous and devoted attempt to force nature into the conceptual boxes supplied by professional education.

Thomas Kuhn

VICTOR SHELFORD, one of the most distinguished of the early ecologists in the USA, defined ecology as the 'science of communities' (chapter 1). 'A study', he wrote,

> of the relations of a single species to the environment conceived without reference to communities and, in the end, unrelated to the natural phenomena of its habitat and community. . . is not properly included in the field of ecology.[1]

In the 1930s, the Oxford ecologist Arthur Tansley coined the term 'ecosystem', which he defined as a community or association of species taken together with its äbiotic environment.[2] It is probable that, were Shelford alive today, he would see ecology as the 'science of ecosystems'. Eugene Odum, possibly the most distinguished ecologist of modern times (and one of the few to have remained true to holism), defines ecology as 'the study of the structure and function of nature'[3] or 'the structure and function of Gaia',[4] as James Lovelock refers to the biosphere (and which the American ecologist LaMont Cole refers to as the 'ecosphere'). For Odum, ecology is therefore a superscience or *unified science*—as it was for Barrington Moore, the first president of the Ecological Society of America. For him, ecology was not just another scientific discipline but a science 'superposed on the other sciences', a science of synthesis essential to our understanding of the structure and function of the biosphere. He asked his colleagues in his address to the St Louis branch of the society in 1919,

> Will we be content to remain zoologists, botanists, and foresters with little understanding of one another's problems, or will we endeavour to become ecologists in the broad sense of the term? The part we will play in science depends upon our reply.[5]

His words would sound singularly out of place at a meeting of the Ecological Society today—and still more so at a meeting of its British counterpart.

The British theoretical biologist J.H.Woodger also considered that

> there ought to be a most general science, not immersed in a particular subject matter but dealing with the relationship between the various special sciences and trying to synthesise their most general results.[6]

Neither the biosphere nor any of its constituent processes can be fully explained in terms of the separate impermeable disciplines into which modern knowledge has been divided. As Russell Ackoff, a pioneer of operations research, notes,

> Some of the questions that we ask of Nature—in contrast to the problems it presents to us—can be classified as physical, chemical, biological, and so on, but not the phenomena themselves. . . . Automobile accidents can be viewed at least as physical, biological, psychological, sociological, and economic phenomena. To study them in any one of these ways is to exclude variables that are relevant from other points of view.[7]

Kenneth Craik makes the same point, 'Getting used to the dark,' he asks, 'is it physics, chemistry, or physiology?'[8] For him, it is at once quantum physics, chemistry, photochemistry, physiology, and psychology. Even what appears to be a purely physical phenomenon—like tracing the movement of planets—cannot be understood in purely physical terms. As Ackoff writes,

> Experience of planetary motion is as much a biological, psychological, sociological, and economic phenomenon as it is physical.[9]

The biosphere, in fact, cannot be understood in terms of the arbitrary divisions into which knowledge has been divided. Even the best established barriers turn out to be of relative value only. Thus, when Friedrich Wöhler synthesised urea the barrier between the *organic* and the *inorganic* was suddenly shattered—as was that between the *animate* and the *inanimate* once the virus was found to manifest certain conditions associated with life on being confronted with a source of protein, while at other periods displaying the normal behaviour-pattern of a crystal. A.N. Whitehead even refused to accept that there was any fundamental barrier separating physics from biology, famously stating that, 'Biology is the study of the larger organisms; whereas, physics is the study of the smaller organisms.'[10] Ludwig von Bertalanffy, the father of General System Theory (GST), showed that, at a certain level of generality, the behaviour of all living entities or natural systems is very similar and must be governed by the same laws. This basic principle underlies his General System Theory (chapter 42).

The compartmentalisation of knowledge into different disciplines makes possible the erection of artificial barriers between different life processes, permitting them to be viewed in isolation from all the others so that they can be made to appear subject to laws of their own that have nothing in common with those that govern other life processes.

In this way, totally aberrant theories have been constructed and have, in some cases, remained to this day the official doctrine of science—

theories whose absurdity would be apparent to all were we to accept the fundamental unity of life processes. An example is the mechano-morphic theory of life that sees living things as being akin to machines (chapter 38).

René Descartes divided the things of this world into two categories—the realm of the outer corporeal or physical world (*res extensa*) and the realm of the inner mental or 'metaphysical' world (*res cogitans*). The former, Descartes maintained, was the domain of science—the latter, the domain of theology. The object of this totally artificial division was to carve out a sphere of influence for science so that it would be freed from the shackles of theological control and, at the same time, to reassure the Church that science was not threatening to take over its territory.

This may have been politically expedient, but it was undoubtedly a sort of intellectual Yalta—the frontiers it established were as arbitrary and as pernicious as those set up by that infamous treaty, for it is impossible to understand the *res extensa* without reference to the *res cogitans*, the soma without reference to the germ, the body without reference to the mind.

The compartmentalisation of knowledge has also led to the erection of a barrier that separates economic activity (*i.e.* the distribution of resources within a society) from the society itself and from the rest of the biosphere. As a result, the economic process, as Nicholas Georgescu-Roegen points out, is depicted as a 'circular diagram, a pendulum movement between production and consumption within a completely closed system.' It is thus seen as governed exclusively by its own laws rather than by those that govern all the other processes occurring within the natural world. As a result,

> between the economic process and the material environment there exists a continuous mutual influence which . . . carries no weight with the standard economist. And the same is true of Marxist economists, who swear by Marx's dogma that everything nature offers man is a spontaneous gift. In Marx's famous diagram of 'reproduction', too, the economic process is represented as a completely circular and self-sustaining affair.[11]

Once it is admitted that the economic process influences and is in turn influenced by biological, social, and ecological factors—generally known as 'externalities'—then an effort is made to 'internalise' them by quantifying them in the language of economics. This may be a reasonable procedure, as Herman Daly and John Cobb concede, when the externalities involved are of a minor nature—but once it is the very capacity of the earth to support life that has to be internalised, then 'it is time to restructure basic concepts and start with a different set of abstractions that can embrace what was previously external.'[12] This means, in effect, completely rewriting economics in the light of a unified theory of the biosphere (chapter 35).

Further barriers separate the disciplines in terms of which we study the behaviour, individual development, and evolution of organisms, with equally obscurantist consequences—for these life processes are part of the same *biospheric process* (chapter 37), governed by the same general laws; they cannot be understood separately from each other. Thus, to say that a population has evolved is to say that neither its embryological development nor its behaviour is the same today as it was at some moment in the past. To understand evolution we therefore need to understand development and behaviour (the processes that have actually undergone change) not separately, as do the neo-Darwinists, but as part of the whole evolutionary process to whose constraints they are subjected.

The development of an individual organism (*ontogeny*) is clearly goal-directed, since it proceeds from a fertilised egg to become a fully-formed adult. It is also dynamic and highly coordinated, since all its different stages are closely interwoven into a single process. The developing system can also monitor its responses and correct diversions from the course it must take to achieve its goal and hence implement its strategy (chapter 21). That the day-to-day behaviour of non-human animals also displays these same features few will deny—yet neo-Darwinists, indeed all mainstream scientists, deny it to the evolutionary process itself. The geneticist Theodosius Dobzhansky, for instance, while accepting that the development of the individual organism is purposive, since organs grow to fulfil future functions, still dogmatically insists that this is not true of the evolutionary development of the species (*phylogeny*).[13]

Furthermore, with the hardening of Darwinian theory under the auspices of August Weismann and William Bateson, any feedback between behaviour and development on the one hand and evolution on the other is also fervently denied (appendix 4). This means that the instructions that determine the evolutionary process are seen as issued blindly, uninfluenced by the effects of the processes to which they give rise—a phenomenon that is unknown in the living world and impossible from the point of view of a self-regulating adaptive life-process. However, once behaviour, development, and evolution are seen together as part of a single integrated process, the operation of feedback processes of some sort becomes incontestable (chapter 37 and appendix 4).

The compartmentalisation of knowledge also makes possible the totally artificial distinction between behaviour occurring within the highly orderly and cooperative internal environment of an organism and that occurring *outside* it. It is only by insisting on this arbitrary dichotomy that the idea of natural selection—closely associated as it is with the 'survival of the fittest' (Charles Darwin suggested the two might be different terms for the same thing)—can possibly be postulated as the basic means of evolution. Indeed, the notion put forward by the German biologist Wilhelm Roux that selection occurs at different levels of organisation within the internal environment of an organism[14]—for instance at the level of the cell and the tissue—did not gain full acceptance because natural selection and the struggle for existence were so difficult to envisage within an internal environment, where cooperation and *homeostasis* are so well marked.

In general, it is only by studying evolution in a restricted context that it has been possible to perpetuate the neo-Darwinian myth that the process is individualistic, competitive, blind, and hence non-directive—one that is not subject to biospheric regulation and hence that cannot be distinguished from the anti-evolutionary enterprise to which our industrial society is committed (chapter 65).

If ecology is to become Barrington Moore's superscience—in terms of which we can understand the structure and function of the biosphere—then it must be non-disciplinary or super-disciplinary and serve, above all, to provide the *generalities* of a coordinated set of ecologically inspired disciplines, in terms of which the *particularities* of biospheric life-processes may alone be understood.

PART II

THE NATURE OF KNOWLEDGE

HUMAN BEINGS ARE COGNITIVELY ADJUSTED
TO THE WORLD IN WHICH THEY EVOLVED

> . . . it is by Earth that we see Earth . . .
> *Empedocles*

> How exquisitely the individual Mind
> (And the progressive powers perhaps no less
> Of the whole species) to the external World
> Is fitted; and how exquisitely, too—
> Theme this but little heard of among men—
> The external World is fitted to the Mind;
> And the *creation* (by no lower name
> Can it be called) which they with blended might
> Accomplish—this is our high argument.
> *William Wordsworth*

What a curious idea it is, this fear that has haunted us since the age of Bacon, that knower and known cannot be trusted alone in one another's company but must be chaperoned by a sober and censorious methodology . . . lest they should have illegitimate intercourse and produce bastards of fantasy.
Theodore Roszak

THE PERFECTION of humankind's cognitive endowment for the purpose of assuring our adaptation to our biological and social environment is an essential principle of the ecological worldview. This principle was always clear to traditional peoples and has been expressed in a wide variety of ways. Philosophers since the days of Parmenides have insisted that the mind can understand reality only because they both have the same structure or *logos* ('the order of things'). It was also the first article of faith of Goethe's philosophy of nature that there is 'a perfect correspondence between the inner nature of man and the structure of external reality, between the soul and the world'.[1] Henry David Thoreau referred to it as 'nature looking into nature'.[2] Paul Tillich refers to what he regards as the rational structure of the mind as 'subjective reason' and to the rational structure of reality as 'objective reason'.[3]

This principle is incompatible with the scientific assumption that subjective knowledge is necessarily imperfect and that only objective scientific knowledge displays sufficient accuracy to provide the basis of rational and hence adaptive behaviour. Darwin followed a similar line of reasoning. Intuitively, he felt that the natural world could not really have been brought into being by random changes. However, he did not feel that he could trust 'the convictions of man's mind', for it 'has been developed from the mind of lower animals', and he asks, 'would anyone trust in the convictions of a monkey's mind if there are any convictions in such a mind?'[4] This is also the view of the neo-Darwinists and sociobiologists. Thus, R.L. Trivers, a noted sociobiologist, regards as 'very naïve' the view that 'natural selection favours nervous systems which produce ever more accurate images of the world'.[5] On the contrary, as the philosopher Michael Ruse notes, sociobiologists take the view that 'our genes are deceiving us and filling us full of a glow of having achieved absolute truth.'[6] Indeed, Edward O. Wilson attacks intuitionism based on the notion that we cannot depend on our innate judgments precisely because they are 'relics' of our evolutionary past, some of which, he asserts, are 'likely to be outdated' (see also appendix 3).[7]

It is also true that in terms of the neo-Darwinian theory of evolution an individual need not be capable of correctly apprehending his environment in order to survive, for behaviour is not taken to be part of the evolutionary process (appendix 4). What is more, living things are not seen as correctly apprehending or understanding their relationship with their environment but as reacting to it blindly like Pavlov's dogs (chapter 31).

Behaviour, like evolution, is thus regarded as a passive process, stagemanaged by an anonymous environment.

It is encouraging, however, that a number of our more thoughtful scientists have, by implication at least, rejected such assumptions, realising that the living brain, after millions of years of being shaped by the environment, is suited to it with an accuracy that is both remarkable and profound. C.H. Waddington points to a 'congruity between our apparatus for acquiring knowledge and the nature of the things to be known' and suggests that the human mind 'has been shaped precisely to fit the character of those things with which it has to make contact'.[8] Konrad Lorenz goes still further. He notes that the way we experience the outside world, as well as our *a priori* forms of intuition, are 'organic functions' determined by the physical form and structure of our sense organs and nervous system, which in turn have been adapted to the 'circumstances and laws of the external world' by millions of years of evolution.[9] Jean Piaget goes so far as to say that our cognitive functions are an extension of organic regulations and must be seen as differentiated organs for regulating our relationship with the external world, which must therefore clearly serve the ends of human life.[10]

8

PRIMARY KNOWLEDGE OF THE
WORLD IS INHERITED

No proposition can be said to be in the mind which it never yet knew,
which it was never yet conscious of.
John Locke

Deductivism in mathematical literature and inductivism in scientific papers
are simply the postures we choose to be seen in when the curtain goes up
and the public sees us.
Sir Peter Medawar

From childhood on, we are taught not to believe in our instinctive knowledge. We are told that parents and teachers know best and that when our
feelings do not concur with their ideas, we must be wrong. . . . The loss of
faith in our innate expertise leaves us turning from one book to another as
each successive fad fails.
Jean Liedloff

IT IS FUNDAMENTAL to the reductionist paradigm of science that all knowledge is obtained by empirical observation. This is often taken to imply, among other things, that a child is born with a virgin mind—the 'tabula rasa' of the empiricist philosophers—on which empirical knowledge is systematically registered during its upbringing (chapter 15). This thesis is consistent with the view that a living thing is a temporal isolate, existing only for the present, but it is incompatible with our knowledge of the continuity and stability of natural systems (chapters 36 and 37).

The psychologist Robert Fantz noted how new born chicks pecked one hundred times more often at spherical than at pyramidal objects.[1] The Nobel Laureate Niko Tinbergen found that newly hatched herring gull chicks preferred pecking at objects that resembled the bill of the parents from which they were fed.[2] Marked preferences for certain specific objects were also established among baby chimps. Fantz also showed that children displayed a greater interest in flat objects that were painted to look like human faces than at flat objects on which the features of a human face were painted in a scrambled pattern, while they largely ignored similar objects on which no human features were painted. Fantz regarded his experiments as demonstrating that living things are born with an 'innate knowledge of the environment'—a knowledge that 'provides a foundation for the vast accumulation of knowledge through experience'.[3]

But we already know that animals of all kinds possess the instinctive knowledge and skills necessary for them to engage in far more complex behaviours from the moment they are born—the ability of spiders to spin their webs; of termites, ants, bees, and birds to build their nests; of beavers to erect and maintain their dams;[4] not to mention the innate ability of animals everywhere to swim, walk, fly, navigate, feed, fight, court, groom, mate, nurture, and act in all manner of highly complex ways that fulfil their particular needs within their respective habitats—all of which may subsequently be refined and adapted by their inborn intelligence and instinctive learning skills (chapter 32).

This must be so, for each generation of living things inherits genetic information that reflects the experience of its ancestors going back into the mists of time. Only in this way can a species (and the biosphere of which it is part) display continuity or stability. The growth and development of an organism's features (*morphogenesis*)—including that of the individual's brain and hence of its capacity to build up knowledge—must also display continuity or stability. But what is true of morphogenesis is also true of behaviour, for these processes are but different stages in the same biospheric process (chapter 37). It follows that the behaviour of successive generations also displays continuity—which in any case we know empirically to be true—and this requires that an individual inherit a rudimentary model of its relationship with its environment, reflecting the long-term behavioural experience of its cultural group, its race or variety, and its species.

We know that the evolutionary development of all life processes proceeds from the general to the particular, and this is also true of the development of the knowledge on which behaviour is coordinated (chapter 11). The generalities of this knowledge, what is more, being relatively inelastic, must colour the rest of the information that is acquired through experience.

It is thus the most general and hence the most fundamental (or primary) knowledge that must be inherited, while that which is accrued through experience is derived from this inherited knowledge during the interplay between the individual's behaviour and its natural habitat—the ordered environment within which behaviour occurs (chapter 49). In this respect, there is no reason to suppose that human beings are any different from other forms of life.

9

PRIMARY KNOWLEDGE IS PROVIDED BY OUR INSTINCTS, INTUITION, AND OUR INNATE SENSE OF ÆSTHETICS

What we cannot speak of, we must be silent about.
Ludwig Wittgenstein

The *dào* that can be told is not the eternal *dào*.
Laozi

The intuitive powers of the investigator are always dominant and decisive.
Michael Polanyi

When you have satisfied yourself that the theorem is true, you start proving it.
George Pólya

The servant of *dào*, realising the perfect beauty of the universe, attains understanding.
Zhuangzi

F OR EMPIRICIST PHILOSOPHERS—and hence for our mainstream scientists—knowledge must be entertained consciously and must be expressible in language, for only such knowledge is observable. However, there is every reason to suppose that knowledge that is entertained subconsciously, and cannot thereby be articulated, plays an essential part in determining the pattern of our behaviour.

Michael Polanyi refers to this nonverbal knowledge as 'tacit' or 'ineffable' and notes how all professionals possess a mass of knowledge of this sort,

> they know many more things than they can tell—knowing them only in practice (as instrumental particulars) and not explicitly (as objects).[1]

The use of such knowledge to guide our behaviour he takes to be 'an ineffable process of thought'.

Arthur Koestler notes that our emotions are 'notoriously inarticulate'.

> We can describe intellectual processes in the most intricate detail but have only the crudest vocabulary even for the vital sensations of bodily pain—as both physician and patient know to their sorrow.[2]

Neurophysiologically, the seat of our instincts and emotions (and thus of our values too) lies in the oldest structures of the brain—the first to have developed during the course of our neurobiological evolution. It is the knowledge organised in these older parts that we are normally unaware of and cannot articulate. The seat of our readily articulated conscious knowledge, on the other hand, seems to lie in the newest structures of the brain, such as the neocortex.

Significantly, attempts to control functions at the 'higher' conscious level that are designed to be coordinated at a 'lower' one lead to maladjustments and failures. The psychologist Viktor Frankl notes how many psychological problems and failures on the part of patients to fulfil basic behavioural functions are attributable to this cause.

> In clinical practice, often we are confronted with patients who are, so to speak, over-conscious of what they are doing—and this interferes with performance, be it the performance of the sexual act (sexual neurosis) or the performance of any artistic work (vocational neurosis).[3]

In Frankl's terms, this is the phenomenon of *hyper-reflection*—to be countered by *de-reflection*, which means turning a patient's attention away from themselves and their own activity.

Polanyi describes the same phenomenon in slightly different terms.

> If a pianist shifts his attention from the piece he is playing to the observation of what he is doing with his fingers while playing it, he gets confused and may have to stop. This happens generally if we switch our focal attention to particulars of which we had previously been aware only in their subsidiary role.[4]

This is usually referred to as self-consciousness. In the example of 'stage fright', it consists in 'the anxious riveting' of the would-be actor's attention on the next word (or note or gesture) to be remembered. This accent on the details 'destroys one's sense of the context, which alone can smoothly evoke the proper sequence of words, notes, or gestures'. The cure is to allow our minds to 'operate with a clear view to the comprehensive activity in which we are primarily interested'.

This suggests that different types of behaviour (if they are to be adaptive) must be coordinated *at the appropriate neurological level*. An essential part of the skills displayed by Polanyi's professionals, pianist, and actor—and by Frankl's lover and artist—is closely bound up with their instincts, emotions, and values, and must be coordinated by the older structures of the brain. This is even more obviously true of our basic physiological functions, such as the digestion of our food and the circulation of our blood. If they were to depend for their proper functioning on the conscious knowledge organised in our neocortex, we would probably not survive for a single day.

It is probably also true of our most fundamental knowledge of our relationships with the world around us. Thus, the basic features of the behaviour of traditional or *vernacular* people towards their society and their environment are coordinated on the basis of their traditional worldview, which is primarily organised by the older parts of the brain. But once the conscious and rational mind, associated with the neocortex, seeks to take them over, disaster follows, for it was simply not designed for that purpose. This primary, but ineffable, knowledge must also be passed on from generation to generation largely intact. It is only the particularities of such knowledge that can be modified with impunity by articulate consciousness. The process whereby we acquire ineffable knowledge is usually referred to as 'intuition'. It is itself mysterious and ineffable.

A fundamental principle of the vernacular worldview is the unity or 'oneness' of the living world. For the Bantu, as Father Placide Tempels writes, this is the supreme wisdom, which cannot be acquired in schools or universities.[5] For Alexander von Humboldt, the 'harmonious unity' of nature lies beyond the realms of positive knowledge and is accessible only to the 'vivid and deep emotions'.[6] The Haiku scholar R.H. Blyth also feels that only our intuition can enable us to understand the whole, while the intellect can understand something as a part but not as a whole.[7] For deep ecologists this 'oneness' of the natural world is 'the central intuition of deep ecology'[8]—but they do not stress its ineffable and *intuitive* character.

Our sense of æsthetics is closely related to our intuition. It is also an important means of apprehending and of understanding our relationship to the world around us, as it is of attaching us emotionally to that which is important to us and to the wider cosmos of which we are part.

It is above all the natural world—in which our primary æsthetic sense, like all our other innate faculties, evolved—that we find beautiful, as we do the human artefacts that mimic it. A Gothic cathedral, for instance, is seen as beautiful, for its vault resembles that of the forest canopy, its pillars the towering trunks of the forest trees.

On the other hand, we tend to abhor what is foreign to nature—unnatural colours, the jutting lines of modern buildings, the regimented uniformity of a conifer plantation that contrasts only too sharply with the mosaic of varied shapes and mottled greens of a natural forest.

Things that are beautiful also tend to be socially and ecologically desirable. Thus, the traditional farm carved out of the woods, with its diminutive fields, its patchwork of different crops enclosed by hedgerows, looks good and is good. As William Cobbett would say, 'Farm right and you may be sure the land will look right.'[9] On the other hand, the modern intensive farm, with its huge corrugated sheds and its endless stretches of monoculture enclosed by barbed wire fences, looks wrong and is wrong —very wrong.

We see beauty, too, in the natural pattern and order of nature. For Paul Weiss, the beauty of natural forms is not a 'random configuration, scattered haphazardly through the universe' but rather the outcome of lawful and orderly processes in nature.[10]

Not surprisingly, then, we see beauty in the *wholeness* of living things and of the natural world in general. As American poet Robinson Jeffers notes,

> A severed hand
> Is an ugly thing, and man disseuered from the earth and stars and
>   his history. . . for contemplation or in fact . . .
> Often appears atrociously ugly. Integrity is wholeness, the greatest
>   beauty is

Organic wholeness, the wholeness of life and things, the divine
    beauty of the universe. Love that, not man
Apart from that, or else you will share man's pitiful confusions,
    or drown in despair when his days darken. [11]

10

UNDERSTANDING DEVELOPS BY ORGANISING KNOWLEDGE IN THE MIND

Overt intelligent performances are not clues to the workings
of minds, they are those workings.
Gilbert Ryle

How can scientific discovery and artistic originality be explained or
described without reference to mind and imagination?
Arthur Koestler

The proper understanding of matter requires the imagination to invent
entities not apparent in everyday phenomena. It is the enduring miracle of
creative thought that the mind is equal to this task.
Gerald Feinberg

Complex concepts are not built up out of simple ones—simple concepts
are abstracted from complex ones.
Russell Ackoff

I F THE CONCEPTS of 'ineffable knowledge' and 'intuition' are foreign to the modern paradigm of science, so too (until the development of the new 'cognitive' or 'mentalist' school in the 1970s) was that of the mind itself, for its workings are not observable in the sense in which material objects are. Thus, to David Hume, only impressions (sensations) and ideas were real, the mind being regarded as no more than the sum total of our impressions and ideas.[1] The linguistic philosopher Gilbert Ryle insisted that there could be no mind as distinct from its workings and that any statement about the mind was meaningless.[2] This, in broad terms, has been the position of empiricist philosophers ever since.

When John B. Watson and the American behaviourist school sought to eliminate from their field of study all the metaphysical speculation of their predecessors and turn their subject into a 'hard science', they denied the existence of the mind in the same way as did Hume and Ryle. Any introspective concept that could not be observed and quantified was taken to be non-scientific and had to be eliminated. Consciousness, for instance, which empiricists since Descartes had always taken to be the seat of knowledge, Watson regarded as 'neither a definable nor a usable concept' and as 'merely another word for the "soul" of more ancient times'.[3] As he pointed out, 'No one has ever touched a soul or has seen one in a test tube.' This too was E.C. Tolman's position. 'All that can ever actually be observed in fellow human beings', he insists, 'is behaviour'[4] —and he intimates that this is all we can talk about scientifically. Also, since all behaviour is seen as random, there is no need for the mind as an instrument of coordination.

According to Watson, when a dressmaker designs a new gown, they do not have any picture in their mind of what the gown is going to look like when it is finished—this would be teleological behaviour, which is quite unacceptable to science (chapter 2). Besides, how can we quantify a picture and explain it in the scientifically respectable terms of physics and mechanics? The dressmaker merely

> calls his model in, picks up a new piece of silk, throws it around her; he pulls it in here, he pulls it out there. . . . He manipulates the material until it takes on the semblance of a dress.[5]

A painter, too, plies their trade in this way. 'Nor can the poet boast of any other method.' Indeed, we get new verbal creations, such as a poem or a brilliant essay, he insists, 'by manipulating words—shifting them about until a new pattern is hit upon'. The same attitude is displayed by the members of the behaviourist school of sociology. Thus, George A. Lundberg considers the search for human motives to be unscientific on the grounds that it is 'an animistic pursuit'.[6] It is under the influence of such ideas that sociology degenerated into the study of the observable atoms of social behaviour.

Evolution is seen by neo-Darwinists and sociobiologists in just the same way. As Watson writes,

> by manipulating at random the organic raw material—putting a tail here, putting a pair of wings there . . . a suitable pattern is hit upon and re-tained owing to its fitness to survive.[7]

The only scientifically acceptable method of acquiring 'synthetic' knowl-edge is referred to as *induction*, which involves the acquisition of data by cumulative individual observations and correlations. The more often a correlation can be made, the more are we justified in believing that the events will continue to occur together and, indeed, that they constitute a 'cause and effect' relationship.

This method of acquiring knowledge fits in perfectly with the dominant paradigm of science. It is a reductionistic concept, since each observation can be regarded as an 'atom' of cognition, just as each 'bit' is an atom of information, each 'reflex' an atom of behaviour, each sense-datum an atom of perception, and each 'meme' (to use Richard Dawkins's term) an atom of culture. Each of these reductionist concepts can be quantified, since observations can be counted. It also fits in with the view of behav-iour as random or blind rather than orderly or purposeful, and as passive and robotic rather than dynamic and creative (chapters 26, 27, 28, and 29). But it has very serious failings. David Hume was the first to point to the limitations of induction. There was no logical reason, he argued, for sup-posing 'that instances of which we had no experience must resemble those of which we have had experience',[8] which means that

> even after the observation of the frequent or constant conjunction of objects, we have no reason to draw any inference concerning any object beyond those of which we have had experience.[9]

However, in spite of this failing, Hume considered that induction still provides the only valid way of building up knowledge. Indeed, he is usu-ally regarded as its original proponent.

Other epistemologists, including both Immanuel Kant and later Karl Popper, have taken the logical objection to induction more seriously.[10] However, this issue does not seem to be the critical one, for no method of acquiring 'synthetic' knowledge can provide us with logically indubitable knowledge. What we require is a means of acquiring knowledge that has the greatest *likelihood* of being true—different degrees of likelihood being required for different purposes. The critical question is whether induction is the means of satisfying even this more modest criterion, and it can be shown that it is not. One reason is that we can push Hume's argument against the validity of induction a stage further. Because of the nature of life processes themselves (which logicians do not appear to be concerned with), the fact that events have been observed to occur together does not mean that they will continue to do so indefinitely. As Michael Polanyi notes,

> Our expectation of life does not increase with the number of days we have survived. On the contrary, the experience of living through the next 24 hours is much less likely to recur after it has happened 30 000 consecutive times than after only 1000 times. Attempts to train a horse to do without food will break down precisely after the longest series of successes; and the certainty of amusing an audience by one's favourite joke does not increase indefinitely with the number of its successful repetitions.[11]

The truth is that the building up of knowledge requires more than the accumulation of individual observations. These must be *interpreted* in the light of a model of our relationship with our environment (chapter 11). Thought is required—a non-quantifiable, non-reductionistic, non-mechanistic activity, whose very existence is not consistent with the underlying paradigm of science. Without it, 'without theoretical interpretation,' in Popper's formulation, 'observation remains blind—uninformative.'[12]

Cause and effect relationships established on the basis of indiscriminate empirical observations must indeed provide very questionable conclusions. After the 'race riots' in Britain in 1981, a public enquiry was set up under the chairmanship of Lord Scarman to determine its causes and propose measures to prevent their recurrence. The Brixton residents group Concern argued that simply to engage more policemen would not solve the problem. To confirm this thesis, they published a study establishing that between 1977 and 1980, the period during which crime really began to escalate in Brixton, 'the number of policemen exceeded the established level for the area by 113 per cent.' From this they drew the conclusion that 'more police increased the crime rate.'[13] They may, of course, have been right, but it is perhaps more realistic to see the growing crime rate in Brixton and elsewhere as but a symptom of social and cultural deprivation, against which the police, however numerous, can do very little (chapter 51).

It is only among the most simple forms of life, for whom mental activity (*i.e.* thinking) is still relatively rudimentary, that knowledge is acquired by something approaching the inductive method. To train an earthworm to find its way through a maze must require considerable patience. The correlation between taking the wrong path and receiving an electric shock is made only after repeated lessons. On the other hand, as we move to more complex forms of life (chapter 24), so there is a corresponding increase in the complexity of their *mental model* of the world (*i.e.* an increase in their *cybernismic* complexity—see glossary) and hence in the ability to think about and interpret experiences—consequently, the number of empirical observations required before learning occurs is proportionately reduced. In fact, we could formulate a law to the effect that the role of induction is inversely proportionate to the complexity of the mental model an animal develops of its relationship with its environment. Indeed, the more we know about something, the smaller the number of observations needed to understand it and predict how it is likely to change. Otherwise, why should an authority on the subject be better at doing this than one who knew nothing about it at all?

As we shall see (in chapter 15), perception or observation involves actively *detecting* rather than just passively receiving signals—a living thing detecting only those signals that appear to be relevant to the achievement of its behavioural goal. Such signals are said to attract its 'attention'—the role of which is simply ignored by behaviourists and other inductive scientists. Popper tells of an experiment that he carried out with his students in which he simply asked them to 'observe'. The students looked a little flummoxed. He then said,

> I hope you are all cooperating and observing! Yet, I fear that some of you, instead of observing, will feel a strong urge to ask, 'What do you want me to observe?'[14]

If this were so, he told them, then his experiment had been successful, for its object was to show that 'in order to observe, we must have in mind a definite question which we might be able to decide by observation.'

Interestingly enough, Darwin, in his autobiographical sketch, insisted that he 'worked on true Baconian principles, and, without any theory, collected facts on a wholesale scale'.[15] But later in the same book he admitted that he could not resist forming a hypothesis on every subject. In a letter to the naturalist Henry Fawcett, he observed 'how odd it is that anyone should not see that all observation must be for or against some view,'[16] and later in a letter to H.W. Bates he agreed that for him 'a good observer really means a good theorist.' Sir Peter Medawar considers that these comments reflected 'his true opinions as opposed to the opinions which he felt became him'.[17]

Polanyi also denies that a scientist's discoveries are the product of the inductive method. He considers that 'de Broglie's wave theory, the Copernican system, and the theory of relativity were all found by pure speculation guided by criteria of internal rationality.'[18]

W.H. Thorpe sees scientific progress as being largely achieved by

great leaps of imaginative insight—leaps which, at the time they were made, may have had very little experimental or observational basis . . . In some respects . . . , many of the most important theories in the history of science are arrived at as much by the modes of thought of the artist and the pure mathematician as by those popularly considered to be characteristic of scientists.[19]

They were achieved by a mysterious process, he might have put it, that could well be referred to as intuition (chapter 9).

11

THE KNOWLEDGE ORGANISED IN THE MIND
CONSTITUTES ITS WORLDVIEW
AND LIFE STRATEGY

The assembly of simple constituents into complex macromolecules in organic systems always requires the presence of a readymade model of the product . . . to guide the proper order of assemblage.

Paul A. Weiss

[It is] functionally necessary for every person in society to maintain a mental image of the society and its culture, as well as of his own body and its behavioural regularities, in order to act in ways which reduce stress at all levels of the system. . . . The [model] is nature, society, culture, personality, and body image as seen by one person.

A.F.C. Wallace

All cognised models encode values, but all do not value the same things equally. . . A model dominated by . . . the postulates of economic rationality would propose that an ecosystem is composed of elements . . . that qualify as 'resources', those that are neutrally useless, and those that may be regarded as pests, antagonists, or competitors. In contrast, the Ituri pygmies take the forest encompassing them to be the body of God. These two views of the world obviously suggest radically different ways of living in it.

Roy Rappaport

F OR A NATURAL SYSTEM to be capable of undertaking a coordinated sequence of actions to achieve a particular endstate (a baby in the case of an embryological process or a climax ecosystem in the case of an ecological process), it must be endowed with the requisite set of instructions. Furthermore, it must also possess a model of the relationship between itself and its endstate, of the developmental path to be followed, and of all the likely sources of disturbance that must be counteracted if the endstate is to be achieved.

The living body of information into which this model and its related set of instructions are organised, I refer to (generically) as a living system's *cybernism*.

For Norman Horowitz, the gene provides such information.

> It seems evident that the synthesis of an enzyme—a giant protein molecule consisting of hundreds of amino acid units arranged end-to-end in a specific and unique order—requires a *model* or *set of instructions* of some kind. These instructions must be characteristic of the species; they must be automatically transmitted from generation to generation; and they must be constant yet capable of evolutionary change. The only known entity that could perform such a function is the gene. There are many reasons for believing that it transmits information by acting as a *model* or *template*.[1]

The relationship between the *genome*—which is more realistically seen as providing such a model and set of instructions—and the proteins that it synthesises must be functionally the same as that existing between *any* cybernism and the life process that it helps to coordinate. In each case, information organised in a cybernismic medium is translated into behaviour. The information it contains must therefore be highly purposive or goal directed—not objective or, in Keith Oatley's words, 'neutral in the sense that . . . an encyclopædia typically is'.[2] On the contrary, the information is best seen as formulated subjectively in the system's own language (chapter 15). For instance, it is because a traditional society's fundamental instructions are of a moral nature that its cultural model is formulated in the language of morality.

The instructions and potential instructions it contains are organised in accordance with the stage in the process at which they will be required—in accordance, too, with the probability of their being required and hence of the occurrence of conditions to which the behaviour they coordinate is adaptive. The cybernism thereby provides a *relevant* picture of the system's relationship with its environment in the face of predictable obstacles. This is the very essence of *cybernetic* or self-regulating behaviour.

In a military campaign, the commander issues orders arranged according to their scope and priority, as all orders must be (chapter 42). The most general order, and thus most critical, will be to defeat the enemy—the less general orders specify how, in the changing conditions of the battlefield, this goal is best to be achieved. The instructions will be constantly revised in the light of the data gathered by intelligence officers on the deployment of friendly and enemy troops. Of course, they will not just be piled up somewhere, for adaptive behaviour cannot be coordinated on the basis of data alone, or even a database. For behavioural purposes, the data must be organised to constitute a model—only then can they be taken to constitute *information*.

Specialised staff officers do this, ensuring little symbols representing friendly and enemy formations move across a map that is usually displayed on a wall of the room, tent, or caravan that serves as the general's headquarters. It is only by consulting this 'dynamic map' that the general knows what instructions, at any given point in the campaign, will make victory more probable. Any other approach would simply be 'muddling through', very much as our politicians do today. But theirs is not the way of nature. The behaviour of the biosphere and its component subsystems we know to be coordinated and committed to a *long-term strategy* of survival. Thus, we can postulate that all behaviour, including the evolutionary process itself, must be coordinated with the aid of a dynamic model analogous in some ways to that used by the general in our example.

It is a comparatively recent idea that humans and other animals possess in their minds a dynamic model of their relationship with their environment. The neurologist Henry Head was possibly the first to suggest that information was organised in the brain to form representations or 'schema'.[3] This idea was taken up by Karl Lashley, who found it useful as a means of understanding the behaviour he observed in his own animal experiments.[4] In 1932, F.C. Bartlett published his classic *Remembering*. He showed that remembering can only be understood if it is realised that 'the past operates as an organised mass rather than as a group of elements, each of which retains its specific character,' and that 'remembering is not the reëxcitation of innumerable fixed, lifeless, and fragmentary traces—*it is an imaginative reconstruction.*'[5]

Thus, if a group of people are told a story and are, at a later date, asked individually to repeat it, each will likely do so quite differently, for each will reconstruct it in the light of their personal mental model or worldview. What remains of the original story is a person's general attitude to it, which reflects all the attitudes and prejudices (if we like to call them such) that underlie their own particular worldview. Their principal preoccupation, thereby, is not to recall the events with the greatest possible precision but to reconstruct the story in accordance with their mental model.

At about this time, C. Judson Herrick also noted that in order to explain the subtleties of behaviour, we must postulate the existence of stable arrangements of information in the brain, which he referred to as 'neurograms'.[6] The first really explicit statement of the thesis, however, was Kenneth Craik's. He contended that the brain, in order to fulfil its function, must provide a 'model' of the physical world.

> If the organism carries a 'small-scale model' of external reality and of its own possible actions within its head, it is able to try out various alternatives, conclude which is the best of them, react to future situations before they arise, utilise the knowledge of past events in dealing with the present and future, and in every way to react in a much fuller, safer, and more competent manner to the emergencies which face it.[7]

Michael Polanyi also found it necessary to explain learning in this way.

> A rat which has learned to run a maze will show a high degree of ingenuity in choosing the shortest alternative path when one of the paths has been closed to it. This behaviour of the rat is such as would be accounted for *by its having acquired a mental map of the maze*, which it can use for its guidance when faced with different situations within the maze.[8]

In this way, a rat does not have to rely on induction—and hence on random trial and error—to find its way out of the maze, any more than does a human.

The rat, in fact, can best be regarded as being endowed with a *mind*. This mind must be seen to be the seat of its instincts, emotions, values, and sociability, which provide it with the appropriate body of instructions or strategy for an adaptive, whole-maintaining behaviour pattern. It also provides the rat with a closely associated dynamic model of its relationship with its world. Each move the rat makes, what is more, will be that which seems most likely to prove successful in the light of its mental model, which is constantly brought up to date with the experience of each successive move. And what is true of the rat must be true of *all* self-regulating natural systems, whether they be organisms, vernacular societies, ecosystems, or the biosphere itself (see glossary—*cybernism*).

12

A PROPOSITION CAN ONLY BE VERIFIED
IN TERMS OF THE WORLDVIEW
OF WHICH IT IS PART

A new scientific truth does not triumph by convincing its opponents and making them see the light, but rather because its opponents eventually die, and a new generation grows up that is familiar with it.

Max Planck

Scientific knowledge in any era is what the scientists actively take as such, and the scientific knowledge of one era may be rejected as error in the next.

Harold Brown

The test of proof or disproof is in fact irrelevant for the acceptance or rejection of fundamental beliefs, and to claim that you strictly refrain from believing anything that could be disproved is merely to cloak your own will to believe your beliefs behind a false pretence of self-critical severity.

Michael Polanyi

IF MAINSTREAM SCIENTISTS assure us that a thesis, however likely it may seem, has not been verified empirically, it will be branded as unscientific and thereby unworthy of being taken seriously. The consecrated formula is that there is 'no scientific evidence' that it is true, the evidence being exclusively provided by empirical verification in 'controlled laboratory conditions' and hence in isolation from the world of living things. If complementary evidence is admitted—epidemiological evidence in the field of health, for instance—this too must be empirical. Empirical verification can also be complemented by theoretical arguments, but these are considered of secondary importance.

Logical positivism is the *epistemological* doctrine that justifies this position. Its main tenet is that the criterion for the acceptability of a proposition—distinguishing a scientific from a metaphysical proposition or 'sense from nonsense'—is empirical verification. Verification is based on induction and is invalid on that count alone (chapter 10). The reason is that neither an observation, an experiment, nor even a series of observations and experiments can establish a thesis or general principle. At best, these procedures can only show that the observation or experiment is *compatible* with that thesis. But, of course, most propositions can be shown to be compatible with a large number of different theses, many of which are likely to be irreconcilable with each other. The philosopher of science Jerry Ravetz shows that we could 'verify' in this way 'the hypothesis that the moon is made of mouldy cheese. One need only deduce that it would then have spots and then establish that the predicted spots do exist.'[1]

The philosopher Harold Brown regards the fact that 'universal propositions cannot be conclusively verified by any finite set of observation statements' to be the 'central difficulty' of logical positivism. To be consistent, logical positivists would have to regard universal propositions as but meaningless metaphysics, but this they clearly cannot do without losing all credibility. They have got round the problem by insisting that they are not propositions at all but merely 'rules which allow us to draw inferences from observation statements to other observation statements'.[2] This is playing with words in the worst tradition of mediæval casuistry (chapter 2).

On the other hand, more sensible logical positivists have given up the strict verificationist position. While they require that a meaningful proposition must at least be testable by observation and experiment, they accept that the results need not be conclusive. Rudolf Carnap, one of the leading exponents of logical positivism, proposed replacing the principle of verification with that of 'gradually increasing confirmation'.[3] This marked the establishment of a new school of epistemology called 'logical empiricism'.

Another problem with empirical verification is that it is based on observation. As we have seen (chapters 10 and 11), to observe something means forming a hypothesis about it in the light of our worldview, while the act of observation that serves to verify the hypothesis is itself the product of this paradigm or worldview and hence no more objective than the proposition it serves to verify (chapter 15).

Thus, Karl Popper noticed as far back as 1919 how accepted theories of the time, such as Marx's theory of history, Freud's psychoanalysis, and Adler's individual psychology, seemed to explain almost everything in terms of their own field of study—so much so that those who studied them underwent what could be described as an 'intellectual conversion or revelation'. 'Once your eyes were thus opened,' Popper writes, 'you saw confirming instances everywhere—the world was full of verifications of the theory. Whatever happened always confirmed it.'[4] Arthur Koestler, who in his youth in Hungary was a member of the Communist Party, later admitted that this is precisely what used to happen to him.

> My party education had equipped my mind with such elaborate shock-absorbing buffers and elastic defences that everything seen and heard became automatically transformed to fit the preconceived pattern.[5]

Popper regards such behaviour as 'uncritical'. Scientists do not behave that way. Science is distinguished from metaphysics by its application of the 'critical approach', which means that scientific theories must be formulated in such a way that they can be refuted or 'falsified' by empirical means. Newton's theory, for example, predicted deviations from Kepler's laws (due to the interactions of the planets) that had not been observed at the time. It exposed itself thereby to attempted empirical refutations whose failure would invalidate the success of the theory. Einstein's general theory of relativity was, in turn, tested in a similar way —predicting both the orbital precession of the planet Mercury and the bending of starlight produced by the sun's gravitational field. 'Only if a theory successfully withstands the pressure of these attempted refutations,' Popper asserts, 'can we claim that it is confirmed or corroborated by experience.' Scientists, in formulating a theory, are thereby 'taking a risk', which astrologers, Marxist historians, psychoanalysts, and individual psychologists do not take. In other words, 'the criterion of the scientific status of a theory is its falsifiability, or refutability, or testability.'[6]

This thesis has in turn been much criticised on a number of obvious counts. To begin with, falsifiability still depends on observation and is thereby still subject to all the limitations applying to the empirical method. As Sir Peter Medawar notes,

> We could be mistaken in thinking that our observations falsified a hypothesis—the observations may themselves have been faulty or may have been made against a background of misconceptions; or our experiments may have been ill-designed. The act of falsification is not immune to human error.[7]

Popper himself admits this.[8] Falsifiability, what is more, is also based on induction, and, as we have seen (chapter 10), we cannot argue from observations to theories—nor can we disprove theories—in this way.

C. H. Waddington considers that the falsifiability principle does not properly apply to complex events, such as those studied by biologists.[9] The reason is that all sorts of devices can be resorted to in order to maintain the validity of a hypothesis concerning the behaviour of complex natural systems. Imre Lakatos sought to replace Popper's principle of 'naïve falsification' with 'sophisticated falsification', which involved confronting the scientific theory with an alternative one. 'There is no falsification', he wrote, 'before the emergence of a better theory,'[10] though this is still not enough—what is required is a 'series of theories . . . usually connected by a remarkable continuity which welds them into research programmes'.[11] This, Lakatos admits, is roughly what Thomas Kuhn refers to as 'normal science'. However, a programme takes a long time to develop, and it must not be killed off prematurely by pointing to a single inconsistency. For this reason, 'one must treat budding programmes leniently,'[12] for it is unfair to falsify theories until they are fully developed. Falsifiable theories must therefore be tolerated, at least in their early stages.

For Kuhn, this is not sufficient. He rejects Popper's view that science is still concerned, as was Greek science, with fundamental issues (the deeper paradigmatic or metaphysical theories). This is simply not true of modern science, in which the accent shifts from the discussion of fundamentals to that of what he calls 'problem solving'. Those involved in this latter activity share the same *paradigm*, whose validity is taken for granted and hence does not require testing. Kuhn actually goes so far as to say that 'it is precisely *the abandonment of critical discourse* that marks the transition to a science,' after which 'the critical discourse recurs *only at moments of crisis* . . . when [scientists] must choose between competing theories,' and it is only then that they behave like Greek scientists or philosophers.[13]

Of course, in normal conditions, testing still occurs—but it is not the fundamental issues (the current underlying theory) that are tested but only the details or technicalities of the theory (the experimenter's skill at 'problem solving'), while the paradigm itself is never tested *and could be guaranteed to emerge unscathed even if it were.* As John Watkins notes,

> If the outcome of such a 'test' is negative, it does not hit the theory but backfires on the experimenter. *His* prestige may be lowered by the failure of his attempt to solve a puzzle—but the prestige of the paradigm, within whose framework he makes the attempt, is so high that it will scarcely be affected by any such little local difficulties.[14]

Not surprisingly, Kuhn considers that it is only very superficial propositions that are falsified, except when the paradigm of which it is part is in crisis and is due to be replaced with a new paradigm.

The trouble is that when there is a confrontation between two paradigms the victor is not necessarily that which would be chosen on the basis of any sort of empirical verification or falsification. *For there is no rational discourse between the proponents of different paradigms.* They speak different languages, see things in a fundamentally different way, *and therefore cannot really communicate.* Moreover, as Michael Polanyi observes, scientific controversies never lie altogether within science,[15] which is perhaps an understatement. Indeed, such controversies are likely to be highly emotive, even quasi-religious, affairs. In general, we can say that people, whether they be primal peoples, businessmen, bureaucrats, or professional scientists, will do everything they can to preserve their paradigm in the face of knowledge that appears to undermine it. This is referred to by the anthropologist A.F.C. Wallace as 'the principle of conservation of cognitive structure'.[16]

Polanyi describes three strategies used for preserving a cognitive structure (or 'conceptual framework' as he refers to it) when confronted with experiences that would appear to invalidate it. The first is to defend the principle that seems to be invalidated with reference to another principle —this is possible because of the self-enclosed or circular nature of worldviews and paradigms. Edward Evans-Pritchard notes how this is done by the Azande tribe of Uganda when faced with such experiences.[17] For them, 'the contradiction between experience and one mystical notion is explained by reference to other mystical notions.' Polanyi points out that belief in the usefulness of mathematics as a means of understanding the world is based on the same self-reinforcing circularity, since every assertion of a deductive system can be demonstrated by, or else shown to be implied as axioms of, the others. Therefore, if we doubt each assertion in its turn, each is found confirmed by circularity, and the refutation of each consecutive doubt results in strengthening our belief in the system as a whole.[18]

Another technique mentioned by Polanyi for maintaining the stability of beliefs in the face of conflicting evidence is the 'expansion of the circle in which an interpretive system operates'.[19] In this way, an 'elaboration of the system' can be readily supplied to cover 'almost any conceivable eventuality'. This device he calls 'the building up of ancillary hypotheses'. Scientific theories that 'possess this self-expanding capacity', he writes, are 'epicyclical'—an allusion to the epicycles that were used in the Ptolemaic theory to explain the apparent motion of the planets. According to Polanyi, all major interpretive frameworks have an epicyclical structure 'which supplies a reserve of subsidiary explanations for difficult situations'.[20] Polanyi cites Evans-Pritchard's description of the epicyclical character of Azande beliefs.[21]

The Azande believe in the powers of the poison oracle. The oracle answers questions through the effects on a fowl of a poisonous substance called *benge*. The oracle poison is extracted from a creeper gathered in a traditional manner, which is supposed to become effective only after it has been addressed in the words of an appropriate ritual. Suppose that the oracle, in answer to the same question, says 'yes' and immediately afterwards, 'no'. For us, this would discredit the oracle, but Azande culture provides ready-made explanations for such contradictions. Evans-Pritchard lists no fewer than eight ready-made explanations that can account for the oracle's failure.[22] They may insist that the wrong type of poison had been used, or a breach of *tabu* committed, or that the spiritual owners of the forest where the poisonous creeper grows had been insulted and avenged themselves by making the poison ineffectual.

Scientists, Polanyi points out, behave in just the same way. They are no more likely than an Azande medicine-man to accept evidence that could invalidate any aspect of their beliefs. This could not be better illustrated than by Lakatos's story of the imaginary pre-Einsteinian physicist.

On the basis of Newtonian mechanics—of Newton's law of gravitation (N) and of the accepted initial conditions (I)—the physicist calculates the trajectory of a newly discovered small planet, (p). Unfortunately, however, the planet does not follow the expected trajectory. How does the physicist react to this? Does he accept that Newtonian mechanics are wrong? That the law of gravity (N) does not apply? Undoubtedly not. He suggests that there must be a hitherto unknown planet, (p^1), which perturbs the path of p. He calculates the mass, orbit, *etc.* of this hypothetical planet and then asks an experimental astronomer to test his hypothesis. The planet p^1 is so small that even the biggest available telescopes cannot possibly observe it—the experimental astronomer applies for a research grant to build yet a bigger one. In three years' time, the new telescope is ready. Were the unknown planet p^1 to be discovered, it would be hailed as a new victory of Newtonian science. But it is not. Does our scientist abandon Newton's theory and his idea of the perturbing planet? No. He suggests that a cloud of cosmic dust hides the planet from us. He calculates the location and properties of this cloud and asks for a research grant to send up a satellite to test his calculations. Were the satellite's instruments (possibly new ones, based on a little-tested theory) to record the existence of the conjectural cloud, the result would be hailed as an outstanding victory for Newtonian science—but the cloud is not found. Does our scientist abandon Newton's theory together with the idea of the perturbing planet and the idea of a cloud which hides it? No. He suggests that there is some magnetic field in that region of the universe which disturbed the instruments of the satellite. A new satellite is sent up. Were the magnetic field to be found, Newtonians would celebrate a sensational victory. But it is not. Is this regarded as a refutation of Newtonian science? No. Either yet another ingenious auxiliary hypothesis is proposed or . . . the whole story is buried in the dusty volumes of periodicals and the story never mentioned again.[23]

The third technique proposed by Polanyi to maintain the stability of a hypothesis in the face of evidence that refutes it is to 'deny to any rival conception the ground in which it might take root'.[24]

Polanyi refers to this third technique or 'defence mechanism' as the principle of 'suppressed nucleation'. He regards it as complementary to the operations of circularity and self-expansion.

While these latter protect an existing system of beliefs against doubts arising from any adverse piece of evidence, suppressed nucleation *prevents the germination of any alternative concepts* on the basis of such evidence.

Again, this is not only done by members of vernacular societies but by mainstream scientists, who will purposefully ignore and, if necessary, suppress any information, however well-documented, that appears incompatible with the paradigm of science.

In this way, scientists are both ignoring and suppressing the holistic and ecological knowledge that makes nonsense of their methodology, of many of the practices of the Promethean enterprise to which they are committed (*i.e.* of the systematic transformation of the living biosphere into a lifeless *technosphere*), and of the reductionist paradigm of science itself.

For Polanyi, to preserve the stability of our conceptual framework, worldview, or 'paradigm' is entirely human. To suppose that it can be avoided by developing a more objective science is no more than a pious hope based on no serious knowledge of any kind. It is also an error to suppose that this is a human failing. It is not. It is, in fact, *highly adaptive, indeed essential in order to maintain the continuity or stability of a human social system.* All organisations of information in the natural world (or cybernisms—chapter 11) are, and must be, capable of maintaining their stability in the face of environmental challenges.

The problem, as Polanyi does not fail to point out,[25] is that the devices used for stabilising a true or adaptive view of the universe may equally stabilise an erroneous or maladjusted one. That, of course, is in the nature of things. The faculties that make possible whole-maintaining life processes (chapter 46) can be misdirected to promote whole-disrupting ones instead (chapter 47). But the possibility of such errors is systematically reduced as a society moves from an unstable 'disclimax' or 'neo-pioneer' stage (chapter 65)—in which people's ideas are largely random and individualistic—towards a stable *climax* stage, in which people are imbued with a worldview consistent with the behaviour that best assures the preservation of the critical order of the *cosmos*.

13

ECOLOGY IS QUALITATIVE

What, except for its exactitude, is exact about mathematics?
Johann Wolfgang von Goethe

The further away economics strays from reality, the better
it can be sold as 'scientifically precise'.
Jude Wanniski

It is perfectly meaningless to measure something with higher and
higher degrees of precision, if the thing you measure is
more or less meaningless.
Ralph Gerard

. . . not everything that can be counted counts, and not everything
that counts can be counted.
William Bruce Cameron

While you and i have lips and voices which
are for kissing and to sing with
who cares if some oneëyed son of a bitch
invents an instrument to measure Spring with?
e e cummings

T HE BASIC KNOWLEDGE of traditional or vernacular people was contained in their myths, in the language of gods and spirits. It was also formulated in the language of abstract concepts, such as 'fate', 'justice', and 'law'—concepts that had a clear meaning to them in terms of their worldview. It was a language of the people, a human language. Plato also sought to understand the world in terms of abstract ideas or 'universals', while abstract concepts, such as 'origins', 'essences', 'qualities', and 'goals', continued to be in vogue during the mediæval period.

Quantification, on the other hand, came with the search for objective and precise knowledge. That which was non-quantifiable, therefore, was to remain outside the field of science.

The new philosophy of nature developed by Descartes and Galileo anticipated the Newtonian idea that nature could be understood in terms of physical atoms moving through space and time. To isolate the characteristics of matter in motion (which could be measured and related by mathematical laws) was to understand the workings of nature. As Descartes himself famously put it, 'Give me extension and motion, and I will construct the universe.'[1]

Quantifiable concepts, such as space, time, weight, velocity, acceleration, inertia, force, and momentum, were the subject matter of Galileo's new science, replacing the more subjective knowledge that could not so easily be quantified. The seventeenth century saw the development of further quantifiable abstractions, such as 'the force of gravity', 'space-pervading ether', 'mass', and also 'power' and 'energy'. The two great eighteenth century works on mechanics, Joseph Louis Lagrange's *Traité de Mécanique Analytique* (1788) and Pierre-Simon Laplace's *Traité de Mécanique Céleste* (1799), purported to prove that nature is governed by precise and all-embracing mathematical laws—they served to enshrine the quantitative method.

Since then, science has not looked back. As Morris Kline writes,

> The history of modern science is the history of the gradual elimination of gods and demons and the reduction of vague notions about light, sound, force, chemical processes, and other concepts to number and quantitative relationships.[2]

This process has been a great success in the field of physics, where the concepts used have been relatively simple and hence easy to quantify, especially when employed in isolation from the more complex systems studied by biologists and sociologists. As C.F.A. Pantin notes, 'physics and chemistry have been able to become exact and mature just because so much of the wealth of natural phenomena is excluded from their study,[3] and the more complex the natural system studied the more must be excluded. But surely, as Paul Weiss argues, 'There is no reason for us to downgrade nature' to meet the physicist's inadequacy,[4] which, of course, is precisely what science has done and continues to do.

If scientific method is unsuitable for the study of complex systems, so are the concepts that science uses. Few have even been defined. As the theoretical biologist J.H. Woodger notes,

> Nothing is more striking [in biology] than the contrast between the brilliant skill, ingenuity, and care bestowed upon observation and experiment, and the almost complete neglect of caution in regard to the definition and use of the concepts in terms of which its results are expressed.[5]

This is also a problem in psychiatry. The Nobel Prize-winning novelist Isaac Bashevis Singer notes how accurately the textbooks have defined the idiot, the cretin, the imbecile, the epileptic, the hysteric, the hypochondriac, and the neurasthenic. But, as he observes, 'instead of admitting that little was known about what went on in the human brain, either healthy or sick, the professors stacked up Latin names.' What do the impressive Latin words actually refer to? A vague set of symptoms at best. As the cynic puts it, the psychotic builds a castle in the air, the neurotic lives in it, and the psychiatrist collects the rent.[6]

Similarly, the most basic terms used by ecologists have never been properly defined. Thus, G.H. Orians distinguishes between nine types of stability,[7] and David Merrell notes twenty-one different ways in which scientists use the term competition.[8] In the philosophy of science the terms used are equally vague. Margaret Masterman once accused Thomas Kuhn of using the term paradigm in twenty-two different ways.[9] The term diversity (chapter 25) is used at once to denote the number of species in an ecosystem ('species richness') and at the same time the relative population sizes of these species ('equitability'). These are basically two different concepts that could only be represented by a single quantity if they were known to be precise functions of each other, so that a change in the value of one would automatically lead to a predictable change in the value of the other. This is not so. In fact, the relationship between the two concepts has yet to be determined with any sort of accuracy. Other terms used in ecology are also very difficult to quantify. Biomass is an example. Ramón Margalef points out that a tree 'includes much dead tissue' to which the term biomass cannot strictly apply.[10]

The preoccupation with quantification has led scientists to develop concepts and indeed whole theories, partly at least, because they could be quantified, regardless of whether or not anything in the real world corresponded to them. Many of the concepts of neo-Darwinism fall into this category, natural selection being a case in point. It should realistically be seen as acting on the *phenotype* (the living features of an organism). As C.H. Waddington notes, if a horse is to survive in the natural world, it must run fast enough to escape from predators, and 'it is irrelevant whether it can run fast because it has been trained by a good race-horse trainer or because it has got a nice lot of genes.'[11] However, natural selection acting on the phenotype is extremely difficult to quantify, for which reason selection has been seen by neo-Darwinists, misleadingly, as acting on the genotype—a process very much easier to model.

'Complexity' is also defined in terms that makes it easily quantifiable. A 'complex' system is simply seen as one made up of many interacting parts *without reference to the way they are organised*, for organisation is very difficult to quantify. Such 'complexity', however, corresponds to nothing in the real world (chapter 24).

If modern ecologists are so preoccupied with energy flux, it is also largely because this concept is particularly easy to quantify. R.J. Putman and S.D. Wratten, who see ecology as 'a quantitative exact science with certain underlying principles and laws as fundamental as the laws of pure physics', assure us that it is via energy that an ecological science can be developed. They also insist that it is by studying organisms in terms of their energy flux that it is possible to see them 'in context' and 'to define their actual function'.[12]

Modern ecologists have been at pains to define ecosystems in such a way as to rationalise this thesis. Thus, Robert O'Neill states explicitly that the ecosystem is fundamentally an 'energy processing system'.[13] Putman and Wratten also see a biological system—individual, population, or community—as a 'system for the transfer, storage, and dissipation of energy';[14] a thesis with which Robert McIntosh seems to concur.[15]

This is but a gratuitous dogma. Why should energy be the currency of nature? Why not resources, or information, or organisation? Why should we not seek to understand nature in terms of a model that makes use of *all* these and many other relevant variables?

Quantifiable or not, the idea that the basic role of living things is to process energy cannot really be very much more simplistic and naïve. It is, of course, reconcilable with the dominant paradigm of science—which sees living things as no more than machines—but it bears no possible relationship with reality.

Michael Polanyi has shown how mental knowledge undergoes simplification as it is translated into language, for all that cannot be articulated must be left out.[16] As it is further translated into mathematics, still more information is left out—all that cannot be quantified—which is often information that is most relevant to the understanding of any given issue.

Scientists are unlikely to entertain the possibility that a proposition about the behaviour of complex systems couched in the language of mathematics can provide *less* rather than more accurate information. Robert Mann of Auckland University, however, accepts that it can. He distinguishes between precision and accuracy. By formulating a proposition quantitatively, he argues, we undoubtedly make it more precise but only at the cost of reducing its ability to represent the real world.[17] Precision, in fact, is only achieved at the cost of accuracy.

14

ONLY QUALITATIVE KNOWLEDGE CAN PROVIDE
THE BASIS FOR ADAPTIVE BEHAVIOUR

> Anything can be proved with a model if the
> right assumptions are specified.
> *Cheryl Payer*

It is only in quantitative ecosystem ecology that the rich details of natural history become reduced to 'brute' transfers of conservative substances, because the real details have so far proved too diverse, complex, and generally difficult to represent and quantify. Every ecologist who has ever made an energy or material flow model of an ecosystem is painfully aware of its deficiencies in terms of relevant information omitted . . . The model reduces the intricate beauty and awesome complexity of a piece of living nature to what is by comparison a flat, pallid image of the reality. . . An ecosystem model, no matter how sophisticated or difficult to produce, is but a shadow of its prototype.

B.C. Patten and *Eugene Odum*

K NOWLEDGE IS SEEN by mainstream science as organised into artificial structures, such as logic or mathematics, from which propositions can then be deduced. Thus, it is increasingly considered by scientists that to understand the structure and function of a complex system, such as a society or an ecosystem, requires modelling it mathematically. This involves first determining what are the relevant variables to take into account (systems analysis) and then determining just how they are interrelated (modelling). A change occurring in the real world can then be simulated by modifying the value of the appropriate variables and interrelationships—the effect that this will have on all the other variables and interrelationships providing an indication of how the change is likely to affect the real world. Simulation can thus be seen as a very much more sophisticated form of deduction. It is particularly attractive because living things seem to proceed in a very similar way when they seek to understand events in the real world (chapter 11). Unfortunately, however, this methodology is fraught with problems.

To begin with, there is no established methodology for choosing the variables and interrelationships. They are chosen first of all because they are easily modelled—which means above all that they can be easily quantified (chapter 13), and unfortunately many of the most relevant variables and interrelationships of a complex system (or rather of a *mental model* of a complex system) are too difficult, or even impossible, to quantify.

In turn, there is no valid methodology for choosing which of these quantifiable variables and interrelationships should be taken into account. This is left to the initiative of the modellers, and inevitably the choice will faithfully reflect the worldview with which they have been imbued. In view of the very high cost of building mathematical models of complex systems, which can often run into hundreds of thousands if not millions of dollars, the chances are that it is the worldview of *modernism*—which is most fanatically entertained by governments, multinational corporations, and international agencies—that the choice of the variables and interrelationships will reflect.

The same problem occurs in the choice of the basic assumptions underlying a mathematical model, which the modellers are expected to state explicitly. Such assumptions are not those that must underlie the model if it is to represent the real world with the greatest accuracy, but those that are required for purely technical model-building reasons. Thus, among the assumptions underlying a model built by the ecologist and entomologist A.J. Nicholson to mimic the stable relationship between predators and their prey are firstly that the predator and the prey have synchronised generations, which means that they are of the same length and start at the same time.[1] Needless to say, this simply does not occur in the real world.

Further assumptions in Nicholson's model are equally unrealistic. The generations are assumed to be discrete, with no overlap between them. The predator searches randomly, contrary to the known behaviour of predators, which is dynamic, intelligent, and consistent with a specific interpretation of the situation in which they find themselves (chapters 28, 32, and 31). The predator never becomes satiated and goes on eating members of the prey species indefinitely, which again we know not to be the case. Finally, the machine-like predator has a 'constant searching efficiency', which means that it is unaffected by the food it eats, the mood it is in, or the time it has spent seeking out its prey, which is also very unrealistic.

In short, to build a mathematical model at all, its architect must simplify their creation until it bears very little relationship to the real world it is supposed to be modelling. This does not seem to concern our modellers unduly, their principal preoccupation being to assure that their model is a self-contained and logically consistent construct. At this they are very skilful.

Consider the mathematical model provided by R.J. Putman and S.D. Wratten of the process of ecological *succession* towards a climax (chapter 22).[2] For them, succession, rather than being a goal-directed ecological strategy that ends once its goal (the climax or most stable state) is achieved —a scientifically unacceptable thesis that makes nonsense of the notion of 'progress'—is simply an example of a statistical process known as a 'regular Markov chain', in which 'transitions among various "states" occur with characteristic probabilities that depend only on the current state and not on any previous state,' and which, as the chain develops, eventually settles into a pattern 'in which the various states occur more or less randomly with characteristic frequencies that are independent of the initial state'. Further,

> It is argued that this final 'stationary distribution' of states is the analogue of the climax community, and that climaxes *must* occur by the statistical certainty that the Markov process always settles into a stable pattern.

What is more,

> If a community is temporarily disturbed, something like the original community returns. This, too, is a function of Markovian processes. Finally, Markovian developments, like succession, are characterised by rapid

changes followed by undetectably slow changes. (Hence stability, in the naïve sense of 'absence of change', increases tautologically as succession proceeds.)[3]

What is important is that 'none of these characteristics', Putman and Wratten insist, are 'necessarily of biological origin'. In other words, it is not in terms of the behaviour of biological systems, let alone of natural systems in general, that we must seek to explain succession but in terms of a mathematical formula that can be fed into a computer. Researchers, they inform us, have shown the 'close fit' between Markovian processes and succession. The most 'sophisticated' of such researchers, we are told, is H.S. Horn, who insists that 'several properties of succession are direct statistical consequences of a species-by-species replacement process and have no uniquely biological basis'.

The whole argument is an example of a fallacy we can best refer to as 'mathematical realism'. Children often think that because a word exists there must be something in the real world to correspond to it, a notion known as 'nominal realism'. Jean Piaget cites many examples from children, who may say things such as 'pigs are rightly named because they are so dirty' and 'the sun is rightly named because it is so hot'.[4]

The Oxford linguistic philosophers were similarly guilty of what might be called 'linguistic realism' when they assumed that there must be some intrinsic and universal wisdom in the structure of the English language that casts light on the workings of the cosmos, when in reality what they offered was only the very crudest of representations.

Putman and Wratten, like Horn and other modern ecologists, are in fact committing the same error. They suppose that because someone has developed a mathematical model that simulates in a rudimentary manner some aspects of the real world, then it must be capable of simulating accurately all aspects of the real world. It is, of course, astonishing that a mathematical model of a Markov chain can imitate, however crudely, any aspect at all of such real-world processes as succession to a climax. That we must thereby be able to derive from it other ecologically acceptable information about succession is absurd, just as absurd as to suppose that because a puppet can be made to resemble a policeman, an examination of the cotton wool with which it is stuffed will enable us to understand the policeman's digestive system or the circulation of his blood. What they are proposing is in fact little more than a modern form of divination—but because the diviners are scientists, performing their rituals on scientifically consecrated premises, they enjoy credibility among the naïve and the faithful (chapter 22, and appendices 2 and 3).

Simulation on a mathematical model is no substitute for the interpretation of real-world situations in the light of a *qualitative* model of an individual's relationship with their environment, such as that provided by a traditional or vernacular worldview. It can, of course, be argued that such a model is not 'scientific' in that it does not conform to 'objective' reality. However, the role of knowledge is not to depict reality in the manner of an encyclopædia but to help coordinate behaviour *adaptively* so as to maintain overall well-being (chapter 11).

Roy Rappaport sees vernacular knowledge as organised to constitute 'cognised models', which he sees as providing populations with a distinctive means of maintaining themselves in their environment. Thus, rather than being objective or encyclopædic, such models are primarily developed *for the achievement of this adaptive goal.* Nor, as Rappaport writes, should they be simply judged in accordance with

> the extent to which they are identical with what the analyst takes to be reality but the extent to which they direct behaviour *in ways that are appropriate to the biological well-being of the actors and of the ecosystems in which they participate.* The criterion of adequacy for a cognised model is not its accuracy but its *adaptive effectiveness.*[5]

The Colombian anthropologist Gerardo Reichel-Dolmatoff also sees the mythology of a vernacular society as providing its members with a model of their relationship with the society and to its natural environment, in the light of which they seek to interpret environmental changes and monitor their behaviour pattern so as to assure that such changes are reduced to a minimum and their society's stability is maintained.[6] A vernacular model is naturally formulated in the language of the society's mythology. The interrelationships that are seen to exist between the gods and spirits who maintain society and the natural world are carefully established and explained in mythological terms (chapter 63). Thus, among the indigenous Canelos-Quichua of Ecuador, as N.E. Whitten tells us,

> playing flutes, singing songs, and telling myths punctuates discussion of Amasanga (who controls the weather, the thunder and lightning), Nungüi (who controls the soil-base for the roots of garden-life and pottery clay), and Sungui (who controls water).

These activities

> are, among other things, mechanisms for associational or analogic linking of cosmological and ecosystem knowledge to social rules and breaches, and social dynamics to cosmological premises.[7]

Problems, such as a shortage of game, soil erosion, a lack of clay for making pots, and bad weather, can all be interpreted in terms of the model and attributed to some maladjustment in the relationships between the various gods that maintain these resources, which in turn can be related to some failure on the part of society to fulfil its obligations towards them. The model is holistic rather than reductionistic—the spirits are not atomised components of the natural world but, on the contrary, reflect its truly organised and interrelated nature. In addition, the model, rather than being divided up into watertight disciplines between which interrelationships are almost impossible to establish, is totally non-disciplinary, which is necessary if it is to permit the coordination of an integrated behaviour pattern, as opposed to that mere patchwork of expedients that is the policy of a modern nation state.

A vernacular model, what is more, is usually formulated in a language that each member of the society can understand and that can guide the behaviour of the society as a whole. This is in stark contrast with a mathematical model, formulated in an esoteric script, which only a handful of specialists can really understand and act on.

What is more, the interrelationships on which it is based are constantly brought home to people in songs, dances, plays, and other ritual activities, so that everyone is properly imbued with the worldview it reflects. Also, because it is couched in the moral and emotional language of the society's mythology, people are emotionally motivated both to entertain it and to adopt that behaviour pattern that is consistent with it, and indeed feel morally bound to do so.

For all these reasons a qualitative vernacular model satisfies the basic self-regulatory (cybernetic) requirements of a social system in a way that the scientific mathematical model cannot. A vernacular model, in fact, is alone capable of providing the informational basis for the behaviour required to ensure cohesion and stability at the social level (see glossary —*cybernism*).

15

ECOLOGY IS SUBJECTIVE

Te mātauranga o te Pākehā
The white man's wisdom
He mea whakatō hei tinanatanga
is propagated
Mō wai rā?
for whose benefit?
Mō Hātana!
For Satan's!
Kia tūpato i ngā whakawai.
Be wary of its temptations.
Kia kaha rā, kia kaha rā.
Be strong and firm!
Te mātauranga o te Pākehā
The white man's wisdom
Patipati, ā, ka mura whenua.
charms you, then takes away your land.
Kia kaha rā, e hoa mā.
Be strong, friends.

Ka mutu anō
Land is all we have
Te tānga manawa,
to rest a beating heart,
oranga, a oranga.
to sustain us!
Te mātauranga o te Pākehā
The white man's wisdom
Ka tuari i te penihana oranga.
doles out social-security benefits.
Hei aha rā?
Why?
Hei patu tikanga,
To suppress our customs,
patu mahara,
to confuse us,
mauri e.
to destroy our vital force.

Tuīni Ngāwai of the Māori tribe of *Ngāti Porou*

SCIENTIFIC KNOWLEDGE purports to be objective—that is seen to be its main virtue, distinguishing it from the sort of knowledge entertained by most ordinary people. Objective knowledge is knowledge that is free of the personal beliefs, values, and metaphysical ideas of its entertainer—hence, it is knowledge that is neutral with regard to the achievement of any specific goal.

In actual fact, scientific knowledge is epistemologically no different from other forms of human knowledge. We like to think that the latter (whether scientific or not) is something very special, but it is simply a particular kind of information, and there is every reason to suppose that it is organised and made use of in the same way as other forms of information. It is thus significant that objective information plays no part in the strategy of the biosphere. The information used by natural systems at all levels of organisation is not objective but *subjective*.

Thus, the information contained in a fertilised egg is not objective—it consists of that which is required to permit the development of the embryo into a child. The information contained in the cultural 'cognised' model of a vernacular society is not objective. As Roy Rappaport makes clear, its role is to ensure the adaptation of a particular society to the specific environment in which it lives (chapter 14)—*it is thus only in terms of its ability to achieve this goal that it can be judged.*[1]

Though most scientists will deny it, this is also how scientific models are really judged. Francis Bacon, 'the father of modern science', was the first to insist that science be ruthlessly separated from values ('the idols of the understanding')—but he did nothing of the sort. His scientific knowledge, far from being 'value free', set out explicitly and purposefully to give humanity power over nature. 'Truth . . . and utility are . . . perfectly identical,' he wrote in *Novum Organum* (1620), and, 'that which is most useful in practice is most correct in theory.'[2]

Instead of putting aside the old values of good and evil to create a value-free factual knowledge, Bacon simply replaced them with the values of 'useful' and 'useless'. It was a critical time in the history of human affairs. The New World had just been explored and the financial opportunities provided by plunder and the slave trade seemed limitless. It is not surprising, as Benjamin Farrington notes, that the Christian values of mercy and love should, in such circumstances, have been so easily forgotten, nor that the cynical values of Baconian science should have been so readily accepted.[3] After all, they were precisely those that best served to rationalise the efforts made to exploit these new opportunities. 'In Baconian ideology,' Donald Worster writes, 'the good shepherd of the Christian tradition had become a scientist and technocrat. Science offered the means for building a better sheepfold and creating greener pastures.'[4]

All the models developed by human societies, including the worldview of modernism and the closely associated paradigm of science, are necessarily *cognised* and hence subjective. One reason is that we, like all other living things, are *participants* in the life of the biosphere, whereas in the Western philosophical tradition we are regarded as *spectators* and hence as entertainers of 'objective' knowledge. The former position has now been accepted, in theory at least, in modern physics. Werner Heisenberg showed that it is impossible to eliminate the influence of the observer, and this led him to formulate his famous 'principle of uncertainty'. Unfortunately, this principle has yet to affect the way most physicists look at the world, let alone the practitioners of such disciplines as chemistry, biology, anthropology, sociology, and ecology.

For vernacular people, however, there was what Ashis Nandy calls 'a continuity between the observer and the observed'.[5] For the Japanese scholar Toshihiko Izutsu,

> The highest degree of knowledge is always achieved when the knower, the human subject, becomes completely unified and identified with the object [of knowledge], so much so that there remains no differentiation between the two. For differentiation or distinction means distance, and distance in cognitive relationships means ignorance.[6]

The view that knowledge, whether scientific or not, must be subjective also follows from the fact that the faculties with which our evolution has equipped us for perceiving our relationship with our specific environment are purely subjective—for, contrary to the assumptions of our empiricist philosophers, they are simply not designed to provide us with an objective representation of the world. This principle is worth looking at in some detail.

Observation or perception, which is supposed to be the source of all our knowledge, begins with the detection of data (chapter 28). This process is *active* rather than passive—data being detected, rather as a mine is detected by a mine detector, not just *received*—and it is *highly selective*. Instead of accumulating available data in a random fashion, as empiricists assume we do, we isolate those that appear relevant to our behaviour pattern (a minute percentage of the total) from those that do not. As C. Judson Herrick notes,

The skin is sensitive to mechanical vibrations up to 300 per second but beyond that point feels only a steady push. The ear is aware of sound waves from 20 to 20 000 cycles per second but does not hear sounds above or below these limits. The skin is aware of heat waves from 20 to 80 trillion cycles per second (THz), and the eyes are sensitive to light waves from 400 to 800 THz, but our senses miss electric waves, as well as ultraviolet waves, X-rays, gamma rays, and cosmic rays running from frequencies of 800 to 30 000 000 THz and beyond.[7]

We have no biological means of apprehending sense data outside these ranges, presumably because during the course of our evolution they have not proved of any relevance to the achievement of our behavioural goal.

This biologically determined selection is complemented by a culturally determined one. At any given moment, we detect only a minute proportion of the data that we are biologically equipped to detect—those that our upbringing and experience within a particular culture have taught us to regard as relevant to our behaviour. Thus, it is in the light of our *mental model* (chapter 11)—whose generalities reflect the experience of the species and whose particularities are largely those of the individual within their cultural group—that the relevance of different data to the individual's behaviour pattern is determined.

Furthermore, what we detect with our sensing apparatus is not what we *see*. We do not detect the actual constituents of our environment, such as dogs, trees, and rocks, but only patterns of light and shade. These are then *interpreted* by us in the light of our mental model. A perception is thus a *hypothesis* based on a particular conceptual framework or paradigm (chapters 10, 11, and 12). Only in this way can we explain how we can differentiate between movements in our environment and shifts of the image on the retina due to the movement of our own eyes, or how we are able to perceive an object's colour as constant, even as the lighting conditions change (so called 'perceptual constancy'). Only in this way can we understand why babies see everything the right way around, for if they were to depend on their optical faculties alone, they would see everything upside down.

Only in this way, too, can we understand our extraordinary ability to handle fragmentary data. When we read a page of print we may not even notice printing mistakes, such as missing letters or even missing words. We subconsciously fill in the gaps. This is possible, Keith Oatley points out, because we have a prior knowledge of what we are looking at.[8] More precisely, we interpret the signals we detect in terms of the mental model we have built up of the subject matter, and which provides the basis for our particular way of seeing.

There are many classic experiments that demonstrate this tendency of seeing things according to our previous expectations. For example, when incongruous playing cards, such as a red six of spades or a black ace of diamonds, are placed among normal cards, players will initially *see* what they are accustomed to—the six of hearts or a normal ace of diamonds in this instance (a phenomenon known as 'perceptual priming'). Equally, the well-known Necker cube, 'rabbit–duck', and 'wife & mother-in-law' illusions demonstrate how our perception can dramatically shift from seeing one thing to quite another without the particulars of the original image having changed at all (a so-called '*gestalt switch*'—see appendix 6). Indeed, other experiments, including those carried out by Solomon Asch at Harvard, reveal that people can also be induced by suggestion and the force of public opinion to *see* things very differently from the way they previously saw them.[9]

Thomas Kuhn wrote that this is precisely what occurs in the scientific world after a 'paradigm shift'. Thus, Antoine Lavoisier, who discovered oxygen, '*saw* oxygen' where Joseph Priestley had *seen* dephlogisticated air and where others had *seen* nothing at all. In learning to see oxygen, however, Lavoisier also had to change his view of many other more familiar substances. He had, for example, to see a compound ore where Priestley and his contemporaries had seen elementary earth, and there were other such changes besides. At the very least, as a result of discovering oxygen, Lavoisier *saw* nature differently. We might even say that he 'worked in a different world'.[10]

If observation is a subjective process, then so are the other means whereby we acquire knowledge, such as intuition and thought itself. Thus, we judge the validity of a proposition or hypothesis by determining to what extent it fits in with our subjective model of our relationship with our environment.

The truth is that we are simply not designed by our evolution to entertain objective knowledge. As Karl Popper put it, 'Knowledge in the objective sense is knowledge *without a knower.*' Empiricist philosophers have totally failed to realise this. For this reason, Popper discards the epistemology of John Locke, George Berkeley, David Hume, and even Bertrand Russell, for they all assume the possibility of objective knowledge in the conventional sense of the term.[11] He thereby dismisses the entire school of empiricist philosophy that they created, and which provides the basic epistemological foundations of modern science.

Michael Polanyi goes further than Popper. If knowledge is objective, he considers, then 'we must accept the virgin mind (bearing the imprint of no authority) as the model of intellectual integrity'. Only a newborn child possesses such a virgin mind and is thereby able to pass judgments on all questions 'without any preconceived opinions'. But such judgments would necessarily be of a rudimentary nature, as a child would not yet be intelligent enough to understand fully the issues it was called on to judge. To do so, it would have to grow up—but for its mind to remain virgin, and hence objective, the child

> would have to be kept unshaped until then by any kind of education. It must be taught no language, for speech can be acquired only äcritically, and the practice of speech in one particular language carries with it the acceptance of the particular theory of the universe postulated by that language. An entirely untutored maturing of the mind would, however, result in a state of imbecility.[12]

For these reasons, Polanyi considers that objective knowledge is an illusion and that we should accept that knowledge, whether scientific or not, is necessarily subjective or 'personal', as he refers to it.

Popper, on the other hand, still thinks that objective knowledge is possible—even though it may be, strictly speaking, 'knowledge without a knower'. Such scientific knowledge he sees as made up of logical constructs of different sorts—'conjectural theories', 'arguments', and presumably mathematical models. It is precisely the role of science to build up such constructs. Popper postulates 'three worlds'. The first world is the real world, the second that of subjective knowledge of the real world, and the third that of objective knowledge of the real world, which he sees as the product of humans, just as 'honey is the product of bees, or spiders' webs the product of spiders'.[13]

It is true that such constructs have a measure of autonomy, in that changes occurring in the real world can be translated into or 'simulated' by changes in the structure of the construct in accordance with clear rules. If the construct is a particular language, for instance, simulation is achieved in accordance with the grammatical rules of the language in question. If it is symbolic logic, it is done in accordance with the rules of symbolic logic—if a mathematical model, in accordance with the rules of mathematics. Changes occurring within these constructs, it can be argued, are insulated from human subjectivity by virtue of the fact that they occur in accordance with the laws that govern them.

That is undoubtedly the case once the constructs have been brought into being—but we must not forget that the constructs *are of human origin in the first place* and, for that reason, reflect human cultural patterns, which are clearly highly subjective. Indeed, Benjamin Lee Whorf maintained that each language faithfully reflects the metaphysical system of the society that developed it,[14] a thesis much discussed and generally confirmed by semanticists and anthropologists over the years. That a mathematical model reflects the metaphysical system of the society that developed it is perhaps even more evident. It is generally accepted that a mathematical model is no better than its basic assumptions. If these are wrong, then the answers obtained by simulating real-life changes on the model will also be wrong. As the critics of model building put it, 'garbage in, garbage out.'

The subjectivity of all the various disciplines into which we have divided modern knowledge is equally clear. Their function is, above all, to help rationalise, and hence legitimise, different aspects of the enterprise of economic development or 'progress' to which our society is so resolutely committed. Thus, Adam Smith's *The Wealth of Nations* (1776) postulated that by behaving in the most egoistic way possible we maximise not only our own material interests but also those of society at large—a cheerful philosophy that rationalised the individualism and egoism that marked the breakdown of society during the industrial era. Darwinism was rightly described by Oswald Spengler as 'the application of economics to biology'[15]—Darwin's 'natural selection' being but a biological version of Smith's 'invisible hand' and serving, above all, to legitimise the Promethean enterprise to which our modern society is committed by making it appear to be a natural process.

Scientific knowledge, as is pointed out throughout this book, serves to rationalise the reductionist paradigm of science and hence the worldview of modernism, on the basis of which economic development or 'progress' is seen to be justified. There is no reason to suppose that ecological knowledge—in its different variants—is any more objective, less value-laden, or less purposive. It is, or rather ought to be, designed purposefully to rationalise the worldview of ecology and the associated ecological society, geared as it must be to maintaining the critical order of the cosmos.

16

ECOLOGY IS EMOTIONAL

The physiologist is no ordinary man—he is a savant, seized and possessed by a scientific idea. He does not hear the cries of suffering wrung from racked and lacerated animals, nor see the blood that flows. He has nothing before his eyes but his idea and the organisms that are hiding the secrets he means to discover.
Claude Bernard

Reason is, and ought only to be, the slave of the passions.
David Hume

Reason flows from the blending of rational thought and feeling. If the two functions are torn apart, thinking deteriorates into schizoid intellectual activity and feeling deteriorates into neurotic life-damaging passions.
Erich Fromm

. . . people need more than to understand their obligation to one another and to the earth—they need also the *feeling* of such obligation.
Wendell Berry

NINETEENTH-CENTURY naturalists were unashamedly emotional in their descriptions of nature. This is particularly true of Alexander von Humboldt, who described the tropical forests of Brazil with emotion and with awe. Darwin, who particularly admired Humboldt, wrote of the Brazilian forests in the same vein in a letter to John Henslow,

> Here I first saw a tropical forest in all its sublime grandeur—nothing but the reality can give any idea how wonderful, how magnificent it is. . . . I formerly admired Humboldt, I now almost adore him—he alone gives any notion of the feelings . . . on first entering the tropics.[1]

This is very different from the detached, impersonal, 'objective' approach of today's scientists, for whom, as Donald Worster notes, the natural world is but a collection of resources to be mapped and dissected, and whose constituents are classified and catalogued increasingly for the benefits of some organisation that is only interested in their utilitarian potential.[2]

Modern science has banned the emotions. This is the inevitable consequence of decreeing that scientific knowledge must be objective—a vain decree, since we are, by our very nature, incapable of entertaining objective knowledge (chapter 15), just as we are incapable of effectively suppressing our emotions. Michael Polanyi speaks of 'the overwhelming elation felt by scientists' at the moment of making a scientific discovery, 'an elation of a kind which only a scientist can feel and which science alone can evoke in him.'[3] He cites as an example Kepler's elation at discovering his Third Law, 'Nothing holds me,' he wrote, 'I will indulge my sacred fury.'

The same degree of passion is displayed by scientists in their diatribes against those who attack their beliefs and threaten their 'conceptual framework' (chapter 12). Against these critics, veritable witchhunts have been mounted comparable to those the mediæval Church launched against the proponents of new heresies. Take the case of Rachel Carson, who dared to suggest that synthetic organic pesticides, whose development in the 1940s was seen as one of the great scientific achievements of that period, actually did more harm than good and should be phased out. Rachel Carson's message was undoubtedly a very subversive one. 'The "control of nature" is a phrase conceived in arrogance,' she wrote,

> born of the Neanderthal Age of biology and philosophy, when it was supposed that nature exists for the convenience of man. The concepts

and practices of applied entomology, for the most part, date from that Stone Age of science. It is our alarming misfortune that so primitive a science has armed itself with the most modern and terrible weapons, and that in turning them against the insects it has also turned them against the earth.[4]

This was clearly more than mainstream scientists could take—the reaction was quick and venomous. Dr William B. Bean wrote in *Archives of Internal Medicine* that her pivotal work *Silent Spring* (1962), from the scientific point of view, is 'so much hogwash'.[5] The reaction to *The Limits to Growth* (the first report to the Club of Rome, published in 1972 by Donella and Dennis Meadows and others)[6] was equally emotional. It was lambasted by the editors of both *Nature* and *Science*, the two principal scientific journals in the English-speaking world, and by Lord Zuckerman, then chief scientist to the British Government, who referred to it as 'arbitrary speculation' and 'unscientific nonsense'.[7]

The reaction of the scientific world to Immanuel Velikovsky's heretical book *Worlds in Collision* (1950) was even more hysterical, as is well documented by Harold Brown.[8] Among other things, there was a concerted effort to force the publisher to take the book out of print. Scientists wrote numerous infuriated letters to the publishers and actually boycotted their salesmen and text books. The attack was so powerful that the publishers simply had to give in, even though it was one of their most profitable books. This does not seem to be the way that truly objective scientists would react to the publication of a dissenting book, as was eloquently acknowledged by the American cosmologist Carl Sagan in response to the affair.[9] Rather, it was the reaction of highly emotional, indeed, almost hysterical people who felt that the dissenter threatened to undermine scientific doctrines to which they were professionally and psychologically committed.

The truth is that human beings (whether scientists or not) are simply not designed to behave in a non-emotional way, which is one of the reasons why we are incapable of entertaining objective knowledge and behaving 'rationally'. Those imbued with the paradigm of science see this insuppressible human emotionality as a terrible human failing. Some go so far as to attribute it to a defect in our neuropsychological evolution that has prevented our neocortex—the seat of our intelligence—from dominating the older 'reptilian' parts of our brain—the seat of our emotions (chapters 9 and 37).

Arthur Koestler considers that this terrible evolutionary blunder can only be remedied by systematically subjecting ourselves to some form of chemotherapy.[10] But the suppression of our emotions would mean the eclipse of our closely associated values, our religiosity, our spirituality, our ability to sing and dance, laugh and weep, love and hate, *everything, in fact, that makes us human*—all in the interests of making us more rational and machine-like and hence better adapted to the aberrant and necessarily short-lived surrogate world that science has helped bring into being.

Up to a certain point, we can 'isolate' ourselves, to use Sigmund Freud's expression, from our emotions—splitting cognition from affect.[11] Freud saw this as an 'ego defence' or, in Ashis Nandy's words, 'a psychological mechanism to help the human mind cope with unacceptable or ego-alien inner impulses and external threats'.[12] It involves distancing oneself emotionally from a situation or an act that, to a normal human being, would otherwise be intolerable—'distancing' (as Bruno Bettelheim notes[13]) being, in the words of Nandy, a 'psychological device which both the victim and his oppressor have to use'. It is precisely by reducing a victim to the status of an object that one can face treating them in an inhuman way, which is why Aimé Césaire equates colonialism with 'thingification'.[14]

Scientists involved in designing instruments of mass destruction, such as nuclear bombs, must also be capable of distancing themselves emotionally. Robert Jungk describes his encounter with a mathematician he met on his last visit to Los Alamos,

> His face was wreathed in a smile of almost angelic beauty. He looked as if his gaze was fixed upon the world of harmonies. But in fact, he told me later he was thinking about a mathematical problem whose solution was essential to the construction of a new type of H-bomb.[15]

Jungk adds that this scientist never bothered to watch the trial explosion of any of the bombs he had helped produce. To him, 'research for nuclear weapons was just pure mathematics, untrammelled by blood, poison, or destruction.'

But is Jungk's mathematician as unemotional as he seems? Undoubtedly not. Scientific education does not suppress the emotions—*it merely displaces the object of the emotions*. Instead of teaching people to feel emotional about their family, their community, their traditional culture, their religion, and the beauty of their natural environment, they are taught instead to feel emotional about the scientific enterprise and the surrogate world of industrial artefacts it brings into being. Nor is the emotional attachment of the scientist to their work irrelevant to its achievement. Polanyi notes that 'scientific passions are no mere psychological by-product.' Instead, they have a logical function that contributes an indispensable element to science. . . . Passions charge objects with emotions, making them repulsive or attractive—positive passions affirm that something is precious.

It follows that

the excitement of the scientists making the discovery is an intellectual passion, telling that something is intellectually precious and, more particularly, that it is precious to science.[16]

In the same way, it can be argued that the witch-hunts mounted by the scientific community against those who threaten the credibility of the scientific enterprise are also 'precious to science'.

The ecology we need is not the ecology that involves viewing the biosphere on which we depend for our survival at a distance and with scientific detachment. We will not save our planet by means of a conscious, rational, and unemotional decision—a sort of 'ecological contract' based on a cost-benefit analysis. A *moral* and *emotional* commitment is required. Indeed, one of the key tasks of ecology must be to redirect our emotions so that they may fulfil the role they were designed for—to commit us to what should be the overriding human enterprise of maintaining the critical order of the biosphere.

17

ECOLOGY IS A FAITH

Unless ye believe, ye shall not understand.
St Augustine

Science is the new religion, and disinfectant is its holy water.
Anon.

[Science] has remained predominantly an anti-rationalistic movement
based upon a naïve faith.
A.N. Whitehead

We must now recognise belief once more as the source of all knowledge.
Michael Polanyi

V ERNACULAR PEOPLE BELIEVED unquestioningly in the sacred
principles underlying the cultural pattern with which they were
imbued. Since these principles had first been formulated by their ancestors who lived at the beginning of time, they had to be true. Who
were they to doubt the ancestral wisdom that these principles so clearly
embodied?

For Augustine of Hippo, knowledge was a gift of grace for which we
must strive under the guide of antecedent belief.[1] He dominated Christian thought for over a thousand years, until the end of the seventeenth
century. Then came the development of 'objective science', which was,
and still is, seen as being free of all contamination from subjective and
'irrational' human emotions, values, and beliefs.

John Locke, in particular, distinguished between faith and knowledge,
persuasion and certainty. It was particularly important to root out faith
or belief, for it was associated with religion and superstition. As Michael
Polanyi writes, 'all belief was reduced to the status of subjectivity—to
that of an imperfection by which knowledge fell short of universality.'
Without belief, however, there can be no knowledge. 'For all truth', as
Polanyi notes, 'is but the external pole of belief, and to destroy all belief
would be to deny all truth.'[2]

This is the overall theme of his seminal work *Personal Knowledge* (1958).
'Into every act of knowing', he writes, 'there enters a tacit and passionate
contribution of the person knowing what is being known,' and this, rather
than being imperfect, is 'a necessary component of all knowledge'.[3] For
him, the idea that reason and intelligence alone are the source of our understanding is sheer illusion.

> Tacit assent and intellectual passions, the sharing of an idiom and of a
> cultural heritage, affiliation to the like-minded community—such are the
> impulses which shape our vision of the nature of things on which we rely
> for our mastery of things. No intelligence, however critical or original,
> can operate outside such a fiduciary framework.[4]

That this must be so follows from the fact that the human neocortex,
which seems to be the seat of our intellectual activities, has not been
designed by its evolution to function by itself as an autonomous instrument of control any more than has the gene. The older parts of the brain,
which may be regarded as the seat of our values and emotions, have an
equal, and indeed possibly greater, role to play in determining adaptive
human behaviour.

Our leading philosophers of science and our more thoughtful scientists fully realise that science, too, is a faith, in that scientists accept uncritically the basic assumptions that underlie it. Karl Popper considers that 'scientific discovery is impossible without faith in ideas which are of a purely speculative kind,' and that this is 'completely unwarranted from the point of view of science'.[5] A.N. Whitehead considers that 'faith in the order of nature, which has made possible the growth of science, is a particular example of a deeper faith,' which 'cannot be justified by any inductive generalisation'.[6] C.H. Waddington agrees that scientists' work is influenced by their metaphysical beliefs[7] (a point also made by Ludwig von Bertalanffy, Thomas Kuhn, Paul Feyerabend, and others). To say this is no more than to say that the nature of scientists' work reflects the paradigm by which they seek to understand it and, indeed, the wider paradigm of science that has shaped their whole professional life.

Science, in many respects, is just another religion. Kuhn actually describes the scientific community in theological terms—intimating that it is a sort of priesthood.[8] John Passmore compares 'aristoscientists' with mediæval theologians.[9] In many ways, they are the priests of our industrial society. It is they who provide the information on the basis of which the industrial process is administered and without which it could not occur. It is they who have formulated the worldview that provides its rationale, and like other priesthoods, they have couched their holy texts in an esoteric language of their own that no outsider can understand. What is more, they have defined truth in such a way that they alone have access to it, for it must be established by a set of scientific rituals that only they can perform, for only they possess the necessary scientific skills, only they are equipped with the requisite scientific technology, and only they have access to the holy places where, in order to be effective, these rituals must be performed.

It is not surprising that their writings are imbued with an aura of sanctity previously reserved for the holy texts of the established religions. Indeed, if a proposition is classified as 'scientific', then it must be true, indeed incontestable—if, on the other hand, it is branded as 'unscientific', then it must be the work of a charlatan. This has provided the scientific-priesthood with the power to prevent any undesired deviation from scientific orthodoxy, just as the Catholic establishment of the Middle Ages could excommunicate any heretic whose teachings were a challenge to its authority. Science, thereby, has not banished faith. It has merely substituted faith in modern science for faith in conventional religion.

The worldview of 'ecology', with which we must replace it, is also a faith. It is a faith in the wisdom of those forces that created the natural world and the cosmos of which it is part; it is a faith in the latter's ability to provide us with extraordinary benefits—those required to satisfy our most fundamental needs; and it is a faith in our capacity to develop cultural patterns that can enable us to maintain its integrity and stability.

18

ECOLOGY REFLECTS THE VALUES OF
THE BIOSPHERE

Nature has . . . to be recognised as the first ethical teacher of man.
Peter Kropotkin

For primitive man, the universe as a whole is a moral or social order
governed not by what we call natural law but rather by what we must
call moral or ritual law.
A.R. Radcliffe-Brown

A thing is right when it tends to preserve the integrity, stability, and
beauty of the biotic community. It is wrong when it tends otherwise.
Aldo Leopold

FOR VERNACULAR PEOPLE, the laws of nature were essentially moral laws. In Ancient Greece, the natural world was seen to be governed by abstract cosmic forces, in particular, Moira (fate) and Dike (justice, law, and morality). These concepts are not really distinguishable. As F.M. Cornford notes, 'the ordinance of Fate is not a mere blind and senseless barrier of impossibility—*it is a moral decree*; the boundary of right and wrong.'[1]

Hesiod states clearly that, for him, the course of nature is governed by a moral law. 'When men do justice', he said,

> and do not go aside from the straight path of right, their city flourishes and they are free from war and famine. 'For them, the earth brings forth food in plenty, and on the hills the oak tree bears acorns at the top and bees in the middle; their sheep have heavy fleeces; their wives bear children that are like their parents.'[2]

On the other hand, if they do not do justice, if they divert from 'the straight path of right' and hence violate the moral laws of the cosmos, then—taking the form of Nemesis—the cosmos will strike back. Thus, when Œdipus committed incest, even if his crime was an unconscious one, both he and the whole land of Thebes were made to pay the penalty for violating the cosmic laws.

That the order of nature was a moral order, Cornford considers, was for the ancient Greeks an 'obvious, unchallengeable truth' and, indeed, 'the most important truth about the world'[3]—and this could probably be said of all vernacular people, even today. Furthermore, their idea of what constitutes morality is likely to be exactly the same as it was for the ancient Greeks.

The moral philosophers of today, on the other hand, do not see morality as in any way connected with our behaviour towards society, nature, or the cosmos. Instead, morality is seen as a unique and isolated phenomenon. Thus, Anthony Flew writes of G.E. Moore, probably the most influential moral philosopher of the twentieth century, that his 'argument proceeds as it were in suspense outside space and time—and, incidentally, in complete isolation from the progress of the natural and the human sciences'.[4] He could have said much the same for the arguments of most of the other moral philosophers of recent times (appendix 3).

The importance of ethics is today also seriously downplayed. Thus, T.L.S. Sprigge tells us that 'our moral life is not the most important aspect of our life,' and that 'we should conform to morality but seek our satisfaction elsewhere.'[5] The so-called 'emotivist' school of moral philosophy goes even further, regarding moral statements as 'non-factual'— neither true nor false, but merely reflecting someone's non-rational emotions.[6] This is clearly the view that best fits the paradigm of science.

The ethical attitudes of leading modern biologists and sociologists cast considerable light on the metaphysical assumptions and worldview underlying their scientific beliefs. The social Darwinists, such as Herbert Spencer in the UK and William Graham Sumner in the USA, saw nature as random, chaotic, atomised, competitive, and aggressive. They felt that it was natural, desirable, and indeed moral that people should behave in the same way. Another school of thought on morality is represented by T.H. Huxley, George Gaylord Simpson, and Jacques Monod, as well as Edward O. Wilson, Richard Dawkins, and the other sociobiologists. They agree that nature is 'red in tooth and claw', but they consider that it is humanity's duty, on the contrary, to declare war against nature. As Huxley puts it, 'the ethical progress of society depends not on imitating the cosmic process, still less in running away from it, *but in combating it.*'[7]

The third school can be represented by C.H. Waddington and Julian Huxley. They, too, saw nature as 'red in tooth and claw'. However, they rejected T.H. Huxley's view that people's behaviour is equally unpleasant, and also that we should wage war against nature. They felt that nature was evolving and would become more cooperative as it did so. It was thus by observing the laws of evolution that humanity could be moral.

In spite of their obvious differences, the scientists of all three schools have much in common—above all, their view of morality faithfully reflects the fundamental principles underlying the modernist paradigm of science. Thus, they all agree that morality begins with modern people and that we cannot talk of primal peoples or of other forms of life as being 'moral'. This was the view of both T.H. Huxley and Julian Huxley after him. Waddington felt that it is only when we pass on from the subhuman world to deal with the evolution of humanity that ethics must, in its own right, enter the picture. In a similar vein, Simpson tells us that 'there is no ethics but human ethics—and a search that ignores the necessity that ethics be human, relative to man, is bound to fail.'[8]

This theme of a transcendent humanity born into a fallen world is one of the main tenets of what is, in effect, a secular religious cult—one that follows a direct line from a number of well-documented religious cults and related philosophical movements that flowered in the early history of the Western world. One of the best-documented is Gnosticism, the 'heretical' early Christian movement that, like mainstream science, saw the natural world as fundamentally flawed—indeed, positively evil. The

Gnostics did not deny that there was order and law in the cosmos, but they believed that it was a 'rigid and inimical order—a tyrannical and evil law, devoid of meaning and goodness, alien to the purposes of man and to his inner essence.'[9] Hence, for them, God and the cosmos were no longer intimately related, as they were in the classical world (chapter 63). They had become alien to one another—indeed, opposites. Humanity, therefore, was condemned to cosmic solitude,[10] as we are condemned, too, in the minds of our leading scientists.

In this way, ethics is seen as being dependent on all those endowments supposedly unique to humanity—namely, the very consciousness, knowledge, and purpose denied to the natural world—for it is only by means of these that there can be reason and choice and thus morality. Monod and Simpson actually preached an 'ethic of knowledge'. The former saw this as being the only possible ethic for modern people and regards them as differing from 'animistic' or primal peoples, who, by contrast, believed in a purposive world, which is irreconcilable with objective or 'authentic' knowledge (chapter 2).[11] Julian Huxley also considers that scientific knowledge is good—its acquisition being essential for assuring the march of progress. It must follow that 'social morality' includes 'the duty of providing an immense extension of research, and its integrated planning, to provide the basis for desirable change'.[12] Scientific knowledge alone is also regarded as making democracy possible. Joseph Needham goes so far as to say that 'Democracy might . . . be termed that practice of which science is the theory,' while 'the subjective and the irrational are anti-democratic—they are the instruments of tyranny.'[13]

Monod tells us that the ethic of knowledge differs from all other previous ethics in that it has been adopted by an act of *objective* choice.[14] Simpson insists that 'choice' is morally good. 'Blind faith', on the other hand, 'is morally wrong.'[15] It must follow that as knowledge builds up our rational choices will change or rather 'evolve'. This means that our ethics must be flexible rather than absolute or universal. Change, insists Simpson, is 'the essence' of evolution—and for that reason alone, there can be no absolute standard of ethics. Simpson also considers that an evolutionary ethic 'cannot be expected to be absolute but must be subject to evolution itself'—in particular, it must 'be the result of responsible and rational choice in the full light of such knowledge of man and of life as we have'.[16] This was also essentially the view of Waddington and Julian Huxley.

The ethic of modernism is also an individualistic ethic. Simpson argues that even if we wished to derive an ethic from nature, it would still be individualistic, for evolution tends towards individualisation as opposed to higher integration, as ecologists once maintained. Humanity must be aware of 'the goodness of [the] maintenance of this individualisation' and promote 'the integrity and dignity of the individual'.[17] For sociobiologists, only an individualistic ethic is even conceivable, for an individual's overriding goal is the proliferation of their genes. The notion that in the natural world this goal may be subordinated to the needs of the community, the species, or the natural world itself is considered 'unscientific', and those who suggest such a notion, as does V.C. Wynne-Edwards,[18] are mercilessly derided. The occasional occurrence of such 'altruistic behaviour' is acknowledged but is explained away as merely serving to provide, in specific circumstances, the best means of satisfying the individual's overriding goal of maximum gene-proliferation.

There is a terrifying logic to this argument. For 'conscious' and 'rational' modern man—supposedly bereft of a subconscious, of emotions, of faith, who is allowed no attachments save of a rational and contractual nature, and who is deprived of any identity in an anonymous megasociety committed to perpetual growth—*there can be no alternative to the individualistic ethic.*

It is logically justified in another way. The ethic of modernism is the product of the conscious choice of the individual, who is seen to be external to the natural world or biosphere and thus free of the laws that govern its behaviour. Based on 'objective' and hence 'scientific' knowledge, this ethic can be sanctioned or authenticated by no authority *but that of the individual themselves*, endowed as they supposedly are with unique intellectual and moral gifts and armed with the unique potentialities of scientific knowledge. Not surprisingly, Simpson tells us that humanity can cherish values if it wishes to, *but they are its own self-imposed values*. No absolute ethics can be found 'outside of man's own nature'.[19] Monod is of the same mind. 'The ethic of knowledge', he writes, 'would not be imposed on man. It is he, on the contrary, who would impose it on himself.'[20] For the evolutionists (among them Julian Huxley and C.H. Waddington), modern people also authenticate their own moral choices —although these choices are further authenticated if they are natural and reflect the fundamental direction of the evolutionary process.

Above all, the ethic of modernism is the ethic of *progress*. As Julian Huxley writes, 'Social organisation should be planned not to prevent change, nor merely to permit it, *but to encourage it.*'[21] This is also logical, for if all benefits are derived from the technosphere (the surrogate world of industrial artefacts) and are thereby the product of economic development, which brings that world into being (chapter 39), then ethical behaviour must clearly be that which most favours this fatal process and best serves to preserve the order of the technosphere while continuing to improve and expand it.

Fortunately, others—mainly non-scientists—have returned to a more realistic view of morality. The Romantic poets, for instance, reacted against the ethic of modernism, as did the early ecologists. For Aldo Leopold, 'that land is a community is the basic concept of ecology, but that land is to be loved and respected is an extension of ethics.' 'We abuse land', he wrote, 'because we regard it as a commodity *belonging to us*,' but 'when we see land as a community *to which we belong*, we may begin to use it with love and respect.'[22] This is Leopold's famous 'land ethic'—it remains today the basic principle of ecological ethics.

In the 1940s, Ralph Gerard and the other members of the Chicago school of ecology saw nature as providing moral inspiration. The nature they saw was essentially cooperative rather than 'red in tooth and claw'. 'If nature is found to be a world of interdependence,' Gerard wrote, 'then man is obliged to consider that characteristic a moral dictum.' The evolutionary trend towards closer integration was, he argued, 'like a straight path through a dense wood, requiring of the pathfinder that he remain on the track and follow it through'.[23] The only problem is that Gerard's path seems to lead to an *over*-integrated biosphere—one that does not respect its critical order. He does not realise—and the same can be said for all those who believe integration or cooperation to be a good thing *in itself*—that the relative degree of integration that characterises an individual biological organism, for example, is incomparably higher than that which characterises a family, which in turn is greater than that required at the level of a community, still more so than at the level of society at large, and still more so again than at the level of an ecosystem, or indeed of the biosphere itself.

It follows that the path or 'Way' that is truly moral must be that which leads to the maintenance of the *appropriate degree* of integration required by natural systems at their particular level within the holarchy of the biosphere (chapter 38). Only if this condition is respected can they fulfil their essential whole-maintaining functions towards it (chapter 46), and only in this way can its critical order be maintained.

PART III

THE NATURE OF LIVING THINGS

·STABILITY·

19

STABILITY RATHER THAN CHANGE IS THE
BASIC FEATURE OF THE LIVING WORLD

Wherever we seek to find constancy, we discover change.
Daniel B. Botkin

Nature, left undisturbed, so fashions her territory as to give it almost un-
changing permanence of form, outline, and proportion, except when shattered by geologic convulsions—and in these comparatively rare cases of
derangement, she sets herself at once to repair the superficial damage and
to restore, as nearly as practicable, the former aspect of her dominion. . . .
A condition of equilibrium has been reached which, without the action of
man, would remain with little fluctuation for countless ages.
George Perkins Marsh

What is it that holds so many groups of animals to an astonishingly constant form over millions of years? This seems to be the problem now—the
problem of constancy rather than of change.
W.H. Thorpe

THE ATTENTION of those imbued with the paradigm of science and hence with the worldview of modernism is monopolised by change. For them, the world is in perpetual flux, constantly changing in a direction seen to be desirable and progressive. This is true of species that are seen to be 'evolving' and societies and their economies that are seen to be 'developing'. Reality is quite different. It is continuity or *stability* that has been the most striking feature of the world of living things.

Darwin himself was highly impressed by the constancy of the natural world and once even suggested that it may be more important than 'the struggle for existence' with which he was so concerned. In a letter to the geologist Charles Lyell, he wrote, 'If I had to commence *de novo*, I would have used "natural preservation".'[1] A similar view has also been expressed by George Gaylord Simpson, one of the founders of the *synthetic theory* of evolution, who admits that

> Heredity is, on the whole, a conservative factor tending to keep succeeding generations within a common pattern. The acorn produces an oak similar to the tree that produced the acorn, except in unessential details, and the egg produces a chicken essentially like the hen that laid it.[2]

But he cannot avoid highlighting that 'nevertheless . . . offspring are never precisely like their parents,' and that, 'since evolution is a process of change, these differences are of special concern to us . . .'

Theodosius Dobzhansky was also struck by the conservatism of nature, noting that

> the bones of Cretaceous opossums are similar to some modern ones; . . . modern horseshoe crabs (*Limulus*) do not differ greatly from those having lived some two hundred million years ago; the brachiopod *Lingula* changed little, if at all, for four hundred and fifty million years.[3]

W.H. Thorpe was also impressed by the constancy of living things. He fully realised that the constancy of certain biological forms is more difficult to explain 'than it is to account for their evolution'. He notes, for instance, that

> [the] wagtail (*Motacilla*), there in the garden, was here before the Himalayas were lifted up! This constancy is so extraordinary that it seems to demand a special mechanism to account not for the evolution but for the fixity of some groups.[4]

Paul Weiss also realised this. There is so great a preoccupation with change, he noted, that we have totally neglected the less glamorous but more fundamental constancy of the living world. 'In our educational system,' he writes, 'we are acting very much like newspaper editors, who highlight the spectacular and neglect the far more constant phenomena.'[5] Thus, we highlight evolution, but we do not impress on our children that the most fundamental features of all living things are exactly the same and 'have remained the same from the simplest living system that we know, all the way up to man'. They should also know that

> all the biochemical mechanisms of macromolecular synthesis, energy utilisation, respiration, storage, proliferation, cell division, membrane structure and function, contractility, excitability, fibre-formation, pigmentation, and so forth. All of these processes have remained unaltered in essence through the ages.[6]

This has been noted by the Harvard palæontologist Stephen J. Gould and his colleagues Steven Stanley and Niles Eldredge, who, between them, developed the theory of punctuated equilibrium, in terms of which long periods of stability are punctuated by short periods of dramatic and rapid evolutionary change. Like the similar notion put forward in the 1940s by Richard Goldschmidt (appendix 4), it is difficult to reconcile with the neo-Darwinian view that evolution occurs as the result of a gradual succession of small changes. Punctuated equilibrium is much easier to reconcile with the fossil record, as has always been known, and fits in much better with our knowledge of life processes.

What then explains this stability? Dobzhansky notes that 'we do not know what caused the living fossils to stop evolving.' A possible answer, he suggests, is that evolution simply stopped when a sufficient degree of adaptiveness was achieved. However, he admits that it is not obvious that opossums or horseshoe crabs are in any way better adapted than mice, cats, or lobsters. His own tentative answer is that 'the living fossils occupy ecological niches that have become perhaps more confining but otherwise not much altered for a long time.'[7] In what way, though, are they more confining? Why should this confinement not imply a better degree of adaptation? Dobzhansky provides no answers to these questions.

For Jacques Monod, the answer is to be found in the

> extreme coherence of a *teleonomic* system, which during evolution at once played the role of guide and of break, and has preserved, amplified, and integrated but an infinitesimal fraction of the astronomic number of possibilities offered to it . . .[8]

However, a teleonomic system is one that is programmed to achieve a specific goal (chapter 2)—but what is the goal? Monod does not say. He implies that it is to 'preserve, amplify, and integrate' the favoured minority of living things—the 'fittest' in Darwinian language—but why should this be so? For Monod, as for the rest of the scientific establishment, the explanation lies in the mysterious workings of 'the roulette of nature'—randomness, once again, being introduced to play the role of the *deus ex machina*.

C.H. Waddington more realistically attributes the 'resistance to change' of the living world to the relatively 'inert and stable' nature of the genetic material throughout the evolutionary period, and the continual shuffling and recombination of these existing genes within populations—the results being subject to further stabilising constraints exerted by the organism's developmental processes (see *chreods*, chapter 21).[9]

These are critical considerations. None of the scientists mentioned, however, entertains the possibility that it is the overriding goal of all living things to maintain their own stability within the context of the critical order of the wider biosphere, and that the dynamics of this process are such as to assure that this goal—in normal conditions—may be achieved (chapters 43 and 46).

If gradual evolutionary change were the norm, as neo-Darwinists assume, then we would expect that the incidence of random mutations would be high and that it would increase as systems become more highly developed. But the opposite seems to be the case. Random mutations are extremely rare, and this is no coincidence, as natural systems develop the most elaborate processes to avoid their occurrence and reduce their incidence to a minimum. Monod realised this. He notes that because of the conservative nature, as well as the perfection, of the process of replication, individual mutations are very rare events. What is more, once mutations do occur, special processes, which are perfected during the course of evolution, exist for assuring their elimination.[10] As Bryn Bridges points out, cells that have mutated as a result of exposure to radiation and to other mutagenic agents are, in normal conditions, eliminated by the body's immune system.[11] If it were not for this, the incidence of cancer would be even higher than it is today.

This must lead us to ask an embarrassing question. If genetic mutations play such an important part in evolutionary change, as neo-Darwinists tell us, yet a natural system does everything to prevent their occurrence and indeed seeks desperately to neutralise their effects when they do occur, how can it be considered to be geared to the achievement of such change? Richard Dawkins is fully aware of the contradiction in the neo-Darwinian thesis. He asks, 'Can we reconcile the idea that copying errors are an essential prerequisite for evolution to occur with the statement that natural selection favours high copying-fidelity?' The answer, he suggests, is that

> although evolution may seem, in some vague sense, a 'good thing', especially since we are the product of it, *nothing actually 'wants' to evolve.* Evolution is something that happens . . . in spite of all the efforts of the replicators (and nowadays of the genes) to prevent it happening.[12]

A point also made by Jacques Monod in his Herbert Spencer Lecture.

Quite clearly, natural systems are not geared towards change but towards the *avoidance* of change. Change occurs, not because it is desirable *per se*, but because, in certain conditions, it is judged to be necessary *as a means of preventing predictably larger and more disruptive changes.* This must be true of social evolution as well as biological evolution. The main feature of vernacular societies (within which humanity has spent well over ninety per cent of its experience on this planet) has also been their stability. This is particularly true of hunter-gatherer or 'forager' societies. During the Lower Palæolithic Period, for instance, flint-knapping techniques hardly changed for over 100 000 years, nor did the way of life of Australian Aborigines for at least 30 000 years. The anthropologist W.E.H. Stanner describes how the Australian ethos is one of continuity, constancy, balance, symmetry, and regularity. There are no great conflicts for power, no great contests for place or office. There is no idea of a formal chief in fact. They do not fight over land, there are no wars or invasions to seize territory, and they do not enslave each other. On the contrary,

> They place a very special value on things remaining unchangingly themselves, on keeping life to a routine which is known and trusted. Absence of change, which means certainty of expectation, seems to them a good thing in itself. . . . The value given to continuity is so high that they are not simply a people 'without a history'—they are a people who have been able, in some sense, to 'defeat' history, to become ähistorical in mood, outlook, and life.[13]

It is likely that much the same could be said of hunter-gatherer societies and tribal societies in general when living in the environment to which their cultural pattern has been adapted.

All this is unlikely to impress anyone. We have all been imbued with the notion of change as desirable in itself. Hunter-gatherers, most of us feel, must have had a very boring life, for they underwent no change— they had no 'history'. But is it so desirable to have such a history? It is very doubtful. Our history books are highlighted by wars, invasions, massacres, revolutions, assassinations, and intrigues. It makes for very depressing reading and does little more than illustrate the extreme squalor of human behaviour once vernacular communities and their cultural patterns have broken down. Indeed, if 'no news is good news' then we can equally well say that 'no history is good history'. The fact that hunter-gatherers did not have one reflects above all the orderliness and harmony of their lives, which were not afflicted by the increasingly intolerable discontinuities that today are rendering our lives ever less supportable.

In ecology, one of the problems with the term 'stability' is that it is used differently by different ecologists. Eugene Odum distinguishes between two different types of stability. The first is 'resistance stability', which he defines as 'the ability of an ecosystem to resist perturbations ... and maintain its structure and function intact' (*i.e.* its immunity to disturbance). The second is 'resilience stability', which he takes to be the 'ability to recover when a system is disrupted by a perturbation'[14] (*i.e.* its ability to heal itself). An example of the former is provided by the California Redwood, which is resistant to fire by virtue of its thick bark and other features, but which, if it happens to burn, will recover but very slowly or perhaps never at all. An example of the latter is provided by the Californian chaparral vegetation, which is very easily burned but recovers quickly.

G.H.Orians, who distinguishes between no fewer than seven different types of stability, makes a similar distinction between 'inertia' or 'the ability of a system to resist external perturbations', and 'amplitude', which he defines as 'the area over which a system is stable'[15] (*i.e.* the range or extent to which it can be displaced from a previous state and yet return to it), a concept similar to Odum's 'resilience stability'.

The Canadian ecologist C.S.Holling refuses to accept that either Odum's 'resistance stability' or Orians's 'inertia' is a viable strategy for survival, one that leads to 'persistence'.[16] For him, a stable system is one that returns to 'an equilibrium state' after a temporary disturbance and 'with the least fluctuations'. He includes in this category living things that have not been subjected to change for a long time. These are very vulnerable to environmental change and thereby cannot be regarded as 'persistent'. He then contrasts stable systems with resilient systems that are characterised by large fluctuations and that alone are 'persistent'. He does not seem to notice the irony of classifying as 'non-persistent' such organisms as the horseshoe crab, which has remained virtually unchanged for some two hundred million years at least, while reserving the term persistent to 'resilient' species like the fruit-fly that is constantly developing new forms. This is quite clear to Waddington. The distinction that Holling makes between stability and resilience he sees as based on 'a confusion between two different types of stability'.[17]

But Holling is a disciple of Ilya Prigogine and thus committed to the most extreme form of the paradigm of science and the worldview of modernism. For him, stability means stagnation, a bad word. In the world in which we live, in any case, it is not an option. Increasingly, he writes, 'we must learn to live with disturbances and live with variability and live with uncertainties.'[18] Discontinuities, such as floods, droughts, epidemics, wars, pollution disasters, the erosion of the ozone layer, and climate change, are presumably desirable because out of such 'fluctuations' emerge progress and order.

I think we can reject Holling's views on stability. Eugene Odum's distinction between 'resistance' and 'resilience' stability, on the other hand, seems very sensible. Of course, we can refine the concept as Orians sought to do. In particular, we can regard a resilient system as more or less stable in accordance with the size of the discontinuities that affect it, and from which it must then recover (chapter 48). What is important is that if a system evolves, so it becomes capable of reducing such discontinuities to a minimum. As this occurs, it comes to enjoy a more cooperative relationship with the other systems that make up the larger system of which it is part (chapters 44 and 45). And as this larger system becomes more highly integrated, so 'resilience stability' evolves into 'resistance stability'.

20

LIFE PROCESSES SEEK STABILITY

. . . all the vital mechanisms, varied as they are, have but one purpose—that of preserving whole the conditions of life in the internal environment.
Claude Bernard

[Homeostasis refers to] the coordinated physiological processes which maintain most of the steady states in the organism . . . a condition which may vary, but which is relatively constant.
Walter Cannon

Health is a continuing property, potentially measurable by the individual's ability to rally from insults, whether chemical, physical, infectious, psychological, or social.
J. Ralph Audy

B IOLOGICAL ORGANISMS are self-regulating cybernetic systems capable, by their own efforts, of maintaining their stability (both resistance and resilience) in the face of internal or external challenges—a quality referred to as *homeostasis*. A natural system controlled by an agent external to the biosphere, however, cannot be stable. Because the external agent is not an integral part of the wider biosphere, it is not subject to its regulatory influence and so cannot act towards the maintenance of its integrity. Instead, the external agent will steer the natural system towards its own specific goals, which are external—and thus random—to those of the biological, social, and ecological systems it attempts to control.

Hippocrates considered that diseases were cured by the natural actions of the body. As the physiologist Walter Cannon notes, this implies the existence of agencies that are ready to operate correctively when the normal state of the organism is upset. The nineteenth-century French physiologist Claude Bernard was also impressed by the way in which living cells maintain the constancy of their 'internal environment' (*milieu intérieur*). For him, 'the constancy of the internal environment is the condition for the free and independent life'[1]—a principle still fundamental to physiology. The same principle was noted in 1885 by the German physiologist Eduard Pflüger and also by his Belgian colleague, Léon Frédéricq. 'Each disturbing influence', the latter wrote,

> induces by itself the calling forth of compensatory activity to neutralise or repair the disturbance. The higher in the scale of living beings, the more numerous, the more perfect, and the more complicated do these regulatory agencies become. They tend to free the organism completely from the unfavourable influences and changes occurring in the environment.[2]

For Bernard, to achieve this must be the fundamental goal of all living things.

The term 'homeostasis' was first coined by Cannon in his seminal book *The Wisdom of the Body* (1932). It is worth considering the concept in some detail. Cannon was struck by the fact that organisms,

> composed of material which is characterised by the utmost inconstancy and unsteadiness, have somehow learned the method of maintaining constancy and keeping steady in the presence of conditions which might reasonably be expected to prove profoundly disturbing.

For instance, mammals can maintain the constancy of their body temperature in spite of external changes.

For a short time, men may be exposed to dry heat at temperatures from 115 to 128 degrees Centigrade (239 to [262] degrees Fahrenheit) without an increase of their body temperature above normal. On the other hand, arctic mammals, when exposed to cold as low as 35 degrees Centigrade below freezing (31 degrees below zero Fahrenheit), do not manifest any noteworthy fall of body temperature.[3]

Resistance to changes induced by external circumstances (resistance stability), Cannon notes, is not the only evidence of adaptive stabilising arrangements. Natural systems are also capable of resisting disturbances from within. For instance,

the heat produced in maximal muscular effort, continued for twenty minutes, would be so great that, if it were not promptly dissipated, it would cause some of the albuminous substances of the body to become stiff, like a hard-boiled egg. Again, continuous and extreme muscular exertion is accompanied by the production of so much lactic acid (the acid of sour milk) in the working muscles that within a short period it would neutralise all the alkali contained in the blood if other agencies did not appear and prevent that disaster.[4]

The constancy that living things achieve, some might be tempted to term equilibrium. That word, however, has come to have a fairly exact meaning as applied to relatively simple physico-chemical states in which physico-chemical forces are balanced. Homeostasis is a far more complex condition. It is not 'something set and immobile, a stagnation,' but a dynamic condition. What is more, 'the coordinated physiological processes' required to maintain it 'are . . . complex and . . . peculiar to living things—involving, as they may, the brains and nerves, the heart, lungs, kidneys, and spleen all working cooperatively'.[5]

Homeostasis also develops through time. All the cooperating factors can be brought into action successively as well as at the same time. Cannon notes, as did Frédéricq, that as an organism evolves, the homeostatic processes that assure the constancy of its internal environment also become correspondingly more elaborate. Thus,

lower animals, which have not yet achieved the degree of control of stabilisation seen in the more highly evolved forms, are limited in their activities and handicapped in the struggle for existence.[6]

A frog, for instance, is not capable of preventing water from evaporating from its body, nor can it regulate its own body temperature. This means that if it leaves the pond in which it normally lives, it soon dries up, and when it gets cold, it must seek refuge in the mud at the bottom of its pond and hibernate until spring.

Reptiles have developed more effective homeostatic processes against rapid loss of water, which means that they no longer have to remain close to ponds or streams and can even survive in very dry conditions. But like amphibians, they have no homeostatic processes to insulate their internal environment against changes of temperature. They are still 'cold-blooded', which means that during the winter they too must give up an active existence. As Cannon writes,

> only among the higher vertebrates—the birds and mammals—has there been acquired that freedom from the limitations imposed by cold that permits activity throughout the year in any climate.[7]

Interestingly enough, Cannon considers the probability that such processes may not only be operative in biological organisms but also in other natural systems, which could also explain their constancy. A comparative study, he suggests, might show that every complex organisation must be capable of 'more or less effective self-righting adjustments in order to prevent a check on its functions or a rapid disintegration of its parts when it is subjected to stress'.[8]

Significantly, B.C. Patten and Eugene Odum also see homeostatic processes or 'checks and balances (or forces and counter-forces) that dampen oscillations' as operating 'all along the line' and hence not only at the level of the individual, where, for instance, they 'keep our body temperature constant, despite fluctuations in the environment' but also at the level of the population, the community, and the ecosystem.[9]

Roy Rappaport was probably one of the first anthropologists to show that tribal societies are also capable of such behaviour. In his seminal book *Pigs for the Ancestors* (1967), he interpreted the ritual cycle of a small social group in New Guinea in cybernetic terms, showing it to be, above all, a means of controlling its impact on its natural environment so as to assure its sustainability or stability.[10] Gerardo Reichel-Dolmatoff, quite independently of Rappaport, interpreted the cultural pattern of the indigenous Tukano of Colombia in much the same way.[11] Thomas Harding also sees tribal societies as capable of homeostatic behaviour and thereby of maintaining their stability.

> When acted upon by external forces, a culture will, if necessary, undergo *specific* changes only to the extent of, and with the effect of, preserving unchanged its *fundamental* structure and character.[12]

That ecosystems are geared to the maintenance of their homeostasis is denied by mainstream ecologists today, as it is difficult, if not impossible, to reconcile with the reductionist paradigm of science. However, if ecosystems are not cybernetic (and hence self-regulating), as Patten and Odum ask,[13] *then by what other means could the perceived harmony of the biosphere have evolved?* Most modern ecologists would give the neo-Darwinian answer—by natural selection from random mutations and hence by a crude and rudimentary mechanism largely determined by external factors, such as competition and selection. Thus, R.J. Putman and S.D. Wratten insist that self-regulatory behaviour at the level of an ecosystem is largely due to *intra*specific competition for a resource. They nevertheless admit that such competition seems to achieve an equilibrium 'well before the limiting resource starts to act as a finite shortage'.[14] This suggests that natural systems are capable of foresight and planning (chapter 30)—but Putman and Wratten deny this. Such a notion is irreconcilable with the reductionist paradigm of science.

Eugene Odum and B.C. Patten, on the other hand, do not believe that competition alone can explain the order displayed by ecosystems.

> Either the ecosystem is orderly... or its lack of chaos just happened to develop from unregulated Darwinian struggles between competing populations all alone and uninfluenced, except by each other, on the neutral slate of life. The latter seems implausible for us.[15]

Odum notes how ecosystems are endowed with the necessary means for self-regulation and hence homeostasis.

> Besides energy flows and material cycles... ecosystems are rich in information networks comprising physical and chemical communication flows that connect all parts and steer or regulate the system as a whole. Accordingly, ecosystems can be considered cybernetic... in nature, but control functions are internal and diffuse rather than external and specified, as in human-engineered cybernetic devices.[16]

Howard Odum (brother of Eugene) refers to these physical and chemical information networks as the 'invisible wires of nature', which are 'analogous to, but far less visible than, the nervous or hormonal systems of organisms'.[17]

A number of experiments have been carried out to determine whether ecosystems display resilience stability (chapter 19), and if so, whether this can be attributed to their own efforts (and hence whether they are cybernetic or self-regulating systems capable of maintaining their homeostasis).

The best known of such experiments are those conducted by Daniel Simberloff and Edward O. Wilson. They removed all the fauna from several small mangrove islets and then closely watched the way these were recolonised by terrestrial arthropods. They established that, though the islets were eventually populated by usually very different species from the original ones, the total number of species was very much the same as before.[18]

Three years later, Harold Heatwole and Richard Levins examined the same data. Their interest was to classify the different species to be found there in terms of trophic organisation (the roles and relationships within the food web), noting the number of species in each of the trophic categories (herbivores, scavengers, detritus feeders, predators, *etc.*). The results were highly significant. They showed that the trophic *structure* of the communities on the different islets displayed a remarkable stability, even though the actual species composing each of the trophic categories had undergone a considerable change.[19] This experiment clearly illustrates the principle of homeostasis, though this is denied by Putman and Wratten. They insist that what Heatwole and Levins witnessed was not 'the recovery of a disturbed system' *but the creation of a completely new one*, which means that there is no evidence for any cybernetic process at work.[20]

Putman and Wratten's error is that they assume that a goal-directed life process (that they refer to as 'deterministic') must, like a machine, display '*micro*-determinacy'. But, as Paul Weiss has taken so much trouble to show, it only displays '*macro*-determinacy' (chapter 43). In other words, to be stable, a natural system need only preserve its basic pattern or basic features, *not every detail of its structure*, as in the case of a homeostatic machine. Indeed, the details must necessarily change in answer to changing environmental conditions, as it is only in this way that bigger and more devastating changes can be avoided. What is important is that *the underlying trophic structure* of the ecosystem studied by Heatwole and Levins was restored. The fact that the actual species that took over the different trophic functions were no longer the same is beside the point. Indeed, that the same functions can be taken over in this way by different species demonstrates just how adaptive are the processes assuring the homeostasis or stability of ecosystems. It provides a perfect illustration of Weiss's 'principle of conservation of *overall* pattern',[21] which is really but another way of stating the principle of ecological homeostasis.

James Lovelock, in his seminal book *Gaia—A New Look at Life on Earth* (1979), shows that the biosphere itself displays homeostasis. Dorion Sagan and Lynn Margulis are also struck by the extraordinary stability of the earth's living conditions.[22] It must have been maintained very much as it is now, at least 'since the time that air-breathing animals have been living in forests'—or for about 300 million years. Fossil records show that the climate has varied relatively little since life first appeared on earth about 3500 million years ago. Yet the output of heat from the sun, the surface properties of the earth, and the composition of the atmosphere have almost certainly varied greatly over the same period.

For the incredible stability of world climate to have been the result of pure chance is for Lovelock 'as unlikely as to survive unscathed a drive blindfolded through rush-hour traffic'.[23] Again, the only explanation is that life must have developed the capacity for self-regulation, so maintaining its own stability. Lovelock refers to Cannon's work on the homeostasis of biological organisms and considers that there must be a similar homeostatic process regulating the temperature of the planet, a conclusion that has the widest possible implications for our view of the natural world and our interrelationship with it.

The principle of homeostasis is somewhat of an embarrassment to reductionist science. It is difficult to reconcile with the dogma that living things are in a permanent state of flux, as it is with the notion that they learn only by the crude process of trial and error, or that their adaptive responses are selected by an undefined environment, or, alternatively, are simply impromptu responses triggered by specific environmental stimuli. Nonetheless, that biological organisms are geared to maintaining their homeostasis is now difficult to deny, but that vernacular societies or ecosystems do as well is accepted only by a small minority of social scientists and ecologists, and that the biosphere itself does so, by a still smaller minority.

What is missing from the whole discussion of homeostasis, however, is the realisation that natural systems are integral parts of the wider *holarchy* of the biosphere (chapter 42), and that a system cannot maintain its homeostasis *unless the holarchy of natural systems of which it is part is also capable of doing so.* In other words, a system can only be stable if the larger system of which it is part is also stable. There is no stable economy, for instance, within an unstable society, no stable society within an unstable ecosystem, and no stable anything when the biosphere itself is being destabilised, as is happening today. Hence, for a natural system to maintain its own homeostasis, its behaviour must act in such a way that simultaneously maintains the integrity of the larger system of which it is part (chapter 43), which means its overriding consideration must be that of maintaining the critical order or stability of the biosphere.

21

LIFE PROCESSES SEEK A STABLE
COURSE OF DEVELOPMENT

Homeorhesis makes homeostasis possible by ensuring the structural
composition [or development] of the organs.
Jean Piaget

We use the word homeorhesis when what is stabilised is not a constant
value but is a particular course of change in time.
C.H. Waddington

IN SPITE OF THE BASIC TENDENCY IN NATURE towards relative constancy, living things are changing dynamically all the time. Thus, a fertilised egg develops into a fœtus, a child into an adult, a pioneer ecosystem into a climax ecosystem, and unicellular organisms (sometimes) into multicellular organisms. How do we reconcile this tendency towards change with the thesis of overall stability?

From the evolutionary point of view, these processes of change do not violate the principle of stability so long as we see them holistically. Individual generations of organisms (ontogenies) can thus be regarded as 'feelers' enabling the long-term evolutionary process—the biospheric process—to monitor its interactions with, and thereby permit its adaptation to, its environment (chapter 37).

Seen cybernetically, the development of an individual organism occurs along a closely integrated constellation of set-paths, which C.H. Waddington refers to as *chreods* (from the Greek root χρή (*chre*), it needs, and ὁδός (*hodos*), a path or way). The total constellation of chreods along which a system needs to develop constitutes what Waddington refers to as the 'epigenetic landscape'—the developmental path the system is constrained to follow by virtue of the instructions with which it is endowed in addition to the constraints it is subject to from the larger system of which it is an integral part (chapter 5). A developing system thereby displays 'a certain lack of flexibility'—its development has

> a strong tendency to proceed to some definite end-point. For instance, the adult tissues, such as muscle, nerve, lung, kidney, *etc.*, are quite distinct from one another, and it is rather difficult to persuade developing cells to differentiate into something intermediate between these main types. Again, the animal as a whole will very often succeed in 'regulating', that is to say, in reaching its normal adult state in spite of injuries or abnormal circumstances it may have met during the course of its development.[1]

This ability has been noticed by many students of development, among them Hans Driesch, who noted the remarkable 'equipotentiality' of the sea-urchin embryo (chapter 38). He and others also pointed to the ability of a fertilised egg to develop into a normal embryo even after undergoing severe amputations. This goal-seeking behaviour of a developing embryo remains inexplicable in terms of mechanistic science.

The tendency of a developing system to maintain itself on its preset path along its constellation of chreods and to correct any disturbances that might divert it, Waddington refers to as *homeorhesis* (from the Greek ὅμοιος (*homeos*), same, and ῥέος (*rheos*), stream). Homeorhesis is the principle of homeostasis applied to a predetermined path or trajectory rather than to a fixed point in space-time. G.H. Orians refers to it as 'trajectory stability', that he defines as 'the property of a system to move towards some final end point or zone, despite differences in starting points.' This, he tells us, is the sort of stability that plants tend to achieve during plant succession, 'where a single "climax" state may be reached from a variety of starting points,'[2] (*i.e.* equifinality—see also chapter 2).

It is reasonably clear that a climax is not a point fixed in space and time. Life processes are dynamic, creative, intelligent, and anticipatory (chapters 28, 29, 32, and 30). This means that in changing environmental conditions a living thing can develop in a new direction so as to achieve a new endstate or climax—one that, on the basis of its model of its relationship with its environment, would appear to constitute a position of still greater stability, one in which discontinuities would be still further reduced.

Of course, this process is itself subject to the constraints of the larger system of which it is a part. It is the homeostasis of the biosphere that homeorhetic processes ultimately seek to achieve—since this is a prerequisite of their own stability (chapter 20).

During the course of this book, I shall seek to show that all life processes, *including evolution*—the biospheric process—are homeorhetic in this way, regardless of the level of organisation at which they occur (chapter 37).

22

LIFE PROCESSES DEVELOP SEQUENTIALLY
TOWARDS THE MOST STABLE STATE

Pioneer species are outcompeted not solely because the environment no longer suits them but also because they are by nature poor competitors. . . . As soon as a relatively stable community develops, in which competition between organisms for available resources becomes more intense, such organisms cannot persist.

R.J. Putman and S.D. Wratten

That ecological succession is a developmental process and not just a succession of species each acting alone remains one of the most important unifying theories in ecology.

Eugene Odum

Development does not occur by chance through encounters with the physical and social environment but follows a certain direction—in the development of thought, particularly, there are sequences or stages of progressive structuration.

Bärbel Inhelder

ALL LIFE PROCESSES are sequential. This implies that their various
stages must occur in the right order, so much so that if one stage is
left out, then the succeeding stages will not occur or will occur only imperfectly. It also implies that each stage of development must occur in
the specific environmental context to which it is adaptive (chapter 49).
Let me try to make this a little clearer.

All behaviour must be seen as modifying the environment, not in a
random way but as part of a wider strategy. Thus, the new environment
will be that which best serves to elicit the behaviour that leads to the next
stage in the strategy. This does not mean that the whole process is predetermined in a precise way, for at each stage there may be a large number
of variants of a basic behavioural response—the given conditions determining which of these (whether one or more) will be adopted.

Jean Piaget was struck by the 'sequential character of development' that
exhibits 'a series of stages, of which each one necessarily results from the
preceding one'.[1] Indeed, that embryological development, occurring as it
does within a highly protected and ordered environment, constitutes a
planned and sequential strategy, is fairly obvious—but so is the learning
process. Piaget and Bärbel Inhelder pointed out at Arthur Koestler's important Alpbach symposium that

> learning is definitely dependent upon the subject's developmental level.
> Generally, in all this research, it has been shown that the child never man-
> ages to accomplish more than the passage from one sub-stage to the next,
> without ever jumping a stage.[2]

An essential feature of sequential development is that it must occur at the
appropriate rate. If it is speeded up or slowed down, the end product is
unlikely to be optimum. The reason is that any behavioural process or
strategy, because of the holarchical organisation of the biosphere (chapter 42), is likely to be part of a larger process or strategy with which it
must be synchronised. Rupert Riedl refers to the inertia caused by the
need to synchronise a process with a host of others as its 'burden'.[3] Piaget
and Inhelder note the impossibility of accelerating the passage from one
stage to the next. Indeed,

> if mechanisms in mental development can be compared to what [C.H.]
> Waddington (in embryology) calls 'chreods', or necessary paths with a
> 'time-tally', it appears obvious that development always has an optimum
> rate, neither too slow nor too fast.[4]

For Piaget and Inhelder, cognitive development is governed by precisely the same laws that govern embryological development. This is not very surprising, since the development of a fœtus within the womb and a child's upbringing within its family clearly form a single process. The notion that they should be governed by different laws is only conceivable because scientific knowledge is arbitrarily compartmentalised, and those two sub-processes are thereby studied in terms of separate disciplines.

The sequential principle in ecology is known as 'ecological succession'. Succession was regarded by Frederic Clements, one of the founders of holistic ecology in academia, as fundamental to the developing science of ecology. Nature, he considered, did not move aimlessly but in a steady flow towards stability. In a specific environment, a clear progression could be plotted through what Clements called a 'sere', which begins in the pioneer stage with an unbalanced and relatively unstable assemblage, and ends with a complex and stable equilibrium-community capable of sustaining itself indefinitely. Clements emphasised the role of climate in determining the nature of the sere, and he also established the principle that in any given habitat the sere could only end in a single climax (monoclimax).[5] Both these positions later came under serious attack.

Clements's theory of succession to the climax, as Donald Worster notes, undoubtedly reflected his 'underlying, almost metaphysical faith that the development of vegetation must resemble the growth process of an individual plant or animal organism'.[6] This view is unacceptable to modern science and hence to modern scientific ecology on a number of counts. Firstly, it tends to confirm the scientifically unacceptable idea that an ecosystem is a kind of superorganism or 'complex organism', as Clements maintained, or at least that it resembles an organism in a significant way. Secondly, it implies that the development of an ecosystem is not the result of random changes selected by an undefined environmental 'invisible hand' in accordance with the neo-Darwinian thesis but occurs instead according to an orderly strategy. Thirdly, it implies that this strategy is carefully coordinated by the ecosystem, which means that ecological development is at once purposeful and holistic—which is doubly anathema to mainstream scientists and scientific ecologists for whom life processes are blind, random, and atomised.

It is unacceptable for another closely associated reason. It implies that the goal of ecological development is the achievement of stability, whereas our modern industrial society is committed to perpetual change in a single direction, one that requires the reversal of the successional process or sere in order to assure the artificial maintenance of an ecosystem at its most productive *but highly unstable* pioneer stage.

To accept the principle of ecological succession to a climax is thus to accept the implication that economic development is inherently destructive, and, not surprisingly, ecologists had to reject Clements's thesis. Of course, Clements may well have gone too far—for instance, climate is clearly not the only factor in determining the nature of the climax; nevertheless, his *basic* thesis must be regarded as correct.

As ecology became increasingly distorted to make it conform to the paradigm of reductionist science, succession came to be seen, not surprisingly, as largely random. As Henry Gleason, who first formulated the new view of succession, wrote in 1927, 'In the centre of an association . . . we see only the fluctuations in structure from year to year.' He even suggested that succession might be retrogressive.[7]

The whole question of succession to a climax came to a head during the debate over the Dust Bowl that had devastated the Great Plains of North America in the 1930s. Ecologists at the time showed that the crisis was the result of human activity. Ploughing the delicate southern plains, ecologists maintained, should never have been undertaken. It caused the land to diverge from its climax stage, and the Dust Bowl was the inevitable consequence. During the debate that followed, the very notion of a 'climax' came under attack. Arthur Tansley was particularly keen to discredit the concept. He insisted that humanity, with its great ingenuity, was capable of creating its own climax—an 'anthropogenic climax' as he referred to it—which he insisted could even be superior to the natural variety.[8]

Clements's climax was also attacked very bitterly by the agricultural historian, James Malin. For him, the large-scale mechanised agriculture, which was seen by ecologists as responsible for the Dust Bowl, was another step in the march of progress. The plains had benefited from it, nature needed to be ploughed up, and blowing dirt around was necessary for it 'to remain vigorous and fertile'.[9] Clements was the bogey man. His writings provided the rationale for the 'hysterical' conspiracy against 'progress' and had to be discredited.

> The conventional or traditional concept of the state of nature must be abandoned—that mythical, idealised condition in which natural forces, biological and physical, were supposed to exist in a state of virtual equilibrium, undisturbed by man.[10]

Malin never bothered to disguise his motives. The idea of a climax 'assumes the end of change' and hence of economic development, which he and his colleagues saw as a panacea for every possible problem.

Ironically, it is the anti-ecological ideas of Gleason, Tansley, and Malin that have come to be regarded as the ecological orthodoxy. It is the view of R.E. Ricklefs that

> in recent years the concept of the climax as an organism or unit has been greatly modified to the point of outright rejection by many ecologists, with the recognition of communities as open systems whose composition varies continuously over environmental gradients.[11]

In line with current scientific dogma, ecological succession is now explained in terms of competition and related to the properties of populations rather than whole ecosystems. This is the view put forward today in most ecological text books, such as that written by R.J. Putman and S.D. Wratten.[12]

It is difficult to see how scientific ecologists can really believe this. The operation of all sorts of internally generated negative feedback processes (Howard Odum's 'invisible wires of nature'—chapter 20), which inhibit the growth of species that are displaced in the succession towards a climax, should be evident to all. Ricklefs alludes to the operation of such a process when describing succession on abandoned farmland in the Piedmont region of North Carolina. He describes how

> decaying horseweed roots stunt the growth of horseweed seedlings—this self-inhibiting effect, whose function and origin is not understood, cuts short the life of horseweed in the sere. Such growth inhibitors presumably are the by-product of other adaptations that increase the fitness of horseweed during the first year of succession. If horseweed plants had little chance of persisting during the second year, owing to invasion of the sere by superior competitors, self-inhibition would have little negative selective value.[13]

Putman and Wratten also refuse to accept that the development of an ecosystem towards a climax is part of a long-term strategy. This means that the climax cannot be taken to its logical outcome—instead it must be seen as 'thrust upon' the system from the outside. For this reason, they suggest that we abandon the use of the term climax altogether and use instead the term 'end community'.[14]

How, then, do Putman and Wratten propose that succession occurs? They offer the sort of simplistic explanation that can be quantified and modelled by systems ecologists (chapter 14). They suggest that succession is the result of 'an accumulation of biomass' that stops when the process comes up against gross features of the environment that are immutable, such as a shortage of resources for further growth. Alternatively, they see it in purely energetic terms as 'an imbalance within the energy relations of the community resulting in the accumulation of biomass by the community'.[15] Both these explanations are based on the notion that the behaviour of an ecosystem is random, mechanistic, and individualistic and thereby uncoordinated, passive, and externally controlled, like all the life processes that have been made to fit, Procrustean-like, into the reductionist paradigm of science.

Putman and Wratten go further. Productivity, they tell us, is often low in a climax compared to earlier stages in the succession, 'Due to the complexity of web-design, cycling of material through the system is extremely slow.'[16] Such features of a climax have traditionally been regarded as beneficial. But Putman and Wratten wonder if they really are. They point out that there are 'many examples of far more productive, indeed far more diverse communities characteristic of earlier pre-climax seral stages.' They then ask whether a climax is, in fact, tantamount to over-maturity.[17] The argument assumes that *productivity* is the yardstick for judging ecosystems—the position taken by Tansley and Malin when they opposed the application of any constraints on humanity's ecologically destructive agricultural activities in the southern plains.

Unfortunately, Putman and Wratten are thoroughly representative of modern ecologists, whose work serves, above all, to rationalise technological progress. For Putman and Wratten, a biological explanation of succession towards a climax is not necessary. All we are witnessing, they tell us, is a phenomenon equivalent to 'a class of statistical processes known as a "regular Markov chain"',[18] which, as we have seen (chapter 14), bears but the most superficial resemblance to the ecological strategy required to achieve a stable endstate or climax.

Eugene Odum is one of the few modern scientific ecologists to retain a holistic view of succession. For him, the main features of the process are the more or less directional and predictable sequence of populations, its ability to correct divergences from its optimum course (Waddington's chreods) that will lead to the requisite climax, and its achievement of an increasingly refined and stable state as it reaches its climax, thereby converting 'an inorganic environment to a more organic one' (chapter 65).[19]

In an earlier textbook, Odum is still more explicit. Succession, he tells us, is

(1) . . . the orderly process of community changes—these are directional and therefore predictable. (2) It results from the modification of the

physical environment and population structure by the community. (3) It culminates [in] the establishment of as stable an ecosystem as is biologically possible on the site in question.[20]

He also points out that ecological succession '*is community controlled*' and insists that 'each set of organisms changes the physical substrate and the microclimate (local conditions of temperature, light, and so on),' thereby making conditions favourable for another set of organisms, and that 'When the site and the community has been modified as much as it can be by biological processes, a steady-state develops—at least in theory.'[21]

In the same book, he highlights the similarity between the development of an organism and that of an ecosystem. He asks us to think of the temporary communities as developmental stages analogous to the life-history stage through which many organisms pass before reaching adulthood.[22] At the same time, he notes that the mature community, with its greater diversity, larger organic structure, and balanced energy flows, is often able to buffer the physical environment to a greater extent than the young community, which is often the more productive. Thus, the achievement of a measure of stability or homeostasis, rather than a mere increase in productivity in a fluctuating physical environment, may well be the primary purpose (that is, the survival value) of ecological succession when viewed from the evolutionary standpoint.

It is unlikely that any other leading ecologist today would dare state this unfashionable principle quite so explicitly—yet, if it is not faced, there is no way in which the behaviour of an ecosystem can be understood; no way, either, in which we can realise just how unnatural and how destructive is the idea of economic development or 'progress', which seeks to maximise production, regardless of its destabilising effects on biological, social, and ecological systems.

23

INTERNALISING COORDINATION
LEADS TO GREATER STABILITY

The operation of ritual among the Tsembaga and other Maring helps to
maintain an undegraded environment, limits fighting to frequencies which
do not endanger the existence of the regional population, adjusts man–
land ratios, facilitates trade, distributes local surpluses of pig throughout
the regional population in the form of pork, and assures people of high-
quality protein when they are most in need of it.

Roy Rappaport

Animals . . . are metaphors for survival. By analysing animal behaviour,
the Indians try to discover an order in the physical world, a world-order to
which human activities can then be adjusted.

Gerardo Reichel-Dolmatoff

A S NATURAL SYSTEMS DEVELOP towards their climax stage, their homeostatic processes become increasingly refined and, consequently, their relationship with their environment becomes more stable. Regulatory controls are thus progressively *internalised*. In the early stages of development, however, controls are relatively crude and are often applied by external factors. The limit to the expansion of a population, for instance, is set directly by the resources of its environment. If it expands beyond that limit, the population will be reduced by starvation and disease to a level that the environment can support. This is the only sort of population control that is reconcilable with the reductionist paradigm of science, which sees living things as passive, robotic, and manipulated by external agencies—as indeed they largely are under the aberrant conditions imposed by industrial society.

One method of internalising the coordination of behaviour is through *ritualisation*—a principle alien to industrial society's emphasis on bringing about the maximum change with the minimum human effort. Ritualisation does the opposite—it minimises change (and hence social and environmental damage) by *maximising* the effort required to achieve it. Contrary to what we have all been taught, it is this latter strategy that in normal conditions is most adaptive.

V.C. Wynne-Edwards describes in detail how different living things have internalised restraints on their population growth. He notes that external factors—disease, starvation, accidents—play an insignificant role in controlling animal populations and concludes that 'the animals themselves must exercise the necessary restraint.' Thus 'the threat of starvation tomorrow, not hunger itself today, seems to be the factor that decides what the density of a population ought to be.'[1]

The territorial system of birds, and also of some animals, helps to make this possible. Wynne-Edwards notes that in the breeding season the male of many species of birds

> lays claim to an area of not less than a certain minimum size and keeps out all other males of the species—in this way, a group of males will parcel out the available ground as individual territories and put a limit on crowding. It is a perfect example of an artificial mechanism geared to adjusting the density of population to the food resources. Instead of competing directly for the food itself, the members compete furiously for pieces of ground, each of which then becomes the exclusive food preserve of its owner. If the standard territory is large enough to

feed a family, the entire group is safe from the danger of overtaxing the food supply.[2]

There are many variations on this theme. Wynne-Edwards refers to them as 'social conventions' and sees them as providing the 'homeostatic machinery that prevents the growth of the population from departing too far from the optimal density'.[3]

In vernacular societies, these internal controls are even more developed. Many societies have tabus against sexual activity during lactation, or during the first year of widowhood, or before taking part in all sorts of different rituals and ceremonies. In India, among the Brahmins and related castes, widow remarriage is not permitted. This was, at one time, of considerable significance, since it was customary for children to get married at the age of five or six, and if the bridegroom were to die a few years later, his widow would never be allowed to remarry. Indeed, when the British first went to India they were horrified to find that there were literally hundreds of thousands of widows under the age of eight or nine. In Tibet, a significant proportion of young men entered and remained in monasteries and young women in nunneries.

Indeed, there is every reason to suppose that traditional people employed a veritable constellation of population-control strategies that best fitted into their particular cultural behaviour pattern.[4] This was maintained by society as a whole via public opinion and the council of elders (chapter 54), and was justified by its mythological and religious beliefs. Thomas Malthus was obviously unaware that in climax societies restraints on population are internalised in this way, or he would not have declared that populations necessarily expanded until they were reduced by food shortages (chapter 45).

Gerardo Reichel-Dolmatoff explains how the mythology of the indigenous Tukano of Colombia serves to rationalise a whole system of prohibitions against such undesirable trends as 'population growth, the exploitation of the physical environment, and aggression in interpersonal relations', which could otherwise destroy their ecological balance and threaten their survival. In their mythology, the superior forces of the Earth frequently punish animal species that have become overindulgent, aggressive, or improvident. They serve as examples not only to other animal species but to humans as well.[5]

The prohibitions against overhunting, eating different types of food, and indulging in different types of sexual activity are very elaborate. All animals are governed by the 'Master of Animals' who jealously guards his flock of deer, tapir, peccary, agouti, paca, monkeys, and other species that the Tukano rely on for food. Before anyone can go out hunting, they must first obtain permission from the Master of Animals, and this will only be granted if they undergo a rigorous preparation that consists of sexual continence, a restricted diet, and purification rites, including cleansing the body by bathing and emetics. For some days before going on a hunting excursion, the hunter should not have had any dream with an erotic content. Moreover, it is necessary that none of the women who live in the hunter's household be menstruating. To make things even more difficult, a species can only be hunted after the constellation with which it is associated in the Tukano mythology has risen over the horizon. Even then, Reichel-Dolmatoff notes, the hunt is not a purely utilitarian affair devoid of internalised controls. Highly ritualised, it is best regarded as 'a courtship in which the prey has to be seduced to submit to the hunter'.[6]

When the game is scarce, it becomes even more difficult to obtain permission. The prospective hunter must visit the Master of Animals 'in a narcotic trance' and promise to send to the Master's abode the souls of the persons who, at their death, must return to this great storehouse to replenish the energy of those animals the supernatural gamekeeper gives to the hunters. In this way, the necessary regulation for preventing overhunting and overfishing are built into the cultural pattern of the Tukano. What is more, fear of retribution from the superior powers of the Earth —that usually takes the form of illness or misfortune in hunting—further strengthens the prohibitions against overtaxing the environment (chapter 64). It follows that it is not the ecosystem in which they live as a physical entity that is coordinating their behaviour but the ecosystem *as a product of their own worldview*, formulated as it is in the language of their mythology (see glossary—*cybernism*).

With the breakdown of traditional societies under the impact of economic development, such culturally internalised (and thus *homearchic*) constraints cease to operate. Unfortunately, the external (or *heterarchic*) controls applied by the state and its specialised agencies are no substitute (chapter 43).

As self-regulating processes are undermined, behaviour gets out of control and becomes increasingly disruptive (heterotelic). Only crude external controls—such as those exerted by the proverbial 'Four Horsemen of the Apocalypse'—can, in such conditions, bring population growth and environmental devastation to an end. Massive discontinuities become the order of the day as we move towards a social and ecological *disclimax*.

24

INCREASING COMPLEXITY LEADS
TO GREATER STABILITY

The stability of complex continental ecosystems was no armour against the Japanese beetle, European gypsy moth, or Oriental chestnut blight (*Endothia parasitica*) in North America . . . It is trivial, but not irrelevant, to observe that stability was hardly enhanced by the extra links added to the trophic web in these instances.

Robert M. May

The term 'complex' [in general usage] need imply no more than a haphazard conglomeration, whereas in the living system we find distinctive orderliness of the complexes.

Paul A. Weiss

UNTIL RECENTLY ecologists have tended, along with the famous British ecologist Charles Elton, to assume that as a system becomes more complex, it also becomes more stable—though Eugene Odum considers that complexity tapers off some time before a climax (the most stable stage) is achieved. Today, however, this link between complexity and stability is denied by most mainstream ecologists.

One of the books that has played an important role in changing this attitude is R.M. May's *Stability and Complexity in Model Ecosystems* (1973). Underlying it is the assumption that a system's complexity can be measured by the number of its constituent parts *without considering the way they are organised*, let alone the role they play within the wider body of the biosphere.[1] In other words, it does not distinguish between the kind of 'complexity' arising from a random and disintegrated confusion of (heterotelic) parts and that arising from an ordered and integrated organisation of (homeotelic) parts. This means that because a highly destructive ecological invasion, such as the introduction of the rabbit into Australia or the walking catfish into Florida, increases the number of the constituent parts of ecosystems in these countries, it is seen as increasing their 'complexity'. The fact that it also tends to reduce their health, integrity, and stability can be construed as confirming May's preposterous thesis that 'complexity' reduces stability.

In reality, all it does is confirm the indubitable principle that to introduce into an ecosystem a living thing that has been designed by its evolution to fulfil a very different role as a constituent of a very different ecosystem, can only increase the former's randomness and reduce its *organised* or real complexity.

Ilya Prigogine also insists that increased 'complexity' is associated with growing instability. This for him is confirmed by the fact that the world is becoming ever more 'complex' yet, at the same time, increasingly unstable. It is this instability that is reflected in the ever-growing fluctuations—floods, droughts, epidemics, and wars—that are everywhere on the increase. In his particular scheme of things, however, such fluctuations are highly desirable because they give rise to economic development or 'progress'.[2] The 'complexity' that Prigogine refers to is again of the random or haphazard kind. It offers no basis for distinguishing between the biospheric complexity required to maintain the integrity and stability of the real world, and the technospheric 'complexity' created by economic development, which is alien to the biosphere and necessarily disrupting of its critical order and stability.

If neither Prigogine nor May can handle organised complexity, it is because, among other things, *it is extremely difficult to quantify and hence to model mathematically*. Not surprisingly, the model that May builds to prove that complexity reduces stability bears little relationship to the real world. Among other things, the underlying assumptions are totally unrealistic (see chapter 14). Thus, May admits that his model only applies to systems with an even number of species—a 'disquieting' thought, he agrees, but not one that leads him to question its intrinsic value because, for his purposes,

> whether or not the Lotka–Volterra equations [on which the model is based] are applicable to real-world situations is beside the point being made here, which is that simple mathematical models with many species are in general less stable than the corresponding simple mathematical models with few species.[3]

In other words, he is not concerned with the relationships between complexity and stability in the real world *but only in his mathematical model*. In the real world, May admits (though only as an afterthought) that things may be different. 'Natural ecosystems, whether structurally complex or simple,' he writes,

> are the product of a long history of coëvolution of their constituent plants and animals. It is at least plausible that such intricate evolutionary processes have, in effect, sought out those relatively tiny and mathematically ätypical regions of parameter space which endow the system with long-term stability.[4]

However, as May himself states, such an ecosystem is 'mathematically ätypical' and hence, he intimates, of little relevance to a mathematical model—and, to him, it is this that is important.[5]

In the real world, complexity must first be distinguished from diversity (chapter 25), as a natural system can increase the number of its constituent parts so as to better achieve two different and indeed rival strategies.

The first (complexity) is to seek to fulfil *particular* adaptive functions with greater accuracy and refinement, thereby increasing its homeostasis *within a specific environment*.

The second (diversity) is to increase the *range* of environmental challenges it can deal with adaptively (chapter 25).

The first strategy is the most adaptive in an orderly and *predictable* environment—the second, in a disorderly and hence *unpredictable* environment. The first strategy has been referred to by the German biologist Bernhard Rensch as 'anagenesis', the second as 'cladogenesis', terms that have been adopted by a number of theoretical biologists, such as Julian Huxley and C.H. Waddington.

Let us consider the first strategy. Real complexity is organised and purposive. A complex system does not come into being by the random accumulation of unrelated parts but by the *differentiation* of parts that are already integral to it. Differentiation thus *implies* integration, as the constituent parts of a natural system must be able to act in coordination with one another so as to achieve a particular adaptive function or endgoal.

In a simple ecosystem, for instance, different species of herbivores are relatively *undifferentiated* eaters. A mountain goat must be able to eat practically anything if it is to survive in its inhospitable habitat, so much so that an increase in the population of another species is sufficient to cause a shortage of the basic foodstuffs they both have in common.

Complex ecosystems, however, are far less vulnerable to such discontinuities. Impala and eland in the African savannah, for example, each have a much more specific diet. They will not only eat different plants from one another but often different parts of the same plants. This means that they make the best use of their environment, which will thereby support a greater diversity of herbivores without being degraded. An increase in the number of predator species must also further differentiate and hence further refine the quantitative and qualitative controls applied on prey populations. In these, and a host of other ways, a system becomes more stable as it becomes more complex.

There is a cost however—the greater the specialisation and the commitment to specific environmental conditions, the smaller the range of possible responses that a system is capable of dealing with, and hence the fewer the environmental challenges to which it can respond adaptively (unless *cybernismic* diversity is increased—see glossary). This means that the more highly integrated a complex ecosystem, the less capable it is of tolerating improbable internal or external challenges.

Thus, a tropical rainforest is a highly integrated ecosystem judged by the standard of other ecosystems. For this reason, it is less likely to withstand improbable disturbances. Cut down its trees, for instance, and it does not readily recover, whereas a simpler and less integrated system, such as a savannah, can recover from similar treatment much more readily. A mammal living within the rainforest, being still more highly integrated, is correspondingly more vulnerable to a disturbance. Deprive it of the organs that ensure essential metabolic functions, such as the liver or the kidneys, and it too will fail to recover.

Natural systems can only function adaptively (maintain their homeostasis) within specific conditions (chapter 48). In the case of complex integrated systems, these conditions are often very specialised. For this reason, certain ecologists have maintained that such systems are 'nonpersistent'. But this is not so, for on the basis of a very long experience such living things can predict, usually with justification, that these specialised conditions will be maintained (chapter 30).

What is more, why such conditions have been maintained can very easily be explained. A system together with its environment constitute a larger system or 'field' (chapter 49). This larger system, by maintaining its own stability, assures the orderliness of the environment in which its sub-systems are embedded and hence the stability of their relationship with this wider holarchy (chapter 43). Thus, an embryo will tolerate only minor changes to the highly ordered environment it requires. However, it cannot, on this account, be regarded as unstable. Similarly, a child can only flourish in an environment displaying a certain measure of order—that of the family. This does not mean that it is unstable or 'nonpersistent', as this orderly environment is preserved by the normal behaviour of the various members of the family unit. The family itself is designed to live in an environment that also displays a certain measure of order (though less so than that required by its individual members), and this is provided by the community—and so on, all the way through the various levels of organisation of the biosphere. In other words, though a complex integrated system may only be able to adapt to a limited range of environmental conditions, changes that are outside this range *are unlikely to occur* because of the orderly and predictable environmental conditions provided by the wider holarchy of natural systems of which it is an integral part. That is but another way of saying that it displays high '*resistance* stability' (chapter 19).

A less complex and less integrated system may be able to adapt to a wider range of environmental conditions, but it is not insulated in the same way from these conditions, which are correspondingly more likely to occur. For this reason it must be more capable of dealing with discontinuities, displaying the requisite level of '*resilience* stability'—the ability to restore or heal itself after a disturbance (chapter 19 and next).

In both cases, the system's capacity to deal with change in the environment to which it has been adapted by its evolution corresponds to the *likelihood* of the occurrence of such change. It clearly must be if the system is to maintain its stability or continuity and hence, by definition, survive.

25

INCREASING DIVERSITY LEADS
TO GREATER STABILITY

No single organism can make use of all forms of energy and nutrient resources, attack all host genotypes, survive in all temperature and moisture conditions, or itself resist all parasitism and predation . . .
David Pimentel

Monocultures are almost invariably prone to diseases.
Miguel Altieri

THE TERM 'DIVERSITY' is used by mainstream ecologists to denote the number of different species that inhabit a complex ecosystem. Diversity is generally considered as having two components. The first is 'species richness', a measure of the total number of species present in an ecosystem. The second is 'species evenness' or 'equitability', a measure of the relative population sizes of the different species present and of the extent to which the most abundant ones dominate (chapter 13). It is difficult to see what is to be gained by including these two different and not necessarily connected notions under the same heading of 'diversity'. How can such a concept help us to understand the role of natural systems within the biosphere, let alone their role in maintaining its critical order?

Eugene Odum sees diversity as a measure of redundancy. There is considerable apparent redundancy in the natural world. Flies, ticks, herrings, and many other forms of life produce a vast number of offspring, of which but a minute fraction will survive and reproduce. Only a very small proportion of the genes that make up the human genome encode for proteins. The others, often referred to as 'junk-genes', were (until recently) regarded as redundant. A human can lead an apparently normal life even when deprived of half of the neurons that make up their neocortex. This might lead us to regard the rest as being 'redundant' or 'junk neurons'. A population, too, can be reduced drastically without its ability to survive being noticeably impaired, at least in the short-term.

It would be presumptuous to suppose, however, that the systems involved have not been affected in some way by the reduction in the number of their constituents. Eugene Odum obviously thinks they have, for he considers that to increase an ecosystem's 'redundancy' must also increase its stability, for there would then be more than one species capable of fulfilling a specific function, and hence, if one were to become extinct, the others could take over.

However, redundancy is a misleading term to use. One of the basic techniques used in biotechnology is cloning, which means growing large numbers of plants or other forms of life that are all genetically identical. However, for Pat Mooney, genetic uniformity in crops amounts to an invitation for an epidemic to destroy that crop.[1] The world has already experienced the terrible consequences of an agricultural system's dependence on too narrow a genetic base. The best known example is the fate of Ireland's nineteenth century potato economy. The bulk of the population of that country lived off the potato, with cereals being produced largely for export to England. Since the potatoes were of a single variety, it was only a matter of time before the whole crop would be struck by a disease. When this happened, some two million people died and several million more were forced to seek a new life in North America. In 1970, the world was reminded of this danger when the USA lost fifteen per cent of its maize crop to corn-blight. Fortunately, the superpower did not depend on maize for its sustenance—but in many Third World countries, such a blight would have been catastrophic.

Genetic uniformity also reduces a population's adaptive capacity. Thus, David Merrell and J.C. Underhill failed to induce resistance to DDT among inbred strains of the fruit-fly *Drosophila melanogaster* after two and a half years exposure to that poison.[2] In contrast to this, resistance to DDT was induced in normal wild populations in less than six months. C.H. Waddington also found that the 'genetic assimilation' of new physical traits (appendix 4) 'fails completely—at least over periods of fairly small numbers of generations—in inbred strains lacking genetic variability'.[3]

Not surprisingly, '*uniform* redundancy' does not occur in the natural world. It is not part of the strategy of nature. Natural 'redundancy' is highly *diversified* and the biosphere's capacity to create this diversity is astounding. We all know just how many different words can be constructed by using an alphabet of twenty-six letters. Similarly, it would seem that an almost limitless number of instructions can be issued by using the genetic code of four basic nucleotides—and an almost limitless number of different forms of life can be generated from the twenty different amino acids required to make proteins. Not surprisingly, the biosphere is not only capable of generating an incredible number of different species but also of different sub-species, varieties, and individuals.

This *organised* diversity enables a natural system to deal with a wide range of both internal and external challenges—not a random but a *specific* range—that range which, in the light of the system's evolutionary (phylogenetic) and developmental (ontogenetic) experience, is most likely to threaten it and most likely to materialise.

As the diversity of the system increases, so it is capable of insuring itself against an increasing number of the less common and less immediately threatening of these challenges. This also implies that its sub-systems are capable of acting more autonomously, as each must be specialised in dealing with different possible challenges.

On the other hand, a *complex* system (displaying very little diversity and organised to adapt with greater accuracy to very specific environmental conditions) would only be capable of dealing with the most common and most threatening challenges—unless it had developed the requisite *cyber-*

nismic diversity (in which case it would have the reörganising or coordinating capacity for responding to a greater variety of challenges, as in the case of human beings and other highly adaptable organisms).

It might be useful to think of the role of diversity as one that insures against discontinuities. Thus, the most significant feature of tribal agriculture is the incredible diversity of the crops and varieties of the same crop that are grown. Floribert Jurion and J.M. Henry tell us how, among Central African farmers,

> fields of sorghum and millet are commonly composed not only of different varieties but even of different species of the same genera. As for rice, maize, groundnuts, and voandzu, it is more a matter of mixtures of different types than of varieties distinguished one from another.[4]

In peasant societies, the same principle applies. Peasants are imbued with what has been termed the 'subsistence ethic'. Their concern is not to maximise yields but to *reduce vulnerability* and hence discontinuities, such as droughts, floods, or plant epidemics. As James Scott writes,

> the local tradition of seed varieties, planting techniques, and timing was designed over centuries of trial and error to produce the most stable and reliable yield possible under the circumstances. . . . Typically, the peasant seeks to avoid the failure that will ruin him rather than attempting a big, but risky, killing.[5]

Such prudence, however, is inimical to the development of commerce and hence to the interests of industrialists and politicians. To satisfy them, production and consumption must be maximised and insurance sought via market mechanisms. This motivates farmers to adopt precisely those biologically, socially, and ecologically disruptive methods that will maximise rather than minimise risk. The results can only be disastrous, as in the long-term, *there is no effective substitute for diversity as an insurance against discontinuities.*

It is often very difficult to determine which of the constituents of a natural system contribute to its complexity and which contribute to its diversity. The planting of a large number of different crops by traditional agriculturalists increases not only the diversity but also the complexity of the agricultural ecosystem. In a well-planned intercropping system, early established plants tend to reduce soil temperature and produce the appropriate microclimate for other plants. Plants also complement each other in terms of nutrient cycling—thus, deep-rooted plants can act as 'nutrient pumps', bringing up minerals from deep down in the sub-soil. Minerals released by the decomposition of annuals are taken up by perennials. The nutrient intensity of some plants is compensated for by the addition of organic matter to the soil by others. Thus, cereals benefit by being grown in conjunction with legumes, which have deeper roots—permitting a better use of nutrients and soil moisture; and whose root nodules host bacteria specialised in fixing nitrogen.[6] All these crops thereby play a significant role in the metabolism of an agricultural eco-system and hence contribute to its complexity. On the other hand, such crops retain their ability to react individually to many environmental challenges. They can thus fulfil two roles, contributing both to the eco-system's complexity *and* to its diversity.

It is interesting to note that some natural systems that are organised to achieve great diversity can—if required to deal with new environmental changes—transform this diversity into complexity and vice versâ. A typical example is the cellular slime mould, a small amœba-like creature that normally lives in colonies that display considerable diversity. When there is a shortage of *Enterechia coli*—the bacteria on which they feed—they undergo an impressive metamorphosis, joining together to form a highly differentiated multicellular organism displaying a corresponding degree of complexity. As soon as their food supply increases, this organism breaks down once more into its constituent parts—complexity yielding once more to diversity.

The same occurs among vernacular human communities. When faced with an external challenge, they organise themselves to form larger social groupings—as did the Bushmen in their struggle against the Bantu invaders and as occasionally did the indigenous tribes of North America in their struggle against the colonial invaders. There is every reason to suppose that had these native peoples won their struggle and kept out the invaders, they would afterwards have resumed their normal way of life in the traditional social groupings within which such ways of life are best led—complexity once more giving way to diversity.

Thus, the diversity and complexity of a natural system must be thought of as representing not only the relative abundance of its parts but also the way in which those parts are *organised* in relation to particular challenges.

THE NATURE OF LIVING THINGS

·INITIATIVE·

26

THE PROCESSES OF THE BIOSPHERE
ARE NOT RANDOM

... Man is the product of causes which had no prevision of the end they were achieving—that his origin, his growth, his hopes and fears, his loves and beliefs are but the outcome of accidental collocations of atoms... all these things, if not quite beyond dispute, are yet so nearly certain that no philosophy which rejects them can hope to stand. Only within the scaffolding of these truths, only on the firm foundation of unyielding despair, can the soul's habitation henceforth be safely built.

Bertrand Russell

It is upon the notion of randomness that geneticists have based their case against a benevolent or malevolent deity and against there being any overall purpose or design in nature.

Sir Peter Medawar

To assert ... that life appeared and evolved quite by chance is a gratuitous supposition, which we consider to be wrong and not in accordance with the facts.

P.P. Grassé

THE NOTION THAT THE BIOSPHERE and everything in it are the product of pure chance and blind selection is critical to the reductionist paradigm of science. Jacques Monod refers to the process of determining the evolution of life and of culture as 'a gigantic lottery' or as 'nature's roulette'. 'Chance alone', he sees

> as the source of every innovation, of all creation in the biosphere. Pure chance, absolutely free but blind, at the very root of the stupendous edifice of evolution—this central concept of modern biology is no longer one among other possible or even conceivable hypotheses. It is today the *sole* conceivable hypothesis, the only one that squares with observed and tested fact. And nothing warrants the supposition—or the hope—that on this score our position is likely ever to be revised.[1]

Many neo-Darwinists, however, (including Theodosius Dobzhansky and Julian Huxley) have adopted a less extreme position. They admit that mutations may well be caused by factors that we ignore. However, they insist that

> in all cases they are random *in relation to evolution*. Their effects are not related to the needs of the organism or to the conditions in which it is placed. *They occur without reference to their possible consequences or biological uses.*[2]

This means that although something makes a mother feed her child, that something is unconnected with the child's need to be fed by its mother.

In the real world, however, life processes are not random, even in this less extreme sense of the term. Art styles, for instance, closely reflect the character of the cultures in which they developed. The clothes people wear are indicative of the image of themselves they wish to communicate to others. The way people walk, eat, light cigarettes, blow their noses, do up their shoelaces—all convey some information as to the personality of the individuals concerned.

Behaviour is indeed so ordered, so little random, that it is questionable whether people are capable of behaving in a random way. This appears to be confirmed by various experiments, such as those described by the psychologists Anne Broadhurst and W.R. Ramsay, who experimented with a panel of seventy-two people by asking them to repeat in time to a metronome a series of numbers, one to nine, in as random a manner as possible. They found that 'even when subjects try to be random, there is a high degree of stereotype.'[3] They suggest that it is even possible to 'fingerprint' and thus identify an individual by their particular response to the tests, and also that a pathological configuration of the tests may reveal a mental illness. A set of random numbers has actually been used to enable a practitioner to differentiate between mentally ill patients and normal subjects.

The British cybernetician Stafford Beer also rejects the view that randomness is a natural feature of behaviour in the natural world.

> There are random number tables on my bookshelf; there are computer tapes for producing pseudo-random numbers next door; there is a large electronic machine for generating noise upstairs; down the road there is a roomful of equipment designed to hurl thousands of little metal balls about in a random way; and I use ten-sided dice as paper-weights. The up-keep of this armoury is considerable—think of all the time we spend trying to ensure that all these artefacts produce results which are 'genuinely random'; whatever that may mean. This tremendous practical problem of guaranteeing disorderliness ought to be enough to satisfy any systems' man that *nothing is more unnatural than chaos.*[4]

How, then, do scientists know that a process is random? How do they know it is not part of an orderly pattern that they simply have not been able to identify? Darwin himself had pointed out—along with many others before him—that the word 'chance' merely signifies our ignorance of causes.[5] C.H. Waddington said much the same thing, in particular with regard to the randomness of genetic mutations.[6]

Various studies have tended to confirm this view (see also appendix 4). Biologist John Cairns and his colleagues at Harvard University, for example, conducted studies which suggested that mutations are not random but are, on the contrary, directive (although, he later began referring to them as 'adaptive'—a far less controversial notion).[7] At first, Cairns's studies were dismissed by the scientific establishment—however, Barry Hall of Rochester University produced similar results. He found that certain mutations in bacteria occur more often when they are useful to the bacteria than when they are not (referring to them as 'Cairnsian' mutations, thus deftly avoiding the controversy surrounding Cairns's original term).[8]

There is every reason to doubt, too, the concept of 'genetic drift' that has been postulated to explain evolutionary changes that do not appear to have been 'selected'. This concept is increasingly seen as yet another convenient device for masking our ignorance of the role of such changes.

Indeed, more and more processes that originally appeared to be random are found on closer examination to be highly functional—indeed, *purposive*.

However, we do not need experimental 'evidence' for rejecting the idea that evolution is based on random mutations. We know that single gene mutations can only determine extremely superficial changes. Significant changes can only be brought about by alterations to a whole constellation of associated genes or polygeny. This means, as Rupert Riedl notes, that for a functional unit to make an adaptive change requires not just one happy accident but 'an accumulation of happy accidents.'[9] Does this seem likely? Waddington did not believe it, in spite of his insistence on remaining within the neo-Darwinian fold. He admitted that to suggest that evolution was based on selection from random mutations was 'like suggesting that if we went on throwing bricks together into heaps, we should eventually be able to choose ourselves the most desirable house'.[10] Murray Eden rejects the thesis on the grounds of its sheer mathematical improbability. It is as unlikely as it is that 'a child arranging at random a printer's supply of letters would compose the first 20 lines of Virgil's *Æneid*'.[11]

How then can the notion of the randomness of life processes have been raised to the elated status of 'the central concept of modern biology'? I shall suggest some possible answers.

To begin with, randomness was postulated as an argument against teleology (chapter 2), which was seen as ushering in all sorts of unacceptable supernatural principles, such as God or various forms of *vitalism*. Secondly, it is essential in order to rationalise the reductionist nature of modern science. If the biosphere displays order, worse still, if the whole evolutionary process is seen as a *single coordinated strategy, involving all life processes at all levels of organisation* (chapter 37), then the reductionist approach would make no sense. Thirdly, the postulate of randomness is also required to justify statistical method, which in turn rationalises other key features of the modern paradigm of science—the principle of *causation*, for instance, and reductionism itself.

Finally, randomness is seen as essential because it is impossible to justify the Promethean enterprise to which our industrial society is committed if the biosphere is seen as organised to achieve a grand overall project of its own. By seeing the biosphere as random, on the other hand, it is possible to make out that what order there is in the world has been created by science, technology, and industry rather than by God or the evolutionary process. 'The cardinal tendency of progress', as J.D. Bernal writes, 'is the replacement of an indifferent chance environment by a *deliberately created one.*'[12]

The insistence by mainstream scientists on maintaining the principle of the randomness of life processes in the teeth of all the evidence, both empirical and theoretical, shows what a negligible role is played by 'scientific method' in the formulation and acceptance of even the most fundamental principles of modern science (chapter 12). This particular principle, like many others, is accepted for one reason only—it is essential in helping the reductionist paradigm of science, and hence its corollary 'progress', appear to make sense, serving to rationalise and hence legitimise it in people's minds.

The truth of the matter is that scientists know very little about the incredibly complex and beautiful world we have inherited. As Wendell Berry puts it, 'We are up against mystery,' and

> To call this mystery 'randomness' or 'chance' or a 'fluke' is to take charge of it on behalf of those who do not respect pattern. To call the unknown 'random' is to plant the flag by which to colonise and exploit the unknown. . . . To call the unknown by its right name, 'mystery', is to suggest that we had better respect the possibility of a larger unseen pattern that can be damaged or destroyed—and with it, the smaller patterns.[13]

27

THE PROCESSES OF THE BIOSPHERE
ARE INHERENTLY PURPOSIVE

... the problem [of evolution] is now essentially solved, and ... the mechanism of adaptation is known. It turns out to be basically materialistic, with no sign of purpose as a working variable in life history, and with any possible Purposer pushed back to the incomprehensible position of First Cause ... Man is the result of a purposeless and materialistic process that did not have him in mind. He was not planned.
George Gaylord Simpson

'Purpose' is not imported into nature and need not be puzzled over as a strange or divine something-else that gets inside and makes life go ... It is simply implicit in the fact of organisation.
Herbert J. Muller

THE EVIDENCE FOR the purposiveness of life processes at every level of organisation within the biosphere is so great that its denial seems inconceivable. Who could deny that the evolution of gills and fins by fish is purposive to enabling them to breathe and move about in their aquatic environment, or that the development of mammary glands by the females of all species of mammals is purposive to feeding their young, or that the milk provided in this way is designed to satisfy the nutritional needs of their young in the earliest stage of their lives?

To Charles Sherrington, it seemed obvious that the embryological process, whereby 'a pin's-head ball of cells in the course of so many weeks becomes a child,' is purposive.[1] He points to the

> levers laid down in gristle becoming bone when wanted for the heavier pull of muscle which will clothe them. Lungs—solid glands, yet arranged to hollow out at a few minutes' notice when the necessary air shall enter. Limb-buds—futile at their appearing and yet deliberately appearing in order to become limbs in readiness for existence where they will be all-important.[2]

Sherrington is particularly impressed by the development of embryonic organs—useless at the time to their possessor but indispensible later on during the course of their development. 'Organs of skin, ear, eye, nose, tongue,' he writes, 'superfluous all of them in the watery dark where formed, yet each unhaltingly preparing to enter a daylit, airy, object-full manifold world which they will be wanted to report on.'[3]

Purposiveness is also evident in physiology. As Gavin de Beer notes,

> The structure of an animal shows a number of exquisitely delicate adjustments—the splinters inside a bone are situated exactly where they are required to withstand the pressure to which the bone is subjected; the fibres of a tendon lie accurately along the line of strain between a muscle and the bone to which it is attached; centres of nerve cells in the brain are situated close to the ends of the nerve-fibres from which they habitually receive impulses.[4]

The same principle is equally evident in animal behaviour. For Bierens de Haan,

> that the weaving of the web by the spider is purposeful to the catching of insects, and the collecting and storing of caterpillars by the wasp pur-

poseful to the nourishing of its future larva are facts that are so self-evident that it is not necessary further to elucidate them.[5]

If life processes achieve their purpose, it is because they are controlled or *coordinated*. But they could not be coordinated in the first place unless they had a goal to achieve. Coordination serves to ensure that life processes achieve their goals. This is clear if we consider that a basic ingredient of coordination is 'negative feedback', *which is totally useless to a non-purposive system.*

An essential constituent of coordination is perception, and perception is essentially purposive. As Keith Oatley notes, 'the way we see is in terms of our human purposes in the environment.'[6] What we see depends on our particular purpose at the time—what we are trying to do and what aspect of the thing we are seeing that is relevant to what we are trying to achieve. Furthermore, it is not just in terms of a short-term purpose that we see things but, ultimately, in terms of our long-term strategic purpose, which itself must be seen in the overall context of the purpose of our society, our ecosystem, and the entire biosphere.

Thoughtful scientists recognise this as a serious problem. Jacques Monod for instance, as Gunther Stent notes, insists that

'. . . the cornerstone of scientific method is the postulate that nature is objective. In other words, the systematic denial that *true* knowledge can be got at in terms of *purpose*.' Thus, while the purposive character of life is *prima facie* apparent, scientific objectivity obliges us to deny it.[7]

Monod admits that 'this self-same contradiction is in fact the central problem of biology.'[8] But it is only a problem for modern scientists, for their ability to understand the functioning of the biosphere is seriously hindered by their adherence to the paradigm of reductionist science. In the light of the worldview of ecology, on the other hand, purposiveness is a necessary feature of life processes at all levels of organisation and, in particular, at the level of the biosphere—whose critical order they seek purposefully to secure.

28

LIVING THINGS POSSESS INITIATIVE

We [in the West] hold a *static* conception of 'being',
they [the Bantu] a *dynamic*.
Father Placide Tempels

Even under constant external conditions, and in the absence of external
stimuli, the organism is not a passive but a basically active system.
Ludwig von Bertalanffy

The lowliest creature and the highest, the moment it is hatched or born,
lashes out at the environment . . . with cilia, flagellæ, or contractile muscle
fibre; it crawls, swims, glides, pulsates; it kicks, yells, breathes, feeds, and
sucks negative entropy from its surroundings for all its worth. . . . In fact,
the animal does not merely adapt to the environment but constantly adapts
the environment to itself. It eats environment, drinks environment, fights
and mates environment, burrows and builds in the environment . . .
Arthur Koestler

THAT LIFE PROCESSES are dynamic was self-evident to vernacular people. For Father Placide Tempels, author of the seminal book on Bantu philosophy, *La Philosophie Bantoue* (1945), it is traditional people's accent on the dynamic aspect of living things that characterises their view of the world. This view contrasts only too starkly with the reductionist view of living things as essentially static and passive, a view that is consistent with the modern paradigm of science but not with our knowledge of the real world.

All the different processes involved in adaptive behaviour are necessarily dynamic. Perception is dynamic. Signals are not merely received, they are detected—the organism seeks out those signals that are seen to be relevant to its behaviour pattern in the light of its mental model of its relationship with its environment (chapter 15). Mental activities do not merely occur to interpret external stimuli, they also occur quite spontaneously. Even in the absence of any external stimuli, the brain remains constantly active. We think, in fact, even when sitting in an armchair in a dark room.

Erich von Hoist has shown that primitive motor activities function without the aid of external stimuli. Movements continue to occur even after 'the connection of motoric to sensory nerves' have been severed.[1] Konrad Lorenz has pointed to the existence of what he calls 'innate releasing mechanisms', which play a central role in our behaviour and can function without the presence of external stimuli.[2] This fits in very well with Ragnar Granit's description of nerve cells that are specified at birth, that are not affected by outside stimuli, and that are subject to the presence of genetically determined instructions—whether or not they are in use and whether or not they are triggered off by an environmental stimulus.[3]

It must be clear from our own experience that we are not only led to do things by the mere presence of an external stimulus. When I am hungry, I shall look for food—it is not just the sight of food that triggers off my food-seeking behaviour. It may undoubtedly stimulate my appetite, but appetite there must be. A good indication that this must be so is furnished by the possibility of redirecting different behavioural trends, such as aggression, into relatively harmless activities, such as sport, rather than into destructive ones, such as war (chapter 45).

When the normal outlet for a behavioural tendency or urge is unavailable, living things can even imagine it or create it. Thus, the Comanche tribe of Nevada, once they were confined to a reservation and deprived of their hereditary enemies, compensated for this by increasing the number and the threatening nature of the evil spirits with which they saw themselves surrounded, thereby creating or imagining the stimuli needed to trigger off their aggressive tendencies.[4] In the field of sex this could not be more evident. If the normal stimulus that triggers off sexual behaviour is not available, others are sought out, and the degree of improvisation seems considerable. In other words, we modify—or even invent—by our own efforts, the stimuli that alone are supposed to trigger off behavioural responses. This dynamism, what is more, does not only occur at the behavioural level but is a feature of all life processes.

Alister Hardy, like Jean Piaget, has pointed to the close relationship between the dynamism of behaviour and that of evolution.

> It is adaptations which are due to the animal's behaviour—to its restless exploration of its surroundings, to its *initiative*—that distinguish the main diverging lines of evolution; . . . giving the lines of runners, climbers, burrowers, swimmers, and conquerors of the air.[5]

Evolving systems are not puppets controlled by the whims of a distant environmental puppeteer, as Darwin and his successors have implied. On the contrary, it is the dynamism and initiative of living things themselves that makes evolution possible.

29

LIVING THINGS ARE CREATIVE

One is astonished at the amount of creative force, if such an expression
may be used, displayed on these small, barren, and rocky islands
[The Galapagos].
Charles Darwin

[A.N. Whitehead's dictum] 'creativity is ultimate'. . . is not a philosophical
postulate. It is an observed fact that creative activity, or 'formative process', is an intrinsic property of everything in the natural cosmos that is
known to man.
C. Judson Herrick

C LEARLY, humans have a vast capacity for improvisation and have
developed diverse and highly imaginative cultural patterns for dealing with the challenges of life in different environmental conditions. The
creative capacity of non-human animals is also well documented. Living
things have developed the most diverse strategies for adapting to different
and often highly challenging environments. Thus, a warm-blooded animal can learn to survive the rigours of the winter by developing a thick
fur coat, by going into hibernation, by migrating to a warmer area, or by
lighting a camp fire. Desert plants can learn to avoid desiccation by developing leaves covered with oily substances, or that become spine-like, or
that are simply shed during the dry season, or by changing their life cycle
so that it is compressed into the wet season.

The creative development of new and often more complex forms of
life is an essential feature of evolution. For instance, the development of
the lichen provides a remarkable example of innovation arising from the
partnership of different organisms—a fungus and an alga and-or cyanobacterium. Lichens possess many physical, chemical, and physiological
features that are absent from the partners when living independently.

Not only is nature creative and innovative in the extreme, but creative
and innovative changes can occur very quickly as adaptations to environmental challenges. Consider how mosquitoes have adapted to DDT. According to David Merrell, resistance was first reported in 1946, and by
1965 it had been noted in one hundred and sixty-five pest species. More
impressive than the speed at which this resistance had developed were
the very different strategies exploited by the mosquitoes for dealing with
this new menace. Some mosquitoes learned not to alight on the walls
that had been sprayed with DDT, others developed a thick cuticle that it
could not penetrate. Others accumulated more body fat, thereby increasing their capacity to assimilate fat-soluble DDT. The nerves of others
became less sensitive to DDT. Still others developed an enzyme that
breaks down DDT into a harmless compound. The diversity of different
approaches used by mosquitoes to adapt to DDT spraying programmes,
as Merrell notes, is 'testimony to the opportunism of evolution'.[1]

Mainstream science seeks to explain this extraordinary innovativeness
and creativity in terms of the neo-Darwinian thesis. The genetic resistance to DDT, Merrell insists, 'already existed in the populations and was
not induced by exposure to DDT'.[2] But the DDT molecule did not exist
in nature before it was produced synthetically in the 1940s. How then
could the mosquito's gene-pool have prior knowledge that this foreign

substance would one day be synthesised by science and released into the environment? The answer, we are told, is by chance—by random preädaptation. This is the only scientifically respectable explanation of creativity—the only one reconcilable with such essential features of the mainstream paradigm of science as causality, mechanomorphism, and statistical theory. Chance, in the context of evolution, means random mutations. It is only to them that evolutionary creativity can be imputed. 'Natural causation', the biologist R.A. Fisher writes,

> has a creative aspect . . . because it has a causal aspect . . . Looking back at a cause we can recognise it as creative—it has brought about something which could not have been predicted; something which cannot be referred back to antecedent events.[3]

It is like a 'game of chance', he tells us, where it is possible to conceive all the possible outcomes of the game—indeed, to calculate the relative probability of each one of them—but it is not possible to foresee exactly which one it will be. The scientific notion of causality is not thereby creative in the true sense of the term, for a like cause must create a like effect, and all Fisher is saying is that we cannot predict which particular causal relationship is going to occur, as that will be decided by natural selection.

But natural selection from random mutations, in spite of what our mainstream scientists tell us, cannot be a source of creative evolutionary change. We can understand that by selecting the most viable living things and allowing them to reproduce, their characteristics will be transmitted to the next generation, which will become correspondingly more viable—but this is only possible if living things *already possess* the capacity to transmit such characteristics to the next generation. Billiard balls cannot (and it is difficult to see how they might) be made to evolve by natural selection, however much variability they might exhibit. As Ludwig von Bertalanffy notes,

> selection presupposes self-maintenance, adaptability, reproduction, *etc.* of the living system. These therefore cannot be the effect of selection. This is the oft-discussed circularity of the selectionist argument. Proto-organisms would arise and organisms further evolve by chance mutations and subsequent selection. But in order to do so, *they must already have the essential attributes of life.*[4]

For J.H. Woodger, the neo-Darwinian thesis is unacceptable on this count alone. An 'explanation' of this kind, he writes, can only make out a case for itself by 'begging the fundamental question at issue'—the essential characteristics of an organism have to be surreptitiously introduced in 'vague general language'.[5] They are so introduced largely by attributing to natural selection—the mechanical sorting machine—qualities, such as creativity, *which no machine can possibly display*, and that are in effect little more than the very 'internal factors' whose role in determining the evolutionary process neo-Darwinists are at such pains to deny.

That the extraordinary and highly complex biosphere can be regarded as the product of such a crude process as selection from random mutations has to be seen in the context of other clumsy efforts by mainstream science to maintain the myth that living processes are essentially machine-like in nature (mechanomorphism). Machines cannot create—their output (the effect) is a function of their input (the cause). It was to make sure that embryogenesis or *development* conformed to this principle, that the theory of 'preformation' became popular, according to which a fertilised egg contained a miniature replica of a fully grown organism—the end product of the process. However, it eventually became clear that the information contained in the fertilised egg was nowhere near sufficient to give rise to a fully grown organism, and preformation gave way to *epigenesis*—a theory that is very difficult to explain in terms of the reductionist paradigm of science (appendix 4).

One of the most astonishing feats of creativity in the natural world is the working of the immune system, the most likely explanation for which is the process of genetic recombination. Immunologists tell us that a biological organism can produce 10^7 or so different antibodies—that is to say 10^7 different proteins designed to repel specific threats. All sorts of attempts have been made by mainstream scientists to explain this in the language of the neo-Darwinian orthodoxy. They have failed. One possibility with regard to our mosquito populations, for instance, is that although they were not endowed before the development of DDT with the genes that would confer resistance against that poison, they were nevertheless endowed with cells containing bits and pieces of the genes (a 'kit of components', as Philip Leder puts it [6]), and those components are shuffled in the cells of the immune system, which can lead to a different result in each of millions of lines of cells. Individual mutations amplify the diversity and, as a result, in the mature descendants of each line, a unique gene is assembled whose information is expressed in the form of a unique antibody.

If this is so, then it must be extremely unlikely that the mutations referred to are in any way random. The immune system, like the genome, is self-regulating and capable of maintaining its homeostasis in the face of external or internal challenges. That mutations are often not random but highly directive or purposive has now been established by Cairns and others (chapter 26 and appendix 4). It seems more likely that such mutations are brought about by the whole-maintaining (or homearchic) regulatory action of the genome, or of any other cybernismic system, such as that associated with the functioning of our immune system. Whether recombinations together with such induced mutations provide a sufficient explanation for the massive evolutionary leaps that have given rise to metazoans, vertebrates, and mammals is uncertain. Susumu Ohno and P.P. Grassé consider that this requires the development of new gene loci that previously had no particular functions (a process referred to as 'neofunctionalisation').[7]

All in all, the creativity of the living world is only a problem if we insist on trying to reconcile it with the reductionist paradigm of science. It *is* wholly reconcilable, on the other hand, with—and is indeed an essential feature of—the worldview of ecology.

30

LIVING THINGS HAVE FORESIGHT

The essential nature of mind is to govern present action by anticipation of the future in the light of past experience—to make, in short, effects precede and determine their causes.

William McDougall

Every perceptual act anticipates its own confirmation by subsequent acts.

H.H. Price

Man has lost the capacity to foresee and to forestall. He will end by destroying the earth.

Albert Schweitzer

FOR NATURAL SYSTEMS to achieve their goal of maintaining their own stability and that of the wider biosphere, they must be able to predict the environmental changes to which they may have to adapt as well as the environmental effects of such adaptations. There is every reason to suppose that they are well capable of doing so—providing such changes occur within their *tolerance range* (chapter 48).

Thus, the *Didiera*, Baobab tree, and certain cacti of Madagascar seem able to store just the right amount of water required to help tide them over dry periods. It does not stretch the meaning of the word too far to say that they must be *predicting* the weather changes involved. Green turtles travel more than two thousand kilometres from the coast of South America to Ascension Island, in the middle of the Atlantic Ocean, where they lay their eggs. When embarking on such a journey, they can only be seen as predicting that their reproductive period is approaching and that by laying their eggs on Ascension Island, rather than anywhere else, they will give their young the best chance of survival.

Many insects, such as monarch butterflies, ladybird beetles, hoverflies, noctuid moths, and other species, migrate to warmer climes when winter approaches. They do not do so, however, because the cold has become insupportable, for they begin to migrate long before cold weather sets in. As C.G. Johnson notes,

> Neither food shortage nor 'intolerable overcrowding' are evident to the human observer at the time of departure. . . . The migration, therefore, usually comes in advance of any obvious change for the worse in living conditions.[1]

Such examples are not exceptional (chapter 52). As Hans Kalmus writes,

> Anticipatory actions occur widely in the organic world. A predator catching a moving prey, a tennis player hitting a ball, a spider constructing a web, even a flower displaying its visual and olfactory attractions, all can be said to anticipate future events in their environments.[2]

Prediction is an essential component of perception, the first step in self-regulation. What people see is not a static image but a hypothesis—as to its history, why it is there, how it is likely to change, and what the consequences will be (chapter 10). Perception, in fact, involves *prediction*.

Reductionist science cannot admit that living things predict. They are supposed to be passive and stage-managed by an external agent. In any case, they cannot predict the future, for, we are told, knowledge is only acquired by observation, and we cannot observe what has not actually occurred. This explains to what lengths mainstream scientists have gone to deny that prediction plays a necessary role in adaptive behaviour. Thus, the behaviour of dogs in Pavlov's famous experiments has been interpreted in such a way *as to avoid having to admit that the dogs are making predictions*. When a dog is trained to salivate at the sound of a bell announcing food, it is seen as responding in a blind and unintelligent manner to the ring of a bell *as if the bell were food*. A 'conditioned stimulus' is seen in this way as simply replacing the 'unconditioned stimulus'.[3]

It is becoming increasingly difficult to maintain this myth. Indeed, C.L. Hull, a behaviourist and experimental psychologist inspired by Ivan Pavlov, sought towards the end of his life to modify his theories so as to reconcile them with the fact that living things display interest, planning, foresight, foreknowledge, expectancy, purpose, and so on— qualities whose very existence his predecessors, and he himself, had previously denied.[4]

Prediction is not only possible on the basis of the information contained in the brain but also on that organised in the genome. J.Z. Young has pointed out that 'the genes have to perform a task analogous to prediction.'[5] The genes of the polar bear, for instance, are predicting that this great beast will live in the Arctic snow and that the snow-white coat will help to camouflage it from its prospective prey. If suddenly there were a radical warming of the Arctic area, these predictions might then prove to be wrong, and, partly as a result, polar bears might not survive.

W.H. Thorpe is also struck by the ability of the genes to predict the sequence of chemical processes in metabolism. He quotes Malcolm Dixon and Edwin Webb who ask

> how the gene-forming enzyme 2.4.2.14 'knows' that phosphoribosyl pyrophosphate will be converted by the consecutive action of ten or more different enzymes into a purine nucleotide . . . , or how the gene for the first enzyme of histidine biosynthesis, which acts on the same compound, 'knows' that its product will be converted into histidine by a different series of enzymes. Even with this information, how do these genes 'know' what amino acid sequences in their enzymes will act as specific centres combining with purine nucleotides or histidine respectively?[6]

For Dixon and Webb, this ability to predict is only possible if we postulate a means 'whereby information derived from the metabolic processes themselves is transmitted back to the genes and there incorporated in the form of polynucleotide sequences'.[7] However, the existence of such a feedback process violates Francis Crick's 'central dogma' and is irreconcilable with the neo-Darwinian thesis (see appendix 4).

C.H. Waddington accepts that evolution must be based on prediction. He tries to reconcile this with the neo-Darwinian thesis by attributing to the environment—that neo-Darwinists have never bothered to define— the capacity to select species for their ability to deal with future as well as present problems, producing 'a system which is stable enough to deal with difficulties that may arise many generations in the future'.[8] However, if it is to selection that we must attribute the capacity to achieve this long-term stability, then this crude mechanical agency must be endowed with the ability to predict the future, for how else can it result in precisely those genes and gene combinations required to permit an organism to adapt to conditions that have not yet occurred?

Without the capacity to predict, natural selection would not, among other things, be able to bring into being an organ that is still in its embryonic stage and is not yet really functional, for how else could embryonic and non-functional organs have an adaptive function in the short-term that would justify their selection by the environment? Clearly they could not. For P.P. Grassé, this provides yet another reason for rejecting the notion that natural selection plays a determining role in evolution. If it did, then we would have to attribute to natural selection 'the gift of divination or of prophecy'.[9]

For a living thing to predict the future is only possible on the basis of a model of its relationship with its natural habitat. The accuracy of its predictions will not only depend on the accuracy with which its mental model represents this relationship *but also on the stability of its natural habitat* and hence the stability of the wider biosphere of which it is an integral part. Equally, it will also depend on the extent to which the living thing has adapted to its habitat—biologically, socially, and cognitively (chapters 50, 51, and 52).

Early *chthonic* or earth-centred peoples, for example, would have had no difficulty in predicting the future, for they inhabited a climax ecosystem and knew how to earn their living in it without disrupting its critical functioning. In such conditions, they would have predicted with reasonable certainty that the future would be very much like the present and that the present would closely resemble the past—an environment, in fact, that constituted a stable continuum (chapters 36 and 37).

One important reason is that traditional practices are based on detailed knowledge accumulated over centuries, and in some cases over millennia. Such knowledge is based on a remarkable understanding of natural phenomena which, as Madhu Ramnath notes, can only come 'from a lifestyle which has a direct day-to-day contact with its surroundings'.[10]

This knowledge enables tribal peoples in the forests of central India to know exactly when key seasonal events that play a critical role in their agricultural activities are likely to occur. Thus, they can predict the onset of the annual monsoon when black ants begin to appear in long winding rows from cracks in the ground; when the 'goborliti' birds begin to migrate away from the forest; when certain plants, like the 'kodoma' and the 'thummi', which has a root like that of turmeric, begin to flower; and when the 'kenil' red ants, which build their nests in the folds of the green leaves of certain trees, stop laying their eggs. These tribal people can even tell which stage of the monsoon is in progress, because they know that certain mushrooms that appear during the wet season do so in a very specific order, and they know how the order relates to the different stages of the monsoon.

This knowledge also enables them to predict and interpret the nature of slight diversions from the norm. In 1987, for instance, the monsoon was an abnormal one, and the plants and animals strayed from their usual patterns of behaviour (chapter 47). Thus, the 'manai' mushroom, which normally appears at the end of the monsoon, was seen in the first days of September. The wild boars, which normally dig up the thick roots of the 'thummi' plant after the monsoons, dug them up and ate them well before the rains ended. Nests of the 'kenil' red ants with eggs and young continued to be found as late as August, and the 'goborliti' bird prematurely returned to the forests in the first days of September.

For the tribal people, these ants, mushrooms, and boars, as Madhu Ramnath notes, 'are not just food to be gathered and hunted, they are also the guides and calendars of the forest'. As he says, 'Their behaviour tells the people when to plough their land and whether their grain should be sown on sloping ground or flat ground,' and a host of other things besides. This invaluable knowledge, however, is only of use if these diversions from the climatic norm occur within certain limits (see chapter 48).[11]

Today, we are bringing about the most dramatic possible changes to the world, and our scientists have no hope of predicting their consequences, for the methodology that enables scientists to understand the functioning of the constituents of the biosphere (for the purpose of making such changes) does not enable them to understand the effects of these changes on the biosphere as a whole. Our scientists are capable of producing synthetic organic chemicals but quite incapable of determining how exposure to them will affect the health of living things. They have developed methods of extracting fossil fuels from the bowels of the earth, using them to generate power that drives countless devices to achieve all sorts of different and often impressive goals. However, they are quite incapable of predicting with any sort of accuracy what the effect will be on biological organisms, societies, ecosystems, and now on global climate.

If we are to be capable, once again, of predicting the future with any sort of accuracy, it will not be by developing new technologies for this purpose—however ingenious and however sophisticated—but by dramatically *reducing* the impact of our activities on the biosphere, thereby creating the conditions in which its critical order (and hence its predictability) can begin to restore itself.

31

LIVING THINGS SEEK TO UNDERSTAND THEIR RELATIONSHIP WITH THE WORLD

Nature has placed mankind under the governance of two sovereign masters—pain and pleasure. It is for them alone to point out what we ought to do, as well as to determine what we shall do.

Jeremy Bentham

. . . animals and people deploy highly structured strategies for solving problems that confront them . . . Learning takes place not simply as the emission of a new response when an error occurs. Rather, it involves *understanding* the particular structure of the mistake and *deciding* what to do next.

Keith Oatley

A LIVING THING apprehends its environment by detecting data that appear relevant to its particular behaviour pattern. It interprets this data in the light of its mental model of its relationship with the world (chapter 15), doing so within as wide a context as is necessary to determine the appropriate adaptive response. In other words, it seeks to establish their meaning—to *understand* them.

This thesis is, of course, irreconcilable with conventional wisdom on the subject. Behavioural psychologists fall into a number of schools, but for a long time, the dominant one was that of behaviourism. It is associated with the work of Edward Thorndike and E.R. Guthrie, also with John B. Watson and particularly with B.F. Skinner. Though many behavioural psychologists, such as the members of the Gestalt school, and of the 'cognitive' or 'mentalist' school that we associate with the name of R.W. Sperry, did not accept behaviourism, it remains true that it still underlies much of the thinking in this field. One reason is that it is the view that best fits in with the reigning paradigm of science, which rationalises the methodology that experimental psychologists and ethologists must use if they are to be taken seriously by the scientific community. This highly reductionistic theory of behaviour is roughly as follows.

Living things apprehend their environment by acquiring sensations or 'sense data'—the atoms of perception—which provide them with measurable atoms of information or 'bits' (appendix 2). It is accepted that living things have a memory, but the memory, too, is atomised—the atoms of memory being referred to as 'engrams' or memory traces. The atom of behaviour is the reflex, a mechanism whereby an environmental event referred to as a 'stimulus' triggers off a blind and automatic response. As far back as 1906, Charles Sherrington wrote that the 'simple reflex is probably a purely abstract conception . . . if not a probable fiction'.[1] C. Judson Herrick describes it as 'a pure abstraction', a mere manifestation of what is clearly a very coordinated pattern of behaviour.[2] However, such criticisms have not deterred others from presenting the process even more mechanistically, in terms of inputs and outputs—the stimulus being the input and the response the output, like a machine that switches on when the button is pressed.

Learning has to be explained, of course, and mainstream scientists have done so very ingeniously, making it appear blind, atomistic, and mechanistic, as is required by the modern paradigm of science. The learning process is not seen by them as occurring in any necessary order—living things are seen as simply responding to their environment in a purely random manner. A rat trying to find its way out of a maze, for instance, will try out a whole series of trial and error moves corresponding to the Darwinist's random variations and the random genetic mutations of the neo-Darwinists. If one such move is crowned with success, it is said to be 'reinforced'—the equivalent of Darwinian 'selection'. In laboratory experiments, rats are given rewards for making what the experimenter judges to be the right moves and are often also given penalties, such as being administered electric shocks, for what are considered the wrong moves—rewards and penalties being seen in the Benthamite tradition as the only motivations of living things.

Behaviourists attribute remarkable powers to reinforcement, just as neo-Darwinists do to selection. Thus, Skinner informs his readers that 'a man talks to himself . . . because of the *reinforcement* he receives;'[3] that thinking is in fact 'behaving which automatically affects the behaviour and is *reinforcing* because it does so';[4] that 'just as the musician plays and composes what he is *reinforced* by hearing, or as the artist paints what *reinforces* him visually, so the speaker engaged in verbal fantasy says what he is *reinforced* by hearing or writes what he is *reinforced* by reading;'[5] while the creative artist is 'controlled entirely by the contingencies of *reinforcement*'.[6]

It is astonishing that serious people can really believe that the highly developed and incredibly subtle behaviour of living things can be explained in terms of so crude and rudimentary a mechanism. If we really believed it, as Michael Polanyi points out, we would also have to accept that

> if a dog were consistently offered food whenever it was shown the radiogram of diseased lungs and no food when shown the radiogram of healthy lungs, it should learn to diagnose pulmonary diseases.[7]

Pure trial and error learning, however—except perhaps in the most rudimentary possible forms of life—is mere fantasy. This has been realised even within the ranks of experimental psychologists. Thus, Karl Lashley has insisted strongly that normal animals do not behave in a random fashion. Keith Oatley agrees, 'In animal or human behaviour,' he maintains, 'trials are not chosen randomly.'[8] On the contrary, as Herrick notes, 'the learning process is ordinarily directive, and it is an organised activity, never a mere random fumbling.'[9] Isadore Krechevsky considers that 'we must change our description of the learning process so as to recognise the existence of organised and systematic responses at all stages of the process.' Indeed, the rat, when placed in an unsolvable situation, does not respond in a helter-skelter chance fashion but makes a series of integrated, unified attempts at solution. These systematic responses are, partly at least, initiated by the animal himself and are not altogether merely a resultant of the immediately presented external situation.[10]

This means that such animals are not just reacting blindly to various stimuli but are seeking to interpret them correctly and thus *understand their meaning*—that, of course, involves establishing the role of the thing or event that attracts their attention within the context of the larger dynamic system of which it is part.

When the Tahitians first saw a horse (introduced to the island during a voyage made by the English missionary William Ellis), they immediately classified it in terms of the mammal they knew most resembled it —the pig.[11] It was obviously closer to the horse than the other two mammals of which they had any experience—the dog and the Polynesian rat. Very sensibly, they referred to the horse as a 'man-carrying pig'. This was not a blind response—it was an intelligent attempt to understand this strange beast in the light of their experience of similar beasts. There is no reason to suppose that rats do not do likewise.

Some of Lashley's experiments cast considerable light on this question. He showed that rats with large cortical lesions could learn to solve a problem in about the same time as normal rats, but their behaviour was simplified. They did so less elegantly. They stumbled on the solutions rather than seeking them in a more systematic or logical way. In other words, they did not really *understand* the nature of the problems they had to solve.[12]

This is similar to the behaviour of children brought up in isolation, whose model of the world remains stunted and rudimentary. Peter the Wild Boy of Hanover, the celebrated eighteenth century isolate brought to London as a curiosity by the Royal Family, ended up working as a farm labourer. He would perform his tasks well but could never really *understand* their meaning. When asked to load a cart with manure, he would do so very efficiently but—not understanding the point of what he was doing—would proceed to empty it and fill it up again repeatedly until made to stop.[13]

To understand something is to determine its function within a larger system. This means that *widening the context* in which we study it will increase our knowledge of its function. This is how a detective tries to understand a crime. Each clue is related to an increasingly wider set of events, gradually acquiring ever greater meaning. Other clues are treated in the same way until, eventually, the crime is reconstructed, and the detective can be said to have *understood* exactly what has occurred. There is no other way of proceeding. The clue in isolation from its context cannot be interpreted, for it has no meaning and merely constitutes data, not *information*.

Living things, except perhaps for the very simplest ones, do not behave like passive robots. They are intelligent beings, and—whether mainstream science likes it or not—they seek desperately to understand their relationship with the world about them.

32

LIVING THINGS ARE INTELLIGENT

Of all the fictions with which mankind has allowed itself to be fooled, none is vainer than the belief that the 'instinct' of animals is absolutely different from the 'reason' of men and that the lower races are dumb and soulless automata separated from the human by a deep and impassable gulf.

Henry S. Salt

The existing scientific data indicate a greater degree of intellectual communality among the primates, and probably a greater communality among all animals, than has been commonly recognised.

H.F. Harlow

THE NOTION THAT human mental processes are categorically distinct from those of other animals is a gratuitous assumption based on no valid knowledge of any kind. In particular, it is gratuitous to insist, as mainstream science has done, that only humans are *intelligent*—especially since the term has never even been satisfactorily defined. Admittedly, we have intelligence tests, but as C. Judson Herrick notes, 'we do not know just what it is that they measure.'[1] Some authors, among them Ashis Nandy, suggest that intelligence is little more than 'that which is tested by intelligence tests'.[2]

Alfred Binet and Théodore Simon, the pioneers of intelligence testing, consider that 'to judge well, to comprehend well, to reason well, these are the essential activities of intelligence.'[3] For Alice Winifred Heim, 'intelligent activity consists in grasping the essentials in a given situation and responding appropriately to them.'[4] H.F. Harlow defines intelligence as all round intellectual ability—to learn, understand, improvise, and create;[5] qualities that all living things, in varying degrees, tend to display. With regard to learning, for instance, Harlow considers that

> there is no scientific evidence of a break . . . between primate and non-primate forms. Emergence from the ocean to the land produced no sudden expansion of learning ability. Indeed, there is no evidence that any sharp break ever appeared in the evolutionary development of the learning process.[6]

Richard Hingston would have agreed with Harlow. For seventeen years he observed the behaviour of lowly insects in the tropical forests of India, and he concluded that they solved their problems much the same way as we do. The notion that 'insects are nothing but animated machines,' he wrote, and 'that they lead purely reflex lives, these assertions I believe to be quite unfounded.'[7] Regardless of what particular mental qualities we judge as important, Hingston showed that insects seem to display them. For example, they are quite capable of 'reasoning'. Hingston noted how dung-rolling beetles, when their ball was pinned to a long stake, examined the ball, discovered the stake, and freed the ball by cutting it in two and putting the separate bits together. They are also quite capable of adapting means to ends. Thus, the wasp *Mellinus arvensis*, Hingston found, can capture flies on pads of dung. It normally does so by sneaking about. But on one occasion, when the flies were particularly active, one of these wasps was seen to lie on the dung simulating death, simply waiting for the victims to walk into its grasp. 'Have we not here a particular plan adapted to meet a particular end?' Hingston asks.[8]

Insects are quite able to improvise strategies for dealing with environmental challenges. Hingston describes how Swynnerton's ants dealt with a poisonous spine caterpillar. They ingeniously blocked the poisonous openings with crumbs of earth and then amputated the spine.[9] They are also capable of displaying judgment. Hingston describes the wasp that dragged its large victim to the opening of its nest. Before trying to get its victim in, the wasp went backwards and forwards between its victim and the hole, until, having determined that the victim would not fit, it set about methodically to enlarge the hole.[10]

They are also capable of forethought—foreseeing the results of their present activities (chapter 30). Hingston describes a mason wasp that, in building its nest, did not just build one cell after another in a random way but started off by laying the foundation plan for all the cells of the finished nest.[11] They are similarly well able to remember past experiences. A particular ant, Hingston assures us, can remember the place where it has found food after a prolonged period of time. A hive-bee can do the same thing. Wasps, he assures us, can not only remember one spot but can 'keep in their minds a geographical picture of the territory over which they work'.[12]

From all this evidence, Hingston claims that

> we are not justified in making barriers between insect and human mentality. I mean, we have no right to regard their minds as being totally different in kind. In their main essential characteristics, *the minds of these humble creatures operate in the same way as the mind of man*, and this harmonises well with those laws of continuity, which, as our knowledge of this world grows, become more and more firmly established.[13]

Reductionist science is unimpressed by these arguments. Non-human living things are indeed capable of very remarkable achievements, but these, it is insisted, are merely the products of instinct not of intelligence.

Yet human behaviour is as much governed by its instincts as is that of other animals (chapter 8). The advantage of our intelligence does not lie in substituting new goals for those set by our instincts. Rather, our intelligence enables us to satisfy those very instincts *with greater discrimination and in a greater variety of conditions* than can other animals. In normal conditions—those that fall within our tolerance range (chapters 48 and 49)—there is no conflict between our instincts and our intelligence. Our instincts do not lure us, as Paul MacLean and Arthur Koestler suggest, into primitive types of behaviour against the better judgment of our intelligence (see chapter 37).

If the term intelligence is to be used in a meaningful and functional manner, there is no reason why it should be limited to the behaviour of complex organisms—on the contrary, it should be applied to all life processes. Lucien Cuénot, the French theoretical biologist, went so far as to attribute to the cell 'a sort of intelligence and, indeed, an immanent power equivalent to the purposiveness that is apparent in human behaviour'.[14] Piaget felt that Cuénot had gone too far, and accused him of 'psychomorphism'[15]—but if the function is the same at both levels of organisation, why not use the same term? Not to use it is to mislead people into supposing that the processes are different, helping to perpetuate the myth of the uniqueness of humanity, on which the paradigm of modern science depends.

Sherrington was filled with awe at what we could refer to as the intelligence of the developmental process,

> The body is made up of cells, thousands of millions of them—in our own instance about [100 million million]. . . .The one cell, the original fertilised cell, grows into two, and those two each into two, and so forth. When that has gone on in the aggregate some 45 times, there are 26 million million magic bricks, all of a family. That is about the number [of cells] in a human child at birth. They have arranged themselves into a complex, which is a human child. Each has assumed its required form and size in the right place.[16]

How do we explain this? 'It is as if an immanent principle inspired each cell with knowledge for the carrying out of a design.'

Perhaps the most quoted miracle of nature is the eye. Even the eye of a relatively modest form of life, such as an insect, is of a degree of intricacy that defies the imagination. The Spanish neurologist Santiago Ramón y Cajal describes it thus,

> From the insect's faceted eye proceeds an inextricable criss-cross of excessively slender nerve-fibres. These then plunge into a cell-labyrinth, which doubtless serves to integrate what comes from the retinal layers. Next follow a countless host of amacrine cells, and with them, again, numberless centrifugal fibres. All these elements are, moreover, so small, the highest powers of the modern microscope hardly avail for following them. The intricacy of the connections defies description. Before it, the mind halts, abased.[17]

The complexity and precision of the eye was an embarrassment to Darwin. As he wrote in *The Origin of Species* (1859),

> To suppose that the eye—with all its inimitable contrivances for adjusting the focus to different distances, for admitting different amounts of light, and for the correction of spherical and chromatic aberration—could have been formed by natural selection, seems, I freely confess, *absurd in the highest degree.*

However, he pointed out,

> When it was first said that the sun stood still and the world turned round, the common sense of mankind declared the doctrine false—but the old saying of '*Vox populi, vox Dei*,' as every philosopher knows, *cannot be trusted in science.*[18]

Reason, for him, was a better guide, and it told him that the eye, however intricate, could still only be the product of natural selection.

It is ironic that to explain what are the paltry, not to mention socially and ecologically destructive, achievements of scientific and technological society, such as the invention of the internal combustion engine and the atom-bomb, we invoke our consciousness, our creativity, and our intelligence—yet we categorically deny these qualities to all other living things, let alone to the miraculous processes of evolution and morphogenesis that have brought them and ourselves into being.

33

CONSCIOUSNESS IS NOT A PREROGATIVE
OF HUMAN BEINGS

... only human beings guide their behaviour by a knowledge of what happened before they were born and a preconception of what may happen after they are dead—thus, only human beings find their way by a light that illuminates more than the patch of ground they stand on.

Sir Peter Medawar

... the evidence for some degree of consciousness, certainly in the higher animals and perhaps far down the animal scale, is overwhelming.

W.H. Thorpe

E VEN IF IT BE ADMITTED that all natural systems are intelligent (thus allowing the term to be used in a meaningful way), it will still be maintained by many that humanity remains unique, as we alone display consciousness. We are told that without consciousness there can be no reason and hence no real choice, no purposiveness, and no morality (chapter 18). Also, because we are conscious, our evolution (as opposed to that of all other creatures) is seen as freed from all the biological, social, and ecological laws (or constraints) that govern the rest of the natural world, which means that we can in effect determine our own evolution. Erich Jantsch puts this idea into religious language—it is because of consciousness, he maintains, that 'Mankind is not redeemed by a god but redeems itself.'[1]

Evolution, he tells us, is usually seen as the history of the organisation of matter and energy. However, it can also be viewed as 'the organisation of information into complexity or knowledge'.[2] This 'may be understood as the evolution of consciousness',[3] the highest state of evolution, consistent with Pierre Teilhard de Chardin's 'noösphere'. Once this stage is achieved, he argues, the whole universe can be identified with consciousness, and it is this consciousness that determines the course of further evolution. In this way, by identifying the universe with human consciousness, Jantsch has reconciled—to his satisfaction at least—the idea of a conscious humanity determining its own evolution with his principal thesis that the universe is a self-organising entity.[4] The Promethean enterprise to which modern society is religiously committed is thereby effectively justified.

Along with C. Judson Herrick,[5] I think we can best regard consciousness as a state of awareness associated with enhanced mental activity, which may be required when it is necessary to identify and interpret very carefully an important environmental challenge to which an immediate and often *innovative* response is required—the subconscious mind being largely concerned with routine matters.

W.H. Thorpe is perfectly willing to accept that the human species is not the only living thing to possess this faculty. He sees the same degree of consciousness in the higher animals (chimpanzees, like other 'higher' animals, denoting specific states of mind by different facial expressions) and the possibility of its presence far down the animal scale.[6] Conscious awareness, he feels sure, provides some adaptive advantage over a purely unconscious apprehension of the environment. Julian Huxley talks of the 'mind intensifying' organisation of animals' brains. He sees this as providing a fuller awareness of both outer and inner situations and as enabling living things to deal with chaotic and complex situations.[7]

For some authors, all natural systems are endowed with consciousness, or 'bioconscience'. Teilhard de Chardin goes so far as to attribute a rudimentary consciousness to the atom and molecule (a thesis known as 'panpsychism').[8] We can, at least, consider consciousness as being a feature of biological organisms—embryonic among the simpler forms and more highly developed with the evolution of the brain and, in particular, the neocortex.

But it is important not to overrate the importance of consciousness as a factor in determining our behaviour. As motivation research has revealed, humans themselves are not normally conscious of their basic underlying motivations—the reasons we give to explain our actions being largely those that best serve to *rationalise* them (chapter 12). It is indeed one of the principal failings of modern epistemology that it is only concerned with *conscious* knowledge, completely ignoring the subconscious or ineffable knowledge that plays an incomparably greater role in shaping our worldview and in determining our particular behaviour pattern, and hence the way in which we interact with the living world on which we depend (chapter 9).

34

THERE IS NO FUNDAMENTAL BARRIER SEPARATING HUMAN BEINGS FROM OTHER FORMS OF LIFE

The fact that primitive man draws no strict line of cleavage between the animal, vegetable, and mineral kingdoms on the one hand, and human beings on the other, has been so often emphasised that it can be regarded as an anthropological commonplace.

Raphael Patai

To man in the totemistic stage of thinking, Dike and Themis—natural order and social order—are not distinguished, not even distinguishable. Plants and animals are part of his group—factors in his social structure. It is not that he takes them under his protection—they are his equals, his fellow-tribesmen; naturally, they obey the same law, or rather . . . they follow the same social custom.

Jane Ellen Harrison

We have seen that the senses and intuitions, the various emotions and faculties—such as love, memory, attention, curiosity, imitation, reason, *etc.*, of which man boasts—may be found in an incipient or even sometimes in a well-developed condition in the lower animals.

Charles Darwin

We and the beasts are kin. Man has nothing that the animals have not at least a vestige of—the animals have nothing that man does not in some degree share. Since, then, the animals are creatures with wants and feelings, differing in degree only from our own, they surely have their rights.

Ernest Thompson Seton

THERE IS NO FUNDAMENTAL DIFFERENCE between the structure and behaviour of vernacular people and that of other living things. Both are governed by the same laws that govern the behaviour of the natural systems that make up the holarchy of the biosphere.

That the fellowship between humanity and other animals was strongly felt in classical antiquity, during the Middle Ages, and even as late as the nineteenth century in rural areas of Western Europe is well documented by Edvard Westermarck in his *Origin and Development of the Moral Ideas* (1906). It played an essential part in the worldview of vernacular peoples, for without it there could be no animism (chapters 62 and 63), nor could vernacular people see themselves as an integral part of the total living structure or *holarchy* of the biosphere, let alone realise that this holarchy is governed throughout by the same fundamental laws (chapter 61). As Raphael Patai notes, it is 'merely a recognition of the true state of things, the perception of the fundamental similarity underlying the apparent diversity of forms'.[1]

It is particularly marked among 'totemic' societies—those whose members were imbued with an earth-centred or chthonic worldview. For Sir James Frazer, this 'sense of close relationship of man with the lower creatures' is the very essence of totemism.[2] He notes how a Bushman, when questioned by a missionary, could not see any difference between humans and other animals—for instance, 'He did not know but a buffalo might shoot with bows and arrows as well as a man, if it had them.'[3] The Giliaks of the Amur attach no importance to the physical differences separating human beings from other animals.

> In substance, every beast is a real man, just like a Giliak himself, only endowed with an intelligence and strength which often surpass those of mere ordinary human beings.[4]

The clans into which many tribal societies are organised are named after specific animals with whom they see themselves as very closely related. Indeed, they often actually identify themselves with their totemic animals. F.M. Cornford tells us that, among Australian Aborigines, a member of a group that has the Kangaroo as its totem literally believes that he is a kangaroo.

> His belief that he is a kangaroo is so unquestioned that he has no need to pretend that he is one . . . ; all he has to do is to be a kangaroo by behaving as one.[5]

Among the Ojibwe, as Frazer notes, the members of the bear clan behave in a surly and pugnacious way, and members of the crane clan affect 'clear ringing voices like cranes'.[6]

Needless to say, tribesmen will desist religiously from killing animals of the species that they identify with. Frazer tells us how a Mandingo porter offered to forego a whole month's pay in order to save a python, because the python was his totem and to kill it would threaten the survival of his whole family.[7] Such an attitude is a serious impediment to economic development, for if the tribesmen are to participate in this Promethean enterprise, they cannot have any such qualms about killing living creatures. It requires a very different attitude—rather than being our brothers and sisters, non-human animals must be seen as vastly inferior 'beasts' or 'brutes' to whom such qualities as purpose, creativity, intelligence, consciousness, even morality are denied. Instead, their behaviour must be seen as blind and robotic. In this way, we can avoid any qualms and feel justified in exploiting and killing them as much as we like in order to satisfy our sordid short-term economic interests.

Some mainstream scientists have gone further, insisting that 'there is no evidence that animals actually suffer pain.' This is but another pretext for exploiting them—in particular, for torturing them in laboratories in order to obtain whatever 'scientific evidence' will legitimise the use of lucrative new cosmetics, pesticides, and pharmaceutical products.

Many of those who have sought to justify the colonial enterprise have insisted in a similar way that a person born into a tribal society was 'little more than an animal'—hence, little more than a machine. Darwin, for one, wrote in this vein of the Fuegians, the natives of Tierra del Fuego.[8] The domination, indeed the annihilation of tribal cultures, was seen by him and the social Darwinists as part of the beneficial workings of natural selection.[9] If tribal societies failed to survive, it was that they were not fit to do so. The fact that the colonial powers were capable of dominating and eventually of annihilating them was sufficient proof of the former's superiority. It was fully justified in the name of the 'survival of the fittest' and was seen as a necessary condition for human Progress.

All this we must reject. In terms of the worldview of ecology, no fundamental barrier separates us from all the other living things with which we live on this planet—the particularities of their structure and behaviour may be different but the underlying generalities are the same.

PART IV

THE NATURE OF THE BIOSPHERE

·UNITY·

THE BIOSPHERE IS ONE

Academic philosophers, ever since the time of Parmenides, have believed that the world is a unity. . . . The most fundamental of my intellectual beliefs is that this is rubbish. I think the universe is all spots and jumps, without unity, without continuity, without coherence or orderliness, or any of the other properties that governesses love.

Bertrand Russell

For primitive peoples, the highest wisdom consists in recognising a unity in the order of beings in the universe, from which they do not [exclude] the spiritual world.

Father Placide Tempels

The entire range of living matter on earth, from whales to viruses and from oaks to algæ, could be regarded as constituting a single living entity capable of manipulating the earth's atmosphere to suit its overall needs and endowed with faculties and powers far beyond those of its constituent parts.

James Lovelock

TRADITIONAL PEOPLE knew that the world is one, that it is alive, holarchically organised (chapter 42), and that all the myriad living things that inhabit it are closely interrelated and cooperate in maintaining its integrity and stability. Among the ancient Greeks, as Donald Hughes writes, 'the Pythagoreans . . . held that the world is spherical, animate, ensouled, and intelligent.'[1] Plato saw it as 'a living creature, one and visible, containing within itself all living creatures which are by nature akin to itself.'[2] What is more, this living creature is 'endowed with soul and reason'. The Stoics, Hughes tells us, also saw the cosmos as a sentient being that is rational, harmonious, and of which all living things are part.[3] It is also self-sufficient, since it nourishes and is nourished from itself.

This view of the world was largely that of Linnæus and his followers in the eighteenth century and that of the Natural Theologians, such as John Ray, William Paley, and Thomas Morgan. The latter wrote of the 'perfect unity, order, wisdom, and design' of the natural world, 'by which every individual is necessarily related to and made a dependent part of the whole'. For Morgan, the living world could only be the work of a 'universal designing mind' that

> contrived, adjusted, and disposed the whole into such order, uniformity, concordant beauty, and harmony, and who continues to support, govern, and direct the whole.[4]

Aldo Leopold also saw the earth as one,

> in our intuitive perceptions . . . we realise the indivisibility of the earth— its soil, mountains, rivers, forests, climate, plants, and animals—and respect it collectively not only as a useful servant but as a living being . . .[5]

More recently, advances in cytology and molecular biology have led scientists—whose interest had previously been monopolised by the extraordinary diversity of living things—to realise that underlying it all is a basic unity that is very difficult to explain in terms of the modern paradigm of science, in terms of which knowledge is so strictly compartmentalised. Thus, the geneticist Theodosius Dobzhansky notes that underlying the great diversity of living things there are profound similarities.[6] The genetic information in all living things can be read in the language of DNA and RNA, and the protein building blocks of all living things are made of the same twenty standard amino acids. The molecular biologists François Jacob and Jacques Monod also note how similar are all living things at the microscopic level.[7] And if the materials are the same throughout the living world, so is the pattern of construction.

> There are sperm whales and microbes, fleas and giraffes, organisms that thrive at high temperatures and others that thrive in frozen regions. But if we look beneath the variety of forms, we find an amazing similarity of structure and function.[8]

Thus, the French biologist Armand de Ricqlès is struck by the fact that all vertebrates—fish, amphibians, reptiles, birds, and mammals—are built according to the same underlying organisational plan in spite of important anatomical differences. 'What', he asks, 'does this unity of design imply? This is the big question that comparative anatomy began to ask in the eighteenth century and which it has not ceased to ask.'[9]

It implies, of course, that as evolution proceeds, so superficial changes occur to adapt different forms of life to specialised environments, and yet the basic underlying features of life remain the same—an evolutionary achievement that is very difficult to reconcile with currently accepted evolutionary theory. It implies, too, that the overriding goal of living things is to preserve the critical order and hence the stability of the biosphere of which they are part. It also suggests that the biosphere is a single self-regulating natural system and at once a life-process and the unit of evolution (chapters 36 and 37).

The Scottish geologist and natural philosopher James Hutton, writing in 1788, was possibly the first scientist in the modern world to recognise the unity of nature.[10] The idea was put forward once again by the Austrian scientist Eduard Suess in 1875. He saw the earth as a living world that is a system of living animals and plants and coined the term 'biosphere' to apply to this entity together with its geological substrate.[11] The modern idea of the biosphere, however, is usually attributed to the Russian scientist Vladimir Vernadsky, who quite rightly noted that it had the widest possible implications for all the other disciplines in terms of which modern society seeks to understand the natural world and its functioning.[12]

The notion that the world of living things, together with its geological substrate and atmospheric environment, also constitute an entity can probably be traced to Jean-Baptiste Lamarck. He saw the development of living organisms as an integral part of a wider subject (the physics of the earth) that included the study of the atmosphere (meteorology) and of the earth's crust (hydrogeology).[13] None of these disciplines could be understood without reference to the others, pointing to the need for a truly holistic science of the natural world. Suess also saw the biosphere in this way and described plants reaching deep into the soil to feed and, at the same time, rising into the atmosphere above to breathe—thereby highlighting the close interaction between the lithosphere and the atmosphere.[14] Vernadsky's biosphere included 'the whole atmospheric troposphere, the oceans and thin layer in the continental regions expanding down about three kilometres or more.'[15] His position contrasted with that of Frederic Clements and Victor Shelford. Though they were among the fathers of holistic ecology, they nevertheless insisted that the biological community and its geological environment should not be regarded as forming part of the same ecological entity.

Critical to the development of the modern theory of the biosphere was the realisation that the atmosphere was the creation of living things rather than the product of purely physical and chemical forces. This was first suggested by the French scientists Jean-Baptiste Dumas and Jean-Baptiste Boussingault in 1841, and later by Alfred Redfield.[16] In the early 1970s, the idea was taken up by James Lovelock, who described the process of 'geophysiology' in great detail. The atmosphere of dead planets, like Mars and Venus, he notes, is in chemical equilibrium. On the other hand,

> The chemical composition of the atmosphere [of our planet] bears no relation to the expectations of steady-state chemical equilibrium. The presence of methane, nitrous oxide, and even nitrogen in our present oxidising atmosphere represents violation of the rules of chemistry to be measured in tens of orders of magnitude.[17]

What is extraordinary is that many of the gases that compose the atmosphere are unstable in each other's presence. Yet chemically, they should not coexist, which suggests that they have to be continuously emitted on a very large scale if they are to persist in the atmosphere. Lovelock's argument goes as follows,

> we have an abundance of oxygen, 21 per cent of the atmosphere, and a trace of methane, at 1.5 parts per million. We know from chemistry that methane and oxygen will react when illuminated by sunlight, and we also know the rate of this reaction. From this, we can confidently conclude that the coexistence of the two reactive gases methane and oxygen at a steady level requires a flux of methane of 1000 megatons a year. This is the amount needed to replace the losses by oxidation. Furthermore, there must also be a flux of oxygen of 4000 megatons a year, for this much is used up in oxidising the methane. There are no reactions known to chemistry which could make these vast quantities of methane and

oxygen starting from the available raw materials, water and carbon, and using solar energy.[18]

For Lovelock there is only one answer.

> There must be some process at the earth's surface which can assemble the sequence of unstable and reactive intermediaries in the programmed manner to achieve this end. Most probably, this process is life.[19]

As Lynn Margulis and Dorion Sagan also point out, if our planet were a dead one, like Venus or Mars, the atmosphere would be composed of more than 95 per cent carbon dioxide, yet it only contains around 0.03 per cent—that which is required to support life.[20] Why? The explanation is photosynthesis—that essential activity of bacterial, algal, and plant life that is at the same time responsible for maintaining the requisite level of oxygen in the atmosphere. Thus, living things, in taking up carbon dioxide and emitting oxygen, are creating precisely that combination of the two gases in the atmosphere that is required for maintaining life on our planet. They are also creating conditions most favourable to life when generating methane and other atmospheric gases or taking up (or otherwise neutralising) gases in the atmosphere that are surplus to the requirements of life. For Lovelock this suggests

> that the atmosphere is not merely a biological product but more probably a biological construction—not living but, like a cat's fur, a bird's feathers, or the paper of a wasp's nest, an extension of a living system designed to maintain a chosen environment.[21]

It is essential to Lovelock's thesis that living things could not create precisely the atmospheric environment they require nor maintain its stability in the face of environmental change if they were not organised to constitute a single entity—the 'biosphere' (a term he applies exclusively to the organisation of living things on our planet exclusive of its äbiotic constituents). This global living entity, in conjunction with its geological substrate and the atmospheric environment it has created, constitutes a bigger natural system that Lovelock refers to as Gaia, after the Greek goddess of the Earth. The relationship of Gaia to the 'biosphere' (as Lovelock defines it) is thus similar to that of the ecosystem to the biological association or community. Lovelock defines Gaia as

> a complex entity involving the earth's biosphere, atmosphere, oceans, and soil—the totality constituting a feedback or cybernetic system which seeks an optimal physical and chemical environment for life on this planet.[22]

In particular, he stresses that Gaia is thereby capable of maintaining its stability or homeostasis in the face of change, which alone can explain how global climate has remained remarkably stable over the last several hundred million years, even though the heat from the sun has increased by about thirty per cent since life began.

No credible rebuttal of Lovelock's thesis has been published by the mainstream scientific community, nor is one likely to be. Many of its far-reaching implications are considered in this book.

36

THE BIOSPHERE IS A CONTINUUM

Every existing object, whether at rest or in motion, is a strand of
history with some duration.
C.D. Broad

An object separated from its history is clearly not the kind of
thing that could possibly exist.
C.D. Broad

. . . we are beginning to grasp that societies, like the individuals which compose them and like life in general, have a time dimension. They are processes,
and their direction in time is as important a part of their nature as their organisation at any particular time.
Julian Huxley

What are called structures are slow processes of long duration,
functions are quick processes of short duration.
Ludwig von Bertalanffy

THE BIOSPHERE, and indeed all natural systems, exist in time as well as space. As J.H. Woodger puts it,

> A frog without a life history is as impossible as a life history without a frog. A frog in pickle is a cross-section of its history as a living organism, and anatomy is biology with the time dimension omitted. Anatomy studies the organism in 'timeless space'.[1]

The languages of some vernacular societies, including a number of tribes of the American Northwest, characterise time and space as inseparable aspects of the world around them, as Benjamin Lee Whorf has shown.[2] Others, however, including those of European societies, tend to emphasise its spatial aspect, while abstracting time into isolated past, present, and future tenses—thus separating objects from processes.

The members of many North American tribes, as Mircea Eliade tells us, saw the *cosmos* as 'a living unity that is born, develops, and dies on the last day of the year, to be reborn on New Year's Day'. Thus, instead of saying '*a year* has gone by', the Yokuts say '*the world* has passed'.[3]

Similarly, while the sacred houses of the Algonquins and the Sioux are designed to provide a representation of the cosmos, they also provide a representation of the year. What is more, as the cosmos was seen as dying at the end of each year, it was humanity's duty to assure that it was annually reborn. Indeed, many of the ceremonies of vernacular people were reënactments of the original act of creation (*cosmogenesis*) designed to assure the continuity of the cosmos.[4] Vernacular people thus understood that the behaviour of successive generations of people and those of other living things is critical to the maintenance of cosmic continuity and hence to prevent a reversion to the original *chaos*.

Mainstream science, on the contrary, sees no connection between the behaviour of living things, their development, physiology, and the fate of the biosphere—whose very existence as a self-regulating natural system most scientists still deny. They see no connection between the behaviour of human beings and other living things, and the evolutionary process itself—which is seen as occurring independently of the adaptive changes undergone by living things (appendix 4). All these processes are seen as distinct, largely unrelated, and governed by a different set of laws.

Fortunately, a few more enlightened scientists see things differently. In his classical studies of infant behaviour, the psychologist Arnold Gesell notes that the early instinctive reactions of a child are no more than a continuation of the embryological activities that brought it into being. 'The action systems of embryo, fœtus, infant, and child', he writes,

> undergo pattern changes which are so sequential that we may be certain that the patterning process is governed by mechanisms of form-regulation—the same mechanisms which are being established by the science of embryology. . .The growth of tissues, of organs, and of behaviour is obedient to identical laws of development morphology. . .[5]

Henri Bergson also points to the continuity between embryogenesis and behaviour. 'Where', he asks, 'can one draw the line between the constructive processes of the bird's embryonic development and the constructive process by which it builds its nest?'[6] Charles Lumsden and Edward O. Wilson point to the same continuity, asserting that there is no fundamental break in the process between tissue formation and behaviour.[7]

If the anatomical development of an organism (morphogenesis) and its behaviour are both part of the same process, then physiology and behaviour must be similarly linked. Edmund Sinnott notes that breathing, for instance, is a physiological process but also 'a part of the way an animal behaves'.[8] It follows that anatomical development and physiology are also part of the same process. Indeed, 'in any living system,' Sinnott writes, 'changes involved in growth *are essentially the same* as those concerned with the maintenance of vital activities and the repair of tissues.'[9]

It is thus realistic to regard these processes, taken together, as constituting the wider process normally referred to as *ontogeny* (the origin and development of an individual organism). In turn, it is realistic to regard these ontogenies as constituting key units of the evolutionary process itself. That this must be so should be clear from the following consideration. When we say that evolutionary change has occurred, we really mean that *ontogenetic* processes are no longer the same as they were in the past, which means that they have been subjected to morphogenetic, physiological, and behavioural changes. This being so, it seems very unrealistic to study these changes outside their evolutionary context, just as it is absurd to study evolutionary change, as does mainstream science, separately from the changes undergone by the constituent life processes in terms of which it manifests itself.

37

IT IS THE BIOSPHERE AS A WHOLE
THAT UNDERGOES EVOLUTION

The family, from its first ancestor to its latest generation, was a unit.
Erich Bethe

To Freud, the unconscious is chiefly a receptacle for things repressed.
He looks at it from the corner of the nursery. To me it is a vast historical
storehouse.
Carl Jung

It is doubtful whether life can be significantly lived without conscious
relation to some tradition. Those who do live without it live as a kind of
moral proletariat, without roots and without loyalties.
Dorothy Emmet

The continuum of an individual is whole, yet forms part of the continuum
of his family, which in turn is part of his clan's, community's, and species'
continua, just as the continuum of the human species forms part of that
of all life.
Jean Liedloff

IN TERMS OF the neo-Darwinian thesis, the individual organism is seen as the basic unit of evolution. But what is so special about the individual organism? Is there a fundamental difference between its adaptive strategies and those of other natural systems that it can be viewed as totally distinct from them? The answer is, unquestionably, no.

Life processes at all levels of organisation, including the evolutionary process itself, are designed according to the same underlying plan, being purposeful, dynamic, creative, and intelligent (chapters 27, 28, 29, and 32). What is more, their adaptive strategies are geared to maintaining the stability of the larger systems of which they are part—an essential prerequisite for the maintenance of their own stability (chapter 46). In turn, the larger systems (including the biosphere itself) coordinate the behaviour of their constituent parts in such a way that ensures their behaviour maintains the overall stability of the larger systems; a process I refer to as *homearchy*—the coordination of the parts by the whole for the maintenance of the whole (chapter 43).

For these reasons, the individual cannot conceivably be regarded as the unit of evolution. It can only be the larger system—*the biosphere itself* —that is the basic unit of evolution, and we can therefore best refer to evolution as the *biospheric process*.

A process, however, remains an abstraction unless it is considered with regard to its existence in both space *and* time—these being but different aspects of the same singular reality; namely, the total *spatio-temporal* continuum of life that is the biosphere as a whole (chapters 36 and 49).

It follows that, whether we are considering the spatial aspect or the time aspect of the biosphere, there must be a perfect correspondence between the two, just as there is a perfect correspondence between the digestive system considered as a physical entity and the actual *process* of digestion that it engages in—equally, there must be a similar correspondence between the biosphere as a physical entity and the *biospheric process of evolution* that it engages in.

The neo-Darwinian thesis, on the other hand, involves radically isolating the spatial structure of the biosphere from its structure in time—the former being seen in all its complexity and refinement, the latter being reduced to the interplay between two crude mechanisms; namely, a generator of randomness and a blind sorting machine.

In terms of the worldview of ecology, the main features of the biosphere when considered from a purely spatial point of view must also be its main features when considered from the point of view of time and hence its main features when considered properly as a total spatio-temporal entity. Let us look again at a few of its particularly significant features.

The first is that the biosphere, considered from a spatial point of view, is holarchical—being made up of larger systems that are composed, in turn, of organisations of smaller and still smaller systems. The same must also be true of the biosphere when considered from the point of view of time—or, more properly, as a total spatio-temporal process—being made up of long-lived life processes that are further differentiated into ever shorter-lived life processes.

For example, there are many generations of cells within the lifespan of an individual organism. Individuals also have shorter lifespans than do the families of which they are the members. Beyond families stretch communities; beyond communities, societies; and beyond these, the human species, which in turn is but a shorter episode within the much longer history of the biosphere itself.

Another essential feature of the biosphere when considered spatially is that it displays order—where order in space corresponds to purpose in time (chapter 40). This order reveals that the constituent parts of the biosphere must be acting in a way that maintains its critical structure and thus, in turn, their own (chapter 46). James Lovelock sees the development of Gaia and the maintenance of its stability over hundreds of millions of years as the result of the coordinated action of living things—bacteria in particular (chapter 35).

It also implies that the evolution of the constituent species that compose the wider biosphere can only manifest itself in terms of changes occurring to the developmental processes (ontogenies) of succeeding generations (chapter 36). These ontogenies in turn cannot be understood as separate individual processes. They are but the differentiated parts of the ongoing evolutionary process of the species itself (its phylogeny), which in turn is closely integrated with that of the myriad other species (or phylogenies) that make up the total biospheric process—the real unit of evolution.

In relation to this, what then is the underlying role of each generation or ontogeny and its constituent sub-processes (development, physiology, and behaviour)? The answer can only be *to provide the evolutionary process as a whole with the localised and short-term information required to ensure that it remains adaptive to the changing circumstances in which it occurs*. In the language of cybernetics, they provide the *feedback* without which no self-regulating life process is possible. This was implicit at least to the evolutionary theory of Lamarck, but it is hotly denied by mainstream science, which sees evolutionary change as exclusively the result of changes affecting the genes of individual living things. As neither the development of the embryo into a fœtus, the development of a child into an adult, nor its physiological or behavioural experience is considered to affect the genetic material in any way, these processes are seen as totally isolated from the evolutionary process (appendix 4).

Another relevant feature of the biosphere when considered as a spatial or, perhaps more realistically, as a contemporaneous entity is that the smaller constituents are coordinated by the larger ones—the biosphere as a whole coordinating the entire holarchy of members that it embodies. Similarly, when considered in terms of time—as the biospheric process or evolution—both the accumulated experience of its past as well as its endgoals and anticipated future conditions (chapters 2 and 30) must be considered as effectively coordinating its present actions, which are in turn adapting to contemporary conditions. The evolutionary process, in other words, constitutes a *long-term strategy* rather than being just a series of isolated accidents, as is implied by the Darwinian thesis.

In evolution, as in all natural processes, the development of the more general features of the whole precedes that of its more particular features (chapter 59). Thus, the decision that a particular organism was to be a bird rather than a reptile or mammal was taken many millions of years ago. Those required to determine what family, genus, species, or variety it would belong to were taken correspondingly later, and in that order. The more superficial or specific the characteristics that distinguish one species from another, the later its likely period of development.

The German philosopher and naturalist Ernst Haeckel was one of the first to show the similarity between the embryos of different vertebrates, such as chickens, tortoises, and humans, in the early stages of their development and how, as they develop, they grow correspondingly different[1] (an observation also made by Karl Ernst von Baer). This led him to formulate his 'biogenetic law', according to which the development of the individual organism (ontogeny) recapitulates the evolutionary development of its species (phylogeny)—a thesis that was later challenged by Sir Gavin de Beer among others.[2]

It may be more realistic to consider the general similarities of these different embryos at the earlier stages of their respective developments as reflecting the general similarities of their *final* fully developed forms or endgoals, which must of necessity draw upon the common developmental strategies of their shared evolutionary past in addition to the more recent modifications that distinguish each species—the more general, and hence older, strategies being the most critically determining, as the emergence of the more specific, and hence newer, strategies is directly dependent on the prior expression of the more general ones (see *succession*—chapter 22).

Thus, the information that is transmitted from one generation to the next reflects the *whole* experience of that species, not just its recent experience reflected in its more specific developmental strategies. This is essential, since the short-term experience on its own could be unrepresentative, indeed aberrant. Life processes based on it would then be disruptive (heterotelic), serving only to satisfy the short-term needs of individuals of a particular generation without, at the same time, serving those of the larger continuum of which they are but a smaller part—the whole biospheric process losing its continuity or stability as a result.

Put another way, if life processes are to be based on information that reflects the total experience of a species, then the most general and thus longer-term information must be the most stable. It is the more specific and thus more recent information that is variable, and which can thereby change for the sake of preventing larger and more damaging changes affecting the system's long-term generalities (chapters 20, 21, and 22).

In this way, evolution tends to be cumulative and refining. During the evolutionary process, new information does not simply replace the old —rather, it is integrated with the old and thereby supplements it. The nervous system, for example, has evidently evolved by this process of integration and refinement or *differentiation*, whereby the more recent formations have been incorporated without displacing the older ones but by augmenting and enhancing them (chapter 9).

Paul MacLean and Arthur Koestler lament the fact that the neocortex does not completely dominate the older parts of the nervous system— which would be necessary if human beings were, as both of them feel they should be, truly 'rational'. As MacLean writes,

> the reptilian brain is filled with ancestral lore and ancestral memories, and is faithful in doing what its ancestors say—but it is not a very good brain for facing up to new situations.[3]

Neither of them realises that rationality by itself (if there is such a thing) could only lead to chaos—and that it is a prerequisite for the continuity of our species (and hence for its survival) that our 'rationality' be controlled precisely by the 'ancestral lore and ancestral memories' that MacLean and Koestler see as but an undesirable relic of an animal past (chapter 9).

Social behaviour must also be based on information that reflects the society's total experience. How this is achieved is well known. Vernacular and particularly earth-centred or chthonic societies, lacking formal political institutions, such as the state, are effectively governed by a council of elders. These are the living custodians of the society's cultural wisdom that reflects its total continuity of experience and insight. For this reason, a chthonic society has often been referred to as a gerontocracy or *government by the old*. However, the ultimate custodians of the traditional wisdom are the ancestors who formulated it, who are usually conceived of as ancestral spirits directly influencing the day-to-day events of the living. For this reason, such a society is perhaps better seen as a necrocracy or *government by the dead*. Ancestor worship (or rather 'communion with the ancestors' as Jomo Kenyatta refers to it[4]) is an essential feature of the religion of such societies, *as it is the influence and continuity of the values of which the ancestors are the embodiment* that is the determining factor.

Lafcadio Hearn notes how this is true of traditional Japanese society. 'In all matters,' he notes, 'the dead, rather than the living, have been the rulers of the nation and the shapers of its destinies'[5]—as indeed they have effectively ruled and shaped the destinies of all chthonic societies. No voices from the grave have spoken with greater authority than the mythical ancestors, the 'Dawn Beings' as Radcliffe-Brown refers to them,[6] who lived in that sacred period known by certain Australian tribes as the 'World Dawn' or 'Dreamtime'—Mircea Eliade's *in illo tempore*.[7]

In that sacred period, the mythical ancestors enacted the traditional law that was to govern for all time their society, the natural world, and the cosmos itself. The traditional law was sacred on all these counts, and the general immutability of the traditional information that reflected the total experience of the society—and that was passed down from one generation to the next—was thus assured. Adaptation to new environmental changes in such conditions involved only the particular changes that the shaman and the council of elders could reconcile with the society's mythology and the traditional law that it served to rationalise. Such a society can thus be seen as governed by the larger social continuum of which it is part, going right back to the 'Dawn Period' when it first arose. Thus, the principles governing the transmission of cultural information *are precisely the same as those governing the transmission of genetic information* that ensures the stability of natural systems at a biological level of organisation.

But it is not just the past but also the future that regulates the present —for the short-term processes serve the purposes of the longer-term processes *that encompass and outlive them*. Indeed, within the larger biospheric process, individual life processes are designed in such a way as to maintain its critical order indefinitely—that is until such time as massive geophysical change gives rise to conditions that lie outside its 'tolerance range' (chapter 48).

Nothing is undertaken by the biospheric process in the interests of satisfying short-term requirements that could possibly interfere with its long-term continuity or stability and hence with its perpetuation. In the case of economic development or 'progress', the opposite is true (chapter 65). It is exclusively concerned with immediate, short-term political and economic benefits, and its promoters show absolutely no interest in the consequences of such behaviour for future generations—for the latter are not players in today's political and economic games; they neither vote nor invest nor save nor borrow nor produce nor consume. Why then should they be consulted?

It must follow that if evolution is the biospheric process, it cannot be understood by examining only the behaviour of that contemporary segment of which we are part and that is normally taken to be evolving. For such a segment does not evolve simply in order to maintain its own stability but rather the stability of that vast continuous entity that stretches back to the beginning of life on earth, and whose whole experience provides the information on the basis of which it evolves towards its future purpose. It is this total continuum, in fact, that is truly evolving, not the segment, which by itself is not capable of evolution.

Seen from a cybernetic point of view, the total biospheric experience going back into the mists of time *exists*, as does its present experience and its future goals, for altogether they constitute the biospheric process —the true unit of evolution—and hence the total continuum of life or 'Everywhen' of the tribal 'Dreaming'.[8]

A tribal society is said to be made up of the dead, the living, and the yet to be born. That is precisely how the biosphere must be understood.

THE BIOSPHERE IS ALIVE

[Man is] a self-balancing, 28-jointed adapter-base biped; an electrochemical reduction plant, integral with the segregated stowages of special energy extracts in storage batteries, for subsequent actuation of thousands of hydraulic and pneumatic pumps, with motors attached; 62 000 miles of capillaries; millions of warning-signal, railroad, and conveyor systems; crushers and cranes . . . and a universally distributed telephone system needing no service for 70 years if well managed; the whole, extraordinarily complex mechanism guided with exquisite precision from a turret in which are located telescopic and microscopic self-registering and recording range-finders, a spectroscope,
etc. etc. . . . .
Buckminster Fuller

A machine is made to realise some conscious human purpose. Its parts work together to secure that purpose, not to secure its own persistence.
J.H. Woodger

. . . I was born a thousand years ago, born in a culture of bows and arrows . . . born when people loved all nature and spoke to it as though it had a soul.
Chief Dan George

FOR VERNACULAR PEOPLE throughout the ages, nature was alive —and their religious life was, above all, focused on their relationship with the spirits that inhabited all natural things. Theodore Roszak talks of the Pagan view of nature as 'alive and infused with purpose' and 'aglow with seductively sensuous qualities'.[1] Morris Berman tells us that nature was seen, until the scientific revolution, as 'enchanted', 'alive', and as 'a place of belonging'. Humanity was not 'an alienated observer' of the cosmos but 'a direct participant in its drama'. Our destiny was 'bound up with its destiny', and this gave meaning to our lives.[2]

It is no coincidence that vernacular people were animist, for as the anthropologist Weston La Barre writes, animism 'is deeply linked with the biological nature of the human species'.[3] Indeed, it is part of that intuitive heritage that enables people to be cognitively adjusted to the world in which they live (chapter 53). However, with the development of the worldview of modernism and, in particular, of the closely related paradigm of science, the world became 'disenchanted', secularised, and 'mechanomorphised'.

This mechanistic view of the world, like all the different aspects of the paradigm of science, can be traced back to the sixteenth and seventeenth centuries, but it was more explicitly formulated in the eighteenth century by Julien La Mettrie in his *L'Homme Machine* (1747), Joseph Louis Lagrange in his *Mécanique Analytique*, and Pierre-Simon Laplace in his *Mécanique Celeste* (see chapter 13). The mechanomorphic thesis has gone through at least three distinct phases. In the first, with Galileo, Descartes, and Newton, life processes were explained in terms of pure mechanics. Scientists sought purely mechanical explanations of digestion, embryogenesis, nerve reactions, and even the workings of the mind.

During the next phase, living things were compared to heat engines and life processes to combustion. This notion can be traced to Joseph Priestley, who thought that candles and living things like mice emitted a substance known as 'phlogiston' (chapter 15). Since the candle stops burning and the mice die when there is no phlogiston left, living and burning are one.

Antoine Lavoisier replaced phlogiston with oxygen. The process was then reformulated in the language of thermodynamics. It was shown that during metabolism energy is conserved (first law of thermodynamics) and heat is dissipated (second law). It was then noticed that life is more than just the burning up of food to release energy—it also involves synthesis, the use of potential energy to switch one state of matter to another. These considerations led to the third phase, called by Peter Calow 'the chemical plant analogy'.[4] Like a chemical plant, an organism makes use of raw materials and adds them to a 'biological reaction flask' to produce new compounds. This process can also be expressed in the language of thermodynamics—life processes being seen as overcoming the influence of the second law because the biosphere within which they occur is an open system, at least from the point of view of energy (appendix 1).

The mechanomorphic thesis suffers from a very serious flaw. It seems first to have been explicitly formulated by Descartes—who, officially at least, remained a deist. It was God who created 'the man machine', as He created all other living machines that make up the living world. The position of mechanistic science, however, is quite different. God has been abolished, and so human beings and other living things *have neither a manufacturer nor an operator.*

Mechanistic scientists, as J.H. Woodger notes, want to have a machine without a mechanic.

> Their problem is to show how it is possible to have a machine which comes into existence, runs, repairs, and regulates itself, and finally divides into two machines, *without a mechanic.*[5]

They have, in fact, completely forgotten that '*machines presuppose organisms*' and hence all those features of organisms whose very existence the mechanomorphic thesis sets out to deny. Professing to eliminate them, our scientists have merely externalised them on the sly, hoping that no one would notice. In reality, as Woodger notes, 'the choice is not between mechanism and mystery but between one mystery and another.'[6]

It will be argued that this dogma is no longer entertained by physicists today. Quantum mechanics has revealed that behaviour at the subatomic level cannot be understood in terms of Newtonian physics. Quantum physicists, we are told, now view the world in terms of waves, fields, and quanta. But outside the discipline of quantum mechanics, mainstream science remains very definitely Newtonian. If the subatomic constituent is no longer seen as a machine, *molecules, organisms, and ecosystems still are*, and so indeed are human societies.

Why then, we may ask, do mainstream scientists still maintain this untenable thesis? The main reason seems to be that machines are simple and predictable. Their behaviour is explicable in terms of cause and effect and is also eminently quantifiable. They can be studied in isolation from other machines and hence in controlled laboratory conditions (chapter 3). Indeed, scientists should be honest enough to admit, as Woodger does, that living things are taken to be machines largely because they have to be if they are to be studied by means of scientific method.[7] This is of course to admit that scientific method can only enable us to understand the behaviour of living things *once their most important features—precisely those that distinguish them from mere machines—have been eliminated* (chapter 13).

But there is another reason why the mechanomorphic view of life has been adopted by mainstream scientists. If they faced up to the real nature of human beings as complex forms of life, they would also have to face the fact that our real needs—biological, social, cognitive, spiritual, and ecological—are ever less adequately satisfied by 'progress' or economic development. If human beings are machines, on the other hand, we can maintain the notion that our only needs are material and technological—*precisely those that economic development is capable of satisfying*. As Michael Polanyi writes,

> the Laplacean universal mechanics induces the teaching that material welfare and the establishment of an unlimited power for imposing the conditions of material welfare are the supreme good.[8]

Donald Worster makes the complementary point that 'by reducing plants and animals to insensate matter, mere conglomerates of atomic particles devoid of internal purpose or intelligence,' mechanistic science has removed 'the remaining barriers to unrestrained economic exploitation'.[9]

The mechanomorphic view of the world, moreover, is not only alienating but grossly flawed. In their hearts, people have always known this and have constantly reacted against this soul-destroying vision, as did Henry More in the seventeenth century. He was much influenced by the animism of Plato and Plotinus and revived the idea of the 'soul of the world' or 'spirit of nature' or *anima mundi*. He described this as a

> substance incorporeal but without sense and animadversion, pervading the whole matter of the universe and exercising a plastical power therein . . . raising such phenomena in the world . . . as cannot be resolved into mere mechanical powers.[10]

He also posited a vital organising power in plants and animals. It is because of this power, he maintained, that they are more than 'mere motion of matter'.

The notion of the *anima mundi* was taken up by the Romantic poets and writers of the eighteenth and nineteenth centuries in their reaction against mechanistic science and the associated technological ethic. Goethe saw nature 'at work and alive, manifesting herself in her wholeness in every single part of her being'.[11] The Romantics developed a decidedly ecological worldview. Wordsworth, for instance, talked of 'an intertwined togetherness' and a 'community of existence'.[12] A living thing for the Romantics could not be disassembled and then reconstructed like a clock. The world was alive, not dead as the scientists were telling us.

Even scientists began to react against the mechanistic picture of the world. Hans Driesch found that he could not explain, in terms of mechanistic science, the ability of the sea-urchin embryo that he studied in his laboratory to develop into a more or less normal phenotype, even after parts of it had been removed.[13] To do so required that he posit a vitalistic principle that he referred to as 'entelechy'—Aristotle's *entelekhia* (from the Greek έν (*en*), internal, and τέλος (*telos*), end-goal). He saw life processes as controlled by a hierarchy of entelechies that were all derived from and controlled by the organism's overall entelechy.[14]

In his *Creative Evolution* (1907), Henri Bergson also insisted that the evolutionary process could not be explained in mechanistic terms but had to be seen as a 'current of life' flowing from one generation to the next and triggered off by a vital impetus or *élan vital*. 'This impetus', he writes, which he saw as 'sustained right along the lines of evolution, among which it gets divided', is a 'fundamental cause of variations, at least of those that are regularly passed on, that accumulate and create new species.'[15]

The problem with both Driesch's entelechy and Bergson's *élan vital*, however, is that they are very vague notions, so much so that to postulate their existence does not tell us a great deal. Bergson realised this but argued that at least his *élan vital* could serve as a 'sort of label affixed to our ignorance, so as to remind us of this occasionally, while mechanism *invites us to ignore that ignorance.*'[16]

Vitalism, however, is not an alternative to the mechanomorphic thesis. It is just something that is added on to make it more realistic. What is really required is a *totally non-mechanistic theory of life*, and such a theory must, by its very nature, be holistic. As Waddington writes, 'the contrast is not so much between mechanism and vitalism but rather between mechanism and organicism.'[17]

The main features of living things, those that make them alive—their dynamism, creativity, intelligence, and purposiveness—are not apparent if we study them in isolation from the holarchy of natural systems of which they are an integral and organised part. They are alive, in fact, *precisely because they are a part of this holarchy* (chapter 42). As Rainer Schubert-Soldern puts it, 'life is a whole in which the parts, instead of going their separate ways, work together.'[18] If they did not, life would be chaotic, random, uncoordinated. Similarly, Joseph Needham notes how 'the whole requires its components (of all levels) in order to be "alive",' while 'the parts require the whole in order to make their particular contribution to it by virtue of which it is "alive",' expressing in this way what can be referred to as the principle of *holarchical mutualism* (chapter 46). He goes so far as to say that

> a molecule, an atom, or an electron, if it belongs to the spatial hierarchy [*i.e. holarchy*] of a living organism, will be just as much 'alive' as a cell— and one which does not belong to such a spatial hierarchy will be 'dead'.[19]

We can see for ourselves that if we kill a living thing, it loses its wholeness. The parts, in so far as they can survive, regress to a much cruder state of heightened disorder and randomness, and their behaviour can then be more easily considered in terms of the reductionist and mechanomorphic paradigm of science. For instance, general purposiveness in the living world can be identified with the tendency of living things to maintain the whole. Once the whole disintegrates, however, the parts lose their basic purpose and their behaviour can then more seemingly be explained in terms of the crude mechanistic theory of causality.

Though Needham was only concerned with life up to the level of the biological organism, we can apply his criterion of life, with some reservations, to higher levels of organisation, such as that of the society, the ecosystem, and the biosphere itself. At these higher levels, living things are not so closely integrated, which means that their separation from the whole does not immediately entail their demise. However, social isolates are alienated beings incapable of normal whole maintaining behaviour; they can no longer fulfil the basic task for which they were designed—the maintenance of the critical order of the living world, within which their life alone has meaning. Under these conditions, their lives, now largely devoid of meaning, are either devoted to instant gratification, or attempting, via drugs, alcohol, and the like, to cut themselves off from a meaningless world with which they cannot cope, or to recreate, by various contrived means, some illusory semblance of the social environment of which they have been deprived (chapter 51). They have lost their wholeness and are therefore no longer truly alive.

James Lovelock has been criticised for stating that 'Gaia is alive'. 'This notion "alive"', he writes, 'bothers a lot of my scientific colleagues,' and he asks them to think of it as 'no more than the capacity of the earth to regulate itself and to keep cool when things are changing adversely.'[20] In his book *Healing Gaia—The Practical Science of Planetary Medicine* (1991), Lovelock tells us that he sees as alive 'everything that metabolises and self-regulates . . . so that life is something shared in common by cats and trees, as well as by beehives, forests, coral reefs, and Gaia.'[21] In other words, to be alive is to display homeostasis (chapter 20).

However, for a natural system to assure its homeostasis or stability, it must above all seek to maintain the integrity of the larger holarchy of which it is part (chapter 46), *for maintaining the integrity of the whole is the essential prerequisite of homeostasis*. Since, for Lovelock, Gaia is the whole, to assure its homeostasis means maintaining its own wholeness in the face of change. When Lovelock says that Gaia is alive, he must therefore also imply that Gaia (the biosphere) is whole.

39

THE BIOSPHERE IS THE SOURCE
OF ALL BENEFITS

Land left wholly to nature . . . is called, as indeed it is, waste.
John Locke

You can gauge a country's wealth, its real wealth, by its tree cover.
Richard St Barbe Baker

Wilderness is the bank on which all cheques are drawn.
John Aspinall

All that great bare belt of country which now stretches south of the Ganges —that vast waste where drought seems to be perennial and famine is as much at home as is [Shiva] in a graveyard—was once an almost impenetrable wood. Luxuriant growth filled it—self-irrigated, it kept the fruit of the summer's rains till winter, while the light winter rains were treasured there, in turn, till the June monsoon came again. Even as late as the Epic Period, it was a hero's derring-do to wander through that forest-world south of the Nerbudda, which at that time was a great inexhaustible river, its springs conserved by the forest. Now the forest is gone, the hills are bare, the valley is unprotected, and the Nerbudda dries up like a brook, while starved cattle lie down to die on the parched clay that should be a river's bed.
Edward Washburn Hopkins

I T IS FUNDAMENTAL to the worldview of modernism that all benefits are produced artificially—the products of scientific, technological,
and industrial progress made available via the market system. Thus,
health is seen as something that is dispensed in hospitals, or at least by the
medical profession, with the aid of the latest technological devices and
pharmaceutical preparations. Education is seen as a commodity that can
only be acquired in schools and universities. Law and order, rather than
being natural features of human society, are seen instead as provided by
our police force in conjunction with the law courts and the prison system.
Even society is seen as artificial, brought into being by the 'social contract'. Not surprisingly, a country's wealth is measured by its per capita
Gross National Product (GNP), which provides a rough measure of its
ability to provide its citizens with all such artificial commodities—a principle faithfully reflected in modern economics.

For economists trained in these ideas, natural benefits—those provided
by the normal workings of the biosphere, assuring the stability of our
climate, the fertility of our soil, the replenishment of our water supplies,
and the integrity and cohesion of our families and communities—are not
regarded as benefits at all; indeed, our economists attribute to them no
value of any kind; they are simply deemed 'externalities' (chapter 6). It
follows that *to be deprived of these non-benefits cannot constitute a 'cost'* and
the natural systems that provide them can thereby be destroyed with
economic impunity.

Even economists who can see through this preposterous accounting
system still deny that environmental destruction is a problem, because
they have been taught that the market system, in conjunction with science, technology, and industry, can deal with any 'resource shortage'. For
instance, when the farmers of the San Joaquin valley, in the southern part
of the great central valley of California, were faced with a serious water
shortage threatening to put many of them out of business, they did not
appear particularly concerned, making no effort to adapt highly wasteful
water-intensive practices to the new conditions. It was taken for granted
that, sooner or later, some massive water diversion scheme would, as in
the past, bring them the water they required from some other part of
America or even Canada.[1]

The same argument is used to persuade us that the degradation of
our agricultural land is not a problem. For our economists, agricultural
land is just another 'resource'. Gale Johnson, a university professor and
well-known agricultural economist, insists that natural resources play a

relatively minor role in determining the wealth of nations.[2] Emery Castle of Resources for the Future, one of the USA's most influential research organisations, told a meeting on the availability of agricultural land in 1980 that 'the loss of agricultural land is not a high-priority national concern.'[3] The American economist Julian Simon tells us that there can be no permanent shortage of agricultural land—to suppose otherwise is an error that stems from wrongly considering the availability of resources in physical rather than economic terms. Indeed, if some land is unsuitable for agriculture, this is only a reflection of current market conditions. If the land were really needed, then the necessary science, technology, and capital would make it productive.[4]

This aberrant attitude is further rationalised by mainstream scientists, who set out systematically to denigrate natural processes. Thus, Sir Peter Medawar talks of nature's own 'artless improvisations'.[5] Lester Ward attacks the inefficiency of nature—'Rivers, instead of flowing straight and so delivering their water to the sea with minimum expenditure of energy, lazily meander through plains and valleys.' He complains of the 'redundant fertility' of the organic world—the herring lays ten thousand eggs, of which only two will reach maturity; and a large chestnut tree produces up to a ton of pollen.[6] For Ward, nature's shortcomings are an invitation to humanity to become nature's engineer and create a paradise on earth of our own design, whose functioning we can plan and direct in all its detail.

It is a basic principle of the worldview of ecology that real benefits (and hence real wealth) are, on the contrary, derived from the normal functioning of the natural world and of the cosmos itself. Our greatest wealth must be the favourable and stable climate, our forests and savannahs and fertile agricultural lands, our rivers and streams, springs and ground waters, our wetlands and coral reefs, our seas and oceans, and the myriad forms of life that inhabit them all.

It is usual today to depict our remote ancestors—who lived off this great wealth without jeopardising it, as we are doing today—as poor and wretched. They are made out to have suffered from chronic malnutrition, living permanently on the edge of famine. *Nothing is further from the truth.* The incredible biological wealth of the vast area that is now the United States of America is attested by John Bakeless. In the great plains, where modern agriculture has eliminated most of the original vegetation, and where the topsoil is eroding so fast that much of the land will be reduced to low-grade rangeland within a few decades, there were

> prairies teeming with buffalo, in herds that would pass all day without end; lordly moose along the lake shores; deer everywhere. Wild grapes

roofed much of the eastern forests; there were wild fruits of many kinds; plentiful fish in every lake or stream; oysters nine inches long—or longer—in great clusters, which some fortunate dwellers on Manhattan simply pulled out of the clear waters before their shelters; lobsters beyond twenty pounds, easily caught; wild turkeys in flocks so large their gobbling in the morning might be deafening; passenger pigeons that literally did darken the sky. There were grouse, prairie chicken, ducks of every kind, wild geese so fearless that at times they tried to frighten off approaching hunters.[7]

It is straining credulity a little too far to pretend that the dwellers on Manhattan, as it was then, suffered from malnutrition and famine. On the contrary, they were almost certainly considerably better fed than the present inhabitants of that island. In Africa—a continent where famine has now become chronic, and where 27 million people were threatened with starvation in the year 1991 alone[8]—food shortages appear to have been unusual. The anthropologist Richard Lee testifies that !Kung Bushmen had an extremely satisfactory diet and rarely suffered food privations.[9] James Woodburn assures us that the same is true of the Hadza, a tribe of hunter-gatherers in Tanzania.[10]

Mungo Park in his *Travels in the Interior Districts of Africa* (1799), tells us that the Gambia River abounded with fish and that nature 'with a liberal hand' had bestowed on the inhabitants of that area the 'blessings of fertility and abundance'.[11] Two eighteenth-century French travellers, Poncet and Brévedent, note that in the Gezira area of the Sudan, now occupied by eroded cotton fields, there were once 'pleasant forests of flowering acacias full of little green parrots' and 'fruitful and well-cultivated plains', and that it was called God's Country (*Belad-Allah*) 'by reason of the great plenty'.[12] In Kenya, where now an exploding population must be fed from an increasingly degraded environment, food shortages were also uncommon. As B.D. Bowles notes,

> European explorers and Arab traders found little difficulty in obtaining food as they travelled through the area. European conquerors actually burned crops standing in the fields and still survived without the importation of food. They extracted a surplus by force, and they would have been unable to do this if no surplus had been available.[13]

Bengal, which included modern Bangladesh and is now one of the most overpopulated and impoverished areas on our planet, was once known as 'Golden Bengal'. François Bernier in his *Travels in the Moghul Empire* (1670) was particularly impressed by its 'richness'. 'Egypt', he writes,

has been represented in every age as the finest and most fruitful country
. . . but the knowledge I have acquired of Bengal during the two visits paid
to that kingdom inclines me to believe that the preëminence ascribed to
Egypt is rather due to Bengal.[14]

Nor is there any reason to suppose that the Australian Aborigines were
short of food. Sir George Grey, who spent a good deal of time with Australian Aborigines in the early part of the nineteenth century, insists that
he always found the greatest abundance in their huts.[15]

Even if we are forced to admit that malnutrition and famine were not
humanity's natural lot, we still insist that tribal people were poor because
they were 'deprived' of material goods and technological devices. This,
too, is an illusion. For perhaps ninety-five per cent of our tenancy of this
planet we pursued a nomadic way of life as a hunter-gatherer, swidden
agriculturalist, or nomadic pastoralist. For the nomad, material goods that
we associate with wealth are, above all, a burden they see as 'grievously
oppressive', the more so the longer such items have to be carried around.

When Laurens van der Post wanted to give a present to Bushman
friends, with whom he had sojourned, as a token of his gratitude for
their hospitality, he simply did not know what to give them.

We were humiliated by the realisation of how little there was we could
give to the Bushmen. Almost everything seemed likely to make life more
difficult for them by adding to the litter and weight of their daily round.
They themselves had practically no possessions—a loin strap, a skin blan-
ket, and a leather satchel. There was nothing that they could not assem-
ble in one minute, wrap in their blankets, and carry on their shoulders for
a journey of a thousand miles. They had no sense of possession.[16]

To label them as poor *completely misses the point*, for Bushmen living in
their natural environment do not feel in any way deprived by their lack
of material goods. *Their priorities are simply quite different.*

They were even different at the court of the Manchu emperors of
China, before that country had been subjected to Western influence.
Thus, the Emperor Ch'ien-lung was not the least impressed by the gift
of manufactured goods presented to him by the British emissaries of
King George III, who sought to establish diplomatic links with his country. He rejected the British request and sent a letter to King George that
concluded with the following words,

Swaying the wide world, I have but one aim in view—namely, to maintain a perfect governance and to fulfil the duties of the state. Strange and

costly objects do not interest me. . . . As your Ambassador can see for himself, we possess all things. I set no value on objects strange or ingenious and have no use for your country's manufactures.[17]

This attitude could not be more foreign to us. Our appetite for material goods and technological devices seems insatiable. Indeed, it is in terms of our access to them that our wealth, indeed our welfare, is normally gauged. It is undoubtedly true that today we need a lot of material goods and technological devices, but this is not because we have an *intrinsic* need for them but because, in the aberrant conditions in which we live, we have become dependent on them for the pursuit of our biological, social, spiritual, and æsthetic needs—our real needs. The car, for example, when it was first invented, was undoubtedly a luxury. Slowly, however, it became a virtual necessity. As it came to be assumed that people possessed them, so they were expected to travel ever further to their place of work, to the schools where their children were educated, to shopping centres, or for recreational purposes.

It is not religion that is the opiate of the people, as Karl Marx decreed, but *materialism*. The possession of material goods has only been man's chief preoccupation for a very short time, whereas religion permeated every aspect of the life of vernacular people. Material and technological goods can be regarded as little more than bribes and compensations to induce people to accept the systematic annihilation of their real wealth that inevitably accompanies economic development or 'progress'.

It is unlikely that any artificial commodity, however sophisticated, can adequately replace the natural product that it imitates. The reason is that the latter is designed to satisfy the countless requirements of the smaller systems that compose it, as well as those of the larger system of which it is part—whereas the artificial commodity is only designed to satisfy a few of these requirements. A good illustration is our attempt, as part of the developmental process of growing infants, to substitute cow's milk for human milk. Needless to say, it is always easy to find experts who, on the basis of a simplistic notion of human nutrition, assure us of its superiority. We are assured that cow's milk has a higher protein content, for instance. But as Michael and Sheilagh Crawford note, a calf needs more protein because, at birth, it grows more quickly than does a human baby.[18] More important still, as S.H. Katz and M.V. Young point out, is the fact that cow's milk contains less polyunsaturated fat—but this fat is needed for building brain tissue, and what is sufficient for this purpose in a growing calf is insufficient for the development of a human baby's much larger brain.[19] There are a host of other reasons why cow's milk is a poor substitute for human milk in infancy. It contains an almost equal ratio of calcium and phosphorus, unsatisfactory for a human baby, which requires more calcium. The level of sodium in cow's milk is too high and may give rise to primary hypertension. The low level of copper in cow's milk has been related to the reduced transportation of iron and hence to the iron deficiency associated with anæmia, common among North American infants. On the other hand, human milk contains the proportion of long-chain fatty acids that most favours their absorption and conversion to energy in the human baby.

Furthermore, the gastro-intestinal tract of a baby fed on human milk is colonised by the bacterium *Lactobacillus bifidus*. The important role played by this bacillus appears to have been grossly underestimated. Its presence appears to be essential to the absorption of protein and other nutrients in the milk. Equally important is the role played by human milk in ensuring immunisation to disease. Certain antibodies are transmitted by the placenta, which is permeable to them, while other antibodies are excluded. This means that bottle-fed babies are born without immunity to the diseases against which the latter provide protection—including those of gastroenteric origin that happen to be the leading cause of mortality among babies throughout the world. These antibodies, on the other hand, are present in human milk in sufficient concentrations to provide protection against many gastroenteric diseases (though it appears that this immunisation only occurs if the corresponding antigens are present in the child's immediate environment).

There is also growing reason to believe that the intimate relationship between mother and infant during breastfeeding has a significant effect on the child's digestive capacities. Katz and Young also consider that a real synergy is likely to exist among the nutritional, immunological, maternal, and psychoëndocrinological responses that foster infant development.[20]

It is both naïve and irresponsible to suppose that so incredibly sophisticated a natural process as breastfeeding, which has evolved over millions of years, can be advantageously replaced by feeding an infant on milk that is designed by its evolution to satisfy the requirements of a baby ungulate, contained in a bottle that provides but a crude imitation of its mother's teat.

If human milk is one of nature's products that we cannot really do without, so are the natural forests that once covered significant proportions of our planet's land area—in particular, the tropical rainforests. We can draw up an almost endless catalogue of the irreplaceable services that rainforests provide. By means of their elaborate root systems, they literally hold the soil together, preventing erosion from even the steepest slopes. Even in rainforests that are subjected to three hundred inches of rain in a year, the water that runs off into the rivers is crystal clear. Their elaborate root system also ensures that the earth beneath it is sponge-like, which maximises its capacity to retain the rains; by the same token, controlling runoff to the rivers by releasing only a fraction of the water that the earth retains. Once the forests have been cut down and the roots have rotted, the earth hardens and ceases to be capable of retaining water. Most of the water runs off immediately into the rivers, whose beds have been raised by sediment eroded from increasingly deforested slopes, giving rise to ever-worsening floods. The water table sinks; rivers become torrents that only flow during the rainy season; streams and springs dry up.

Forests also provide the perfect habitat for living things—it is said that between half and two-thirds of all the millions of different species of living things inhabit the tropical rainforests. Vernacular people, even after they have become sedentary cultivators, still derive much of their food from neighbouring forests. They also find there the materials required for their houses or huts, their artefacts and tools, their medicinal herbs and their vegetable dyes—indeed, the forests provide the very material basis of their cultural pattern, which necessarily disintegrates once the forests go.

Forests also provide an important sink for carbon dioxide and, at the same time, generate the oxygen required for animals to breathe. The wholesale burning of forests that is occurring today is responsible for a significant proportion of the carbon dioxide released into the atmosphere to cause global warming. Where the destruction is irreversible, it reduces this sink and reduces, too, the availability of oxygen. Forests, via the evapotranspiration from their leaves, give rise to much of the atmospheric moisture that will form into clouds and block much of the sun's heat, providing in this way a cooling system for the planet. Between half and three-quarters of the rain that falls on the six million square kilometres of Amazonian rainforest appears to be generated in this way.[21] Thus, over this vast area, huge amounts of water are constantly falling and rising—yet another way in which these forests act as a cooling system for our planet. James Lovelock has sought to calculate the annual energy cost of achieving the same degree of cooling by mechanical means.

If the clouds made by the forests are taken to reduce the heat flux of sunlight received within their canopies by only one per cent, then their cooling effect would require a refrigerator with a cooling power of six kilowatts per hectare. The energy needed, assuming complete efficiency and no capital outlay, would cost annually $1300 per hectare.[22]

On the basis of this calculation, he regards 'the refrigeration system that is the whole of Amazonia' as being worth about one hundred and fifty trillion dollars. This is probably a conservative estimate, and values only one of the large number of different services that the forest provides. Cattle ranching on the same low-grade land would yield a total income of less than one-thirteenth of this sum, and even then only for a few years, after which this highly vulnerable land would have been largely transformed into dust.

Not surprisingly, even after one hundred and fifty years of economic development, the vast bulk of the services required to keep our planet functioning are still provided by the self-regulating process of the biosphere. This was stated quite explicitly in the seminal MIT report *Man's Impact on the Global Environment* (1970).

At least 99 per cent of the potential pests of man are held to very low densities by natural control. Insects pollinate most of the vegetables, fruits, berries, and flowers, whether they be wild or cultivated. Commercial fish are produced almost entirely in natural ecosystems. Vegetation reduces floods, prevents erosion, and air-conditions the landscape. Fungi and minute soil animals work jointly on plant debris and weathered rocks to produce soil. Natural ecosystems cycle matter through green plants, animals, and decomposers, eliminating wastes. Organisms regulate the amount of nitrates, ammonia, and methane in the environment. On a geological time scale, life regulates the amount of carbon dioxide and oxygen in the atmosphere.[23]

No more than a minute fraction of these essential self-regulating biospheric functions, what is more, could be taken over—very inadequately at that—by the externally-regulated technospheric institutions and corporations of our modern world.

Why this must be so is clear if we compare the lot of the natives of the north-west coast of America before the arrival of the Europeans with that of our astronauts. The region was once covered with luxuriant temperate rainforests, teeming with game and plentifully supplied with all sorts of wild fruits, berries, herbs, and roots. At low tide, so abundant were the shellfish on the beaches that the Tlingit, a tribe of the Pacific Northwest, used to say that 'when the tide goes out, the table is set.'[24] Nor, it would seem, was there any need to build bridges across the rivers, for it was said that you could cross them on the backs of the salmon. All this ecological wealth was made freely available to the vernacular peoples of America by the self-regulating processes of the biosphere, in what (barring unforeseen catastrophes, such as the arrival of the Europeans) was a totally sustainable manner.

The lot of our astronauts circling the planet in their small metal boxes could not be more different. They are deprived of even the most rudimentary ecological wealth. No edible plants grow in their space capsules, there is no game to hunt, no fish to catch, no shellfish to gather from the shores. There are no rivers, no streams, no springs from which they can obtain water to drink. Even the oxygen they breathe has to be brought from afar. Indeed, the very conditions required for sustaining life in their capsules can only be maintained by the most sophisticated technological devices, and the cost of sustaining these astronauts in such degraded and artificial conditions is beyond calculation. The richest person in the world could not afford to enjoy this miserable lifestyle for more than a few days, while only the wealthiest nations, at the height of their economic fortunes, could afford to provide it to a handful of their subjects and then but for a few days, weeks, or, at the most, months.

If the US government follows the geoengineering policies suggested in the National Academy of Sciences' publication *Policy Implications of Greenhouse Warming* (1991), then we may all be condemned to become astronauts on our own planet.[25] Indeed, if we refuse to cut global emissions of greenhouse gases by 60–80 per cent below 1990 levels, which the United Nations' Intergovernmental Panel on Climate Change (IPCC) regards as necessary to stabilise world climate, the only method available to us for preventing a global climatic disaster may well be to resort to the geoengineering 'solutions' of the National Academy of Sciences. Among those suggested by this august body is the placing of fifty thousand, one hundred square kilometre mirrors into earth orbit to reflect incoming sunlight. Another is to use guns or balloons to maintain a dust cloud in the stratosphere to increase the sunlight reflection. Other strategies involve using aircraft to maintain a cloud of dust in the low stratosphere to reflect sunlight, or decreasing the burning efficiency of aircraft engines flying in the low stratosphere to maintain a thin cloud of soot to intercept sunlight.[26]

But how do we know that these ludicrously crude geoengineering strategies would work? Also, what happens if there is a general strike in the country that is responsible for producing them? or a civil war? or a Chernobyl-type accident to a nuclear installation that leads to the compulsory evacuation of large numbers of people, or simply an economic collapse of the sort that occurred in 1929, and that is more than likely to recur in the very near future? Even if it does not, how do we know that the world economy would remain capable of sustaining the cost of applying these geoengineering strategies? How do we know that the resources would always be available or that our planet could sustain the social and ecological costs? or even that the climatic degradation caused by carbon emissions from the burning of the fossil fuels required to power so gigantic a geoengineering enterprise might not neutralise what beneficial climatic effects it might conceivably provide?

That our scientists should even suggest the remote possibility that all this absurd gimmickry could provide a substitute for the homeostatic processes of the biosphere that have regulated world climate so far, indicates to what extent they live in a world of their own—one that seems to be increasingly insulated against social, ecological, and even economic realities.

40

THE BIOSPHERE DISPLAYS ORDER

Order is an expression of conformity to Law.
Rupert Riedl

Order is the condition for understanding the Universe. . . . A world without order would have no meaning. . . . [It] would be neither recognisable nor conceivable.
Rupert Riedl

. . . while, for us, the order of nature is one thing and the social order another, for the [aboriginal] Australian, they are two parts of a single order.
A.R. Radcliffe-Brown

Heaven, Earth, and man have the same *Li* [natural order].
Daoist saying

Li, then, is rather the order and pattern in Nature, not formulated law. But it is not pattern thought of as something dead, like a mosaic—it is dynamic pattern, as embodied in all living things and in human relationships and in the highest human values.
Joseph Needham

Order is a basic feature of the biosphere, as traditional people fully understood. Their own bodies, their homes, their temples, their society, the natural world, and the all-encompassing cosmos, they saw as organised according to the same plan, governed by the same laws, and hence as constituting a single organised whole. The word 'cosmos' itself originally meant order. In many cosmologies, as Mircea Eliade notes, the cosmos came into being once God had succeeded in vanquishing a vast primordial monster or dragon that symbolised the original *chaos*.[1] Often, the monster's body served as the raw material out of which the cosmos was fashioned. Thus, Marduk fashioned the cosmos out of the body of the marine monster Tiamat, and Yahveh built the cosmos out of the body of the primordial sea monster Rahab. However, so as to prevent the cosmos from reverting to the original chaos, that victory had to be reënacted every year (chapter 36).

Evolution and its constituent life processes build up order. Individualistic systems become organised, differentiated, and hence specialised in the fulfilment of various functions. As this occurs, so competition yields to cooperation (chapter 44), so the incidence and severity of discontinuities are reduced, and so the systems become more stable. Indeed, order implies organisation, differentiation, specialisation, cooperation, and stability. *They are but different ways of looking at the same fundamental feature of the living world.* But order cannot increase indefinitely. There is an optimum degree of order at each level of organisation in the holarchy of the biosphere—as there must be for all its associated features. That degree of order required for best assuring the critical order of the biosphere, I refer to as *homeotelic* order (chapter 46).

Order can also be seen as 'the influence of the whole over the parts'[2] —what I refer to more specifically as *homearchic* order (chapter 43). It is often forgotten, however, that this influence takes the form of *constraints* extending from the whole to its constituent parts. Still less is it admitted that these constraints are best regarded as laws, which the parts must observe if they are to fulfil their homeotelic or whole-maintaining functions within the larger system and thereby maintain its integrity and stability (chapter 5). The reason is that this notion cannot be reconciled with the reductionist paradigm of science.

Another implication of order is *limitation of choice*—activities by the constituent parts that are inconsistent with the integrity and stability of the larger systems will be resisted, while those that most favour the achievement of that overriding goal will be facilitated.

Thus, as largely autonomous systems are transformed into the specialised parts of a larger system, so, by the same token, must the larger system's influence over them correspondingly increase. As a result, the parts become subject to correspondingly more effective constraints or laws—that is, their range of choice is reduced.

For example, when the slime mould takes the form of largely autonomous protozoa living in a loose colony, the influence of the whole over the parts is correspondingly weak and the latter are only subject to very loose laws or constraints and thereby enjoy a wide range of choices (chapter 25). When, on the other hand, the loose colony is transformed into a multicellular organism, and its parts become more differentiated and specialised in the functions that maintain its integrity and stability, then the influence of the whole over the parts is correspondingly increased, the constraints or laws to which the parts are subject become more restrictive, and thus the range of their choices becomes more limited.

The pattern of behaviour that the constituents of such orderly systems are led to adopt is that which, in these optimum conditions, they themselves will naturally be inclined to 'choose'—*for it is that which must best satisfy their own needs* by providing them with their optimum environment (or 'field'), outside of which they have no meaning and their life becomes disordered and degraded; hence the principle of holarchical mutualism (chapter 46).

Natural systems display order whether we see them as entities in space, as we usually do, or as processes in time. A disordered or random process can tend towards any end point—its behaviour is unpredictable. As order builds up, however, the process is subject to the influence of the whole of which it is part. Its range of choices is limited as it becomes a differentiated part of the larger biospheric process committed to the achievement of an overriding goal—and consequently its behaviour becomes more predictable. Hence, *purposiveness* is just another word for order applied to life processes—that is, *order in time.*

As Pittendrigh notes, order or organisation without purpose is a meaningless concept.

> There is no such thing as organisation in any absolute sense, pure and simple. Organisation is always relative, and relative to an end. . . . [Thus] the organisation of an army is relative to the end of defeating an enemy —and doing so, moreover, in a particular environment of terrain, weapons, and political system. A room may be organised with respect to relaxation . . . Certainly, neither a room nor an army can be organised with respect to nothing.[3]

Thus, if we state that living systems are organised, then we must be ready to face the question 'With respect to what are they organised?' As von Bertalanffy notes, 'The notion of "organ"—of visual, auditory, or sexual organ—already involves the notion that this is a "tool" for something.'[4] Animals will eat and drink and breathe and reproduce because these processes are as much part of them as are the organs that assure these functions. Indeed, there are no such things as animals that do not eat and drink, breathe, and reproduce, except as photographs, pictures, concepts, and words—nor are there such processes as eating, drinking, breathing, and reproducing taken apart from the organisms involved. This must follow from the fact that living things are systems existing in both space and time, which means that the order they display also exists in space and time, and this necessarily implies purposiveness (see chapter 36 and 37).

If the order of the living world—whether seen in terms of space or time—is not apparent to reductionist science, it is largely because seeing the world as orderly means looking at it *holistically*. Indeed, unless we see a system within its natural habitat or 'field' (chapter 49) as an integral part of the larger continuum of systems in which it evolved—to whose maintenance it is directed and to whose influence it is subject—we cannot see that it is orderly and hence purposive.

Paul Weiss often points out how the parts of a cell are constantly changing, growing, dying, breaking up, recombining in what appears to be a chaotic manner—but the chaos is illusory; the parts are subject to cellular coordination, which is essential if the cell is to remain a viable unit of adaptive behaviour. The cell maintains its order and identity in spite of the apparent disorder of its constituent parts. What is more, it outlives them, for it has greater persistence or stability than its constituent parts.[5]

Mainstream scientists would seek to explain this in terms of statistical method. The individual cells, they would maintain, behave in a disorderly manner, but a large number of cells would behave in an orderly manner. For this reason, we cannot make statements about individual cells, only about large numbers of cells, and these statements are necessarily of a statistical nature. Such statistical statements, however, say nothing about the processes that give rise to this order and hence do not explain why this order comes about. They do not relate order to differentiation, specialisation, cooperation, or stability, nor even to the influence of the whole over the parts, nor to the operation of laws or constraints, nor to the reduction of choice, nor to the need for a system to behave in an orderly or purposive manner so as to maintain the integrity and stability of the whole. On the contrary, the statistical approach is a tool for evading the many fundamental implications of the orderliness of natural systems, all of which are irreconcilable with the reductionist paradigm of science, *which it thereby serves to perpetuate*.

It also makes it possible to avoid recognising that in the biosphere or real world, a single underlying order prevails. In this way, Edgar Morin can tell us that 'there is order in the universe, but not one order.'[6] This is just another way of stating that the biosphere is atomised and random, and that its constituents can thereby be seen as governed by very different sets of laws.

The statistical argument also enables mainstream scientists to avoid recognising that the order displayed by the biosphere is not only distinct from but diametrically opposed to that of the technosphere or surrogate world with which modern society is systematically replacing it. To confuse biospheric diversity and complexity with technospheric variety and sophistication (chapters 24 and 25) is to obscure the essential fact that the expansion of the latter can only occur at the expense of the integrity and stability of the former.

In terms of an ecological or biospheric worldview, the holarchy of the biosphere must be seen as displaying a single order, and this order is sacred (chapter 62). At the same time, the biosphere must be seen as governed by a single set of equally sacred laws, whose generalities apply equally well to biological organisms, vernacular communities, societies, and ecosystems, and to the biosphere itself (chapter 61). This was fully accepted by tribal people, as is pointed out by Jane Harrison, Radcliffe-Brown, and others. Modern people, if they are to have a future, must once more become aware of this fundamental principle.

41

THE ORDER OF THE BIOSPHERE IS CRITICAL

... the atmospheric concentration of gases, such as oxygen and ammonia,
is found to be kept at an optimum value from which even small departures
could have disastrous consequences for life.

James Lovelock

The dominating interest of life [in primal society] is to preserve and perpetuate social harmony, stability, and welfare. Religious cults and magic practices
have chiefly this purpose in view. Everyone who has lived with a 'primitive'
people and has tried to immerse his mind in theirs knows the deep-rooted
dread they foster towards any disturbance of the universal and social harmony *&* equilibrium, and the intimate interdependence they assume as existing between these two. A violation of this harmony *&* equilibrium, whether
this issues from the universal sphere (for example, by an unusual occurrence
in nature) or from the social (by a dangerous transgression of tradition, or
by a disturbing event, such as the birth of twins), calls forth a corporate and
strenuous religious activity towards restoring the harmony (and thereby sav-
ing the fertility) of their fields, their health, the security of their families, the
stability and welfare of their tribe from becoming endangered.

Hendrik Kraemer

Despite every new weapon that man in his frenzy can invent, slowly, but with
inexorable certainty, the legions of the flouted order multiply—the microbe,
the bacillus, the fungus, and the parasite. Behind them, if man does not learn
his lesson, lies the desert.

L.T.C. Rolt

V ERNACULAR PEOPLE knew that the order of the cosmos is critical
—so much so that their overriding preoccupation was to preserve it.
The notion of critical order is reflected in such notions as 'harmony' and
'balance', which were seen by all traditional peoples as being essential
features of the living world and of the cosmos.

The essential principle, built into the cultural pattern of vernacular
people, that everything within the living world has to be recycled was
based on the need to maintain its harmony or balance—as was the principle of reciprocity that governed economic relationships within a vernacular community (chapter 56). The principle of maintaining the balance
between two complementary principles, such as the *yìn* and the *yáng*
among the Daoists, was another means of maintaining the critical order
of the living world, as was Greek medicine, which, as W.H.S. Jones notes,
sought above all to maintain what was referred to as the 'balance of hu-
mours'.[1] The great Swedish naturalist Linnæus also saw the world as displaying balance and harmony, which to him reflected the 'economy of
nature', while for the Natural Theologians of the seventeenth and eighteenth centuries, the 'balance of nature', as Frank Egerton points out,
provided incontrovertible evidence of the wisdom of God.[2]

Unfortunately, economic development or 'progress' cannot occur without disrupting the critical order of the natural world. As the worldview of
modernism and the associated paradigm of science slowly developed to
rationalise and hence legitimise this anti-evolutionary enterprise (chapter
65), so the notion of balance or harmony was conveniently discredited by
biologists, ecologists, and sociologists alike.

When ecology developed, as a reaction against the reductionist paradigm of science, not surprisingly it sought to revive the concept of the
balance of nature. Thus, S.A. Forbes saw 'an ideal balance of nature as
one promotive of the highest good of all the species'.[3] Warder Allee and
the other principal members of the Chicago school of ecology in the
1940s also accepted the principle of the balance of nature, according to
which 'the community maintains a certain balance, establishes a biotic
border, and has a certain unity paralleling the dynamic equilibrium and
organisation of other living systems.'[4]

In the 1930s and '40s, however, ecology was systematically transformed
so as to make it conform with the reductionist paradigm of science, and
ecologists sought to discredit the concept of the balance of nature in the
same way as they questioned the established ecological principles that
ecological succession leads to a climax (chapter 22), that the whole is more

than the sum of the parts (chapter 1), and that complexity gives rise to stability (chapter 24).

Alfred Russel Wallace, who developed the principle of evolution via natural selection at the same time as Darwin and independently of him, had argued that the occurrence of different types of ecological discontinuities made nonsense of the principle of the balance of nature—a principle that was clearly irreconcilable with his theory.

> Some species exclude all others in particular tracts. Where is the balance? When the locust devastates vast regions and causes the death of animals and man, what is the meaning of saying the balance is preserved? [Are the devastations of] the Sugar Ants in the West Indies [and] the locusts, which Mr Lyell says have destroyed 800 000 men, an instance of the balance of species? To human apprehension, there is no balance but a struggle in which one often exterminates another.[5]

The same argument was put forward again in the 1930s by the British ecologist Charles Elton, who stated,

> 'The balance of nature' does not exist and perhaps never has existed. The numbers of wild animals are constantly varying to a greater or lesser extent, and the variations are usually irregular in period and always irregular in amplitude.[6]

This argument, however, takes no account of the fact that in a climax ecosystem everything conspires to *minimise* the incidence and severity of such discontinuities. Their greater occurrence thus indicates that an ecosystem is still at a pioneer stage or has been reduced to a 'neo-pioneer' stage—or 'disclimax'—by an external agent, such as modern society.

This had been fully understood more than two hundred years ago by the famous French naturalist Bernardin de Saint-Pierre. '[. . .] if snails, may-bugs, caterpillars, and locusts ravage our plains,' he wrote in his *Études de la Nature* (1784),

> it is because we destroy the birds of our groves which live upon them; or because that on transporting the trees of foreign countries into our own, such as the great chestnut of India, the ebony, and others, we have transported with them the eggs of those insects which they nourish without importing likewise the birds of the same climate which destroy them. Every country has those peculiar to itself for the preservation of its plants.[7]

It follows that the occurrence of plagues and other similar discontinuities, rather than provide evidence that there is no such thing as the balance of nature, must, on the contrary, be seen as *part of the price we must pay for disrupting this critical balance.* Of course, if we insist that there is no such thing as the balance of nature, if the biosphere has no critical order, then we can argue that it is totally malleable and can be modified with impunity. We can then pretend that plagues are *natural* disasters; and rather than treat them by restoring the critical balance of the affected ecosystems, we can justify waging chemical warfare against their outward symptoms—the remedy that best satisfies the requirements of the agrochemical industry and, it is assumed, of the economy in general, even though it merely serves to mask the underlying affliction.

Scientists have sought in all sorts of ways to deny that the order of the natural world is critical. Lamarck believed that the human genetic material—the genome—was so malleable that it could be moulded into any form by environmental influences. That was his principal error. For René Descartes, living things in general—and for John Locke, the human mind in particular—are but pieces of wax, 'flexible, malleable, ours to shape as we please,' as John Passmore puts it.[8]

If the living world is infinitely malleable, then it can have no needs. Thus, modernist thinkers have attacked the very notion that a society has needs and hence that it has a critical structure. For them, it is only individuals, not societies, that exist and have needs.

The Spanish philosopher José Ortega y Gasset, for example, tells us that humanity does not have a nature, only a history[9]—suggesting, also, that human behaviour is infinitely malleable and that we can adapt to living in just about any social or environmental conditions, including, of course, those that economic development or 'progress' imposes on us. Modern economists would agree with him. They, too, deny that people have needs. They only have 'wants', which means that it can be left to sheer economic expediency to determine with which goods and services they should be provided.

All this is so much nonsense. Living systems or processes at all levels of the biosphere have a critical structure—that which is consistent with the fulfilment of their homeotelic or whole-maintaining functions, and which must therefore be maintained within certain critical limits, *i.e.* within their *tolerance range* (see chapter 48). Thus, the structure of an organism, like that of any other natural system, is clearly critical—its various body fluids, for instance, must have the normal chemical and biological composition, or what would be the point of pharmacological tests? The basic features of a human community are also critical. However much it may differ in its details, it must be composed of extended families that are linked together by intermediary social groupings, which in turn form a larger cohesive society capable of maintaining its stability in the face of change.

Attempts to transform society so as to satisfy a particular ideology—for instance, the systematic annihilation of these social forms so as to 'liberate' people from the constraints society imposes on them, as occurred with the French Revolution—could only fail. The atomised mass-society that it produced could no longer run itself and was inevitably taken over by a ruthless dictatorship, giving rise to the 'total state' committed to war and destruction that ravaged Europe for nearly two decades.

A cultural pattern must also display a critical order, *and cultural traits can only be understood in accordance with their functions within it*. The suppression of vernacular customs and institutions because they appear undesirable (when judged by our particular standard of morality) can have fatal results on the culture involved, very much as the extraction of a key organ can result in the demise of an organism.

Let us take the case of the marital customs of the Comoro Islanders of the Indian Ocean. They practise polygyny and have a high frequency of divorce, so much so that it is perfectly normal for a woman to have been married five to ten times.[10] On the basis of the experience gained in our culture, we would tend to associate this high divorce rate with an equally high rate of emotional instability, drug addiction, juvenile delinquency, and crime. However, things do not work out that way. When I visited the Comoros in 1971,[11] I found that the incidence of all these problems was extremely low. Their society had thus adapted to marital instability, which ours has not. The reasons are twofold. Firstly, the society is both matrilinear and largely matrilocal—a child being partly the responsibility of the mother's clan, with many of the functions of fatherhood being fulfilled by the mother's elder brother (inheritance being primarily through him rather than through the father). Secondly, by custom, the stepfather (or *baba-combo*) also automatically assumes many of the responsibilities of fatherhood with regard to the children that his wife has had with previous husbands. In particular, the stepfather is responsible for the payment of the very large expenses involved in the circumcision ceremony of his stepsons. In addition, the father's role is reduced by the fact that the children are brought up in the mother's home, while, in any case—as the father probably has several other wives —he would probably have only been physically present in one particular house on one or two days a week.

For all these reasons, divorce does not have the same unsettling effect in the Comoros as it does in our society. Now, supposing a busybody missionary or administrator suddenly decided to abolish matriliny and matrilocality, as vestiges of barbarity not to be found in modern 'advanced' societies—the results would be disastrous. Delinquency, crime, alienation, and the other symptoms of social disorder would undoubtedly result, as they do with the breakup of the nuclear family in our society.

If societies have a critical order, so too must ecosystems. They must be made up of green plants that are capable, via photosynthesis, of mobilising the energy of the sun, herbivores that can feed off the plants, predators that can feed off the herbivores (applying quantitative and qualitative controls on their populations), and decomposers that can break down biological material into its constituent parts to serve as the raw materials for the perpetuation of the whole cycle (chapter 56).

Though all terrestrial ecosystems are designed on this same basic plan, they will nevertheless differ in many respects. Very different species will, in different ecosystems, fulfil the basic ecological roles, and these will also display varying degrees of complexity and diversity, cooperation and competition (chapters 24, 25, 44, and 45).

The biosphere itself, the overall ecosystem, must for the same reason display a critical order. That the earth's atmosphere must do so at a chemical level is clearly noted by James Lovelock (chapter 35). Among other things, its carbon dioxide content is critical—if it were too low, the earth would be too cold, and if too high, its temperature would exceed that which most forms of life could tolerate. Its oxygen content is also critical—if it were a little lower, then certain forms of life would not be able to breathe, while if it were too high, the resulting flammability of the earth's atmosphere would lead to uncontrollable fires.

It must follow that adaptive changes occurring to any natural system are those that serve to maintain its critical order and hence its stability within the context of the critical order or stability of the whole biosphere.

In the vernacular world, the obliteration of a society's social and ecological forms would have been impossible, for this critical order was sacred (chapters 62 and 63), and to violate it could only lead to the most terrible calamities. What vernacular people knew, our most highly regarded social philosophers, such as Plato, Hobbes, and Rousseau—whose ideas most influenced the course of the French Revolution—totally ignored, just as, tacitly at least, do contemporary sociologists, who justify the further atomisation of society and the further destruction of the natural world in order to accommodate further economic development and, worse still, its globalisation under the auspices of the World Trade Organisation (WTO).

THE BIOSPHERE IS A HOLARCHICAL
ORGANISATION OF LIVING PROCESSES

The Chinese . . . visualised the universe as a hierarchy of parts and wholes working in harmony—each according to its own *Li* or pattern—but all fitting together in the great pattern.
Dolores LaChapelle

. . . hierarchical organisation . . . is the essential and distinguishing characteristic of life.
Howard H. Pattee

. . . wholes and parts, [considered separately, cannot] exist anywhere, either in the domain of living organisms or of social organisations. What we find are intermediary structures on a series of levels in ascending order of complexity, each of which has two faces looking in opposite directions—the face turned towards the lower levels is that of an autonomous whole, the one turned upward, that of a dependent part.
Arthur Koestler

INSECT SOCIETIES, human and non-human animal societies, eco-systems, and the biosphere itself have been compared to biological organisms. It may be more useful, however, to regard them as instances of a more general category of entities. Ralph Gerard referred to them as 'orgs'—not a particularly attractive term; Arthur Koestler, followed later by Thomas Starr and others, named them 'holons'; while Ludwig von Bertalanffy, Ross Ashby, Paul Weiss, and others called them 'systems' or 'natural systems', a term that is now in general use.

Unfortunately, the term 'system', like most of the other basic terms used by scientists, is defined in many conflicting ways. A.D. Hall and R.E. Fagen originally defined it as 'a set of objects together with relationships between the objects and between their attributes'.[1] It is more often defined as a set of entities in dynamic interrelationship with each other. However, both of these definitions could apply equally well to a disintegrated or 'atomised' entity, such as a cancerous cell or a modern industrial society or any of the groupings into which the latter is organised—such as state institutions or corporations—all of which are alien (heterotelic), rather than innate (homeotelic), to the biosphere.

Arthur Koestler defines a 'holon' as 'any stable sub-whole in an organismic, cognitive, or social hierarchy which displays rule-governed behaviour and-or structural gestalt constancy'.[2] This definition is a little too loose. He should specify which rules govern the behaviour of the holon —though, of course, if a 'sub-whole' displays structural constancy, then it can only be that it is subject to the rule of the larger whole of which it is part (for which Koestler coined the term 'holarchy'—see below).

Other authors have used the term 'system' in a still more general way. Erich Jantsch, for instance, includes 'paradigms, the whole system of science, religions, and the images we hold of ourselves and of our roles in the evolution of the universe',[3] together with cells, organisms, societies, and ecosystems, in this category, which he mainly refers to, like Ilya Prigogine, as 'dissipative structures'.[4] This is simply a device to make it appear that all these things have more in common than they really do. Jacques Monod rightly criticises the use of the term system as being too loose, 'When one embraces everything, one risks embracing nothing at all,' he writes,[5] though he would undoubtedly have used stronger language if he had seen Jantsch's definition.

With Ross Ashby, von Bertalanffy developed an entirely new discipline called General System Theory, whose object was to establish the laws governing the behaviour of all 'natural systems'. He reserves the use of the term system to 'complexes of elements standing in interaction' to which systems laws can be applied.[6] Paul Weiss defines a system still more realistically as

> a complex unit in space and time, so constituted that its component sub-units, by 'systematic' cooperation, preserve its integral configuration of structure and behaviour, and tend to restore it after non-destructive disturbances.[7]

In this way, he stresses the major features of the constituents of the biosphere; namely, their complexity (chapters 24), their existence in space-time (chapter 36), their cooperative, self-regulatory nature (chapter 44), their dynamism (chapter 28), their purposiveness (chapter 27), and their dedication to the maintenance of the larger systems of which they are part (chapter 46)—a prerequisite for the preservation of their own integrity and stability. By defining a natural system in Weiss's way, we also distinguish it from the components of the technosphere or surrogate world, which satisfy none of these conditions. The failure of many of those involved in General System Theory to grasp the significance of this distinction largely explains why this discipline has made remarkably little progress since the death of its founder.

It is clear that the laws governing the behaviour of natural systems that von Bertalanffy tries to establish would have to be as general as the most general category of systems he describes. Thus, the particularities of the behaviour of humans can be seen as governed by a particular set of laws that apply only to humans. More general aspects of their behaviour can be seen to be governed by more general laws that apply to mammals in general, still more general aspects by still more general laws that apply to all organisms in general, and so on. The most general aspects of their behaviour must be seen as governed by laws that apply to all natural systems or holons, whether they be specified to be humans, mammals, organisms, non-human animal societies, vernacular human societies, ecosystems, or indeed the biosphere itself.

The best means of developing a unified science must be to determine what these most general laws are—as von Bertalanffy insists, 'not by a Utopian reduction of all sciences to physics and chemistry' but by virtue of the 'structural uniformity' that exists between the different levels of the natural world.[8] Such a unified science would thereby constitute a truly holistic ecology in which there would be no place for the misleading dualisms that the reductionist paradigm of science has imposed on our understanding of the natural world, such as that which separates the natural sciences from the social sciences.

Von Bertalanffy lists two of the laws or 'principles' that he regards as essential, and which systems, in order to be classified as such, must presumably follow.

The first is the principle of 'biological maintenance', which states that 'the organic system tends to preserve itself,'[9] another way of saying that it maintains its homeostasis (chapter 20).

The second principle is that a natural system is organised *hierarchically* (*i.e.* holarchically—see below). This he sees as applying both to organic systems and also to the inorganic world, 'with its hierarchy of electron, atom, molecule, mycella, and crystal'.[10] This essential aspect of natural systems is also emphasised very forcefully by Weiss, Koestler, and Eugene Odum. The latter sees all natural systems as organised hierarchically from the biotic community, to the population, the organism, the organ, and the cell. He sees them as forming a spectrum that, theoretically, can be extended infinitely in both directions.[11] The upper end of the spectrum, covering populations and ecosystems, is the concern of ecology.

If every natural system is part of such a hierarchy, regardless of its level of organisation, it must have two functions—on the one hand with regard to the larger system of which it is part, and on the other with regard to the smaller systems that comprise it. Weiss considers that the cell, the main object of his studies, must be seen 'in a double light— partly as an active worker and partly as a passive subordinate to powers which lie entirely outside of its competence and control, *i.e.* supracellular powers'.[12] Koestler sees this as applying to all natural systems or 'holons'. He takes the double-faced Roman god Janus—whose two faces look in opposite directions—as the natural symbol of the holon, symbolising its two roles within the hierarchy of nature (or 'holarchy', as he also refers to it—the entire organisation of holons within holons).[13]

Scientific ecologists tend to ignore this key issue. For instance, there is no mention of hierarchy in R.J. Putman and S.D. Wratten's textbook, nor in a later ecology textbook appearing in the United Kingdom by Michael Begon, John Harper, and Colin Townsend.[14] The reason is probably that its many implications are largely unacceptable to those imbued with the paradigm of reductionist science.

To my knowledge, hierarchy (as a concept in the natural sciences) has been the subject of only two major conferences—one organised by Lancelot Law Whyte[15] and the other by Howard Pattee.[16] Neither was particularly enlightening. M.D. Mesarović and D. Macko, who attended the first symposium, note how 'the term "hierarchy" is used to cover a variety of related yet distinct notions;'[17] Marjorie Grene, another participant, also noted how loosely the term was used.[18]

Some of this may be due, as Koestler himself notes,[19] to the quite different way in which the term hierarchy is employed outside the natural sciences, where it is often used to denote structures of command-and-control imposed on a society by external agents, such as the state—quite the opposite of the largely internalised or systemic self-regulation displayed by members of the biosphere (chapter 23). As Koestler's term 'holarchy' better highlights this important distinction, it has been used widely throughout this book (see also glossary).

Among ecologists, however, it is only Eugene Odum whose textbooks take the essentially hierarchical (*i.e.* holarchical) nature of the biosphere into serious account. Yet unless other ecologists do so, they will never understand the structure and purpose of the living world and of its myriad forms of life.

43

THE BEHAVIOUR OF LIVING THINGS IS COORDINATED BY THE HOLARCHY OF RELATIONSHIPS OF WHICH THEY ARE PART

The world is a community of organisms—these organisms, in the mass, determine the environmental influence on any one of them . . . Thus, the community as an environment is responsible for the survival of the separate individuals which compose it, and these separate individuals are responsible for their contributions to the environment.

A.N. Whitehead

Comparative embryology reminds us at every turn that the organism dominates cell-formation, using for the same purpose one, several, or many cells, massing the material and directing its movements and shaping its organs as if cells did not exist . . .

Charles Otis Whitman

L IKE MOST OF THE BASIC TERMS used by mainstream scientists today (complexity, organisation, competition, hierarchy, stability), the term 'environment' has never been properly defined. It is usually used loosely to refer to little more than 'all that is out there', and no one seems interested in asking what exactly it is that is 'out there'.

Once we realise that each system is itself part of a larger system, it becomes clear that the larger system represents its ordered environment—an environment that coordinates its behaviour and whose integrity it seeks to maintain (homeotely—chapter 46). This was clear to J.H. Woodger with reference to the cytoplasm, which provides the nucleus of the cell with its immediate environment.

> The word cytoplasm can be understood . . . simply in a topographical sense as meaning whatever is left after the removal of the nucleus. Now there is, of course, no such entity as this to be found in nature. What is found in nature is a certain recurrent mode of organisation amid the flux of events. And it is to this important fact that the cell concept gives expression.[1]

B.C. Patten and Eugene Odum also complain that, in ecology, the term environment is never defined.

> The theory of ecology is not pat for us. We believe that to understand the organism in nature, its other half—environment—will have to be understood as well. To us, 'environment' means environment unspecified, but 'ecosystem' is environment specified.[2]

Of course, it is not sufficient to see a living thing or a life process as part of a system that provides it with its immediate environment—we must see it, as Paul Weiss reminds us, in the context of its *total* environment— *the hierarchy (i.e. holarchy) of natural systems of which it is part.*

> What has confounded thinking has been that, due to inattention to the hierarchical structure of living beings . . . , the term 'environment' has mostly been used indiscriminately *without specifying the respective boundary.* Sometimes it meant the natural outer environment of the individual (nutrition, meteorological, and social climate, stress, *etc.*), sometimes the *milieu [intérieur]* of body fluids and tissue associations, sometimes the cytoplasm around the cell nucleus—whereas, in reality, as far as the genes are concerned, it comprises all of those to the extent to which they are in [the] last instance relevant for genic interactions. From the earliest stages of development on, every cell of the body constitutes environment for

all the others; every cytoplasm for the nucleus and the cell organelles; every chromosome for the gene-strings in it.[3]

The same argument applies to other life processes, including childhood development, day-to-day behaviour, and the all-embracing evolutionary process itself. All involve feedback interactions, directly or indirectly, with every part of their respective environments and hence with every system that makes up the total continuum or holarchy of the biosphere, or what Claude Bernard referred to as the *'milieu cosmique'*.[4]

To see the environment of a natural system in this way enables us to see one of the main defects of the neo-Darwinian theory of natural selection—the undefined and anonymous environment was, and still is, seen as having mysteriously acquired the capacity to 'select', with the most astonishing discrimination, those individuals that it judges to be the 'fittest', which is taken to mean the most individualistic and competitive. How it is capable of doing this and indeed why it should *want* to do so, has never been explained. It all makes much more sense, however, once we see the environment as the highly organised continuum of life provided by the biosphere itself (chapter 36), which, like all its constituent sub-systems, is endowed with the processes required for coordinating the whole-maintaining behaviour of its constituent parts.

Such coordination or regulation may be referred to as *homearchic* (from the Greek ὅμοιος (*homeos*), same, and ἀρχός (*archos*), leader or ruler) as opposed to *heterarchic* (from the Greek ἕτερος (*heteros*), meaning different—see glossary), which can be applied to control by an external agent, such as the state.

Homearchy can be seen as a form of holistic as opposed to reductionistic causation. The notion has been used in psychology among members of the 'mentalist' school. R.W. Sperry refers to it as 'emergent causation' or 'holistic control',[5] while Karl Popper and John Eccles adopt the term 'downward causation' from Donald Campbell.[6]

Weiss points to the various processes that multicellular organisms develop to coordinate the activities of their constituent cells—'the nervous system, the hormone system, the homeostatic maintenance of the composition of the body fluids'.[7] Eugene Odum also sees ecosystems as possessing very elaborate processes for regulating the behaviour of their constituent parts (chapter 20).

It is significant that the principle of the coordination or regulation of the parts by the whole is almost entirely ignored by modern cybernetics—the science of control and communication within self-regulating systems. This is partly, at least, because cyberneticians are mainly concerned with the control of machines rather than the coordination of natural systems. When controlling a machine, such as a missile along its course towards its target, the environment can be assumed, for practical purposes, to be random. At most, allowances must be made for the action of the wind and of other such strictly physical phenomena. However, this will not do when trying to understand the regular behaviour of a natural system, whose environment, provided as it is by the holarchy of larger systems of which it is part, is highly organised and exerts considerable influence over the behaviour of its constituent parts.

To understand the role of this regulating process we must realise that the sub-systems first come into being as relatively homogeneous individuals with great potentialities. However, they are, as yet, unable to constitute viable, differentiated, orderly natural systems capable of maintaining their homeostasis within the wider holarchy of the biosphere. Whether they be cells or human individuals, this they must *learn*, and the learning process (seen in its widest sense) must necessarily occur within the context of the larger whole of which they must become the differentiated, whole-maintaining (homeotelic) constituents.

This sounds as if it is only the parts that learn while the larger system remains immutable. This is clearly not the case, but undoubtedly the overall pattern of the larger system is more conservative than the constituent parts. The parts change, as already noted, and indeed must do so in order to prevent larger and more destructive changes that could affect the overall pattern or critical underlying features of the whole that must be preserved at all costs (chapters 19 and 37).

Thus, in the words of Paul Weiss, a natural system must display micro-*in*determinacy but macro-*de*terminacy (chapter 20)[8]—the parts are free to change *within certain limits* but not beyond these limits (chapter 48), and it is the role of the entity as a whole to make sure that they do not. Only in this way can their behaviour remain homeotelic to the whole, *i.e.* to the holarchy of the biosphere and, thus, to the wider cosmos.

Homearchy, it should be noted, is really best seen as regulation rather than control. At the level of a vernacular society, rather than force people to behave contrary to their natural inclinations, it only regulates their natural behavioural tendencies—ensuring that their innate behaviour preserves the integrity of (and hence remains homeotelic to) the families, communities, societies, and prevailing ecological conditions or 'cosmos' within which they have evolved, and to which they are normally perfectly adjusted; biologically, psychologically, and cognitively.

In a vernacular society, this kind of regulation is largely internalised (chapter 23). Thus, to prevent disruptive or heterotelic behaviour, such as overhunting or the overuse of natural resources, the appropriate regulations are integrated within the cultural pattern, which is unfortunately no longer the case in the fragmented mass societies of today.

Robert Nisbet, like Ferdinand Tönnies and others, refers to such inherent regulation as being exerted by 'traditional authority' rather than political power. He sees it as 'so closely woven into the fabric of tradition and morality as to be scarcely more noticeable than the air men breathe'.[9] It is very much the sort of regulation that the Daoists referred to as *wú wèi*, that in the words of Wing-tsit Chan means 'taking no action that is contrary to Nature'.[10]

Without this traditional authority, human societies could not conceivably contribute to maintaining the critical order of the cosmos. Political power, on the other hand, has played a key role in disrupting this critical order. It is unnatural or heterarchic control that, instead of being exercised by the whole through its constituent parts, is, on the contrary, imposed by external agents, such as the state or corporations, and is above all designed to satisfy their own interests, which are usually in conflict with those of society, the natural world, and people as a whole.

44

COOPERATION IS THE PRIMARY
RELATIONSHIP OF THE BIOSPHERE

. . . mutual aid is as much a law of animal life as mutual struggle, but . . . *as a factor of evolution*, it most probably has a far greater importance, inasmuch as it favours the development of such habits and characters as insure the maintenance and further development of the species, together with the greatest amount of welfare and enjoyment of life for the individual, with the least waste of energy.

Peter Kropotkin

. . . in nature, the normal way in which trees flourish is by their association in a forest. Each tree may lose something of its individual perfection of growth, but they mutually assist each other in preserving the conditions for survival. The soil is preserved and shaded—and the microbes necessary for its fertility are neither scorched, nor frozen, nor washed away. A forest is the triumph of the organisation of mutually dependent species.

A.N. Whitehead

Cooperation for mutual benefit, a survival strategy very common in natural systems, is one that humanity needs to emulate.

Eugene Odum

THE IDEA OF THE NATURAL WORLD as a 'vast cooperative enterprise' is a very ancient one. It was well understood by traditional people, and in our Western civilisation it was embodied in the concept of the 'œconomy of nature'—a term first used in 1658 by Sir Kenelm Digby and taken up a century later by the Swedish naturalist Linnæus, who, among others, sought to explain 'the grand organisation and government of life on earth—the rational ordering of all material resources in an interacting whole.'[1] Thirty years later, Gilbert White noted how the cattle standing in the Selborne ponds provided, by their droppings, food for insects and thus indirectly for the fish. White marvelled at the ingenuity of the Creator. 'Nature is a great economist,' he wrote, 'for she converts the recreation of one animal to the support of the other.'[2] Darwin himself saw nature as 'one grand scheme' of cooperative integration.[3] In his 'General Observations' on the ecology of Rio de Janeiro, he writes,

> I could not help noticing how exactly the animals and plants in each region are adapted to each other. Everyone must have noticed how Lettuces and Cabbage suffer from the attacks of Caterpillars and Snails—but when transplanted here in a foreign clime, the leaves remain as entire as if they contained poison. Nature, when she formed these animals and these plants, knew they must reside together.[4]

Dov Ospovat considers that it was only after reading Malthus that Darwin abandoned these ideas.[5]

The concept of cooperation also played an important part in the thinking of Eugen Warming, one of the earliest scientific ecologists. In particular, he emphasised *symbiosis*, as in the case of lichens (microässociations made up of a fungus and a green alga and-or cyanobacterium). Warming even regarded parasitism as a form of symbiosis, since the parasite and its host eventually become very dependent on each other.[6]

The academic discipline of ecology that developed towards the end of the nineteenth century regarded mutualism as a basic feature of ecological organisation. Hundreds of articles appeared on this theme in early ecological texts. The American naturalist Roscoe Pound, for example, described in a celebrated article all the various forms of mutualism that were known to occur in ecosystems, including pollination and the fixation of nitrogen by bacteria living on the root nodules of leguminous plants.[7] Mutualism within ecosystems was even compared to forms of cooperation within organisms—a comparison that no academic ecologist would dare make today (chapter 1).

As late as the 1940s, Warder Allee and the Chicago 'Ecology Group' continued to regard mutualism as the most basic feature of ecosystems.[8] However, with the development of the worldview of modernism, with its accent on individualism and competition, interest in mutualism rapidly declined—Eugene and Howard Odum being among the few ecologists who continued to produce work on the subject.

This was particularly so as ecologists strained to adapt their discipline to the paradigm of reductionist science, seeking respectability within the scientific community in which mutualism had little role to play. Consequently, as Douglas Boucher and J.H. Vandermeer note,

> Although some of the most spectacular interspecific interactions in nature are obviously mutualistic, relatively little research, empirical or theoretical, has been aimed at understanding this basic and perhaps prevalent form of interaction.[9]

A survey by Boucher and S.J. Risch of twelve ecology texts published between 1970 and 1975, clearly

> substantiates the claim that practically the entire discussion of organismic interactions has centred on predation and competition. Of a total of 718 pages devoted to interspecific interactions in these texts, 321 pages concern predator–prey interactions, 362 pages concern interspecific competitive interactions, and only 35 pages discuss any kind of mutualistic relationship. In addition to the disproportionate amount of space devoted to the different interactions, predation and competition are presented as important organising principles, while examples of mutualism (such as ant-plants or cleaning symbioses) are presented as interesting but eccentric exceptions to the general rule.[10]

Worse still, when cooperation or mutualism is admitted to exist at all, it is regarded by some of our most prestigious ecologists as thoroughly counter-productive. For instance, Princeton ecologist Robert May's view that mutualism has a destabilising effect on ecosystems has gained general acceptance (see chapter 24). Though this thesis is no doubt consistent with the mathematical model he built of cooperative relations, it bears little relationship with the real world in which mutualism is a basic condition of stability.

Consider a human family. It is the mutualistic relationship between husband and wife, parents and children that holds the family together.

When mutualism is replaced by competition, then the family falls apart
—it ceases to remain a stable unit of behaviour. If the cooperative members of a human community or of the populations that make up an ecosystem suddenly become competitive, so must these natural systems
disintegrate. This is necessarily so. If a mathematical model proves the
opposite, as May's does, *then it must necessarily be wrong*, which in any
case it must be for at least two additional reasons.

The first is that mathematical models of cooperation and competition
can only take into account two cooperators or competitors at a time,
whereas these relationships necessarily involve a large number of different cooperators and competitors—all those that make up the holarchy
of the larger system of which the smaller ones are part and with which
they must necessarily cooperate and compete if they are to ensure its
overall stability.

Secondly, the only sort of mutualism that can be modelled mathematically is 'facultative' or non-dependent mutualism. 'Obligate' or dependent
mutualism—which alone is regarded by Odum as true mutualism—is at
present very difficult to model. In any case, even if it were practicable, it
would probably still not be modelled, for obligate mutualism implies that
organisms are 'selected' for their capacity for mutualistic behaviour, *i.e.*
for their ability to fit into the differentiated system that is an ecosystem
and, by implication, eliminated as 'unfit' if they behave in an individualistic and competitive manner—a notion that is totally irreconcilable with
the neo-Darwinian thesis and hence with the reductionist paradigm of
science and the worldview of modernism.

In the early 1970s, however, there was a sudden resurgence of interest
in mutualism. It seemed to manifest itself independently in the work of
ecologists at different universities, who were often unaware of each other's
work. Well-known ecologists who had previously downplayed the importance of mutualism suddenly changed their minds about it. Thus, Robert
May stated in 1973 that the importance of mutualism 'in populations in
general is small'. However, 'in only a few years,' to quote Boucher, 'May's
appreciation of mutualism changed considerably.'[11] He suddenly announ-
ced that mutualism was now seen as 'a conspicuous and ecologically important factor in most tropical communities'. Indeed, May later became
one of the leaders in encouraging work on mutualism, which he saw as
'likely to be one of the growth industries of the 1980s'.

Renewed interest in mutualism has focused attention (in the work of
Boucher, Sam James, and Kathleen Keeler, for example[12]) on the role
played by microörganisms in the metabolism of complex organisms.
Ecologists have also noted the increasing numbers of parasitic or preda-

tory relationships that, on closer examination, turn out to be mutualistic. Thus, S.J. McNaughton has pointed out that the normal view of the relationship between grazers and the grass they graze is false. Whereas 'ecologists have tended to view plants as relatively passive . . . ,' it now seems clear that plants are capable of reacting in a much more dynamic manner to grazing and indeed are capable of 'compensatory growth and assimilate reallocation'. All in all, McNaughton found nine different ways in which the relationship between grazing animals and the grass on which they graze can be regarded as mutualistic.[13] D.F. Owen and R.G. Wiegert have carried this analysis a step further. They point to the obvious implication that grazers and the grasses they graze have coëvolved 'to an extent that one group would not have been possible without the other'.[14] They quote W.J. Mattson and N.D. Addy, who consider 'that insects can act as regulators of primary production and nutrient cycling and thus perform a vital function in ecosystem dynamics.'[15]

Does this then mean, Boucher asks, that mutualism is 'destined to be part of a new synthesis in which Newtonian ecology is replaced by a more organicist, integrated, value-laden view of the natural world?' He is not too optimistic on this score. The reason is that 'our present theories of mutualism are still basically mechanistic, mathematical, fitness-maximising, and individualistic.'[16] Unfortunately, this is only too true. D.H. Janzen, for instance, considers that 'mutualisms are the most omnipresent of any organism-to-organism interaction.' However, he still sees mutualism reductionistically in neo-Darwinian terms and insists that natural systems larger than the individual cannot be mutualistic. The reason is that

> a mutualism is an interaction between individual organisms in which the realised or potential genetic fitness of each participant is raised by the actions of the other. The participants are called mutualists. Since a species has no trait that is analogous to the genetic fitness of an individual, mutualism cannot be defined with reference to species.[17]

Boucher considers it inevitable that ecologists should see mutualism in this way,

> While arguing that nature is an integrated whole and that everything is connected to everything else, we continued researching with theories that said that communities are no more than sets of individual organisms. The problem, in other words, is one of *cognitive dissonance*—the difficulty of working with two sets of ecological ideas based on different fundamental assumptions and ultimately in conflict.[18]

Mutualism clearly cannot be understood in the light of the reductionist paradigm of science, with which it cannot be reconciled. It is only when seen in the light of an ecological or biospheric worldview that its essential role in maintaining the critical order of the cosmos becomes apparent.

COMPETITION IS A SECONDARY
RELATIONSHIP OF THE BIOSPHERE

> ... all nature is at war...
> *Charles Darwin*

From the point of view of the moralist, the animal world is on about the same level as a gladiator's show. The creatures are fairly well treated and set to fight—whereby the strongest, the swiftest, and the cunningest live to fight another day. The spectator has no need to turn his thumbs down as no quarter is given.
> *T.H. Huxley*

The growth of a large business is merely a survival of the fittest. . . . It is merely the working out of a law of nature and a law of God.
> *John D. Rockefeller Sr.*

Never in history... had there been such a determined, richly subsidised, politically organised attempt to persuade the human race that all progress, all prosperity, all salvation—individual and social—depend on an unrestrained conflict for food and money, on the suppression and elimination of the weak by the strong, on Free Trade, Free Contract, Free Competition, Natural Liberty, Laisser-faire—in short, on 'doing the other fellow down' with impunity...
> *George Bernard Shaw*

It is rare to see two animals, particularly animals of different species, tugging at the same piece of meat. And even when competition is observed, it often appears inconsequential. Perhaps a fiddler crab scurries into a hole on a beach only to come running out again, expelled by the current inhabitant. But the crab simply moves off to find another hole. Competition between species—interspecific competition—thus appears to be little more than a minor, temporary inconvenience.
> *Daniel Simberloff*

THE INDUSTRIAL REVOLUTION transformed our vision of the natural world. Its proponents sought to show that even the most destructive aspects of industrialism were 'natural', indeed beneficial. The disintegration of society and the individualism, interpersonal competitiveness, and aggression that are the inevitable accompaniments of industrialisation, Adam Smith saw as a veritable boon providing, via the workings of 'the invisible hand', the very basis of economic and hence social prosperity (chapter 15).

In his influential work *Social Statics* (1851), Herbert Spencer began formulating the principle of 'the struggle for existence' (later, coining the expression 'survival of the fittest'), which he took to be the basic feature of human society, and which he regarded as a means of creating a more differentiated and hence a more efficient society. Thomas Malthus had earlier argued in *An Essay on the Principle of Population* (1798) that the struggle for food and resources was a mathematical necessity and that poverty, malnutrition, and famine were quite normal. Indeed, this was considered desirable by Spencer, since the victims of the struggle for life or death would make way for the victors—the best adapted—who alone displayed the qualities required for creating an efficient and prosperous society.[1]

Darwin, influenced by both Spencer and Malthus, set out to show how the struggle for existence, which he loosely identified with competition, was also the organising principle of the natural world, providing the means for achieving evolutionary progress. For him, competition was everywhere. It was even the basic feature of interrelationships *within* a biological organism, where mutualism most obviously takes its highest developed form. He makes this view clear in his treatment, in *The Origin of Species*, of the similarity between a real tree and the 'Tree of Life'.

> The affinities of all the beings of the same class have sometimes been represented by a great tree. I believe this simile largely speaks the truth. The green and budding twigs may represent existing species—and those produced during former years may represent the long succession of extinct species. At each period of growth, all the growing twigs have tried to branch out on all sides and to overtop and kill the surrounding twigs and branches, in the same manner as species and groups of species have at all times overmastered other species in the great battle for life.[2]

If he saw competition to be the basic interrelationship *within* a biological organism, such as a tree, in which mutualism is most highly developed, we can imagine what little room there was, in his scheme of things, for mutualism *between* organisms or within an ecological community, where the role of cooperation in its various forms may not be quite so obvious.

It was in 1893 that T.H. Huxley gave his famous Romanes Lecture, *Evolution and Ethics*, in which he stated most clearly what has come to be known as the gladiatorial view of the natural world—a 'cosmic process' that humanity was itself subject to, but which, he believed, was checked in civilised societies by an 'ethical process'.

In answer to these ideas, Peter Kropotkin published his famous work *Mutual Aid* (1890–96). For Kropotkin, cooperation and mutual aid were in evidence everywhere among non-human animals and among 'savages' and 'barbarians' as well as 'civilised men'—how, then, could our scientists possibly ignore this, let alone deny its very existence? 'Sociability', he wrote,

> is as much a law of nature as mutual struggle. . . . If we . . . ask Nature, 'Who are the fittest—those who are continually at war with each other or those who support one another?' We at once see that those animals which acquire habits of mutual aid are undoubtedly the fittest.[3]

Kropotkin's argument fell on deaf ears however, and until recently, other critics of the gladiatorial view of the natural world have fared no better. Everything had to be explained in terms of competition.

If Adam Smith showed that the competitive principle applied to economics, Malthus did the same for demography, Spencer for sociology, Darwin for evolutionary biology, and academic ecologists made sure that they were not left out. Douglas Boucher and S.J. Risch note that

> twentieth century ecology, while usually shying away from analogising the natural and social worlds, has continued the tradition of seeing antagonistic interactions as the basis of community organisation.[4]

R.E. Ricklefs, the author of a famous textbook of ecology, confirms that 'competition [as] a major organising principle in ecology is so widely accepted . . . that it has achieved the status of a paradigm.'[5]

Though competition, like natural selection, is a crude and rudimentary mechanism, ecologists have attributed to it the most sophisticated capacities. No feat is considered to be so daunting that competition cannot achieve it. Thus, the 'competitive displacement principle', otherwise known as 'Gause's Law', tells us that two species with the same way of life and that share the same diet cannot occupy the same niche or coexist on the same territory. In other words, *competition regulates diversity*. Again, since common species of plants, referred to as dominants, are declared the most effective competitors, while rare species, or nondominants, are simply less effective competitors, it follows that *competition determines the relative size of populations*—while, according to R.J. Putman and S.D. Wratten, competition for resources *principally determines ecological organisation as well as ecological succession* (see chapters 20 and 22).[6] Indeed, mainstream ecologists attribute to competition those features of omnipresence, omnipotence, and (presumably) omniscience that are normally attributed to God.

It is the sociobiologists who have taken up the most extreme position. For them, it is individual self-interest that prevails in every sphere, and it is in terms of this self-interest that any form of cooperation must be interpreted—no allusion to the larger system's need for such cooperation being regarded as scientific. This leads sociobiologists to see even the humblest of living things making precise cost–benefit calculations (in the manner of our modern economists) in order to decide whether or not to cooperate with other members of their community, even with those of their immediate family. Even the most intimate mutualistic human relations, such as those obtaining between a mother and her child, are held to be explicable in such terms—displays of affection being seen as masking all sorts of sinister machinations on the part of the child towards its unsuspecting mother and, presumably, vice versâ. Thus, Richard Dawkins assures us that

> we can talk about a conflict between parents and young, a battle of the generations. The battle is a subtle one, and no holds are barred on either side. A child will lose no opportunity of cheating. It will pretend to be hungrier than it is, perhaps younger than it is, more in danger than it really is. It is too small and weak to bully its parents physically, but it uses every psychological weapon at its disposal—lying, cheating, deceiving, exploiting, right up to the point where it starts to penalise its relatives more than its genetic relatedness to them should allow. Parents, on the other hand, must be alert to the cheating and deceiving and must try not to be fooled by it.[7]

Cheating among the partners of apparently mutualistic interrelationships is now even regarded as a legitimate and respectable subject of research in those academic circles that take seriously the ideas of sociobiology.

The concept of competition as the ordering principle in nature, however, is not based on any serious knowledge of any kind. To begin with there is no standard definition of competition, a term used in many different ways. Darwin, for instance, never established very precisely how he related the notion of competition to those of 'the struggle for existence' or 'the survival of the fittest'. Opinions vary as to how he saw these relationships. David Merrell considers that he regarded competition as one aspect of the struggle for existence. L.C. Birch, on the other hand, considers that he used the two terms in a different way.[8] Merrell provides a veritable catalogue of the different ways in which the term 'competition' is defined. In his summing up, he concludes that

> some definitions apply only to animals, others to all organisms—plants as well as animals; some definitions refer only to interspecific competition, others to both intraspecific and interspecific competition; for competition to occur, resources must be in short supply in some definitions but not in others; sometimes . . . the definition is so broad that it does not exclude predator–prey relations, but in others . . . the same trophic level is specified. Given these differences of opinion, it may be hazardous (not to mention presumptuous) to attempt to reach some workable definition of competition.[9]

Nor are the various applications of the competitive principle to ecology any better defined. The competitive exclusion principle, for instance, has been formulated by different ecologists in literally dozens of different ways. Merrell lists many of the formulations. Most of them make reference to limiting resources, but others do not mention resources at all. Furthermore, some definitions state that exclusion occurs if the ecological niches are 'identical'—others only require them to be 'similar'. Worse still, the studies required to justify the thesis that competition is the ordering principle in nature have never really been undertaken. J.H. Connell notes that his review of the literature on the subject yielded only one study involving serious experimental work designed to determine if competition played a significant role in the interaction between species.[10] Peter Price goes so far as to say that

> competition theory lives in a dreamworld where everything can be explained, but the validity of these explanations has not been adequately established in the real world.[11]

In normal conditions, it would seem that competition is a minor feature of the interrelationship between living things, as the ecologist E.J. Kormondy and the entomologist P.S. Messenger maintain.[12] The truth seems to be that animals seek to avoid competition or rather avoid its more destructive manifestations. Thus, living things will learn to occupy a different niche from potential competitors, even if it is one to which they may not be ideally suited and to which they may have to adapt by undergoing behavioural and structural modifications.

Robert Augros and George Stanciu also tell us how different species of living things are known to coexist 'without competing—because they eat different foods or are active at different times or otherwise occupy different niches'. Some plant species, for instance, have learned to live on sandy soil,

> others in rich humus; some prefer acid soil, others alkaline; still others require no soil, such as the lichens; some exploit the early growing season, others the late; some get by only because they are tiny, others only because they are huge.[13]

Some animal species, to avoid competition, will simply move away to occupy a yet unexploited niche—this is why virtually every Galapagos island now has its own sub-species of finch, tortoise, and lizard. In this way, rather than fight to the finish, competing groups spread out and become *differentiated*.

What is more, when real competition does actually occur, it tends to be highly ritualised. *Intra*specific conflict in the animal kingdom is indeed little more than a ritual and is conducted according to a set of rules designed, above all, to prevent the occurrence of death or mutilation. Thus, rattlesnakes, capable of killing each other with a single bite, never actually bite each other. Their conflict, Charles Shaw reports, is a strange ritual resembling Indian wrestling.

> The successful snake pins the loser for a moment with the weight of his body and then lets the loser escape.[14]

The *Oryx* antelopes, which are equipped with horns capable of putting a lion to flight, do not use them in earnest in an intraspecific fight. As Irenäus Eibl-Eibesfeldt writes,

> One hornless bull observed by [F.R.] Walther carried out the full ritual of combat as if he still had horns. He struck at his opponent's horns and missed by the precise distance at which his non-existent horns would have made contact. Equally remarkable, his opponent acted as though his horns were in place and responded to his imaginary blows.[15]

Much the same is true of vernacular societies. For instance, it was the normal procedure in Australian aboriginal warfare for hostilities to cease after only a few casualties.[16] Among the Māori, leadership was all important, and hostilities came to an end once the leader of one of the rival groups was put out of action. Andrew Vayda notes that an attacking force of Māoris, even when 'on the verge of victory', might withdraw on the loss of its leader.[17]

Another form of ritualisation is the substitution of a match or tournament between two or more champions for a conflict between two armies—the contest between David and Goliath being an obvious example. This same strategy of 'single combat' was resorted to a great deal during the Middle Ages in Europe.

Sport also provides a means of ritualising conflict between two social groups. Baseball is apparently used for this purpose on the South Sea island of Truk—as the anthropologist George Peter Murdock tells us—ever since tribal warfare was banned by the then colonial powers.[18] Football has often taken on the form of ritualised conflicts between rival groups of 'fans'—often representing rival ethnic or sectarian groups, as in the case of the Celtic and Rangers football clubs in Glasgow, or between competing nation states.

One of the most sophisticated and highly ritualised of such conflicts is the *Palio* of Siena, in which the *contrade*—mediæval associations, each of which inhabits its own area of the city—compete with each other by means of a horse race round the city's incredibly beautiful central square, the Piazza del Campo. Significantly, there is remarkably little crime in this city—people have learned to live with each other, and the *Palio*, into which their aggressive instincts are channelled, plays a considerable role in enabling them to do so (chapter 55).[19]

The thesis that competition is the ordering principle in nature is based on the fatal error—committed by Malthus, Darwin, the social Darwinists, the sociobiologists, and, indeed, the bulk of mainstream biologists, ecologists, and many sociologists—of regarding the atomised, individualistic, and competitive societies of today as the norm; and seeing them, moreover, as reflecting the basic structure of the natural world. Such societies are, on the contrary, *highly aberrant* and necessarily short-lived, as is the economic system that they have developed.

This was clear to Friedrich Engels when he came to London to study the great towns. He found there 'the war of all against all' and had the wisdom to realise that it was not normal. 'We know well enough', he wrote,

> that this isolation of the individual—the narrow-minded egotism—is everywhere the fundamental principle of modern society. But nowhere is this selfish egotism so blatantly evident as in the frantic bustle of the great city. The disintegration of society into individuals, each guided by his private principles and each pursuing his own aims, has been pushed to its furthest limits in London. Here, indeed, human society has been split into its component atoms.[20]

Today, London has been seriously outdone. It is in the rundown areas of the larger industrial conurbations of North America that the 'war of all against all' is most in evidence. Here crime, delinquency, and violence of all sorts are the rule, and rather than being seen as normal they can only be regarded as symptoms of social deprivation and hence of maladjustment at the social level (chapter 51). If here the community has largely broken down, so has the family—even the nuclear family is no more. A large proportion of households are run by a single woman with children, whose fathers no longer have any interest in their upbringing. Such a society, or rather non-society, is maintained by a state welfare system that serves above all to perpetuate the poverty and the misery it is supposed to combat—a state of affairs in which social relations are as far removed from the norm as they could possibly be.

We have seen that equally aberrant relations among baboons in the London Zoo led Lord Zuckerman to conclude that baboons were individualistic and aggressive creatures, which most people believed for a long time afterwards (chapter 3). Yet when ethologists had the opportunity to study them in the wild, they found them to be, on the contrary, both peaceful and socially integrated. It is important to note, too, that neither in the rundown industrial areas nor among the baboons of the London Zoo is there the food shortage that Malthus and Darwin took to be the norm and that almost all ecologists regard as providing the motivation for competition. Aggression among äsocialised and alienated individuals *is but a symptom of their social isolation and alienation* (chapter 51).

Obviously, competition has a role to play in the behaviour of living things, in particular in a pioneer ecosystem, in which it serves to eliminate randomness and hence to increase the viability of natural systems, helping to maintain the ecosystem's critical order. Competition also serves in such conditions to space out living things, which must also favour the development of increasing diversity, eliciting more numerous patterns of behaviour and structural forms adaptive to a greater range of environmental challenges. As living things evolve, however, *as ecosystems develop from their pioneer stages towards their climax stages*, so are such functions gradually internalised or ritualised (chapter 23), so does competition give way to cooperation, and so is stability correspondingly increased.

THE NATURE OF THE BIOSPHERE

·INTEGRITY·

46

LIVING THINGS SEEK TO MAINTAIN
THE ORDER OF THE WHOLE

[Living beings] are so connected, so chained together, that they all aim
at the same end, and to this end a vast number of intermediate ends are
subservient.

Linnæus

... one cannot help being struck by the way in which the cells in an organism not only cooperate but cooperate in a specific direction towards
the fulfilment and maintenance of the type of particular organism which
they constitute.

Jan Smuts

W E HAVE SEEN that cooperation is the primary interrelationship of the biosphere (chapter 44). But natural systems can only co-operate for the purpose of achieving *a common goal*. If they did not have a common goal, they could not cooperate—the very term would be mean-ingless. Natural systems, as differentiated parts of the holarchy of the bio-sphere, share the common goal of maintaining its critical order or stability, for only in this way can they maintain *their own* critical order and hence their own stability.

At the level of a biological organism, the operation of this principle is clear. Lucien Cuénot notes how birds that fly can do so because a thou-sand details converge—long wing and tail feathers, pneumatic bones, air sacs, breast bone and pectoral muscles, design of the ribs, necks, feet, spinal column, pelvis, automatic hooking of feather barbules, *etc.*[1] All the features of a bird, in fact, conspire to enable it to fly. All are directed to-wards the fulfilment of its flying activities, while flying itself is directed towards the maintenance of the critical order of avian populations within the wider continuum of the biosphere.

The same principle applies to a community and a society. Anthropol-ogists of the 'functional' school saw cultural behaviour as ensuring the integrity and stability of social systems. For A.R. Radcliffe-Brown the function of a behavioural trait is the contribution it makes 'to the *total* activity of which it is a part', while 'the function of a particular social usage is the contribution it makes to the total social life [which is] the functioning of the total social system.'[2]

This same basic principle must clearly apply to all natural systems. Thus, Ludwig von Bertalanffy emphasises the 'whole-maintaining char-acter' of life processes at the level of the biological organism,

> . . . the most convinced representative of an äteleological point of view must admit that actually an enormous preponderance of vital processes and mechanisms have a whole-maintaining character—were this not so, the organism could not exist at all. But if this is so, then the establish-ment of the significance of the processes for the life of the organism is a necessary branch of investigation.[3]

Von Bertalanffy cites Emil Ungerer as being so impressed by the 'whole-maintaining' function of life processes that he decided to replace the bio-logical 'consideration of purposes' with that of 'wholeness' (chapters 2 and 27).[4]

If we highlight the time aspect rather than the spatial aspect of a natural system, seeing it as a *process* rather than a static structure, it is apparent that it is a strategy made up of a number of closely associated steps that must occur in the right order (chapter 22). Only when these successive steps are seen in terms of their specific contributions to the process as a whole do they have any meaning. Thus, the development of an embryo in the womb is not a series of impromptu moves but part of a *carefully coordinated strategy* designed to give rise to an end-product, the human child. Every step in an ecological succession contributes to the achievement of the ecosystem's goal, a climax stage. Superficially, each of these different steps can be seen as cooperating with each other—but in reality *it is with the process as a whole* with which they are cooperating, and such cooperation only makes sense if it is seen teleologically or purposefully as a process serving to promote the integrity and stability of the whole—and hence, in turn, their own.

The coordination of these whole-maintaining processes is particularly impressive. For example, it is clear that the various processes occurring within an organism cannot interfere with each other's functioning—food cannot be properly digested if the blood does not circulate adequately, nor can the circulation of the blood take place in an organism that is no longer capable of digesting its food, and which, as a consequence, is wasting away from starvation. In other words, the sort of trade-offs encountered in a fragmented modern society cannot occur.

It is not so obvious, but it is equally true, that this coordination of the whole-maintaining activities occurs in all natural systems, whether they be stable societies, climax ecosystems, or the biosphere itself. This was fully understood by Radcliffe-Brown. He saw the essential 'functional unity' of a society as

> a condition in which all parts of the social system work together with a sufficient degree of harmony or internal consistency, *i.e. without producing persistent conflicts which could neither be resolved nor regulated.*[5]

He notes that this view of society is in direct conflict with the view that culture is no more than a collection of 'shreds and patches' for which there are 'no discoverable significant sociological laws'.[6] However, without the coordination required to prevent 'persistent conflicts', life processes could not conceivably achieve their common goal of maintaining the critical order of the biosphere.

It is significant that there is no word in the English language that makes explicit the essential goal-directed and whole-maintaining character of cooperation, nor, for that matter, of competition. It is for this reason that I have had to coin a new word—*homeotely* (from the Greek ὅμοιος (*homeos*), same, and τέλος (*telos*), end-goal)—to apply to both. Competition as well as cooperative behaviour serve in different conditions to maintain the critical order of the biosphere, and can therefore be regarded as homeotelic. Thus, the competitive activity that serves to eliminate randomness and disorder within any natural system must be homeotelic to that system and to the holarchy of natural systems of which both are part. Competitive strategies that serve to space out populations and increase diversity are similarly homeotelic (chapter 45).

Predators have an obviously whole-maintaining function to fulfil within an ecosystem. Their role is to apply qualitative and quantitative controls on the prey populations, maintaining their optimum size, organisation, and viability, and helping to maintain in this way the optimum structure of the ecosystem of which they are part. An individual zebra does not see the lion that is stalking it as a benefactor, yet its behaviour is undoubtedly beneficial to the zebra population *as a whole*. It is thus only if we see predator–prey relations holistically that their homeotelic nature becomes apparent.

Significantly, predatory behaviour is encouraged by the prey species itself. Thus, behind a herd of cape buffalo there is often a much smaller herd of stragglers made up of the old and weak. If one of the stragglers tries to join the main herd, it is pushed out. It is on the stragglers, of course, that the lions will concentrate, for to attack the main herd would be too daunting a prospect. In a sense, both predator and prey cooperate to ensure that it is the old and weak—those elements least capable of maintaining the integrity of the whole—that are reduced in this way, so as to maintain the viability of prey populations required to assure the critical order of the wider biosphere (chapter 45).

As we have seen (chapter 4), the homeotelic nature of normal predatory behaviour becomes clearer still when we are faced with the ecological consequences of removing predators from the ecosystems in which they would normally live.[7] In Bangladesh, for instance, frogs were at one time being caught in vast numbers and exported to satisfy the very considerable market for frogs' legs in France and elsewhere. The result was a population explosion of the insects on which the frogs fed, leading to a massive increase in the use of pesticides required for controlling them.[8] It was said that eventually the cost of the pesticides became greater than the income derived from selling the frogs.

The removal of predators has also led to a reduction in the ecological diversity required to maintain an ecosystem's stability. R.J. Putman and S.D. Wratten note that the removal of the starfish *Pisasta ochracens* in the intertidal ecosystem in California caused a dramatic ecological change. Instead of the original fourteen species, only eight remained, of which only four were among the eleven species preyed on by the starfish. They admit, therefore, that predators seem to 'enhance the productivity of individual prey populations' and 'create and maintain diversity within a community'.[9]

The 'exploitation' of prey populations by predators is optimal when it is homeotelic, *i.e.* when it applies those quantitative and qualitative controls on the prey that are required to help maintain the critical order of the ecosystem of which they are part. When there is a breakdown in the balance between predators and their prey populations, these conditions are no longer satisfied, and predation becomes *heterotelic* or whole-disrupting.

Why do living things normally behave homeotelically to the larger systems of the biosphere? One reason must be that they are the differentiated parts of such systems, in isolation from which they have no meaning, cannot survive, or, in the case of a loosely integrated system, can survive only imperfectly and precariously. As Eugene Odum writes,

> Because each level in the biosystem spectrum is 'integrated' or interdependent with other levels, there can be no sharp lines or breaks in a functional sense, not even between organism and population. The individual organism, for example, cannot survive for long without its population any more than the organ would be able to survive for long as a self-perpetuating unit without its organism.[10]

From another perspective, they must behave homeotelically because the holarchy of larger systems provides them with their natural habitat or field, *i.e.* with the ordered environment to which they have been adapted by their evolution and upbringing, and which, as Stephen Boyden points out (chapter 48), must best satisfy their most fundamental needs. For these reasons, we can go so far as to say that *in a stable biosphere, behaviour that satisfies the requirements of the whole must also be that which best satisfies the requirements of its differentiated (as opposed to random) parts.* This may be referred to as the principle of *holarchical mutualism*.

The dependence of the parts on the whole cannot be better illustrated than by the tendency of the parts of a natural system to reorganise themselves after separation—and even after having been shuffled like a deck of cards—into something approaching their original configuration. Jacques Monod notes how this is true of a virus, the bacteriophage T4. When its parts are mixed *in vitro*, they reassemble of their own accord, and the reconstituted virus is quite capable of fulfilling its normal functions.[11] Paul

Weiss has noted, too, how freely floating cells from disassociated embryonic skins, cartilage, and kidney tissue, if thrown together at random, reassociated themselves to form 'higher stages of the tissue in question'.[12]

The same, of course, would be true if we were to shuffle the members of a family or of a climax community in such a way as to create a random assemblage of individuals. Like the parts of the bacteriophage or the embryonic kidney tissue, they would quickly reorganise themselves into their natural groupings. Indeed, we can imagine the frenzied efforts that mothers would make to locate their children; children to find their mothers; fathers to search for their wives and children; elderly grandparents to reintegrate themselves into their families.

Members of different lineage groups and village communities also seek each other out when they migrate to big cities, which in Africa tend to be clearly divided up into distinct tribal areas. Much the same thing occurs in Western cities. In New York, for instance, different ethnic groups, such as the Jews, Irish, Italians, Germans, Puerto Ricans, and African-Americans, live very largely in separate ethnic communities, even when, as is usually the case, the state is committed to integrating them into the anonymous mass society that best suits its own quite alien purposes.

47

WHEN THE INTEGRITY OF THE WHOLE BREAKS DOWN, BEHAVIOUR BECOMES DISORDERED

Creative destruction is our middle name, both within our own society and abroad. We tear down the old order every day, from business to science, literature, art, architecture . . . to politics and the law. Our enemies have always hated this whirlwind of energy and creativity, which menaces their traditions (whatever they may be) and shames them for their inability to keep pace. . . . They cannot feel secure so long as we are there—for our very existence . . . threatens their legitimacy. They must attack us in order to survive, just as we must destroy them to advance our historic mission.
Michael A. Ledeen

We have lived to see a time without order
In which everyone is confused in his mind.
One cannot bear to join in the madness
But if [one] does not do so, [one] will not share in the spoils.
Modern Javanese song

H OMEOTELIC BEHAVIOUR, as we have seen, is normal behaviour
serving the primary purpose for which it was designed by its evolution (phylogeny) and development (ontogeny), which is to maintain the
critical order and integrity of the wider biosphere (chapter 61). *Heterotelic*
behaviour (from the Greek ἔτερος (*heteros*), different, and τέλος (*telos*),
end-goal) is behaviour that is *misdirected*, satisfying up to a point the needs
of the individual but not those of the biosphere as a whole. The critical
distinction between homeotelic and heterotelic behaviour, *i.e.* between
healthy and unhealthy behaviour (from the Old English, *hál*—whole),
is quite foreign to the reductionist paradigm of science. If behaviour is
looked at reductionistically, there is no way in which its purposive and
'whole-maintaining' function can be established and hence no way of determining whether it is fulfilling a homeotelic or a heterotelic function.

Behaviour can be misdirected if it is based on faulty information. It
can also be misdirected if, in new and unpredictable conditions, behaviour based on what has hitherto been sound information ceases to be
adaptive. Heterotelic or whole-disrupting behaviour often occurs when
new environmental conditions *mimic* conditions to which a system is capable of adapting homeotelically *but differ from them in one or more critical
respects*. Thus, when a developing organism is exposed to the radionu-
clide strontium 90, which is chemically very similar to calcium, it treats it
as a raw material for building up bone. This may serve the immediate
requirements of the process in question, *but it does not serve its long-term
purposes* and hence those of the organism as a whole, since its chances
of contracting cancer and other degenerative diseases are considerably
increased.

The Australian biologist Stephen Boyden establishes the difference between adaptation and what he refers to as 'pseudoädaptation'.[1] Studies
conducted in Scotland in the 1970s revealed a very high consumption of
refined white bread, margarine, sweets, and other junk foods, to the point
that almost half of Scottish adults had lost all of their natural teeth.[2] The
homeotelic, adaptive, or healthy response would be to improve the Scottish diet. Only such a response could conceivably *solve* the problem. The
heterotelic, pseudoädaptive, or unhealthy response, on the other hand,
consists in providing the victims with false teeth. Even if we regard false
teeth as a good substitute for real teeth for the purposes of mastication,
to provide them does nothing for all the other symptoms of a faulty diet
—such as diabetes, diverticulitis, peptic ulcers, appendicitis, varicose
veins, various forms of cancer, and the other diseases of civilisation, most

of which have been very convincingly linked with the consumption of junk foods (see chapter 50).[3]

On the contrary, because the provision of false teeth makes one particular symptom of a bad diet more tolerable, it will only encourage people to maintain their poor eating habits, perpetuating the other resulting afflictions. Because each of them in turn will be dealt with heterotelically—their symptoms being suppressed by various patented medicines, all of which have more or less serious side-effects—the victims will be subject to further afflictions, and the cycle of heterotelically treated illnesses will widen until the unfortunate people are consigned to hospitals. There, their symptoms are likely to be suppressed by even more drastic methods, such as surgical operations, causing still more serious side-effects, and so on, in a vicious, self-reinforcing cycle of positive feedback.

There are, of course, exceptions to this rule. Enlightened doctors may well put their patients on a healthier diet and in general cause them to lead healthier lives that minimise the incidence of disease. But this is likely to be the exception, since for medical practitioners health is an artificial commodity—one provided by hospitals and modern medicines (chapter 39).

The heterotelic use of heterotelic medicines on the present scale assures above all the perpetuation of a massive medical industry, increasingly known as the medical-industrial complex, whose sales in the USA in 2004 accounted for some sixteen per cent of Gross National Product (GNP).[4] The medical industry also consumes its share of non-renewable resources, generating a corresponding amount of pollution and other forms of social and ecological disruption.

The same principle applies in almost every other field of activity in the modern world. In no case are the causes of our problems seriously addressed. All such problems as floods, droughts, epidemics, crime, delinquency, poverty, and unemployment are dealt with heterotelically, largely by technological means that our society is geared to providing, and which satisfy the immediate economic interests of the corporations and institutions into which it is organised.

Let us consider another example. A man in a stable society will have been designed by his evolution and his cultural upbringing to fulfil those functions within his family that will assure its stability and survival. He fulfils them spontaneously, because it is by doing so that he best satisfies his own individual needs. Thus, the husbandly behaviour he displays towards his wife, which indeed he must display if the family is to survive, will also satisfy his basic individual needs, such as sex and companionship. In aberrant conditions, however, these same needs may be satisfied by displaying similar behaviour towards a woman who is external to the family unit, and who may be regarded as *mimicking* his wife. In this way, one or more husbandly needs are satisfied—*but in a way that does not lead to the satisfaction of the needs of his family, nor of the holarchy of larger systems of which it is part.* This means that something designed to hold together the key family unit has been mobilised to do exactly the opposite. We are then left with a one parent family, a highly unstable entity that does not provide a satisfactory environment for the children's upbringing, and which can break down still further, leading to the abandonment of the children (as has happened on such a scale in the slums of the major South American cities).

If a man needs a family, so does he need a community. However, with economic development, the community, like the family, breaks down and becomes correspondingly atomised, to be replaced by big corporations or other institutions (Ferdinand Tönnies' *gesellschaft*), which can be regarded as surrogate social groupings that mimic real communities (Tönnies' *gemeinschaft*—see chapter 60). This is particularly so in Japan, where large corporations usurp most of the functions normally fulfilled by the community—paying for their employees' education, looking after them when they are sick, and securing their retirement (mirroring a similar trend that had arisen previously in England—exemplified by the 'model villages' built by the philanthropic industrialists Wedgwood, Owen, Cadbury, and Lever). While this is in many ways admirable, and elicits on the part of the employees a great feeling of loyalty towards the corporation for which they work, it remains true that such behaviour is strictly heterotelic, for although it may serve the interests of the corporations and, for a time, those of their employees, it does not serve the interests of society as a whole, still less those of the natural world to whose rapid destruction these corporations are making such a singular contribution.

If the corporation mimics the family and the community, so does the state. This means that the behaviour of modern society towards the state —on whose many bureaucratic services it has become increasingly dependent—is also heterotelic. For the state is no more a natural constituent of the biosphere than is the corporation. It does not seek to provide that environment for its citizens that is required to satisfy their fundamental needs—whether biological, psychological, or social—but rather that which best satisfies its own immediate political requirements.

Modern society's religion is also heterotelic, since it diverts human religiosity from fulfilling its natural whole-maintaining (or literally *holy*) religious functions towards the natural world—thus, making the latter correspondingly more vulnerable towards exploitation and destruction (chapter 63).

Heterotelic behaviour there will always be. It could be regarded as little more than biological, social, and ecological randomness or 'entropy'. However, in a stable society, *it is the exception rather than the rule,* and all sorts of social means exist for reducing its incidence to a minimum. It becomes the rule rather than the exception once a society disintegrates and the biosphere is replaced by the technosphere. As this occurs, behaviour ceases to be capable of homeostatic self-regulation and thereby loses its capacity for counteracting randomness or heterotely. The society is then out of control—as is our modern society today—and set on a course towards social and ecological disaster. All that can save it then is a cultural 'mega-mutation'—an ecologically-based revitalisation movement giving rise to societies committed, as were the vernacular societies of the past, to a healthy, whole-maintaining behaviour pattern (chapter 66).

48

LIVING THINGS ARE ONLY ABLE TO MAINTAIN THE INTEGRITY OF THE WHOLE WITHIN THEIR TOLERANCE RANGE

Not only may too little of something be a limiting factor . . . but also too much . . . Thus, organisms have an ecological minimum and maximum—[the] range in between represents the limits of tolerance.
Eugene Odum

It is true that a system in homeostasis is more forgiving about disturbances. But this is only when it is healthy and well within the bounds of its capacity to regulate. When such a system is stressed to near the limits of regulation, even a small disturbance may cause it to jump to a new stable state or even to fail entirely.
James Lovelock

In Nature, nothing fails like excess.
John Stewart Collis

THE ECOLOGICAL 'principle of tolerance' states that natural systems can only function adaptively within an environment whose basic features have not diverged too far from the optimum. As their environment diverges, so adaptive behaviour becomes more difficult and eventually impossible. For each particular feature of the environment there are limits beyond which, in the words of Robert McIntosh, organisms 'cannot grow, reproduce, or, at the ultimate extreme, survive'.[1] The same of course can be said for any other natural system, whether it be an ecosystem or a human community.

Today, with global economic development, environments almost everywhere are either reaching these limits or have already passed them. Nuclear tests, for example, have increased radiation fallout, and now the nuclear energy industry is increasing background levels of radiation that could conceivably exceed our level of tolerance. Our various industrial activities, too, are modifying water tables, contaminating groundwater, eroding and desertifying our arable land, and in general, modifying our environment to a point where many of its essential features will no longer fall within our tolerance range.

Limits can be breached in both directions, of course—a living thing can be subject to too little as well as too much of something. In Eugene Odum's words, they have 'an ecological minimum and maximum'. Significantly, most animals in their natural habitat live in the middle of their 'tolerance range'. Thus, according to Odum, the eggs of the brook trout can develop in water with a temperature of between 0°C and 12°C, with an optimum at about 4°C; frog eggs can develop in water with a temperature of between 0°C and 30°C with an optimum at about 22°C; while 'the upper temperature tolerance for hot-spring bacteria is about 88°C and for blue-green algæ about 80°, compared with 50°C for the most tolerant fish and insects.'[2]

The principle of tolerance can be stated in a more subtle way. To begin with, it must be noted—though it rarely is—that the environment most friendly to the needs of living things, that within which their behaviour is most fulfilling and adaptive, can only be that to which they have been adapted by their evolution and upbringing—in other words, their natural habitat. Common sense tells us that this must be so. Thus, a tiger has been adapted by its evolution and upbringing to living in the jungle, which clearly provides its optimum environment. It is the activities in which it is capable of indulging in the jungle that best satisfy its physical and psychological requirements—it is the food that it finds there that it has best been adapted to eating and digesting, and it is the smells encountered there that it has best been adapted to detecting, interpreting, reacting to adaptively, and enjoying. There is no reason for supposing that we are exempt from the operation of this fundamental principle.

But what is our natural habitat? To answer this, we must consider that humankind is by nature a hunter-gatherer. As S.L. Washburn and C.S. Lancaster write,

> The common factors that dominated human evolution and produced *Homo sapiens* were preägricultural. Agricultural ways of life have dominated less than 1 per cent of human history, and there is no evidence of major biological changes during that period of time. . . . The origin of all common characteristics must be sought in preägricultural times.[3]

As Wes Jackson puts it, if a man were designed to be a farmer, 'he would have longer arms'.[4] If he had been designed by his evolution to be an industrialist, Jackson might have added, he would be a robot with no requirement for a family or a community, no feelings for the natural world, no morals, and no emotions. He would also be equipped with a physical constitution that enables him to feed with impunity on devitalised and contaminated food, drink polluted water, and breathe polluted air.

It must follow that the optimum environment for human beings can only be that in which our hunter-gatherer ancestors evolved—a climax society living in a climax ecosystem. As we transform this environment to satisfy the requirements of economic development or 'progress', so it satisfies our basic needs ever less satisfactorily. This principle has been formulated very eloquently by Boyden,

> The important corollary to Darwinian theory that I wish to stress has not been given a name, but I shall refer to it here as the 'principle of phylogenetic maladjustment'. According to this principle, if the conditions of life of an animal deviate from those which prevailed in the environment in which the species evolved, the likelihood is that the animal will be less well suited to the new conditions than to those to which it has become genetically adapted through natural selection, and consequently some signs of maladjustment may be anticipated. Obvious though this principle is, and obvious though [its importance], it is seldom referred to in the literature, and consequently its significance seems to have been largely overlooked. . . . This principle relates not only to environmental changes of a physiochemical or material nature, such as changes in the quality of food or air, but also to various non-material environmental influences, such as certain social pressures which may affect behaviour. Further

more, signs of phylogenetic maladjustment may be physiological, behavioural, or both.[5]

If many of us refuse to face this inescapable principle, it is above all because its implications are so far reaching. Among other things, it makes nonsense of the very idea of 'progress' and hence of economic development. Far from fulfilling its claim to improve our lives, economic development brings about changes that must increasingly cause our environment and our way of life to diverge from the conditions to which we have been adapted by our evolution, giving rise to conditions that lie increasingly outside our 'tolerance range'. It is thus a process that, if allowed to continue for long enough, must lead to the demise of our society or the extinction of our species.

THE TOLERANCE RANGE OF LIVING THINGS
IS THEIR NATURAL HABITAT OR 'FIELD'

The fate of a cell is a function of its position within the whole.
Hans Driesch

Bantu psychology cannot conceive of man as an individual, as a force existing by itself and apart from its . . . relationships with other living beings and from its connection with [the animate and] inanimate forces around it.
Father Placide Tempels

One of the central elements of Buddhism is the concept of *śūnyatā* or 'emptiness'. I had difficulty understanding the meaning of this at first, but over the years, in talking to Tashi Rabgyas, it became clearer. 'It is something that is not easy to talk about and impossible to understand through words alone,' he told me once. 'It is something you can only fully grasp through a combination of reflection and personal experience. But I'll try to explain it in a simple way. Take any object, like a tree. When you think of a tree, you tend to think of it as a distinct, clearly defined object—and on a certain level it is. But on a more important level, the tree has no independent existence—rather, it dissolves into a web of relationships. The rain that falls on its leaves, the wind that causes it to sway, the soil that supports it—all form a part of the tree. Ultimately, if you think about it, everything in the universe helps make the tree what it is. It cannot be isolated—its nature changes from moment to moment; it is never the same. This is what we mean when we say that things are "empty", that they have no independent existence.'
Helena Norberg-Hodge

ONE OF THE MOST glaring deficiencies of both modern development theory (ontogeny) and modern (neo-Darwinian) evolutionary theory is that the information determining these processes is seen to be exclusively contained within the genes. Such a view fits in with the notion of *causality*. The organism's phenotype (observable traits) is seen as the product of a process controlled by an external agent or manager—the genes. It fits in, too, with the mechanistic view of life processes, since machines are run in this way by their human operators, but it bears no relationship with what actually happens in the real world.

According to Paul Weiss, the claim that the gene is 'the sole ordering principle in organisms . . . rests on sheer assertion, based on blind faith and unqualified reductionistic preconceptions.' He accuses the proponents of the genetic view of development of glossing over the difficulty of the problem by bestowing on the gene

> the faculty of spontaneity, the power of 'dictating', 'informing', 'regulating', 'controlling', *etc.* the orderless processes in its unorganised milieu, so as to mould the latter into the coordinated teamwork that is to culminate in an accomplished organism.[1]

But they never explain just how this is done.

The organism is a particular type of natural system. It is organised in a specific way, and these qualities of the organism can neither be attributed exclusively to the action of the genes, to the chromosomes of which they are part, nor even to the genome itself. Thus, an essential feature of the development of an organism is the differentiation of the cells that compose it. These cells, regardless of whether they are liver cells, pancreatic cells, intestinal cells, or cells from the muscles and other tissues, were originally endowed with the same genetic information, yet they have somehow *learned* to fulfil very different functions.

It became clear in the 1920s that this could not be explained in terms of mechanistic science but only in terms of a totally new paradigm. The original inspiration probably came from the new physics of James Clerk Maxwell. Before Maxwell, as Albert Einstein noted, the physical world was seen as made up of little bullet-like atoms or 'material points, whose change consists exclusively of motion'.[2] Maxwell's work led to the development of a new view of physical reality, which came to be seen as 'continuous fields, not mechanically explicable'. An atom could thus no longer be seen in isolation from other atoms but was seen instead as a small volume of an electric field where there is an intense concentration of field force. The French physicist Louis de Broglie saw particles as 'wave fields'. For the new physicists, the field, furthermore, was not regarded in mechanical or even in material terms. It was 'a concept of relation', as Jerome Ashmore puts it,[3] and was seen as exerting an organising or coordinating action on its constituents.

In the 1920s, Paul Weiss and Alexander Gurwitsch sought to apply this new concept of the field to biology. Only in terms of this new paradigm, it seemed to them, could scientists explain the notions of form, organisation, and the differentiation of the parts of any natural system. 'To me,' Weiss writes,

> as an observer of nature, the universe presents itself naïvely as an immense cohesive continuum. However, we usually do not look at it as such. We are used to looking at it as a patchwork of discrete fragments. This habit stems partly from a biological heritage, which makes focusing on 'things', such as prey, enemies, or obstacles, a vital necessity; partly from cultural tradition; and partly from sheer curiosity, which draws our attention and interest to limited 'objects'.[4]

Within this wider 'cohesive continuum', it is the milieu of 'mutual interactions', in which a living system is intimately involved with others, that Weiss and Gurwitsch referred to as its 'field'. C.H. Waddington adopted a similar view of the living world. He defined a field as a 'system of order such that the position taken up by unstable entities in one portion of the system bears a definite relation to the position taken up by unstable entities in other portions.'[5] Viktor Hamburger, one of the original formulators of this view of the living world, saw a field as

> a unit or a whole and not merely the sum of the cellular materials of which it is composed. The field with its organising capacities remains undisturbed if the cellular material which it controls under normal circumstances is diminished or enlarged. The unit character of the field finds its clearest manifestation in these regulative properties.[6]

In this way, the 'field' coordinates the action of the parts and can maintain its stability in the face of internal or external challenges.

The question we must then ask is how a system interrelates with its 'field' in order to assure its own differentiated development. Weiss draws attention to the intimate relationship that a system's own developmental strategy (or cybernism) has with its specific ordered environment at every level of organisation up to that of the individual.

... each cell's genome is, and always has been, a captive of an *ordered* environment. While the genome contributes to the specific properties of that environment in mutual interactions with it during the whole course of embryogenesis, it is only by virtue of the primordial frame of organisation of the *cytoplasm* of the egg that an individual can maintain, from the very start, the unity of overall design ...[7]

In other words, instructions—in this case genetic instructions—are not designed to be transmitted into a random environment. Information, as Anatol Rapoport notes, is not 'something that can be poured into an empty vessel like a fluid or even like energy'.[8] This is one of the most serious flaws in the neo-Darwinian theory of natural selection, in which behaviour is seen as determined by the genes *acting in a random environment*. The genes are not endowed with the power to dictate, as Weiss puts it, but interact in cooperation with the whole of which they are part.[9] The instructions they issue will only be obeyed by systems that have been designed by their evolution and upbringing to receive, understand, and believe them. This must be true of the transmission of instructions in all living processes, regardless of the level of organisation at which it occurs (appendix 2).

As Waddington writes, '... no transmission system can effectively carry information between a transmitter and a recipient *unless the recipient accepts the message as meaningful.*'[10] As the newborn infant develops, for instance, it has to be 'moulded into an information acceptor' and an entertainer of beliefs.[11]

But this is not enough. The receiver of a message must also be structured and motivated in such a way as to be capable of acting on the information adaptively. As Waddington points out,

... it is no use pushing the DNA of your sperm into an egg unless the egg contains the polymerases capable of transcribing it into a messenger and all the rest of the machinery for turning out a protein according to specification.[12]

In the same way, the cries of a baby in distress provide an important message to its mother, who is not only predisposed to hear them and understand their significance but also to respond to them effectively—otherwise, there would be no advantage to be gained from the ability to detect them. In other words, the child's message is only likely to be really effective *within the child's immediate field—that of its family*—within which the mother is the most essential member. Outside this field, the message is likely to lead to a defective response, and if the field is particularly inappropriate, to no response at all.[13]

This is a clear indication of why a child needs to be brought up in its proper family environment that displays the appropriate degree of order and cooperation. This is all the more important in that the experiences of the very early years are the most critical, and if they do not occur in the appropriate conditions, the child is likely to display aberrant psychological traits. Indeed, much of the delinquency and retreatism (drug addiction, alcoholism, schizophrenia) that is a feature of modern society seems to be at least partly due to the breakdown of the family and the community under the impact of economic development (chapter 51).

In spite of institutional education or government welfare services, the child deprived of a family is likely to remain emotionally and intellectually stunted. An extreme case is that of the children who have grown up in isolation, such as Kaspar Hauser, the Wild Boy of Aveyron, or those raised by wild animals, who, in spite of all efforts on the part of those who sought to rehabilitate them, could never achieve a mental age of more than two or three (see also chapter 31).[14]

As children grow older and venture out into the world at large, they undoubtedly require adventure, stimulation, and challenges that they have not previously encountered within the family unit.[15] Indeed, living things can suffer not only from family deprivation but also from family saturation. Thus, a young person brought up for too long in a womb-like family unit, whose every need is anticipated and who is allowed to take no initiative of any kind, is likely to be ill-adapted for dealing with the problems it will encounter when it leaves the family environment and ventures out into the world at large. Living things should develop within an environment or field that displays a specific 'order gradient' or 'gradient of cooperation', in which their insulation from the external world is gradually reduced as they grow up, at a rate and to an extent that will vary in different social and ecological conditions.

It is clear that a natural system's 'field' is nothing more than its ordered environment—in other words, the natural habitat in which it has evolved and developed. Indeed, if it had been realised before that an environment had to be highly structured rather than random, then there would have been no need for the term 'field' or for 'field theory'.

A still more important point is that neither the term 'field' nor the term 'environment' tends to be seen in the context of the wider continuum or holarchy of the biosphere, only in terms of which their structure and function make sense (chapter 43).

50

AS NATURAL HABITATS DIVERGE FROM THE OPTIMUM, BIOLOGICAL DISORDERS INCREASE

Almost all studies that attempt to reconstruct the history of infectious diseases indicate that the burden of infection has tended to increase rather than decrease as human beings adopted civilised lifestyles.
Mark Nathan Cohen

. . . we are witnessing the decay of man—the decay of his teeth, his arteries, his bowels, and his joints on a colossal and unprecedented scale.
Walter Yellowlees

D AMAGE TO THE BIOSPHERE brought about by economic development or 'progress' is drastically altering the environment of the living things that make up its complex holarchical structure. Less and less does it resemble that to which we have been adapted by our evolution and development. For example, we now eat food that is grown by unnatural processes that make use of a host of chemical substances— hormones, antibiotics, biocides (including insecticides, herbicides, nematocides, fungicides, and rodenticides)—of which residues are to be found in nearly all the food commercially available today. Our food is then processed in vast factories with the result that its molecular structure is often totally different from that of the food we have been adapted to eat during the course of our evolution. It is further contaminated with other chemicals, such as emulsifiers, preservatives, and antioxidants, designed to impart to it those qualities required to increase shelf-life and otherwise improve its *commercial* rather than nutritional viability. We drink water contaminated with nitrates, heavy metals, and synthetic organic chemicals, including pesticides that no industrial sewerage works or water purification plants can entirely remove. We breathe in air that is polluted with carbon monoxide, nitrogen oxides, hydrocarbons, ozone, and particulate matter from car exhausts, sulphur dioxides, P C B s, and mercury from chimney flues, radioactive iodine, cæsium, and a host of other radionuclides from the flues of nuclear installations.

It is not surprising that in such conditions we should suffer from a whole range of new diseases, nor that they should be increasingly referred to as 'the diseases of civilisation'. Samuel Epstein, of the University of Illinois, and other scholars attribute a very high proportion of cancers to exposure to chemicals in the food we eat, the water we drink, and the air we breathe—a thesis that is, needless to say, fervently contested by the chemical industry and the experts they sponsor.[1] Ischæmic heart disease, diabetes, peptic ulcers, diverticulitis, appendicitis, varicose veins, and dental caries, like cancer, are also diseases of civilisation.

The incidence of these diseases is extremely low (in some cases, nil) among vernacular people living in their natural habitats, as has been demonstrated by Albert Damon and others for the Solomon Islands,[2] by Ian Prior and his colleagues for Pukapuka in the Cook Islands and the Tokelau Islands over a period of thirty years,[3] and, perhaps most famously, by Weston Price, who studied the health and diets of a wide range of traditional peoples from around the world.[4] Such studies have also shown, however, that as people become exposed to the Western lifestyle, and in particular as they adopt the modern Western diet, the incidence of the same diseases increases dramatically. Infectious diseases, too, become much more common.[5] This should not surprise us—in many ways, development creates ideal conditions for their transmission.

Malaria is transmitted by the mosquito *Anopheles*, which was originally a parasite of monkeys living in the canopy of tropical forests. Well adapted to its hosts, it caused them only mild symptoms of the disease—but once the forests were cut down, the mosquitoes had to find alternative hosts; the most generally available being humans. The cutting down of forests in Amazonia has also brought people into contact with the vectors of leishmaniasis, previously a disease of sloths and armadillos. The pandemic of A I D S, which may once have been a disease of green monkeys or chimpanzees, probably became a human disease once we entered, in different ways, into closer contact with these animals.

Modern agriculture has also put us into close contact with microbes, viruses, and parasites that had previously established a stable relationship with the animals we have domesticated. Many such 'zoönotic' diseases arise from modern highly intensive livestock rearing—in particular, the offensive but presumably 'cost-effective' practice of feeding poultry on the carcasses of their fellows or on their own excrement, causing their meat and eggs to be increasingly contaminated with such pathogenic bacteria as *Salmonella*. The equally offensive practice of incorporating offal and other animal wastes in the feed of dairy cattle has led to an increase in the contamination of milk products with another pathogenic bacterium, *Listeria*, and to the contamination of beef offal, and possibly also beef, with the vectors of Bovine Spongiform Encephalopathy (B S E), which may be transferable to humans. New and deadlier strains of influenza may be yet another side-effect of these highly intensive methods of rearing livestock.

Ironically, the modern preoccupation with hygiene also gives rise to ideal conditions for the proliferation of pathogens. Pasteurised milk products can easily be colonised by microörganisms, some of which could be pathogens, since, in the sterile conditions provided, they do not encounter any competition from other microörganisms. This is the favoured explanation for the epidemic of *Listeria* poisoning in Switzerland in the 1980s.

Poliomyelitis has also been implicated as a disease of hygiene. Vernacular people who as children were exposed to the microörganisms present in soil, and perhaps to animal excrement, and who were at the same time fed on their mother's milk, do not get it—but they become vulnerable if, on the contrary, they are brought up in a hygienic environment and fed on cow's milk.[6]

Greatly increased human mobility has also contributed to the spread of diseases. In a matter of weeks, if not days, any new outbreak will reach the major population centres of the world. Under such conditions, it is not surprising that the incidence of just about every infectious disease, with the exception (for now at least) of smallpox and poliomyelitis, is increasing worldwide. Meanwhile, new diseases, such as AIDS and SARS, are appearing, and there will undoubtedly be more of them, especially once genetic engineering really gets into its stride, for it can only be a matter of time before our scientists release into the environment a genetically engineered pathogen of which our species has had no evolutionary experience, with potentially disastrous consequences.

Large-scale irrigation projects have also provided an ideal habitat for water-borne diseases, like malaria and schistosomiasis—spreading them to parts of the world where they were previously unknown.

If the depletion of the ozone layer increases—which may continue to happen for some time, even if we stop producing CFCs and other ozone-depleting chemicals entirely—we shall be subjected to increasing ultraviolet radiation that will not only dramatically increase the incidence of skin cancer but also disrupt the functioning of our immune systems, making us correspondingly more vulnerable to both degenerative and infectious diseases.

The health consequences of climate change are also likely to be serious for the inhabitants of temperate areas, who will now be exposed to the vectors and pathogens that transmit a host of tropical diseases that make life very much more difficult and more precarious in the tropics than in the cooler areas of our planet. Lacking evolutionary experience of these diseases, we are likely to be all the more seriously affected by them.

To these problems, there is no effective technological solution. Medicine can certainly do little to help, since it is largely concerned with treating the symptoms of diseases, while to control their incidence would mean taking measures that lie outside the brief of the medical profession (chapter 64), and that would in any case be unacceptable, both politically and economically, since it would mean reversing many of the essential processes of economic development or 'progress'.

Some of our scientists have suggested that if we cannot adapt to the world that science is bringing into being, then *we ourselves* must be changed.[7] A new genetically engineered and technologically enhanced human being must presumably be mass-produced—one who can adapt to, and perhaps even thrive in, the polluted and ecologically degraded world that modern society is substituting for the world to which we have been adapted by our evolution. Such a suggestion can only demonstrate to what extent mainstream science has lost touch with the real world in which we continue to live so precariously.

51

AS NATURAL HABITATS DIVERGE FROM THE OPTIMUM, SOCIAL DISORDERS INCREASE

We should have no truck with trendy theories that try to explain
away crime by blaming socioëconomic factors.
Michael Howard (British Home Secretary)

. . . the tendency of unlimited industrialism is to create bodies of men
and women—of all classes—detached from tradition, alienated from
religion, and susceptible to mass suggestion. In other words, a mob. And
a mob will be no less a mob if it is well fed, well clothed, well housed,
and well disciplined.
T.S. Eliot

The poverty in the black and Puerto Rican neighbourhoods on the West
Side of Chicago is worse than any poverty I saw in West Africa. The people [in Africa] are guided by strong traditional values. They do not live in
constant fear of violence, vermin, and fire. You don't find the same sense
of desperation and hopelessness you find in the American ghetto.
Robert Wurmstedt

E CONOMIC DEVELOPMENT causes our social as well as our physical environment to diverge from the optimum. Our species evolved
as an integral part of the extended family, the lineage group, and the small
community together with a host of intermediary associations, such as age-
grades and secret societies. In other words, we evolved within a highly
structured social environment that we can regard as our social field or continuum (chapter 49).

With economic development, however, the community and the intermediary associations disintegrate. Edward Banfield, who made a sociological study of a south Italian village, was particularly struck by the
alienation and demoralisation of its inhabitants, a phenomenon known
locally as *la misèria*. This, he found, was not basically attributable to the
lack of money or material goods—what is normally regarded as poverty—but to *the isolation of the families from each other* due to the absence
of any wider social groupings.[1] This, as we shall see (chapter 60), he attributed to the usurpation by the state of the basic functions that the village should normally assume.

With the development of modern industry, the extended family itself
disintegrates until it is reduced to an atomised society, of which all that
is left of the original social structure is a truncated nuclear family. Even
that is eventually subject to further degradation, and we end up with the
one-parent family, which, in the worst case, disintegrates still further
into its individual members (chapter 60).

There is yet another form of social atomisation. Families, communities,
and societies exist in time as well as in space (chapter 37). To be isolated
from them, therefore, makes of us temporal as well as spatial isolates—
isolated from our ancestors and our children as we are from our contemporaries. This is reflected in our worldview. Whereas people in a vernacular society see their lives as but a link in a long chain of being, people in an
atomised society, such as ours, see their lives as something unique. When
we die, all is over. That is one of the reasons why we in the West have so
great a fear of death, a fear that is not shared by people in a vernacular
society, who see themselves as integral parts of a living continuum extending on into the personhood of their children. In the former atomised society, people are only concerned with the short-term. They are no longer
interested in creating a good world for their children and grandchildren
and great-grandchildren. 'What has posterity done for me?' is a common
refrain in the West today. The notion that we owe nothing to posterity

seems to justify, in the eyes of many people, our terrible egotism and the deliberate pillaging of the world's natural resources, to which our society is so committed, in order to satisfy the requirements of the states and corporations that control it.

Not surprisingly, people in such conditions become increasingly unhappy and depressed. A study undertaken by the US Alcohol, Drug Abuse, and Mental Health Administration (ADAMHA) documented how people born after 1945 are ten times more likely to suffer depression than people born 50 years earlier—a second study found that the people born after 1950 were twenty times more likely to suffer depression than those born before 1910.[2] What is more, such depressions are afflicting much younger people than before.

Émile Durkheim referred to the state of society in which people are alienated from one another and deprived of a satisfactory social environment as *anomie*. Robert MacIver described the individual living in such conditions as having

> the state of mind of one who has been pulled up from his moral roots, who has no longer any standards but only disconnected urges, who has no longer any sense of continuity, of folk, of obligation.[3]

Their life is left empty and purposeless and deprived of meaningful human relations.

The disintegration of the family is possibly the most serious source of anomie or alienation, and it is proceeding today at an unprecedented rate. In the USA, one-parent families were a little more than ten per cent of the total in 1970, but the figure was twenty-seven per cent in 2002—a nearly three-fold increase in just over a generation.[4] Similarly, in the UK, the proportion of single-parent households was about twenty-one per cent in 2001, up from less than fourteen per cent in 1981, representing a fifty per cent increase in less than a generation.[5] As more children are brought up outside the family, it must inevitably bring about a further increase in social alienation. Significantly, the number of abandoned children in the UK increased during the same period. In South America, it had already reached epidemic proportions by the 1980s, with several million abandoned children reportedly roaming the streets of the major cities of Brazil alone.

There is increasing evidence that deprivation of a satisfactory family environment will affect children profoundly and colour every aspect of their later lives.[6] Such children are often referred to as emotionally disturbed. However bright they may be, they will tend to find it very difficult to fit into their social environment—the reason being that the early and most important stages of their socialisation were badly impaired. As D.O. Hebb shows, the earlier deprivation occurs, the more this will be the case.[7]

School education cannot do much for emotionally disturbed children. They tend to have a short concentration span and are particularly concerned with the present and the short-term, are loath to accept social constraints, and are predisposed to all pathological forms of behaviour, such as delinquency, drug addiction, alcoholism, and schizophrenia. When these young people are forced, at the same time, to live in squalid modern housing estates and, as is increasingly likely, to endure long-term unemployment, their lot becomes hopeless. Theodore Dalrymple, a doctor on one such estate in the UK, described the sheer hopelessness of the world in which he lives,

> I live in a wasteland. In the council estate, the glass of many of the windows has been replaced by plywood; such gardens as there are have reverted to grey-green scrub, with empty beer and soft drink cans, used condoms, and loose sheets of tabloid newspaper in place of flowers; and the people trudge through the desolation as disconsolately as in any communist city.[8]

Dalrymple refers to the young men of the housing estates as 'bodily mature but with the mind and inclinations of juvenile barbarians'. They

> eye the world with sullen hostility, which the tattoos on their knuckles, necks, and forearms not infrequently express in words. They are unemployed and often profoundly unemployable—they are intolerant of any external restraint on their behaviour and cannot fix their minds upon anything for more than a few moments. What job could one give them?[9]

What makes matters even more hopeless is that these young people live in a moral and cultural void. 'In the absence of a system of values,' Dalrymple writes, 'adolescent revolt has become a permanent state of mind. The lack of belief in anything is compensated for by shrillness, as if mere noise could fill the inner void.'[10]

The same hopelessness has been a feature of the welfare-maintained ghettos of the larger American cities for decades. Oscar Lewis describes the inhabitants of such areas as having

> a strong feeling of marginality, of helplessness, of dependence, and of inferiority. . . . Other traits include a high incidence of maternal depri-

vation, of orality, of weak ego-structure, confusion of sexual identifica-
tion, a lack of impulse control, a strong present-time orientation with relatively little ability to defer gratification and to plan for the future, a sense
of resignation and fatalism, a widespread belief in male superiority, and a
high tolerance for psychological pathology of all sorts.[11]

He refers to this situation as 'the culture of poverty' and sees it as a feature of the welfare-maintained inner cities of the industrial world. Today,
however, it is manifesting in other sectors of society and, at the current
rate, *it could soon be the culture of industrial society as a whole*. It may be
more accurate, then, to describe this widespread process of social demoralisation or *la misèria* as 'the impoverishment of culture' rather than 'the
culture of poverty'.

Serge Latouche, who worked for decades among the mushrooming
slums of the cities of West Africa, tells us that

> . . . there is not even a word in all the major languages of Black Africa to
> describe the poor in the economic sense. The words that are most often
> used to translate 'poor' really mean 'orphan'. It is remarkable that in all
> the circumstances of everyday life, references to poverty did not refer to a
> lack of money but to lack of social support.[12]

For Jean-François Werner, to be orphaned in Africa is probably the worst
conceivable state of affairs, because, as the saying goes, 'a man is his
family.'[13] This situation is reflected in Mali among the Bambara. Poverty
to them is literally being 'without power, without agency' (chapter 62).
Latouche quotes Chantal Verger, who tells us that they feel 'relegated to
the margins . . . they have lost their entire social foundation, which is primarily the family.'[14]

Latouche notes how our idea of poverty is only conceivable within an
already atomised society, such as that which economic development necessarily gives rise to. He writes,

> economic poverty is a Western invention, not only because it creates new
> material needs to be met, but because the intrusion of Western values
> undermines ancient social practices.[15]

That economic development would lead to this state of affairs was intu-
ited by Adam Smith himself. According to Laurence Dickey, 'Toward the
end of the 1780s, Smith was becoming increasingly alarmed by what [has
been] called "the depleting moral legacy" of commercial society.'[16] His
alarm was well-justified—indeed, a report by James Pattison and Peter

Kim, *The Day America Told the Truth* (1991), showed how Americans appeared to be living in a virtual moral vacuum. The authors of the report found that

> 91 per cent of Americans lie regularly both at work and at home; 68 per cent believe there are no American heroes; 47 per cent are not certain that they would marry the same person again; 31 per cent of married people have had, or are having, an affair; 20 per cent lost their virginity before the age of thirteen; 33 per cent of AIDS victims have not told their partners that they are infected; 72 per cent do not know their nextdoor neighbour; and a majority will not look after their elderly parents.[17]

Equally illustrative is the aberrant behaviour of people when the elaborate mechanisms of the law break down for some technical reason. In Montreal, during a sixteen-hour police strike, shops were pillaged, banks robbed, and people killed.[18] In London, during a power strike, theft increased to such an extent in shops and department stores that many had to close until the lights came on again.[19] In Saint Croix, the capital of the American Virgin Islands, members of the Police and National Guard were among those who took advantage of the chaos that followed a hurricane by looting stores and terrorising island residents, many of whom barricaded themselves into their homes.[20]

Crime has been increasing at record rates in the UK, America, and elsewhere. A 1990 study by Humberside Police's superintendent John Taylor predicted that by the beginning of the twenty-first century the number of recorded crimes in England and Wales would increase from four to six million per year (in fact, it reached the latter figure in 2004), and that only one in four of these would be solved. Taylor considers that recorded crimes are merely 'the tip of an iceberg', no more than a quarter of those actually committed.[21] If this is so, then by 2004 there would have been at least 24 million crimes committed in England and Wales—nearly one for every two inhabitants.

Crime is closely connected with social alienation. The victims react in a number of different ways to their plight. One reaction among young slum dwellers is to organise themselves into street gangs—a rudimentary community that provides them at once with an identity, a goal structure, an embryonic cultural pattern, and a means of achieving recognition and success, at least within their particular group. This gives rise to what Lloyd Ohlin and Richard Cloward refer to as the 'violent gang' subculture.[22]

Another reaction to social alienation, more common among middle-class youths, is to indulge in some form of retreatism, isolating themselves from a lifestyle and an environment that increasingly fails to satisfy basic psychological needs. For American sociologist Robert Merton,

> Defeatism, quietism, and resignation are manifested in escape mechanisms, which ultimately lead him to 'escape' from the requirements of the society. It is thus an expedient which arises from the continued failure to near the goal by legitimate measures and from an inability to use the illegitimate route because of internalised prohibitions, this process occurring while the supreme value of the success-goal has not yet been renounced. The conflict is resolved by abandoning both precipitating elements, the goals and the means. The escape is complete, the conflict is eliminated, and the individual is äsocialised. [23]

One obvious form of retreatism is alcoholism. Another is drug addiction, and the incidence of both these aberrations increases dramatically with social disintegration. Another form of retreatism is schizophrenia, which involves building up and seeking refuge in a world of fantasy. This and other forms of mental disease tend to increase with social disintegration and are particularly in evidence among the members of a society undergoing acculturation (when a culture is breaking down under the influence of an alien one).

Durkheim regarded suicide as the ultimate manifestation of anomie. In one study he found that the suicide rate was particularly low in poor rural communities where social structures were intact, and high in disintegrated affluent society, especially among the working classes, and even more so among Italian immigrants to the cities of Lorraine. He goes so far as to say that 'suicide varies inversely with the degree of integration of religious, . . . domestic, . . . [and] political society.' [24]

The reaction of our political establishment to the increased incidence of all these social aberrations is to blame the victims. They are seen to be deficient in one way or another or 'unfit' in the terminology of social Darwinism. Often this is seen as an inherited problem and attributed to a faulty gene—numerous studies have been conducted to explain why this should be so. Thus, the previously cited US government study on mental health attributed its growing incidence to a genetic cause. Criminals are often made out to be men with an X and two Y chromosomes rather than single X and Y chromosomes, which is a more normal arrangement. Another ploy is to attribute these social aberrations to purely economic factors. They are often seen to be caused by poverty, interpreted in purely economic and material terms, conveniently ignoring that the incidence of these social aberrations is extremely low in the 'poorest' Third World countries where social structures have not yet disintegrated. We can wander, for instance, in total security through the worst slums of Kolkata, where hundreds of thousands of people are condemned to sleeping rough on the pavements, for there the extended family is still largely intact.

Today, such aberrations tend to be attributed in particular to unemployment and the present running-down of the welfare state. These are undoubtedly important factors, but they do not provide a sufficient explanation, since the incidence of these social aberrations was also increasing in the 1960s and early seventies when unemployment levels were low and the social services still highly funded.

Such interpretations conveniently rationalise *further* economic development, which is inevitably seen by our leading thinkers as providing the only means of combating any social, economic, or environmental problem (chapter 64). Thus, it remains the overriding goal of government policies throughout the world; a goal that above all serves the immediate political and economic interests of politicians and their allies within the industrial community, while completely failing to address the social, cultural, and ecological destruction brought about by economic development in the first place—the real cause of human deprivation and misery.

52

AS NATURAL HABITATS DIVERGE FROM THE OPTIMUM, COGNITIVE DISORDERS INCREASE

... it is impossible to overlook the extent to which civilisation is built upon a renunciation of instinct, how much it presupposes precisely the non-satisfaction (by suppression, repression, or some other means) of powerful instincts.

Sigmund Freud

Nature endowed us with the capacity to determine nutritional quality and safety of food so long as it was *natural*. For example, we can distinguish between corn fresh from the stalk and corn a day old. Colour, smell, and texture are all sensations we use in assessing the nutritive value of food. But all this changes in the modern era of fabricated food. Bakery products and candy appear yellow because they have been treated with a coal tar derivative. Bread, soups, and pickles seem tastier because they contain sugar. Meat appears fresher because it contains sodium nitrites to inhibit bacterial growth. Net result—*the taste of fabricated food is no reliable guide to freshness, nutritional quality, or whether the food will eventually kill you.*

Ross Hume Hall

How can man get into harmony with his surroundings when he is constantly altering them?

E.M. Forster

O UR PERCEPTIVE FACULTIES are admirably suited to providing us with the subjective knowledge of our relationship with our environment that we require for adaptive purposes, so long as our environment's basic features *have not been allowed to diverge too much from those to which we have been adapted by our evolution and upbringing* (chapters 7 and 48). As our environment moves beyond these limits, however, our perceptions become ever less useful for understanding it and for helping us to adapt to it—we cease, in fact, to be cognitively adjusted to it.

Ross Hume Hall points out that we are cognitively maladjusted to eating modern processed foods and, as a result, are incapable of behaving adaptively towards them.[1] It is not only our senses but our very intuitive faculties that cease to provide us with the requisite adaptive knowledge (chapter 9). As a result, the solutions to the problems that confront us become increasingly 'counterintuitive', to use Jay Forrester's expression—though this is not because the environment is too complex, as he suggests,[2] but because we have no evolutionary experience of it.

Thus, whereas our ancestors had no difficulty in understanding their relationship with the *living* world, we have no means of understanding our relationship with the artificial surrogate world we have created in its place. What are the implications, for instance, of subjecting our children to X-rays, of permitting a nuclear power station to be built in the vicinity of our homes, of using CFC-emitting cosmetic sprays that erode the ozone layer that shields our planet from ultraviolet radiation, of cutting down the world's tropical forests, or indeed of countenancing the industrialisation process itself? We depend for counsel on experts who are rarely objective and, even if they were, are unlikely to have been trained to take into account all the relevant factors involved.

It is not only our senses and our intuitive faculties that fail us before the brave new world to which economic development is giving rise—our very instincts cease to serve as a guide to adaptive behaviour. As the child learns to become a member of a particular vernacular society via the normal process of socialisation (chapter 59), the instinctive behaviour of the child is channelled in such a way as to assure that it will maintain, and not disrupt, the workings of the biosphere—in other words, its behaviour will become homeotelic to its natural habitat and thus, in turn, to the wider continuum of natural processes that make up the entire holarchy of the biosphere (chapter 46). Once social and ecological systems have disintegrated, however, socialisation can no longer take place properly, and the child's behaviour becomes heterotelic or disruptive to the remaining, and now more degraded, processes of the biosphere.

A typical example is our instinctive aggression. In a vernacular society, like all other forms of competitiveness, it is highly ritualised and serves social, indeed biospheric, ends (chapter 45). Its destructiveness is also limited because vernacular technology is under social control, which means that wars are fought with traditional (and hence not particularly lethal) weapons (chapter 54). All this changes dramatically with economic development, when the associated social and cultural destruction deprives us of the means of managing our aggression and of preventing the development of the most lethal and destructive armaments.

Thus, as we bring into being a world that diverges so drastically from that to which we have been adapted by our evolution, the very faculties with which evolution has endowed us for maintaining the stability of our societies (and hence of our own survival) *now serve to achieve the opposite end.* Julian Huxley, Edward O. Wilson, and other proponents of perpetual 'progress' consider, for that reason, that we must suppress our instinctive drives and our emotions, for they can lead to aggressive behaviour that in the modern world is no longer tolerable (chapters 7, 18, 37, and appendix 3). But if we are to adapt to the brave new world that 'progress' is creating for us, it is not just our aggression that must be suppressed but also those instinctive drives and emotions that make of us *religious* as well as social beings—for only in this way can we adapt to living in the atomised, competitive, secular, and psychologically meaningless world that 'progress' is creating for us. Even if this were possible, it would mean depriving us of just about everything that makes us truly human. But if the Promethean enterprise we call progress requires that we be transformed into unfeeling and emotionless robots, *then surely we have no alternative but to reject it.*

Undoubtedly, the most alarming instance of cognitive maladjustment must be our failure to grasp the critical nature of the global environmental problems that confront us—deforestation, soil erosion, salinisation and desertification, the general chemicalisation of the environment, the depletion of the ozone layer, and the disruption of our climate. Only a small number of our academics—not to mention of our industrialists or politicians—demonstrate any concern for these daunting problems, and even when they do, *few measures of any consequence are undertaken to solve them.* At party political conferences held across the globe, politicians continue to discuss the usual vote-catching topics, obstinately refusing even to mention (save perhaps in a most cursory manner) the real issues that must determine our future and that of our children.

It may not be irrelevant to note that even very modest forms of life, like earthworms, dung beetles, and fiddler crabs, have no trouble identifying the real problems they must deal with if they are to survive.

THE WORLDVIEW OF MODERN SCIENCE IS
MALADJUSTED TO HUMAN BEINGS

. . . man must at last wake out of his millenary dream—and in doing so, wake to his total solitude, his fundamental isolation. Now does he at last realise that, like a gypsy, he lives on the boundary of an alien world—a world that is deaf to his music, just as indifferent to his hopes as it is to his suffering or his crimes.

Jacques Monod

Pursued to its ultimate conclusion, the materialistic theory ends in nihilism, in a world blind and purposeless, signifying nothing, leading mankind—a chance combination of inanimate forces—out of nowhere into nowhere.

L.T.C. Rolt

. . . modern science [has substituted] for our world of quality and sense perception, the world in which we live and love and die, another world—the world of quantity, of reified geometry; a world in which, though there is a place for everything, there is no place for man.

Alexandre Koyré

[Traditional] man feels the need always to exist in a total and organised world—in a *cosmos*.

Mircea Eliade

As MODERN SCIENCE progresses, it depicts the world and our relationship to it in terms that have ever less meaning to the human psyche. The Austrian psychologist Viktor Frankl regards as absolutely basic what he refers to as 'the will to meaning', which he contrasts with Adler's 'will to power' and Freud's 'will to pleasure'. For Frankl, one in four neuroses are of 'noögenic' origin (originating in thought), and most of these, he believes, can be traced to our 'existential vacuum'—the meaninglessness of life in the world about us.[1]

This 'existential vacuum' is deepened by the modern scientific view of human beings as no more than machines responding robotically to environmental stimuli (chapter 10). Our innermost feelings, values, and beliefs are little more than illusions; our family, community, society, even the natural world itself, are no more than a seething mass of atoms and molecules—random, purposeless, and uncaring. Frankl recalls his reaction as a child to being told by his science teacher that life is nothing but combustion—an oxidation process. On hearing this, he jumped indignantly to his feet. 'Dr Fritz,' he asked, 'if this is true, what meaning, then, does life have?' To which key question the teacher presumably had no better answer than have today's mainstream scientists.[2]

People are, nonetheless, psychologically adjusted to entertaining the chthonic worldview, in terms of which all the constituents of the natural world (whether they be animal, plant, or mineral) are intelligible beings that radiate meanings—integral parts of a wider 'cosmic' holarchy (i.e. of an ordered universe—see chapter 40). Vernacular people did not have to be cajoled or coerced into accepting such a worldview. It was the worldview of their ancestors, and they were imbued with it as they learned to become members of their society (chapter 51).

Jacques Monod admits that vernacular or 'animist' people, as he refers to them, could see themselves as an integral part of the natural world. 'Animism', he writes, 'established a covenant between nature and man, a profound alliance, outside of which seems to stretch only terrifying solitude.' But, today, science has revealed to us the terrible truth.

> The ancient covenant is in pieces—man knows at last that he is alone in the universe's unfeeling immensity, out of which he emerged only by chance. *Neither his destiny nor his duty have been written down.*[3]

Monod, nevertheless, considers that we have no choice but to continue along our present path, however meaningless, however alien. But this is not the view of the German philosopher of science Gunther Stent, who notes that

> . . . the dissolution of the covenant . . . presages the end of science, since there is little use in continuing to push the limits of our knowledge further and further if the results have less and less meaning for man's psyche.[4]

In fact, it is this very 'covenant between nature and man' that we must reëstablish, as a matter of urgency, if we are to have any hope of solving the social and environmental crises facing us today (chapter 61).

PART V

THE NATURE OF TRADITIONAL SOCIETIES

54

IN A TRADITIONAL SOCIETY, TECHNOLOGY IS IN ACCORD WITH THE NEEDS OF THE BIOSPHERE

At the heart of the Industrial Revolution of the eighteenth century there was an almost miraculous improvement in the tools of production, which was accompanied by a catastrophic dislocation of the lives of the common people.
Karl Polanyi

Technology, as we know it today, is a historical phenomenon born of a certain idea of nature, of a certain idea of progress, of a certain preconception about the deterministic structure of the world, and also related to specific social ideals and specific visions of the ends of human life.
Henryk Skolimowski

Appropriate technology reminds us that before we choose our tools and techniques we must choose our dreams and values—for some technologies serve them, while others make them unobtainable.
Tom Bender

High technology is merely an instrument for making the plundering of our planet more effective.
Paul Blau

There neither is, nor can be, any simple increase of power on Man's side. Each new power won *by* man is a power *over* man as well. Each advance leaves him weaker as well as stronger. In every victory, besides being the general who triumphs, he is also the prisoner who follows the triumphal car.
C.S. Lewis

The Changthang is a ferocious place. One minute the air is calm and the sun is shining, the next it is hailing. It isn't possible to try to control and alter the Changthang. We don't try—instead, we use our knowledge to adjust to it.
Tibetan nomad

I N A VERNACULAR SOCIETY, technology is embedded in social relations—in other words, it is under social and hence ecological control.
The technology used by a vernacular society in the production of its artefacts or in the cultivation of its fields is not that which maximises productivity but that which best maintains social stability and thereby the stability
of the natural world on which it depends. In order to achieve these social
and ecological goals, technology is necessarily rationalised and legitimised
by the society's mythology.

All economic activities in vernacular societies are highly ritualised. Every stage in an economic activity is marked by a ceremony that endows
it with a cosmical meaning, enabling it to contribute to the maintenance
of the wider cosmos on which the survival of every society depends.

That this was the case among the ancient Greeks is made clear by
Hesiod in his *Works and Days*. The art of agriculture, in order to be effective, he tells us, must above all be in keeping with the Nomos or traditional law, and hence with nature's way (chapter 61). As F.M. Cornford
puts it, '[Man] must keep straight upon the path of custom (Nomos) or
right (Dike) or else the answering processes of natural life will likewise
leave the track.'[1]

Thus, the technology of vernacular people was not designed to transform or master the natural environment but rather *to enable them to live
with it*. Gerardo Reichel-Dolmatoff notes how the native Tukano of
Colombia have

> little interest in new knowledge that might be used for exploiting the
> environment more effectively, and there is little concern for maximising
> short-term gains or for obtaining more food or raw materials than are
> actually needed. But there is always a great deal of interest in accumulat-
> ing more factual knowledge about biological reality and, above all, *about
> knowing what the physical world requires from man*. This knowledge, the
> Indians believe, is essential for survival because man must bring himself
> into conformity with nature if he wants to exist as part of nature's unity
> and must fit his demands to nature's availabilities.[2]

He notes how highly developed is the Tukano's knowledge of ecology
and animal behaviour.

> Such phenomena as parasitism, symbiosis, commensalism, and other
> relationships between coöccurring species have been well observed by
> them and are pointed out as possible methods of adaptation.

They are also well aware of what would be the consequences for them of violating basic ecological laws. Thus, their mythology describes how various animal species have been punished and occasionally made extinct

> for not obeying certain prescribed rules of adaptive significance. Thus, gluttony, improvidence, aggressiveness, and all forms of overindulgence are punished by the superior forces to serve as examples not only to the animal community but also to human society. Animals, then, are metaphors for survival. By analysing animal behaviour, the Indians try to discover an order in the physical world, *a world-order to which human activities can then be adjusted.*[3]

It follows that a society's technology is very much its own, an integral and often sacred part of its cultural heritage. For this reason, there is very little 'technology transfer' among vernacular people. Mary Douglas describes how the Lele, who live on one bank of the Kasai river in DR Congo, persist in making use of their own relatively simple technologies, even though they are well acquainted with the more sophisticated technologies made use of by the Bushong, who live on the opposite bank of the river. It does not occur to the Lele to make use of Bushong technology, *because it does not fit in with their own cultural pattern,* nor is its use rationalised and validated by their metaphysical beliefs and mythology.[4]

Similarly, according to Igor de Garine, the Massa of North Cameroon and of Chad have refused to cultivate sorghum during the dry season, even though to do so would enable them to double their food production. This is not because they do not know about its cultivation, since their neighbours the Tupuri cultivate sorghum very successfully. It is simply that the Massa regard it as more important *to maintain their cultural identity* than to increase their food production.[5]

When the Portuguese introduced the musket into sixteenth century Japan, its use was frowned on, and it took a very long time before it was allowed to replace traditional weapons. Its efficacy as an instrument of war was unquestioned, but it simply did not fit in with the Japanese cultural traditions, in terms of which the use of a device that enabled a small child to kill an experienced samurai, who had devoted his life to mastering the martial arts, was totally unacceptable. The musket had no part to play in their traditional way of life. Indeed, by the eighteenth-century the Japanese had largely abandoned the musket, reverting back to their traditional sword, spear, and bow.[6]

Similarly, the wheel, that we regard as one of the most basic of technologies, was not seen by the native Yequana of Venezuelan Amazonia as capable of playing any useful role in their lives. Jean Liedloff, who lived among them for two and a half years, claims that she has seen the wheel being invented at least eleven times. Children played with it, and it was a source of great amusement for all, but it never occurred to them that it could be put to any other use, and once they got bored with it, it was simply discarded unceremoniously.[7] It was no different in the Golden Age of ancient Athens when, as Henryk Skolimowski notes, all sorts of ingenious gadgets were developed, not for utilitarian purposes but purely for entertainment.[8] According to Plutarch, even Archimedes attached little importance to technological innovations and did not bother to leave any commentary on his inventions.

Robert Fernea, who describes the traditional irrigation system of the El Shabana tribe of Mesopotamia, highlights its sustainability and contrasts this with the non-sustainability of modern irrigation methods. He believes that all the ancient tribal societies who once practised irrigated-agriculture in Mesopotamia achieved a 'congruence or fit' between their methods of cultivation, their land-tenure systems, and 'the nature of the land, water, and climate' that industrial society cannot begin to emulate.[9]

It is, among other things, because vernacular societies *adapted their technology* to their environment that they were sustainable, which modern society, by seeking to *adapt its environment* to its technology, cannot conceivably be.

It is often assumed that this kind of sustainability can only be achieved at the cost of reduced efficiency—but this is untrue. At the turn of the century, the British government sent an agricultural expert, Augustus Voelcker, to study Indian agriculture with a view to modernising it. He was surprised and extremely impressed by what he saw.

> I do not share the opinions which have been expressed as to Indian agriculture being, as a whole, primitive and backward, but I believe that in many parts there is little or nothing that can be improved . . . I make bold to say that it is a much easier task to propose improvements in English agriculture than to make really valuable suggestions for that of India . . .

He was particularly impressed by their traditional technology.

> Anyone who has watched the clever devices of the native cultivators in the implements which they use, for harrowing, levelling, drilling, raising water, *etc.*, will see that if anything is to replace the existing implements, it must be simple, cheap, and effective. He will indeed be a clever man who introduces something really practical.[10]

James Mollison, another British agronomist of that period, formed the same impression.

I believe that the implements in ordinary use are entirely suitable for the conditions of Indian agriculture. . . . To those who are sceptical, I can show in parts of the Bombay Presidency, cultivation, by means of indigenous tillage implements only, which—in respect of neatness, thoroughness, and profitableness—cannot be excelled by the best gardeners or the best farmers in any part of the world. That statement I deliberately make and am quite prepared to substantiate.[11]

The same is true of African agriculture. For example, Robert Mann considers that the Ethiopian *ard* plough cannot be improved on for the conditions under which it has been designed to work. It produces a ridged tilth, does not invert the soil, leaves dead vegetation on the surface, and the unique pivot action between furrow-openers and beam enables the plough point to be lifted up and over obstacles. Yet, as Mann notes, 'there have been many attempts to introduce ploughs of foreign origin into Ethiopia contrary to that accumulated local wisdom.'[12]

If traditional agriculture was so eminently satisfactory, we might ask, why has it been systematically abandoned and replaced by obviously non-sustainable modern agricultural methods? The answer is that there is no place for it in the atomised, corporate-dominated consumer society that economic development has brought into being. The existence of traditional agriculture is not compatible with the achievement of such a society's overall goal, *the maximisation of economic activity and hence of economic growth.* The World Bank, which had a hand in financing economic development in Papua New Guinea, is quite honest about its motives.

Over much of the country, nature's bounty produces enough to eat with relatively little expenditure of effort. . . . Until enough subsistence farmers have their traditional lifestyles changed by the growth of new consumption wants, this labour constraint may make it difficult to introduce new crops.[13]

And new crops must be introduced—the new hybrids in particular, which are designed to be responsive to inputs of fertiliser, pesticides, and irrigation water. Their introduction is required to satisfy the needs of the powerful agrochemical industry and the dam builders. They are specifically designed for export to the industrial world to enable Third World governments to earn the foreign exchange required to finance the purchase of still more of our manufactured products and to pay the interest on the loans that were contracted to modernise agriculture in the first place.

Even in the World Bank's iniquitous Berg Report, it is acknowledged that smallholders 'are outstanding managers of their own resources—

their land and capital, fertiliser, and water'. However, the dominance of this type of agriculture or 'subsistence production' *presented special obstacles to agricultural development*. Farmers had to be induced to produce for the market, adopt new crops, and undertake new risks.'[14]

However, economic development rapidly puts the small farmers out of business, as it does the artisans—and they are replaced by ever bigger, ever more powerful corporations. As this process occurs, so is technology disembedded from its social and ecological context and hence grows increasingly out of control.

Nowhere is the socially destructive nature of modern technology more apparent than when we introduce it into vernacular societies in the Third World. Lauriston Sharp tells a story that has been repeated over and over again in the anthropological literature. It shows how a minute and seemingly inoffensive technological innovation—in this case the substitution of the use of steel axes for stone axes in an Australian aboriginal tribe—is sometimes enough to spell a society's rapid disintegration.

The elders of the tribe in question had a virtual monopoly of the use of stone axes and only lent them out in accordance with a very strict set of rules that ensured that they returned into their possession. The power of the elders, and indeed the whole structure of the society, is shown by Sharp to have depended on the maintenance of these arrangements. However, missionaries eager to modernise this tribal society introduced steel axes that were distributed indiscriminately within the tribe—in this way, the elders were deprived of one of the most important means at their disposal for maintaining the critical order of their society (chapter 57). It soon disintegrated, and it was not long before its now alienated members began to drift to the shanty towns and the mission stations.[15]

Wolfgang Sachs also notes the social implications of the widespread use of the electric mixer—a seemingly innocent technological device.

> Whirring and slightly vibrating, it makes juice from solid fruit in next to no time. A wonderful tool! So it seems. But a quick look at cord and wall-socket shows that what we have before us is rather the domestic terminal of a national, indeed, worldwide system.
>
> The electricity arrives via a network of cables and overhead utility lines, which are fed by power stations that depend on water pressures, pipelines, or tanker consignments, which in turn require dams, offshore platforms, or derricks in distant deserts. The whole chain only guarantees an adequate and prompt delivery if every one of its parts is staffed by armies of engineers, planners, and financial experts, who themselves can fall back on administrations, universities, indeed entire industries (and sometimes

even the military). . . . Whoever flicks a switch on is not using a tool. He or she is plugging into a combine of functioning systems. Between the use of simple techniques and that of modern equipment *lies the reorganisation of a whole society*.[16]

'Disorganisation' may, of course, be a more appropriate term. As Ralph Keyes notes,

> our household conveniences—our whole drive for a convenient life—have cut us off from each other. The cooperation and communication that used to accompany life's chores is being built out of our social systems.[17]

Technology, as J.C. Mathes and Donald Gray put it, 'makes us independent of community and social restraints and traditions but dependent on the technological system'.[18] Patrick McCully refers to Western technology in the Third World as 'a Trojan Horse of Western economic and social values and beliefs'.[19]

It may well be, as Mathes and Gray insist, that the engineer rather than the bureaucrat, the politician, or the economist is the true architect of our 'brave new world'. Indeed, no government edict could possibly have changed society as drastically as did the introduction of the automobile or the television set. There is irony in this, for the engineer is often a conservative in the true sense of the term, who cherishes such things as the family, the community, and their traditional values, all of which their professional activities must inevitably destroy.

It is the gross irresponsibility and, indeed, the unprecedented immorality of many of today's high technology undertakings that are particularly striking. Jerry Ravetz, the well-known philosopher of science, considers that even Bacon and Descartes retained some moral sense. For them, the development of science and technology would still be subjected to moral constraints. Thus, the sages of 'Solomon's House' in Bacon's *The New Atlantis* (1627) decided which knowledge should be revealed to the state and which should remain secret, while Descartes took a 'scientist's oath' not to engage on projects that could be useful to some, only by harming others. Galileo, however, was uncompromising. He saw himself as having the right to state what he took to be the philosophical truth without any concern for its possible social consequences and denied any responsibility for his actions.[20]

This has increasingly become the standpoint of today's scientists in spite of the terrifying nature of the new technologies they have unleashed on the world. Nuclear power is a case in point. When nuclear fission was discovered, in 1938, its military applications were rapidly understood. Some of the atomic scientists—Leó Szilárd for example—wanted to keep the discovery a secret; but others, such as Frédéric Joliot-Curie, refused. For him, scientific progress must never be impeded.[21] Most of our scientists will no doubt agree with him, arguing that they are not responsible for the uses to which their discoveries are put—that science and technology are neutral. Sir Peter Medawar, for instance, insists that 'it is the height of folly to blame the weapon for the crime.'[22] As Dorothy Nelkin notes, 'Many scientists feel that freedom of scientific inquiry is a constitutional "right"—like freedom of speech.'[23]

In 1973 and 1975, John Gofman and Arthur Tamplin resigned their important posts at the Lawrence Livermore Laboratories in Berkeley, California.[24] They had reached the conclusion that there was no peaceful atom, and that the building of nuclear installations to provide electricity was just as much a threat to human survival as the building of nuclear weapons. Very few members of the nuclear establishment have since displayed that degree of responsibility.

Molecular biologist James Shapiro and his colleagues also refused to participate any further in what is perhaps the most threatening of all technological enterprises so far—genetic engineering, the creation of evolutionary new forms of life. Even if this technology were neutral, they argued, the basic control over scientific work in the United States was in the hands of a small minority of corporate executives and bureaucrats who have exploited science for harmful purposes so as to increase their own power. They believed that scientists, and everyone else for that matter, should actively work for radical political changes, and if this means that the progress of science itself may be interrupted, then that is something they would have to accept.[25] Shapiro resigned from his post—but few have followed his lead. So far, all attempts to bring genetic engineering under social control have failed. To quote the Nobel laureate David Baltimore,

> Contemporary research in molecular biology has grown up in an era of almost complete permissiveness. Its practitioners have been allowed to decide their own priorities and have met with virtually no restraints on the types of work they can do.[26]

A few eminent scientists have continued to warn us of the terrible perils of genetic engineering. Erwin Chargaff of Columbia University writes of the

> awesome irreversibility of what is being contemplated. You can stop splitting the atom; you can stop visiting the moon; you can stop using aero-

sols; you may even decide not to kill entire populations by the use of a few bombs; *but you cannot recall a new form of life.* . . . An irreversible attack on the biosphere is something so unheard-of, so unthinkable to previous generations, that I could only wish that mine had not been guilty of it.[27]

Liebe Cavalieri of Cornell University warns that 'a single unrecognised accident could contaminate the entire earth with an ineradicable and dangerous agent that might not reveal its presence until its deadly work was done.'[28] But Chargaff and Cavalieri represent only a small minority of the scientists involved in genetic engineering, which provides the basis of an increasingly big and powerful industry whose irresponsible activities are now totally out of control.

Our inability to control technological intrusions into the workings of the biosphere constitutes an ever growing threat to human survival as the scale of the interventions increases.[29] Already, scientists have exploded a nuclear bomb in the Van Allen belt without bothering to find out its exact function in assuring the habitability of our planet. In the mid-1960s, nearly a hundred million dollars were spent on the Mohole project, which consisted of drilling a hole through the earth's crust[30]—a project that, fortunately, came to naught. At one time, Pentagon officials even talked seriously of using the moon as a missile-testing target.[31]

They were outdone, however, by Alexander Abian, a professor at Iowa State University. The learned professor considers the moon to be responsible for the bad weather on our planet. It apparently exerts a pull on the earth that helps to tilt it on a 23½° axis which alters the angle at which it is hit by the sun's rays. This is seen as causing hot summers in parts of the world and stormy winters elsewhere. If only the moon could be got rid of, the earth would rotate more smoothly and then the sun would warm the planet more evenly, which would enable us to enjoy what the professor refers to as 'eternal spring'. Abian seriously proposes that the moon be blasted with nuclear rockets. If certain romantics really wanted the moon back again, he assures us that this could easily be achieved, as

. . . once human beings learn the secrets to reärranging the universe, scientists will be able to pluck moons from other planets and bring them closer to earth—but not so close that they interfere with the weather.[32]

The professor is shocked that no one has yet sought to do so. 'From the earliest traces of primate fossils, some 70 million years ago,' he writes, 'no one—but no one—has ever raised the finger of defiance at the celestial organisation.' To defy the 'celestial organisation' of the universe is obviously the duty of technological society. God obviously did a bad job —it is clearly incumbent on our scientists to reärrange the universe according to their vastly superior design. What is particularly terrifying is that Abian's suggestion has apparently been taken seriously by various scientific bodies—the Czechoslovak Academy of Sciences, for one (1991).

These and similar tales should make it clear just how urgent it is that science and technology be brought back under social control—embedded once again in social relations. To those who fear that this might compromise our ability to solve our problems, it must be pointed out that technology, though it has many uses, cannot solve the real problems that confront our society today. The root of our crisis is the disruption of *natural systems*, whose proper functioning no technology can restore. There is no technology, for instance, that will recreate a tropical rainforest; none that will bring back into being the countless species that are being made extinct every year, and of which only a fraction have even been catalogued by our scientists. There is no gadgetry that will reconstitute a disintegrated family or community, or restore its degraded cultural pattern. Only nature can do this, and the most our technologists can do is develop, as a matter of urgency, *less disruptive technologies* that exert a much smaller impact on our society and our environment, allowing the return of those conditions in which nature can once more do its work.

IN A TRADITIONAL SOCIETY, SETTLEMENTS ARE IN ACCORD WITH THE NEEDS OF THE BIOSPHERE

A house is a machine for living in.
Le Corbusier

In [vernacular societies], every dwelling is regarded as an image of the cosmos, for the house or the tent 'contains' and 'envelops' man on the model of the great world.
Titus Burckhardt

We need our *marae* [tribal gathering place]
for a host of reasons—
that we may rise tall in oratory,
that we may weep for our dead,
that we may pray to God,
that we may have our feasts,
that we may house our guests,
that we may have our meetings,
that we may have our weddings,
that we may have our reunions,
that we may sing,
that we may dance,
and that we may learn our history
and then know the richness of life
and the proud heritage which is truly ours.
Māori saying

V ERNACULAR SETTLEMENTS through the ages were designed to
satisfy the needs of the whole continuum of life. To begin with, they
were small. Vernacular people usually lived in communities of little more
than a few dozen or a few hundred people. Plato considered that a community should not be composed of more than 5040 citizens—a number
that could comfortably gather in the Athens market-place.[1]

Ecologically, the temporary settlements of nomads are the least disruptive, having, among other things, the smallest impact on the environment. W.E.H. Stanner goes so far as to imply that Australian Aborigines
had less impact on their environment than do many non-human animals.
Unlike beavers, who build dams, and termites, who construct huge nests,
an Aborigine encampment, a year or so after its abandonment, is almost
impossible to identify.[2]

Even among sedentary people, the needs of small settlements for timber and firewood can be met without annihilating local forests, their need
for food does not overtax the soil, and their wastes can be absorbed by the
local ecosystem without degrading it.

This clearly cannot be said of even the cities of antiquity. The decline
and fall of these societies has been attributed to a number of factors,[3] but
among them must surely be reckoned the fatal impact of these massive
conurbations on fragile ecosystems. Thus, around 1500 BCE the great
Indus civilisation drew to an end. Its principal city, Mohenjo Daro, was
built of kiln-baked bricks. Its demise could have been predicted on purely
ecological grounds—among other things, a vast area of forest would have
had to be cleared just to fire the bricks for a city of this size. If this process had continued for centuries, as Sir Mortimer Wheeler notes, it would
have led to such serious soil deterioration that the area would no longer
have been able to support the city.[4] It is not surprising that the sites once
occupied by most of the great cities of antiquity are now deserts. The impact of our modern industrial cities on their environment is, of course,
very much greater and correspondingly more destructive.

From the health point of view, the small settlement is also desirable.
Its inhabitants will be exposed to relatively low levels of pollution, and
it does not provide the niche required to sustain a viable population of
some of the principal pathogens affecting human populations. George
Armelagos and Alan McArdle consider that

> small, isolated populations are incapable of the continuous transmission
> of disease—and outbreaks of endemic infectious disease, where they do

occur, are likely to be periodic or sporadic. This is a consequence of the lack of potential hosts in a small population. If the disease pathogen cannot survive until it comes into contact with a new host, the disease will not be maintained in the population. Many infectious diseases, amongst them measles and influenza, require an interacting population of 500 000 individuals in order to be maintained.[5]

This thesis tends to be confirmed by palæoëcological studies. For instance, R.F. Heizer and L.K. Napton studied fossilised dung of animals from Lovelock Cave in Nevada.[6] They found no eggs or larvæ of parasitic helminths, but because of the extraordinary state of preservation of certain pseudoparasites—mites and nematodes—they were able to conclude, with what they regarded as a fair degree of certainty, that the ancient people represented by these specimens were free of a whole range of intestinal helminths, including flukes, tapeworms, and many nematodes, such as hookworm and Ascaris. This conclusion did not altogether surprise them. They saw it as consistent with our present knowledge of helminthiasis in modern Bushmen and other hunter-gatherers of arid regions.

The American historian William McNeill has shown how infectious diseases, throughout the historical period, have tended to spread in one direction—from the densely populated regions of Eurasia to areas where people still lived in much smaller and more dispersed settlements.[7]

Settlements must also be small so that each person can have contact with nature. Humanity has evolved as part of the world of living things. It is doubtful if we can live in the totally artificial environment that we have created in our cities with biological and psychological impunity. René Dubos went so far as to question whether we can retain our physical and mental health if we lose contact with the natural forces that have shaped our biological and psychological nature.[8] Not surprisingly, urban people often try desperately to create something of nature in the 'concrete jungle' in which they live. Thus, we see balconies in urban apartment blocks shrouded in vegetation sprouting from rows of plastic pots. In the background, we can sometimes even hear recorded versions of the sounds of nature, the wind blowing through the trees, a bubbling brook, or the song of the humpback whale.

Settlements must also be small in order to satisfy social requirements, for the structure of human settlements must reflect that of the societies whose physical infrastructure they provide. The basic social unit is undoubtedly the extended family, and it is this that must first of all be accommodated. But the settlement must also accommodate the lineage group and the community. Each of these social groupings, moreover,

must have an element of privacy. In an Australian aboriginal encampment, for instance, we find that each family has its own space—the area
that the family sweeps several times a day. This place is protected by a
windbreak (*wiltja*), and at the edge of it there is a fire. The family spaces
are grouped around a larger central space. In the darkness of the night,
they cannot see each other and thereby have the privacy they require,
further enhanced by the custom that, once it is dark, people do not leave
their family space for fear of malignant spirits (*mamu*) that lurk around it.[9]

In a traditional Zulu village, according to Eileen Jensen Krige, the huts
are arranged in a circle around the central cattle kraal—the chief's hut is
always situated in the same position, and those of the wives are arranged
in order of seniority. The kinship group (whose blood relationship may
be real or fictitious) that inhabits such a village also enjoys the necessary
privacy, with considerable space left between the grouped huts of each
family.[10]

The Motilone tribe of the Colombian rainforests, according to Robert
Jaulin, live in settlements called *bohio*, which accommodate ten to thirty
families under a single roof. Inside the *bohio* there is semi-darkness. Each
family has a space partitioned off from other families. Each, too, has a
fire in front of its space facing the central circular public space, which
blocks the view from it.[11]

According to Paul Stirling, the traditional Turkish village is made up
of households organised into groups that tend to occupy the same quarters or wards (*mahalle*).[12] The villages of the Ibo of south-eastern Nigeria
and the cities of the Yoruba of western Nigeria are also divided into
areas inhabited by different extended families, which are further organised into neighbourhoods inhabited by closely related families. Those
that inhabit adjoining areas are also related, although less closely.[13] The
traditional city is thus a holarchical or nested system of houses, compounds, neighbourhoods, and clusters of neighbourhoods of related
people—these are closely built, and larger spaces separate less closely
related groups. In this way, *the settlement pattern reflects the social structure
of the society*.

The evidence suggests that it is by following these principles that social problems in modern conurbations are reduced to a minimum (chapter 51). Thus, Valerius Geist points out that successful modern building
designs have been those that

limited people to social groups close in number to those found in primitive societies. We can recognise three limits—one of about 8 persons,
mimicking the size of an extended family; one of about 25, mimicking a

hunting band; one of about 200, which is the limit of people that any one individual can recognise. A successful building, therefore, should have less than 200 inhabitants and should be broken into units housing clusters of about 25 people or 5 families. Had architects designed public housing units keeping these 'magic numbers' in mind, they would have taken one step towards reducing anonymity.[14]

A point further emphasised by the British anthropologist Robin Dunbar. 'The vast majority of people in Tokyo and New York are born, live their lives, and die without ever being aware of each other.' Like Geist, he also notes how tribal societies organise themselves into much smaller social units—the most effective being limited in number to around one hundred and fifty related members. Clans of this size 'appear to be the largest groupings in which everyone knows everyone else, in which they know not simply who is who but also how each one is related to the others.' Dunbar found this same pattern of closely-knit, limited-sized social units appearing again and again throughout the anthropological record, even extending beyond the tribal setting into the realms of church congregations, military units, and businesses, where the limited-sized unit proves to be the most inherently cohesive and stable.[15]

Conversely, a number of anthropological studies have shown how disastrous the disruption of traditional settlements is when they are modernised to satisfy market requirements. Jaulin has shown how such changes led to the disintegration of the society of the Motilone people.[16] The French anthropologist Claude Lévi-Strauss has also described the same process as it affected the Bororo people of Brazil.[17]

A village or small town must also be arranged so as to confer on it a feeling of wholeness and oneness. In the South West of France, the two neighbouring towns of Marmande and Villeneuve-sur-Lot are said to exert very different influences on their inhabitants. The former is stretched out along a main road, the latter, an ancient *bastide*, is built round a central square. Of the two, it is the latter that is known for its spirited community.

Cities, if we are to have them, should also be designed in the same way if they are to satisfy social needs. The central square is a very important feature, offering a place where the citizens can gather to run their affairs. The Greeks could not conceive of a city without its *agora*. Significantly, in the industrial cities of the West, as economic concerns take over from social ones, it is the new shopping precinct with its multistoried car park that is the focal point.

Houses and squares and other parts of the settlement should serve as many purposes as possible so as to maximise social contacts. As Nicholas

Hildyard notes, it is when the whole spectrum of classes, ages, occupations, and activities are concentrated into one localised area

> that the tight mesh of relationships—which form the basis of a community—can develop. Dissect the community and, like a dissected body, it eventually dies. Instead of one community, one gets a series of disjointed, fluid, and highly unstable groupings . . . By fragmenting activities, one quite simply fragments social relations.[18]

That is precisely what we are doing today.

> Work belongs to the industrial estate, play to the playground, leisure to the leisure centre, sleeping and eating to the housing estate, shopping to the shopping centre, growing old to the old people's home, being ill and dying to the hospital, being rich to one area, and being poor to another.

A settlement should also be compact, the houses close together. Instead of expanses of lawn and concrete, resulting in a social 'no man's land', there should be narrow streets, which maximise social contact. As Peter Blake writes,

> What the city needs is not wide open spaces but tightly structured spaces full of shops, restaurants, markets, and all the rest. The one sure way to kill cities is to turn their ground floors into great spacious expanses of nothing.[19]

A society's monuments are also important in that they confer on a settlement its identity, as does its language and customs, which help to differentiate it from its neighbours. More than that, they are associated with its heroes, its founders, its religious leaders, all those who symbolise the city and serve to sanctify it. This contributes to preserving its identity and its continuity and helps to make people proud of it—which they need to be if it is to be a real community.

A settlement must also be æsthetically satisfying, which means providing an interesting and also a diverse environment, which vernacular settlements invariably succeed in doing. Psychologically, this diversity is necessary for maintaining people's morale, while its absence in the faceless conurbations, where increasingly more people are condemned to live, only contributes to their demoralisation. Indeed, as Lewis Mumford writes,

> If man had originally inhabited a world as blankly uniform as a 'highrise' housing development, as featureless as a parking lot, as destitute of life as an automated factory, it is doubtful if he would have had a suffi-

ciently varied sensory experience to retain images, mould language, or acquire ideas.[20]

The depressing effect of living in such conditions was brought home to me during an electoral campaign in Walsall, a suburb of Birmingham, some years ago. My wife Katherine and I, together with a number of our friends, had come from Cornwall to help Jonathan Tyler, then Chairman of the Ecology Party (now the Green Party), to contest that parliamentary seat. In a bar, Katherine met a group of young men with whom she tried to discuss the town in which they lived. They showed little interest in doing so, 'We are ashamed of our town,' they told her.[21]

This could not be in starker contrast with the attitude of young people in Siena towards their beautiful city. Their love for that city is intense, as is their pride in belonging to it. This could not be made more evident than after the *Palio*, when the young people of the winning *contrada* strut triumphantly through the streets all night (and indeed for several days and nights afterwards) singing the traditional *Palio* song,

> In the Piazza del Campo,
> There the verbena grows.
> Long live our Siena!
> The most beautiful of cities.
>
> Long live our square,
> The tower, and the chapel—
> Long live our Siena!
> The most beautiful of cities.

Significantly, Siena is socially an ideal city, one with an extremely low incidence of crime and other social aberrations (chapter 45).

Finally, another essential feature of a settlement must be its sanctity. Vernacular people could not consider living in a house or settlement that had not been sanctified and hence *ritually integrated into the 'cosmic' holarchy*. Thus, before a wild and uninhabited area could be inhabited, sacred rites had to be performed so as to *cosmicise* it. Ananda Coomaraswamy tells us that in the Rigveda, the term *vi mā*, meaning to 'measure out' or to 'lay out', is used to refer to the bringing into being of an inhabitable space or the laying out of 'abodes of cosmic order'.[22]

To build a new village or city meant first building a holy house or temple on the cosmic model. In this way, the settlement that surrounded it was integrated into the cosmic holarchy (chapter 62). The traditional ceremony performed for that purpose was, as Mircea Eliade puts it, a reënactment of the original act of creation (cosmogenesis).[23] Thus, when Romulus founded Rome, he dug a small ditch in the form of a circle. He threw into it some sacred earth that he brought with him from the town where his ancestors were buried, and each of his companions did likewise. In this way, Rome remained *terra patrum*. The ditch was always known as *mundus*, which apparently referred to the place the *manes* or ancestors lived, and which also meant the world or cosmos.[24]

Coomaraswamy notes how 'the erection of a house is . . . an imitation of the creation of the world'—and it is in this connection that the transfixation of the head of the Cosmic Serpent acquires an intelligible meaning, for it is on the head of the Serpent that the world is said to rest. Even today, it appears, 'the mason fashions a little wooden peg from the wood of the khadira tree, and with a coconut drives a peg into the ground at this particular spot in such a way as to peg the head of the Serpent securely down,' otherwise the Serpent might 'shake the world to pieces'. The foundation stone (*pad-ma-śilā*), with an eight-petalled lotus carved on it, is set in mortar above the peg. A Brahman priest assists at all these rites, reciting appropriate incantations or *mantras*.[25]

Significantly, the earth was seen as originally insecure, 'quaking like a lotus leaf', and the gods said, 'Come, let us make steady this support.' This means that the architect who drove down the peg into the head of the Serpent is doing just as was done by the gods in the beginning.[26] The architect is thus reënacting the original act of creation.

Believing that they, their artefacts, their houses, and their settlements were integral parts of the cosmic holarchy, vernacular people saw them all as designed according to the same basic plan. According to Fred Eiseman, in Bali,

> Man is a tiny part of the overall Hindu-Balinese universe, but he contains its structure in microcosm. Man's body has three parts—head, body, and feet—just as the universe (macrocosm) has three parts; the upper world of God and heaven, the middle world of man, and the underworld. Man is a kind of scale model of the universe with exactly the same structure—as is the island of Bali and each village, temple, house compound, building, and occupant on it.[27]

Gerardo Reichel-Dolmatoff shows how true this still is of the temples built by the Kogis of Colombia.

> Kogi temples are meant to be models of man's relationship with the cosmos—models that convey a sense of world order and, simultaneously, are interpreted as the body of the Mother. Each post, beam, or rafter, up to the

smallest detail of roof constructions, thatch, or vines used in tying together the different parts, has its specific symbolic values. A temple construction can be read as an anatomical model, a geographical model, a model of social structure and organisation, or priestly ritual, or of the upper and nether worlds—it also is an instrument for astronomical observation.[28]

This was also true of the ancient Jewish temple. According to the Midrash Tanhuma, it 'corresponds to the whole world and to the creation of man, who is a small world'.[29] In an ancient Jewish legend, Yahveh orders Moses to build him the temple. 'How shall I know how to make it?' Moses asks. Yahveh answers,

> Do not get frightened—just as I created the world and your body, even so will you make the Tabernacle. . . . You find in the Tabernacle that the beams were fixed into the sockets, and in the body, the ribs are fixed into the vertebræ, and so in the world, the mountains are fixed into the fundaments of the Earth. . . . In the Tabernacle, there were bolts in the beams to keep them upright, and in the body, limbs and sinews are drawn to keep man upright, and in the world, trees and grasses are drawn in the Earth. In the Tabernacle, there were hangings to cover its top and both its sides, and in the body, the skin of man covers his limbs and his ribs on both his sides, and in the world, the heavens cover the Earth on both its sides. In the Tabernacle, the veil divided between the Holy Place and the Holy of Holies, and in the body, the diaphragm divides the heart from the stomach, and in the world, it is the firmament which divides between the upper waters and the lower waters.[30]

Titus Burckhardt shows that the early Christian churches were also once designed on the cosmic model. The body of Christ, as Burckhardt puts it, is 'inscribed in the groundplan of the church'. The cross itself was seen as being 'formed by the axes of the heavens'—Christ's head 'lies towards the east, His feet towards the west, His arms and hands extend from north to south'.[31]

Thus, according to the Church Fathers Hieronymus and Basilius, 'the axial cross of the heavens is the preördained prototype of the martyr's wood on which the Saviour was nailed.' Indeed, for the people of antiquity, the cross represented the axes of the heavens and was 'the direct expression of cosmic law'. It was assumed that if a transgressor of this law was executed on a cross, 'this was in order to reëstablish, both symbolically and practically, the disturbed cosmic equilibrium.'[32]

The cosmic symbolism of the early Christian churches could not be clearer than in the case of the Cathedral of Edessa (now called Urfa) in

North West Mesopotamia, which was once one of the greatest centres of Christendom. It was built in the sixth century, like Hagia Sophia in Constantinople (which was dedicated to Holy Wisdom). The description of the cathedral provided by Dionysius the Areopagite could not be more illustrative.

> Wonderful it is that this building, in its smallness, resembles the wide world; not through its size but in its character—water surrounds it, just as the ocean surrounds the world; its roof is wide like heaven, without pillars, vaulted, and everywhere closed and decorated with golden mosaics, as is the firmament with shining stars. Its noble [dome] resembles the Heaven of heavens. . . . Its wide and splendid arches represent the four sides of the world.[33]

By seeing their body, their house, their settlement, and their temples as reflecting the same critical order, which is also that of their society, of the natural world, and of the cosmos itself, it becomes clear to vernacular people that their life is subject to the same single law that governs the cosmic holarchy, and that they are a participant in the great biospheric enterprise, whose goal it is to maintain the critical order of the cosmos.

Needless to say, during the industrial age, those who have planned and built our cities have almost totally ignored such considerations. Since the Second World War, in particular, our settlements have been designed almost exclusively with purely economic and utilitarian ends in view, and the results, as we all know, have been catastrophic.

IN A TRADITIONAL SOCIETY, THE ECONOMY IS IN ACCORD WITH THE NEEDS OF THE BIOSPHERE

'Organise your actions for your own benefit.' God implanted self-interest in the human breast as the motive force of progress. By following self-interest, we follow God's will. Going against self-interest only inhibits God's plan.
Hermann Heinrich Gossen

I owe the public nothing.
J.P. Morgan

The outstanding discovery of recent historical and anthropological research is that man's economy, as a rule, is submerged in his social relationships. He does not act so as to safeguard his individual interest in the possession of material goods—he acts so as to safeguard his social standing, his social claims, his social assets. He values material goods only in so far as they serve this end.
Karl Polanyi

Economics based on *Homo economicus* as self-interested individual commends policies that inevitably disrupt existing social relationships. These social costs can be considered only as externalities and are actually little considered even under that heading. For the most part, they are hardly noticed. We believe these social costs are of enormous importance, that the increase of gross global product at the expense of human well-being should cease. We believe human beings are fundamentally social, and that economics should be re-founded on the recognition of this reality. We call for rethinking economics on the basis of a new concept of *Homo economicus* as person-in-community.
Herman Daly and John Cobb

MODERN ECONOMICS is supposed to determine how scarce resources should be distributed within a society. Its basic assumption, which is never questioned, is that such resources should be distributed so as to maximise wealth. Wealth is measured in terms of per capita Gross National Product (GNP), which is the sum of all economic transactions within a nation state. This means that to maximise wealth, transactions or trade must be maximised.

Neither of these two assumptions can be accepted. If economics concerns itself with the distribution of scarce resources, this is largely because it is only when resources are scarce that they can be sold at a profit, which is when corporations find it worth their while to produce and distribute them. This is so much the case that much of their work involves creating artificial scarcities, firstly by creating a market that did not previously exist for goods that they have developed or plan to develop, and secondly by building into these goods what is generally referred to as 'planned obsolescence'. However, for thousands of years prior to the development of the formal economy, the food and artefacts that were required to satisfy human needs were not necessarily in short supply. Scarcity was not, in fact, a feature of the economy of vernacular people, as Richard Lee and Irven DeVore, Laurens van der Post, and Marshall Sahlins point out over and over again (chapter 39).

For this reason, it would be more appropriate to adopt George Dalton's view of economics as dealing with the provision of material goods to satisfy biological and social needs.[1] This is what Karl Polanyi (brother of Michael) refers to as the 'substantive' use of the term economics as opposed to the 'formal' use. I propose a still more general use of the term economics to refer simply to the study of how resources are distributed within a natural system. In this way, we could expand our study to include the economics of biological organisms, ecosystems, vernacular societies, and the biosphere itself. Clearly, all require resources of various sorts, such as nutrients, to ensure their sustenance and hence to preserve their critical order or stability. In addition, if we accept the thesis of General System Theory (chapter 42), we may also suppose that the same fundamental laws govern the distribution of resources in all natural systems, *regardless of their level of organisation*.

The most fundamental of such laws—and this must be the basic Law of Economics—is that resources are distributed so as to maintain the integrity and stability of the biological, social, and ecological systems within which they are distributed, which also means helping to maintain the integrity and stability of the entire holarchy of the biosphere of which these systems are part.

That resources within a natural system are distributed for the purpose of maintaining its integrity and stability is clear at the level of a biological organism. Thus, oxygen is transported via the red corpuscles to all parts of the body in accordance with its requirements—so are the various nutrients that the body requires. This principle is even clearer when scarcity occurs. In such conditions, a natural system is perfectly capable of setting up its own very effective rationing system, and one that clearly reflects its priorities. Nutrients are provided to the parts in accordance with the importance of their contribution to the preservation, and hence the stability, of the living whole. As Ralph Gerard points out,

> one can get along without a digestive system quite well under starvation conditions, a great wasting of muscles can be tolerated, the reproductive system isn't important, and so on—but if the heart stops pumping or the brain functioning, the whole system is gone.[2]

In the same way, in cold weather, a rationing system becomes operative in preserving the necessary temperature of the critical parts of the body. To begin with, there is a reduction in the blood flow to the surface of the skin, reducing heat radiation and conduction. This may proceed so far that the skin is frozen and dies, the subordinate unit sacrificed 'for the protection of the larger unit'.[3] Such behaviour is an essential part of an organism's homeostatic strategy (chapter 20). The same principle applies within a vernacular society. It is well known that in times of food scarcity hunter-gatherer groups will make food available to the adults who are necessary for assuring the continuity of the society—the old, who are at least partly dispensable, and the very young, who can be replaced, being occasionally sacrificed.

This has many implications. Thus, because our planet's resources are finite (for the biosphere is a closed system from the point of view of materials, though it is an open system from the point of view of energy), materials must be constantly recycled, the waste products of one process serving as the raw materials of other processes. Recycling materials is necessary, too, in order to avoid their accumulation in any part of the system that would give rise to randomness or pollution. Thus, during photosynthesis, carbon is extracted from carbon-dioxide in the atmosphere, and the oxygen is released. Oxygen is a waste product of this particular process, but it is the essential raw material for another process, that of animal respiration. Oxygen is thereby recycled from one living process to another, as are all the chemicals required to sustain the living systems that make up the biosphere and to maintain its critical chemical composition.

Another essential cyclic process is the food chain, which should really be referred to as the 'food cycle'—the primary producers (plants, algæ, and phytoplankton, for example), which alone can harness the energy of the sun, are eaten by herbivores, who in turn are preyed on by carnivores; their dead bodies, together with other dead matter, being eaten by scavengers, and what remains being decomposed by microörganisms into the nutrients required by the primary producers so that the cycle can begin again. All living things cooperate in assuring the success of this cycle, without which life would not be possible.

The need to recycle materials was built into the cultural pattern of traditional societies. It was not seen as a scientific requirement but as a *moral* one—that of reciprocity. Interestingly enough, the principle is formulated in the sole surviving fragment of the writings of Anaximander.

> Things perish into those things out of which they have their birth, according to that which is ordained—for they give reparation to one another and pay the penalty of their injustice according to the disposition of time.[4]

Anaximander intimates here that the development of living things is an injustice—a violation of both fate (Moira) and righteousness (Dike) or morality. Birth was seen as 'a crime', as F.M. Cornford puts it, and growth 'an aggravated robbery'.[5] It must follow that reparations had to be made to the natural world, and the living things that committed the offence must return to the dust from which they came. The same notion is also reflected in the following lines that are recited by the disciples of that remarkable British social philosopher and guru J.G. Bennett before settling down to a meal.

> All life is One
> And everything that lives is Holy.
> Plants, animals, and people,
> All must eat to live and nourish one another.
> We bless the lives that have died to give us food—
> Let us eat consciously,
> Resolving by our Work
> To pay the debt of our existence.[6]

The anthropologist Martín von Hildebrand shows that a very similar notion is built into the cultural pattern of various Amazonian tribes of Colombia.[7]

Modern society violates this fundamental law of natural economics in everything it does and in so doing is spelling out its own doom. Human waste, instead of being carefully returned to the soil—the practice of endless generations of traditional farmers—is simply consigned to the nearest waterway; some two million tons of it every day,[8] depriving the soil of its fertility, poisoning our waterways, and correspondingly reducing their capacity to support fish life. Furthermore, agricultural produce, instead of being consumed locally by those who produce it, is exported as systematically as the timber from our woodlands—a one-way process stripping the land of its essential minerals and organic matter. The American agronomist F.H. King noted in his classic *Farmers of Forty Centuries* (1911) how traditional farmers in Japan, Korea, and China—countries which he visited at that time—meticulously returned all organic matter to the soil, as a result of which its fertility had been maintained for more than 3000 years. In his words, he had travelled 'from practices [in the USA] by which three generations had exhausted strong virgin fields . . . to others still fertile after thirty centuries of cropping.'[9]

The economic activities of modern society are also interfering ever more dramatically with the most fundamental biospheric cycles—such as the water, carbon, sulphur, and phosphorus cycles—thus disrupting the critical order of the biosphere and reducing its capacity to support life. Unfortunately, all this is inevitable if economic development remains modern society's overriding goal. For economic development is a one-way process in which the biosphere is systematically transformed into the technosphere and technospheric waste—a process that cannot continue indefinitely.

If the economic systems of vernacular societies are subject to the same laws that govern the economics of other self-regulating natural systems, then they cannot at the same time be governed by the laws that modern economists have formulated on the basis of their experience of modern market economies, and that they assume to be of universal application. As the economic historian Karl Polanyi showed so convincingly, in the vernacular world, examples of *Homo economicus* are conspicuous by their absence, and economic activities are largely conducted to satisfy *social* rather than commercial goals.[10]

Polanyi also notes that, in behaving in this way, a vernacular society is serving its own immediate interests, for it

> keeps all its members from starving, unless it is itself borne down by catastrophe, in which case interests are again threatened collectively, not individually. The maintenance of social ties, on the other hand, is crucial.

First, because by disregarding the accepted code of honour, or generosity, the individual cuts himself off from the community and becomes an outcast; second, because in the long run all social obligations are reciprocal, and their fulfilment serves also the individual's give-and-take interests best.[11]

The embeddedness of the vernacular economy in social relationships becomes clear if we consider that its units of economic activity are not corporations but *families* and *communities*.

The family is a social, religious, ceremonial, but also an economic unit of behaviour. That is why, once institutions and corporations (*gesellschaft*—see chapter 60) begin to usurp its economic functions, it tends to disintegrate. Economic functions fulfilled at the level of the family, the lineage group, and the community (*gemeinschaft*) occur without any external inducement—a mother looks after her children; a father provides for his wife and also helps to raise the children. Both look after their aged parents and other relatives, as they must do if they are to assure the stability of the family and of the community that, because it is but an association of families, cannot otherwise exist.

In such a society, a man does not act as a purely economic animal. As Sahlins writes, 'A man works . . . in his capacity as a social person, as a husband and father, brother and lineage mate, member of a clan [and] village.' He works as an integral member of these social groups, as a *whole man*.[12]

So alien is the modern concept of 'work' to those living within stable societies, that there is no word for it in their vocabularies. Jean Liedloff tells us that the native Yequana of Venezuela, with whom she lived for two and a half years, did have a word for work—*tarabajo*—which obviously came from the Spanish word *trabajo*, pointing to its relatively recent origin.[13] Mungo Park noted towards the end of the eighteenth century that 'paid service is unknown to the negro. Indeed, African languages ignore the word.'[14]

The economic behaviour of primal peoples is, to quote Sahlins, 'largely an aspect of kinship behaviour and is therefore organised by means completely different from capitalist production and market transactions',[15] and also, we might add, from socialist production and distribution via a state bureaucracy. That in a vernacular society there is sufficient motivation to perform 'work' with enthusiasm and skill is attested by many anthropologists. Richard Thurnwald notes, for instance, that among tribes, 'labour always tends beyond that which is strictly necessary,' and that 'work is never limited to the unavoidable minimum but exceeds the absolutely necessary amount, owing to a natural or acquired functional urge to activity.'[16] Neither are vernacular people alienated from the products of their work, as Karl Marx saw the worker to be in a capitalist economy. As Sahlins tells us,

> the tribesman's relation to productive means and finished products often exceeds ownership as we understand it, moving beyond mundane possession to a mystic attachment. The land is a spiritual value, a beneficent Source—the home of the ancestors; 'the plain of one's bones', Hawaiians say. And the things a man makes and habitually uses are expressions of himself, perhaps so imbued with his genius that their ultimate disposition can be only his own grave.[17]

It is hardly surprising that members of vernacular societies strongly resisted being transformed into mere units of wage-labour. Thus, Agwu Akpala describes the difficulties encountered by the Enugu coal-mining industry in Nigeria in obtaining labour for its mines. Labourers, it appears, could only be obtained by press-gangs. Every day 700 of them disappeared never to be seen again, unless they had the misfortune to be 'grabbed' a second time. Eventually, the chiefs were employed to force their subjects into working for the mining company and paid for each wage-labourer they provided. At first, those who refused to obey their chiefs were fined—eventually it became necessary to sentence them to varying periods of hard labour.[18] This gives some idea of how difficult it is to persuade people leading a fulfilling vernacular life to leave their families and communities for monotonous, soul-destroying work in some large enterprise. Ironically, such enterprises have often been justified on the grounds of relieving 'unemployment' in tribal areas.

Homeotelic or whole-maintaining economic behaviour is well demonstrated by vernacular horticulture and agriculture (family and community activities to which people contribute largely in accordance with their status within the society), the produce being distributed by individual farmers and gardeners according to their obligations to different members of the family and community. The anthropologist Peter Huber, who has studied the agriculture of the Anggor people of New Guinea, goes so far as to argue that they do not just organise themselves in order to produce food—on the contrary, they 'produce food *in order to organise* [*themselves*]'. He sees 'the problem of creating and maintaining sociality' as being 'the central element' in their agricultural system.[19] Social organisation is mainly produced among the Anggor by the hunting and communal distribution of feral pigs. 'These pigs are not valued simply as meat,' he writes, or even simply as pigs, but rather in terms of a complex system of associations which link religion, land tenure, daily life, and social classification. It is because of these associations that the Anggor can produce organisation by killing and distributing feral pigs.[20]

This is not an isolated example. On the contrary, Huber tells us that the ethnographic record 'is replete with instances in which agricultural production is quite explicitly linked—directly and-or indirectly—with ritual events which organise communities on various levels.'

Polanyi sees the distribution of food and other products in a vernacular society as governed by two basic principles—*reciprocity* and *redistribution*. When hunters kill a game animal, they will not sell it or even store it for a rainy day—instead, they will give a feast. In a sense, this will provide them with all the advantages they could have derived from selling or storing it, because they know that their hospitality will one day be reciprocated. Giving a feast is like putting money in the bank or using our friends as a deep freeze, but it enables us to get fresh food instead of frozen food in exchange, and a party to boot. At the same time, the system creates a veritable network of mutual obligations that help knit together the members of their society *and thereby increase its cohesion and viability*.

Once people are provided with the equipment for storing perishable food, much of the apparent need for holding feasts is removed. In some Pacific islands, after deep freezes had been installed at the main population centres, reciprocity ceased to be the favoured means of storing surplus food—there were far fewer feasts and so, of course, social cohesion suffered as a result.

Phyllis Kaberry describes what reciprocity involves among the Lunga of Australia,

> The husband must, from time to time, give kangaroo to his wife's parents and brothers—besides this, he always distributes a little among his blood relatives. Most of what the woman has obtained is consumed by herself, husband, and children—if she has a little extra, she takes some to her mother, sister, mother's mother, father, in fact to any close relative. She, on another occasion, receives similar offerings from them and also meat from her male relatives, which she shares with her husband and children. These gifts are not compulsory as are her husband's to her people. They are dictated by tribal sentiment and her own affection for these individuals—by a kinship system which finds concrete expression not only in attitudes and linguistic usage but also in the exchange of the limited

food resources and the material and ritual objects which are found in the community.[21]

Kaberry regards such behaviour as motivated by 'enlightened self-interest'. The donor may not get anything material in exchange, as elderly relatives do not go hunting and may not have enough strength to do much gathering. But they do benefit from their elders' esteem and also from that of the community at large. They are building up *social wealth*, for which, in many cases, money in the bank may be but a poor substitute.

There is also a redistributive element in many apparently reciprocal transactions. In the Comoros, for instance, gifts of oxen and foodstuffs (*djéléo*) are made to a young man by members of his age-grade on the occasion of his 'grand marriage'—the most important ceremony of his life—and on the lavishness of which his subsequent status within the community will, in great measure, depend. When a lender subsequently prepares his 'grand marriage', he will expect repayment of any loans he previously made. He will not, however, get goods of exactly the same value. Some previous borrowers may return less than they borrowed—most, however, will try desperately to return goods whose value will be, as much as possible, in excess of that of the goods that they themselves once borrowed. The reason is obvious—their status will depend on their generosity. The more the value of the goods they return exceeds that of the goods they borrowed, the greater the prestige they thereby acquire and the more *social* wealth they build up.[22]

This brings us to redistribution proper, as the term is normally used. In some societies, important men (big men, as they are referred to in Melanesia) give large feasts that other members of the society may never be in a position to reciprocate. It is *social prestige* that they obtain in exchange. The best known example of this sort of redistribution is the legendary 'potlatch' (*patlač*) of the tribes of the north-west coast of North America, a practice that satisfies many social requirements. As Bronislaw Malinowski writes, 'The chief, everywhere, acts as a tribal banker—collecting food, storing it, and protecting it, and then using it for the benefit of the whole community.'[23] At the same time, it contributes—as does reciprocity—to the building-up of social bonds.

An economic system based on reciprocity and redistribution also prevents the accumulation of goods that might otherwise be translated into capital, leading to the development of large-scale economic enterprises *that are no longer subject to effective social control* and also to the development of the market system with the corresponding reorganisation of the biosphere to satisfy market requirements.

Economic behaviour in a stable society does not interfere with social and ecological priorities, as it does in our modern industrial society
—instead, it serves to fulfil essential social and ecological functions.
Malinowski came to this conclusion after his exhaustive study of the
life of the Trobriand Islanders. He regarded their elaborate system of
reciprocity and redistribution as 'one of the main instruments of social
organisation, of the power of the chief, of the bonds of kinship, and of
relationships in law'.[24]

That the vernacular economy was 'embedded'—to use Polanyi's expression—in 'social relationships' is critical.[25] What this means is that
such an economy is under *social control*—hence, designed to satisfy the
society's basic requirements and, in particular, the maintenance of its
integrity and stability. Once economic life ceases to be embedded in social
relationships and, worse still, once social relationships actually become
'embedded in the economic system', then the economy ceases to be
under control, becoming random or heterotelic to society and the biosphere, and disrupting their critical order.

IN A TRADITIONAL SOCIETY, MONEY IS IN ACCORD WITH THE NEEDS OF THE BIOSPHERE

[General purpose] money is one of the shatteringly simplifying ideas of all time, and like any other new and compelling idea, it creates its own revolution.

Paul Bohannan

Our money is impersonal and commercial, while primitive money frequently has pedigree and personality, sacred uses, or moral and emotional connotations.

George Dalton

After the last tree has been cut down,
After the last river has been poisoned,
After the last fish has been caught,
Only then will you find that money cannot be eaten.

Cree saying

IN OUR WORLD, money is a medium of exchange in terms of which the value of all commodities designed for exchange on the market can be expressed. It is thus *general purpose* money. It clearly serves to facilitate trade in goods and services, but it does so regardless of whether such trade is desirable on social, ecological, spiritual, or moral grounds. Money, in this sense of the term, does not exist in a vernacular society. In the first place, goods are not produced for exchange (except in special circumstances) but for use; secondly, the system of valuation is different—things are not valued in accordance with what they can be exchanged for but for their importance in maintaining the stability of the social system, the biosphere, and the cosmos itself.

The forms of money developed by vernacular societies, rather than being designed (as is our money) to facilitate economic exchange, are designed instead to serve a *social purpose*—to maintain social structures, strengthen social bonds, and hence build up *social wealth*. Not surprisingly, modern economists criticise what they regard as the irrational nature of primitive money. They find it too bulky and difficult to carry about—worse still, it is not divisible in the way pounds can be divided into pence. Thus, the Rossel Islanders use two different types of shells, *Ndap* and *Nkö*. There are actually twenty-two different classes of the *Ndap* and only a limited number of actual shells in each class—probably no more than a thousand in each of the first thirteen classes. Each shell is known and has a veritable identity of its own and a different value. There is no means of changing a shell of one class into one of another. This means that something that is priced in terms of shells of class twenty, for instance, must be paid for in shells of that class. Thus, under the existing arrangements, if someone wants to buy an object priced in terms of class number twenty *Ndap* shells, they have to borrow an object also priced in terms of this currency.

W.E. Armstrong, an economist who studied Rossel Island money, was keen to show the islanders how their currency could be 'rationalised' so as to greatly facilitate the conduct of their commercial transactions. He pointed out that this elaborate borrowing could be avoided, or much reduced, if the value of the different shells could be related to each other as dollars are to cents. What he completely failed to grasp was that their unsuitability for use in a modern market economy was irrelevant, *for they were designed to fulfil a very different purpose.*[1]

The Kula necklaces and armbands (or 'arm-shells') used in the famous Kula trade described by Marcel Mauss[2] and Bronislaw Malinowski (chapter 58),[3] the coppers (great ceremonial copper discs) used by north-west coast Native American chiefs at a potlatch, Rossel Island shells, and all the other currencies in use in tribal societies may not be convenient, portable, or divisible, but neither, as George Dalton points out, are they the media of *commercial* exchange. Instead, as Malinowski suggests, they should be regarded as treasure items or prized heirlooms, crown jewels or sport trophies. According to Dalton,

> such treasures can take on special roles as non-commercial money; their acquisition and disposition are carefully structured and regarded as extremely important events; they change hands in specified ways, in transactions which have strong moral implications. Often they are used to create social relationships (marriage, entrance into secret societies), prevent a break in social relationships (bloodwealth, mortuary payments), or to keep or elevate one's social position (potlatch). Their 'money-ness' consists in their being required means of (reciprocal or redistributive) payment.[4]

Mary Douglas regards primitive money as more closely resembling coupons than modern commercial money. Their role is not to 'expedite the transfer of goods and services', as our money does, but instead to *restrain* the drive to satisfy individual wants.

> The essence of money is to be transferable. It circulates. But coupons [like primitive money], when spent, return to an issuing point and their acquisition is continually under survey and control. Admittedly, there is a big difference between modern and primitive coupons. In a modern economy, paper coupons, once spent, are returned to the office of issue, counted, and destroyed. But primitive commodity coupons simply return at each transfer into the hands of the senior members of the community, who become by this fact, to all intents and purposes, the issuing authority. This makes it almost impossible to acquire coupons without being acceptable to the senior old men who hold them. Coupons do not circulate—they are continually issued and returned and reissued.[5]

Going further, she suggests that they provide a means of licensing rather than rationing. The object of rationing is to assure equal distribution of scarce resources. The object of licensing, on the contrary, is *protective*. One of its uses is

> to ensure responsible use of possibly dangerous powers, so we have licensing of guns and liquor sales. Licensing pins responsibility, so we have marriage licenses and pet licenses. Licensing protects vulnerable areas of the economy, so we have import licensing, and so on.

But licensing, of course, creates monopoly advantages, both for those who issue them and those to whom they are issued—both parties becoming 'bound in a patron–client relation sustained by the strong interests of each in the continuance of the system'.

Douglas shows that this is precisely what occurs among the Lele of Zaire (now DR Congo). The old men of the tribe, by the workings of the system, obtain a monopoly of the issue of raffia cloth, which is the currency used for paying bridewealth. Because of their monopoly, the older men establish a patron–client relationship with the younger men who acquire the raffia from them if they wish to get married. This serves at once as a means of licensing marriage and hence managing population size (the excessive increase of which can lead to the degradation of the biotic environment); as a means, too, of maintaining the society's basic structure and hence its stability or continuity that, among other things, depends on maintaining the power and prestige of the elders—the custodians of the traditional wisdom—thereby permitting its transmission to succeeding generations (chapter 54).

58

IN A TRADITIONAL SOCIETY, THE ECONOMY IS LOCALISED AND HENCE SELF-SUPPORTING

Whenever the timber trade is good, permanent famine reigns
in the Ogowe region.
Albert Schweitzer

Free trade for a country which has become industrial, whose population
can and does live in cities, whose people do not mind preying upon other
nations and therefore sustain the biggest navy to protect their unnatural
commerce, may be economically sound (though, as the reader perceives, I
question its morality). Free trade for India has proved her curse and held
her in bondage.
M.K. Gandhi

[The *charkha* or spinning wheel] is the symbol of the nation's prosperity
and, therefore, freedom. It is a symbol not of commercial war but of commercial peace. It bears not a message of ill-will towards the nations of the
earth but of goodwill and self-help. It will not need the protection of [a]
navy threatening a world's peace and exploiting its resources, but it needs
the religious determination of millions to spin their yarn in their own
homes as today they cook their food in their own homes.
M.K. Gandhi

. . . let goods be homespun whenever it is reasonably and conveniently
possible—and, above all, let finance be primarily national.
John Maynard Keynes

Free traders, having freed themselves from the restraints of community at
the national level and having moved into the cosmopolitan world, *which
is not a community*, have effectively freed themselves of all community
obligations.
Herman Daly and *John Cobb*

A S EVOLUTION PROCEEDS, so do natural systems become increasingly self-sufficient, reducing their dependence on forces outside their control. This is an essential strategy for increasing their capacity for homeostasis or stability (chapter 20). Thus, Eugene Odum notes how, in the case of ecological succession, ecosystems become increasingly self-sufficient as they develop, and less dependent for their maintenance on resources derived from the outside. Food chains become more complex, with detritus providing an increasingly important source of nutrients.

> In a mature forest, for example, less than ten per cent of annual net production is consumed (that is, grazed) in the living state—most is utilised as dead matter (detritus) through delayed and complex pathways involving as yet little understood animal–microörganism interactions.

Similarly, inorganic nutrients that were originally derived from outside the ecosystem slowly become internalised or *intra*biotic, being constantly recycled within it.[1]

This is an essential homeostatic strategy for increasing an ecosystem's ability to maintain its stability. Similarly, with the development of a vernacular community, self-sufficiency increases as dependency on outside sources decreases. Food and artefacts become largely distributed via procedures that observe the rules of reciprocity and redistribution and that are entirely under social, and hence internalised, control (chapter 56). In many vernacular societies, what appear to be commercial transactions are in reality highly ritualised exchanges embedded in social relations. Thus, certain goods are often traded with goods of another sort and even with socially valuable objects that closely resemble what we would regard as money (chapter 57). But even such trade is not conducted for 'economic' motives, as Bronislaw Malinowski maintains with reference to the Trobriand Islands, for

> there is not even a trace of gain, nor is there any reason for looking at it from the purely utilitarian and economic standpoint, since there is no enhancement of mutual utility through the exchange. Thus, it is quite a usual thing in the Trobriands for a type of transaction to take place in which 'A' gives twenty baskets of yams to 'B', receiving for it a small polished blade, only to have the whole transaction reversed in a few weeks' time.[2]

The same applies to trade with other related social groups. Thus, both Malinowski and Marcel Mauss have described the large trading expeditions of the Kula ring periodically undertaken by the same people (chapter 57). They transported certain types of valuable items (necklaces) to people living in distant islands visited in a clockwise sequence, while other expeditions carried other kinds of valuable items (arm-shells) to islands lying counter-clockwise. The object of these expeditions was not an economic one. 'We describe it as trade,' Karl Polanyi writes, 'though no profit is involved, either in money or in kind.'[3]

Even in the vernacular Indian village, where social structure has diverted somewhat from the tribal norm, what we might regard as commercial transactions were, until recently, under social control. Farmers obtained their pots from the village potter and their tools from the village blacksmith, giving them an amount of food in exchange at a rate established by tradition rather than by blind market forces. What is more, if the local potter were an indifferent craftworker and better pots could be bought elsewhere, this was not regarded as a sufficient reason for abandoning them.

Judged by the values of modern economics, such a system provides no inducement to potters to increase production or, indeed, to improve the quality of their produce—but this objection misses the point. The trading relations between the different members of a traditional Indian village are primarily designed to satisfy *social* rather than economic goals. After all, the quality of the available pots is not the primary consideration. *The maintenance of social cohesion and stability is much more important.*

Walter Rose describes a similar time-honoured tradition involving the keeping of 'contra accounts' between local tradesmen in the English village of his youth. Long-standing debts might be maintained for years and raised as bargaining counters for reciprocal exchange. A form of barter known as 'chop' was also commonly accepted as part-payment on goods. In this way, skills could be employed and goods exchanged locally without money having to change hands—an arrangement that depended, above all, on the strong social ties of the close-knit communities still to be found in England at that time. As a result, 'so little trade went on with neighbouring towns', he recalls, 'that one carrier with a donkey-cart was able to do it all.'[4]

Mahatma Gandhi understood this well. One of the basic concepts of his philosophy was that of *swadeshi*, which he describes as that 'spirit in us which restricts us to the use and service of our immediate surroundings to the exclusion of the more remote'.[5] Sunderlal Bahuguna, the leader of the Chipko environmental movement in the Himalayas, regards *swadeshi* as the most fundamental of Gandhi's teachings.[6]

Economic development, of course, totally undermines the practice of *swadeshi*, since it is based on the very principle that all concerns, whether moral, social, or ecological, must be ruthlessly subordinated to short-term economics. The village community is thereby sacrificed to the overriding ideal of churning out ever greater quantities of bigger and better goods and of influencing villagers, by every possible means, to increase their consumption of them way beyond what they need—equally, there is no concern for whether there are enough resources for producing the goods, or the effect on the environment of extracting the necessary materials, or whether the villagers can afford to buy the resulting products. Production and consumption in such circumstances are no longer subject to any controls, social or ecological. Goods simply proliferate like cancer cells.

In tribal societies, it is only when dealing with complete strangers that the laws of the market are allowed to operate exclusively, free of social constraints. For Paul Bohannan,

> A 'market' is a transaction which in itself calls up no long-term personal relationship, and which is therefore to be exploited to as great a degree as possible. In fact, the presence of a previous relationship makes a 'good market' impossible—people do not like to sell to kinsmen, since it is bad form to demand as high a price from a kinsman as one might from a stranger. *Market behaviour and kinship behaviour are incompatible in a single relationship*, and the individual must give way to one or the other.[7]

This is very much in keeping with the Old Testament precept that 'unto a stranger thou mayest lend upon usury—but unto thy brother, thou shalt not lend upon usury.'[8]

Marshall Sahlins shows that it is possible to distinguish between the economic relations within different sectors, such as the house, the lineage, the village, the tribe, and those outside the tribe. As we proceed from the former to the latter, so reciprocity and solidarity are slowly replaced by haggling and profit-making, and so do economic relations become increasingly commercial.[9] That is why the development of the market system within a society could only occur once solidarity and reciprocity within the inner social groupings had waned and the essential difference between social relations within and without these groupings had become sufficiently blurred—in other words, before economic wealth could become someone's principal preoccupation, *they had first to be deprived of their social wealth*.

David Korten refers to this largely non-monetised economy of the household and the community as the 'social economy'. For him,

> Social economies are by nature local, non-waged, non-monetised, and non-market. Therefore, they are not counted in national income statis-

tics, do not contribute to measured economic growth, and are undervalued by policy-makers, who count only activities in the market economy as productive contributions to national output.

But their function is more important than this. As Korten says,

the very conduct of these activities served to maintain the social bonds of trust and obligation, the 'social capital' of the community.

Korten also notes that

A considerable portion of the economic growth of recent decades is simply a result of shifting functions from the social economy, where they are not counted in GNP, to the market economy, where they are.[10]

He might have added that this is what economic growth or 'development' is all about. Thus, as it proceeds, instead of being provided freely by the family and community, food and clothes now have to be bought in the market, the young brought up in crèches, schools, and universities, and the old and sick looked after in special homes and hospitals. In this way, all these and other critical functions are disembedded from their natural social context, commoditised, and hence ever less available to those who are most in need of them.

Though all societies have possessed an economy of some sort, no economy previous to our time, as Polanyi notes, 'has ever existed that, even in principle, was controlled by markets'.[11] This is not surprising, since only by resisting the power of market forces could the integrity of our social and ecological systems be maintained for so long. Once markets became more than incidental to economic life, the societies in which they operated, together with the ecosystems in which the society existed, were condemned to rapid disintegration.

During the Middle Ages in Europe, only resources of secondary importance—spices, candle-wax, oriental silks, and luxury articles primarily of interest to the Church and aristocracy—were traded via the market at annual fairs held at a few major European cities. In the twelfth and thirteenth centuries, however, an economic revolution occurred—the market expanded rapidly until it came to dominate the economic life of many European societies. Essential to this revolution was the transformation of the key resources—labour and land—into commodities. This was of key significance, for as Polanyi points out,

Labour is only another name for a human activity which goes with life itself, which in its turn is not produced for sale but for entirely different reasons, nor can that activity be detached from the rest of life, be stored, or mobilised—land is only another name for nature.[12]

In mediæval Europe, neither labour nor land had previously been exchanged via the market. Mediæval serfs were bound to their land, but their relationship to their lord was one of mutual obligations rather than of sheer economic expediency, and in exchange they normally had security of tenure. The occupation of land was thus determined by 'status' rather than 'contract'. However, once human life came to be treated as a mere commodity, work ceased to be embedded in social relations, and the integrated or 'whole man' (chapter 56) was replaced by the worker— a new human category. Whereas the members of a vernacular society (the 'whole men') are integral parts of families and communities and have access to ancestral land on which to grow their food, workers live in largely atomised societies, have been deprived of their ancestral land, and can be mobilised to fulfil any function—however socially and ecologically disruptive or morally repugnant—so long as it provides the wage on which they have now become dependent for the satisfaction of their most basic biological and social needs.

The transformation of land into a commodity also had enormous social and economic implications. *Contract*, established via the market system—rather than *custom* and *status*, established by tradition and reflecting the society's social structure—now determined where individual families lived and worked the land (chapter 60). The resulting pattern of land-ownership may well have satisfied the requirements of the new economic system, but it set in train the disintegration of society into a haphazard mass of strangers. The disintegrated community, what is more, was often deprived of its livelihood, since food was sold via the market and bought by whoever paid the most for it, regardless of the community or society to which they belonged.

Indeed, Polanyi attributes the severe famines that occurred in India under the British Raj to the operation of the newly established market system that destroyed the Indian village community.

> While under the regime of feudalism and of the village community, *noblesse oblige*, clan solidarity, and regulation of the corn market checked famines—under the rule of the market, the people could not be prevented from starving according to the rules of the game.[13]

It is the very basis of the market system, once freed of social constraints, that goods should be bought as cheaply as possible and sold at the highest price. This means that there must be one-way traffic of the essentials of life *to* the rich *from* the poor, who are thereby condemned to malnutrition and famine. Thus, Redcliffe Salaman notes how in Ireland, during the great famine, corn continued to be exported to England, even though millions of people were dying of hunger. If it was not available to the local people, it was partly because it was being shipped to England at the rate of 16 000 quarters a week and also because, even if it were not, the Irish could not have afforded it.[14]

Today, this traffic is one of the major causes of malnutrition and famine in the Third World, where a high proportion of the arable land—up to seventy per cent in certain cases[15]—is used for export crops, marginalising the staple food crops on which the local population depends for its sustenance. What is more, according to the rules established by the General Agreement on Tariffs and Trade (GATT—later, the World Trade Organisation), the crops that a country produces must be exported so long as a market demand exists. Only when malnutrition and hunger prevail can an exception be made and export restrictions apply—thus, at the Uruguay Round of the GATT, US delegates insisted that even in such dire circumstances food must continue to be exported.[16] If this advice were to be taken seriously, it would be 'GATT-illegal' for a country to feed its starving people rather than export its goods to the already overfed. For as cynical as this may seem, it is by doing so that it can maximise its expenditure on the manufactured goods of the industrial countries that control GATT, no human considerations of any kind being allowed to compromise the achievement of this sordid goal. This clearly illustrates the principle that production governed by 'market forces' *is not designed to satisfy biological, social, or ecological needs.*

Kenneth Lux points out that economists must deny the very existence of such needs if modern economic theory is to make any sense at all.[17] The market is seen as catering only for our 'wants', which are reflected in 'effective demand', and a country is seen as becoming 'self-sufficient' once this 'effective demand' is satisfied. Thus, the modernisation of agriculture through the adoption of the 'Green Revolution' is said to have enabled India to achieve food 'self-sufficiency'. This sounds very impressive, because it suggests that all the citizens of that country are now properly fed—but nothing could be further from the truth. In 2000, a report by the International Institute for Population Sciences (IIPS) revealed that about forty-six per cent of India's children under three years of age were affected by chronic malnutrition to the extent of being physically and mentally stunted.[18] To state that India is self-sufficient in food merely means that to put more food in the shops would not lead to further sales—for those who are malnourished do not have the money to buy it; their biological needs not being reflected in the pathetic 'effective demand' that they can exert.

Once the market rules our economic life, the natural world is seen to be no more than a source of resources to be commoditised and transformed into cash on the global market. The process is a fundamentally malignant one. By means of it, forests, wetlands, coral reefs, rivers, estuaries, and seas everywhere, together with all the living things that inhabit them, are systematically cashed-in. What happens when all these are gone and the countries are transformed into virtual deserts does not seem to concern either our politicians, industrialists, or economists.

To preserve any resource at all that is capable of being commoditised and cashed-in is only possible by keeping it outside the orbit of the global market. In New Zealand, it is illegal to sell trout in shops. They are reserved for anglers, and it is for this reason that there are still trout to be caught in the country's lakes and rivers. Only by setting up national parks, *in which living things are kept out of the orbit of the market*, can many species be preserved—though we can unfortunately predict that if economic development proceeds for very much longer, the pressures on even these last remaining 'refugia' will become irresistible. Significantly, in certain parts of Tanzania where the economy had largely collapsed and there was not enough money to repair the roads, people were once again beginning to eat properly, for, no longer able to export their food on the global market, they were free once again to eat it themselves.[19]

The export process, what is more, is often as destructive to the importer as it is for the exporter—it is, in E.F. Schumacher's phrase, 'a process of mutual poisoning'.[20] For, the import of cheap food from areas where it can be grown particularly cheaply (or is heavily subsidised by the state) to areas where, for various reasons, it is more expensive to produce, has ruined farmers throughout the Third World. The adoption of modern agricultural methods—imposed by international agencies, such as the I M F, on its debtor countries—increases the dependence of farmers on imported farm machinery, hybrid seeds, fertilisers, and pesticides, which they can ill afford, especially as the prices of these off-farm inputs continue to increase and farmland becomes increasingly degraded from their use. Such farmers are condemned to becoming ever more impoverished, until eventually they must leave their land and seek refuge in the slums that surround the nearest conurbation, a fate that, on current trends, awaits the bulk of the Third World's rural population.

The lot of the traditional craftworker or artisan is very similar. It was a constant theme of Mahatma Gandhi's writings that Lancashire's mass-produced textiles had destroyed India's artisanal, village-based textile industry, causing the degradation of rural life. Carders, dyers, spinners, and weavers—droves of them, who kept the village economy going—were ruined, and the Indian village was deprived of both its economic and social life.[21]

It is for the same reasons that the small farmer and the artisan have been virtually eliminated in Britain and North America and are rapidly disappearing in the rest of Europe. Even the medium-sized farmer and the medium-sized company are everywhere under stress. During the recession of 1991, the European agricultural industry was in a state of near bankruptcy, and only the biggest farms appeared to have any prospect of survival. In the USA, agriculture was in similar straits. The plight of small to medium businesses was scarcely better, with more than nine hundred becoming insolvent every week in the UK during that time.[22]

That the future (temporarily at least) lies with the large corporations —in particular the transnational corporations—no one familiar with recent trends can doubt. As the market expands to encompass the entire world and becomes progressively 'freer', the greater must be the niche it provides them.

Free trade sounds highly desirable—its proponents make it appear that it frees the oppressed individual from yet another set of shackles previously imposed on them and on their ancestors by tyrannical social customs and governments. But it is the transnational corporation that is the 'individual' that benefits from free trade—and the freedom it provides is the freedom to cut down virgin forests in order to produce plywood, lavatory paper, and the Sunday edition of the *New York Times*. It is the freedom to erode, salinise, waterlog, compact, and desertify agricultural land so as to produce the cheap raw materials for the food-processing industry. It is the freedom to pillage the oceans with vast trawlers that literally annihilate fish populations with 'wall of death' drift-nets that are often tens of kilometres long. It is the freedom to grub-up the world's remaining coral reefs, which protect vulnerable islands from the waves and are among the most productive of all ecosystems, in order to provide specimens for souvenir shops. It is the freedom to drain the pathetic remnants of the world's once extensive wetlands in order to provide more pastureland for the world's over-inflated livestock population, or to make available ever more building-land for the developers. It is the freedom to churn out ever greater amounts of ever more toxic chemicals to spread on our fields, release into our rivers and ground waters, dump into holes in the ground, or inject under pressure into deep boreholes—from where they find their way into our food and drinking water. It is the freedom to destroy the ozone layer, which protects us from lethal ultraviolet radiation, in the interests of using patented C F C s and other similar chemicals in cosmetic sprays, refrigerators, and air conditioners, rather than non-patentable substitutes that would reduce the profits of its manufacturers. It is the freedom to increase poverty and misery, malnutrition and disease, to extinguish tens of thousands of species of living things every year, all in order to satisfy the short-term financial interests of these transnational corporations and the industrialists, bureaucrats, and politicians who live off them. This is the freedom that 'free trade' provides, and those are the interests that the G A T T proposals have been designed to serve, and that will deliver the world to its pillagers on a plate to do with it as they please.

What is required is just the opposite—a transition to a world of largely self-supporting communities carrying out their economic activities at the level of the family, the small artisanal enterprise, and the community it-self; primarily to satisfy local needs via local markets. Only in this way can economic activity be subordinated to biological, social, ecological, and moral imperatives, as indeed it must be if we are to survive for long on this beleaguered planet.

IN A TRADITIONAL SOCIETY, EDUCATION IS
IN ACCORD WITH THE NEEDS OF
THE BIOSPHERE

Education *is* the cultural process—the way in which each newborn human infant . . . is transformed into a full member of a specific human society, sharing with the other members a specific human culture.
Margaret Mead

By definition, children are pupils . . . [and] learning is the human activity which least needs manipulation by others. Most learning is not the result of instruction. It is, rather, the result of unhampered participation in a meaningful setting.
Ivan Illich

E DUCATION IN A VERNACULAR SOCIETY is but another word
for socialisation, a process whereby a child born with a potential for
becoming a member of almost any family, community, or society learns
to become a member of a specific family, community, society, and ecosystem. In other words, from the point of view of the society itself, it is
the means of renewing and maintaining itself—progressively integrating successive generations into the critical order of its social continuum
(chapter 37).

A functionally similar process occurs at all levels of organisation. Thus,
a cell, immediately after division, is endowed with the potential for becoming a member of a large number of possible tissues or organs (pluri-
potency), and slowly learns to fulfil its specialised functions within that
tissue or organ in which it is situated (chapters 43 and 49). The process of
cell development or differentiation is also the means whereby the organ or
tissue, and indeed the organism itself, can reconcile the necessarily short
life-span of its constituent cells with its longer-term goal of maintaining its
overall stability and that of the wider biosphere of which it is part.

Not surprisingly, the educational process is governed by precisely the
same general laws that govern the differentiation of a cell, the development of an embryo, and indeed all other developmental life processes at
different levels of organisation (chapter 21).

One such law is that behaviour proceeds from the general to the particular (chapter 37). It is during the earlier phases that the generalities of
a child's behaviour pattern will be determined. It is these earlier stages
that are the most important, and hence why the mother is the most important educator—and the quality of the family environment the most
significant factor—in determining a child's character and capabilities.

Another complementary law is that behavioural processes are sequential (chapter 22), their various stages occurring in a specific order. If one
is left out, the subsequent stages will be prevented from occurring or
will occur only imperfectly. Thus, what a child learns during a formal, in-
stitutionalised education cannot make up for any deficiency in the earlier
phases of its upbringing. This is the conclusion that most serious studies
have revealed. J.S. Coleman, for instance, whose massive study, *Equality
of Educational Opportunity*,[1] led him to examine the career of 600 000 children, 60 000 teachers, and 4000 schools, reported in 1966 that 'variations
in the facilities and curriculum of the schools account for relatively little
variation in pupil achievement,' and that 'family background differences
account for much more variation in achievement than do school differ-

ences.'[2] If the child's upbringing is deficient, then the incidence of the symptoms of faulty socialisation—emotional instability, delinquency, drug addiction, and alcoholism—are likely to increase correspondingly.

Like all life processes, education in a vernacular society is highly dynamic, the child being an active participant rather than a consumer of professional services and educational merchandise. In such conditions, institutions are largely unnecessary. It suffices to introduce children into the dynamic social process—so admirably described by O.F. Raum, author of the seminal work *Chaga Childhood* (1940)—for them to be properly socialised or educated. 'The child is not a passive object of education,' Raum writes,

> He is a very active agent in it. There is an irrepressible tendency in the child to become an adult, to rise to the status of being allowed to enjoy the privileges of a grown up . . . The child attempts to force the pace of his 'social promotion'.[3]

Developmental life processes, such as education, are closely integrated. C.H. Waddington emphasises the close integration of individual developmental pathways or 'chreods' within the larger constellation of pathways that make up the organism's total development (its 'epigenetic landscape'—see chapter 21), noting that 'the sequence of changes by which the fertilised egg becomes an adult animal always involves considerable interactions between neighbouring parts of the embryo.'[4] The development of a child into an adult in a vernacular society proceeds in the same way. The child develops a close interrelationship with different members of various social groupings—its lineage group, its age grade, the secret society to which it may belong—and hence with the community that these social groups constitute.

If education is identified with socialisation, then each society must require its own type of education. Thus, the programme that will transform a Chaga child into an adult member of its society, capable of fulfilling its specific functions within a very distinctive African tribe, cannot conceivably be the same as that which will enable a baby Eskimo to learn its equally specialised but very different functions as a member of a family and small community geared to survival in the inhospitable Arctic regions. A Chaga with the education of an Eskimo is, from the point of view of their society, uneducated, as they would be were they to have been exclusively educated in a Western school or university.

The colonial powers sought to destroy the cultural pattern of traditional societies largely because many of their essential features prevented traditional people from subordinating their social, ecological, and spiritual imperatives to the short-term economic ends served by the colonial economy (chapter 58). *There is, in fact, no better way of destroying a society than by undermining its indigenous educational system.* Thus, as Margaret Read tells us,

> the learning of genealogies of the families and clans, as among the Ashanti and the Baganda, the recognition of social groupings in hierarchical tribal settings and of their reciprocal relationships, the hearing of tribal 'history' in praise songs and legends told at tribal gatherings—these were forms of direct learning which had no place in schools but had set times and places in a traditional situation.[5]

Indeed, they had little contribution to make towards the achievement of the overriding economic goals of the colonial regimes (or, for that matter, of Third World governments today—geared as they are to economic development under the tutelage of the World Bank and the IMF). Unable to renew themselves, traditional societies on whom the Western educational system was imposed are doomed to annihilation and their citizens to becoming social isolates in an anonymous mass society.

In the modern world, we have lost sight of the true role of education. The main reason is that our society has disintegrated—and if there is no society, then there can be no socialisation. In these conditions, education must mean something quite different.

Among other things, it requires that children be educated in specialised institutions instead of in their families and communities—and the isolation of education from the social process has dramatic consequences. For one thing, it ceases to be a spontaneous vernacular process and becomes instead an institutional one. The results are dramatic. As J.S. Coleman writes,

> this setting-apart of our children in schools—which take on ever more functions, ever more 'extracurricular activities', for an ever longer period of training—has a singular impact on the child of high school age. He is 'cut off' from the rest of society, forced inward toward his own age group, made to carry out his whole social life with others his own age. With his fellows, he comes to constitute a small society—one that has most of its important interactions within itself—and maintains only a few threads of connection with the outside adult society. . . . Consequently, our society has within its midst a set of small teenage societies, which focus teenage interests and attitudes on things far removed from adult responsibilities, and which may develop standards that lead away from those goals established by the larger society.[6]

The child is cut off from society for another reason. It is that modern education is concerned with training people for a career in the predominantly urban industrial world. It is said in India that when a young person gets a high school diploma, they leave their ancestral village for the nearest town; when they get a university degree, they move to the city; and when they get a Ph.D., they leave the country for Europe or America. Instead of providing the village with a means of renewing itself, *education now becomes a means of assuring its inevitable demise.*

Education is one of the many key social functions that the state has usurped, which in an ecological society must once again be fulfilled at the level of the family and the community so that young people should learn once again to fulfil their social, ecological, and cosmical roles within the context of their specific culture.

60

IN A TRADITIONAL SOCIETY, THE COMMUNITY IS IN ACCORD WITH THE NEEDS OF THE BIOSPHERE

Concentrated political power is the most dangerous
thing on earth.
R.J. Rummel

. . . it is not by the wax and parchment of lawyers that the independence of men can be preserved. Such things are the mere externals; they set off liberty to advantage; they are as its dress and paraphernalia, its holiday-suit in times of peace and quiet. But when the evil days set in, when the invasions of despotism have begun, liberty will be retained not by those who can show the oldest deeds and the largest charters but by those who have been most inured to habits of independence, most accustomed to think and act for themselves, and most regardless of that insidious protection which the upper classes have always been so ready to bestow that in many countries they have now left nothing worth the trouble to protect.
Henry Thomas Buckle

In notable respects, the mature corporation is an arm of the state. And the state, in important matters, is an instrument of the industrial system.
J.K. Galbraith

The ideal of a future based on ecological principles must have as a fundamental prerequisite the reëmergence of *gemeinschaft* [community] in social relationships.
Alwyn Jones

It is man who creates kingdoms and republics, [but] the community seems to stem directly from the hands of God.
Alexis de Tocqueville

IN THE LIGHT of the worldview of modernism, the state is the only possible instrument of government. It is seen as normal, and indeed desirable, that people should be but the individualistic, competitive, aggressive, and disorderly units of an atomised society. The notion that society is a natural system capable of governing itself and assuring its own homeostasis is foreign to modern sociologists, let alone modern politicians. Margaret Thatcher, while serving as Prime Minister of the United Kingdom, stated quite explicitly that a human society is no more than the sum of the individuals and families that inhabit it.[1] Such a society, or rather non-society, cannot govern itself and must depend on the state and its specialised services to maintain any semblance of order—a situation we are taught to regard as normal. Indeed, we are told that where there is no state there can only be a 'war of everyone against everyone', and life must necessarily be, in Thomas Hobbes's consecrated phrase, 'solitary, poor, nasty, brutish, and short'.[2]

This distorted view of human society can only be entertained by people who have had no experience of a vernacular society of the type within which our ancestors once lived, and which still survives, somewhat precariously, in those areas that have succeeded in remaining, partly at least, outside the orbit of international trade (chapter 58).

A succession of scholars have noted the essential difference between these two types of society. Sir Henry Sumner Maine, in his *Ancient Law* (1861), traced the transition from the familial or tribal form of society to the individualised society—from one governed by personal and sacred law to one governed by impersonal and secular law. For him, behaviour in the former society was based on 'status', while in the latter it was based on 'contract'.[3]

The 'social contract' described by such thinkers as Hobbes, Rousseau, and Locke—one entered into by the citizens of an originally chaotic and disorderly non-society so as to set up a government that would provide them with order and security—is still a generally accepted notion. It fits in perfectly with the worldview of modernism, since the contract is seen as having been entered into *consciously* and *rationally* by *individual* people —and implicit to it is also the idea of *management by an external agency*, just as labour is managed within a corporation.

On the other hand, the notion of a society as a natural and spontaneous biospheric creation is unacceptable to the modernist worldview. Such a society could only be held together by irrational forces, such as *instinct* and *sentiment*, that in Maine's view have no role to play in public affairs and should be limited to the field of personal relations.[4]

The French historian and social philosopher Fustel de Coulanges, in his seminal *La Cité Antique* (1864), stressed the religious nature of the family, community, and larger society, which he saw as providing their cohesion and stability. Of the ancient Greek city state, he wrote, 'The state and religion were so totally fused that it was impossible not only to imagine a conflict between them, but even to distinguish one from the other.' For him, the ancient society died once its law was separated from its religion.[5]

The early American ethnographer Lewis H. Morgan published his *Ancient Society* in 1877. He distinguished between *societas* and *civitas*—the former based on kinship and the latter on territorial connection.[6] This is an important distinction. Real vernacular communities are based on *consanguinity* or 'blood-relationships', whether real or fictitious. With the development of trade and industry, however, normal rules of residence —reflecting the kinship structures of communities and their relationships with other key groupings, such as the clan (chapter 55)—were subordinated to new economic considerations. Thus, among the Hebrews, as Adolphe Lods writes,

> The early groupings, based originally on consanguinity (natural or artificial), tended to become territorial aggregations. The clan finally became synonymous with the population of a town ... Membership of a tribe consisted not in descent from a particular individual but in belonging by birth to a particular locality.[7]

As this change occurred, *contiguity* or 'territorial-relationships' became the main bond holding together the members of a community. Today, even this bond has been eroded as people move to wherever they can find a job. Thus, in the USA more than sixty per cent of the population has moved away from the community in which they were born.[8] In this way, a country's population is shuffled like a deck of cards to satisfy the requirements of the economy, and the community is transformed into a haphazard mass of strangers incapable of governing themselves or of fulfilling their other whole-maintaining functions.

Perhaps the best-known distinction between these two types of society is that proposed by the German sociologist Ferdinand Tönnies in *Gemeinschaft und Gesellschaft* (1887). He saw the *gemeinschaft* or community as constituting a single coherent social unit whose members are bound together by intimate social bonds and common values, whereas the members of a *gesellschaft* or artificial association are, on the contrary, linked by superficial and self-motivated considerations.[9] This is stated very clearly by Fritz Pappenheim,

> Individuals who enter a *gesellschaft* do so with only a fraction of their being; that is, with that part of their existence which corresponds to the specific purpose of the organisation. Members of a taxpayers' association or individuals who own stock in a company are related to each other not as whole persons *but with only that part of themselves which is concerned with being a taxpayer or shareholder.* . . . Thus, they remain loosely connected and essentially remote from each other. . . . So deep is the separation between man and man in *gesellschaft* that . . . [it] becomes a social world in which latent hostility and potential war are inherent in the relationship of one to another.[10]

Roy Rappaport contrasts what he calls a 'general purpose' system or the community with a 'special purpose' subsystem. Whereas the community seeks to satisfy social and ecological requirements, a special purpose subsystem—in which category he includes corporations and governmental institutions, and which corresponds very closely to Tönnies' *gesellschaft* —only seeks to achieve the purpose for which it was set up. Even then, these subsystems are rapidly subject to what he calls 'usurpation' or goal displacement, at which point their foremost preoccupation is to perpetuate themselves and, if possible, increase their power and influence, which can often mean becoming an obstacle to the realisation of their original goals.[11]

In the case of government agencies set up to control the activities of unscrupulous corporations, goal displacement occurs very rapidly. They are nearly always subverted, indeed often completely taken over by corporate interests, whose activities they have been set up to control—a process known as 'regulatory capture' or 'agency capture'. In the UK, the Advisory Committee on Pesticides, which is supposed to advise the government on the control of the use of pesticides, is largely made up of representatives of the agrochemical industry and various academics whose research grants they pay or otherwise control.[12] The United States Department of Agriculture (USDA)—like the UK's Ministry of Agriculture, Fisheries, and Food (later merged into DEFRA)—is dominated by the agrochemical industry; the thousands of agricultural extension offices throughout the USA being little more than agencies for the sale of fertilisers and pesticides. The same can be said of the Food and Agriculture Organisation of the United Nations (FAO), to which subject *The Ecologist* devoted a special issue.[13]

When the Reagan administration came to power in the USA, Anne Gorsuch Burford, an attorney specialised in defending polluting industries against litigation by the Environmental Protection Agency (EPA), was actually made head of that agency and proceeded to dismiss the scientists engaged during the Carter administration—not (on her own admission) because they were incompetent, but because they were 'their scientists' (or scientists with real environmental concerns) and had to be replaced by 'our scientists' (or scientists representing the interests of the polluters).[14]

In general, governments will take no measures that go against the interests of any important industry, however destructive its activities, unless forced to do so by public opinion. The main reason is that governments have an insatiable appetite for money. In a 'democracy', it is money that will enable them to get reëlected by providing material advantages to those sectors of society whose electoral support they particularly require, and it is money that will enable them to sell themselves to the electorate through elaborate publicity campaigns at election times. In a more conventional dictatorship, money will buy the arms and pay the police and troops that maintain the dictator in power. Unfortunately, big corporations have a virtual monopoly of money—hence the inevitable alliance between government and industry. The result is that virtually no important policies are adopted today because they are desirable on human, social, or ecological grounds, but rather because they serve the purpose of powerful special-purpose associations (Rappaport's 'subsystems')—and it is these heterotelic or whole-disrupting policies that are rapidly making our planet uninhabitable.

For the French anthropologist Pierre Clastres, the most basic feature of a vernacular society is probably its capacity to run its own affairs without the aid of formal state institutions.

> On the one hand, there are primitive societies, or societies without a state —on the other hand, there are societies with a state. It is the presence or absence of the state apparatus (capable of assuming many forms) that assigns every society its logical place and lays down an irreversible line of discontinuity between the two types of society.[15]

That a vernacular society can run itself without the aid of formal state institutions is well documented. As the classical American anthropologist Robert Lowie writes,

> the legislative function in most primitive communities seems strangely curtailed when compared with that exercised in the more complex civili-

sations. All the exigencies of normal social intercourse are covered by customary law, and the business of such governmental machinery as exists is rather to exact obedience to traditional usage than to create new precedents.[16]

The power of public opinion, reflecting traditional values, is enough to bring disorderly elements to heel. Often a miscreant is simply laughed at—if this is not enough, people will no longer attend their feasts, and their company will be avoided. This is usually sufficient—if it is not, they will be ostracised; the worst possible penalty, since a member of a vernacular community cannot conceive of life outside it, away from the land where their ancestors are buried and where they may perform their essential religious rites. As British anthropologist Sir Edward Tylor puts it, 'one of the most essential things that we can learn from the life of rude tribes is how society can function without the policeman to keep order.' [17]

A vernacular society is also fully capable of bringing up its own children, looking after the sick and the old, and dealing with any psychiatric disorders. The social psychiatrist Marvin Opler has shown that a vernacular society will automatically provide a cathartic outlet for the particular tensions that, by its specific nature, it must inevitably generate.[18]

A vernacular society coordinates all those activities that contribute to maintaining its stability in the face of change. Above all, this means maintaining the critical order of the holarchy of larger systems of which it is part, and on whose preservation its own stability must ultimately depend (chapter 46). For this to be possible, a vernacular community, together with the families and individuals that compose it, must cooperate in the achievement of this goal—seeking, among other things, to avoid interfering with each other's activities. As a result, the conflict of interests with which we are often faced in the modern world—say, between the use of land for agriculture or for urban development—tend not to occur.

A member of a vernacular society, in Stanley Diamond's words, is

> an integrated person. His society is neither compartmentalised nor fragmented, and none of its parts is in fatal conflict with the others. Thus, he does not perceive himself as divided into *Homo economicus*, *Homo religiosus*, *Homo politicus*, and so forth.[19]

On the contrary, vernacular people perform their various economic, religious, and political tasks as part of a coordinated strategy that is embodied in the cultural pattern with which they have been imbued, and which has regulated their relationship with their society and with their natural environment from time immemorial.

In such conditions, there is clearly no need for the state. The intrusion of such a foreign body into a society's affairs would usurp its most fundamental functions and prerogatives, generating initiatives beyond the influence of traditional law as laid down by the ancestors. In a vernacular society, as Clastres puts it, 'there is no state because the state is an impossibility.'[20]

The state can only come into being *once social structures have been destroyed*. This explains the title of Clastres' seminal work *La Société contre L'État (Society against the State*—1974). Indeed, society and the state cannot coexist. In every country, *the state seeks purposefully to destroy the vernacular features of society*. In India, it wages war against the caste system that, in spite of its obvious abuses, provides the very basis of Indian social structure. It also attacks 'linguism', the preservation of the languages spoken by the different ethnic groups that inhabit modern India, and even rounds on so-called 'statism', where this refers to the residual autonomy of largely ethnically-based realms within India.

In Africa, the governments of the artificial nation-states, whose arbitrary boundaries have been inherited from the colonial period, strive to eradicate 'tribalism' in the interest of creating 'national unity', which really means the bringing into being of vast homogeneous masses of anonymous and alienated people totally dependent, as we in the West have become, on the specialised services provided by an increasingly powerful state.

The close relationship between the development of the state and the disintegration of a self-regulating community is described by Edward Banfield in a study of peasant society in southern Italy (chapter 51). The village, he finds, has been relieved of responsibility for organising its own religious life by the centralised bureaucracy of the Vatican. It has also lost control of its own educational system, since its school has been built and teachers appointed for it by the state. It no longer maintains law and order—the state's police are supposed to do that. As a result, the community has begun to disintegrate—the largest unit of organisation now being the family, with no effective cooperation above that level. In such a society, Banfield writes,

> no one will further the interest of the group or community except as it is to his private advantage to do so. In other words, the hope of material gain in the short-run will be the only motive for concern with public affairs . . . the law will be disregarded when there is no reason to fear pun-

ishment . . . an office-holder will take bribes when he can get away with it. But whether he takes bribes or not, it will be assumed by the society . . . that he does.[21]

Clearly, such a society can only exist because the state provides it with all the services it once provided for itself. 'Except for the intervention of the state,' Banfield writes, 'the war of all against all would sooner or later erupt into open violence, and the local society would either perish or produce [new] cultural forms'—precisely the state of affairs that Hobbes and, later, the social Darwinists took to be the norm (chapter 45).[22]

A peasant society is still only in the early stages of disintegration, since the extended family is still intact. But as economic development proceeds, the extended family breaks down into the very unstable nuclear family, which remains the norm today. Eventually, even that disintegrates until, in the most deprived areas of the industrial world's conurbations, the one-parent family becomes the rule. In such a society, there is little cooperation. It is everyone for themselves, and individualism and competition are the rule (chapter 51). People are thus so alienated that they are no longer capable of looking after their own affairs, and the state takes over more and more of the functions that they are no longer capable of fulfilling. As a Pomo Indian pointed out to a white North American,

> the police and soldiers take care of protecting you, the courts give you justice, the Post Office carries messages for you, the school teaches you. Everything is taken care of, even your children if you should die—but with us, the family must do all that. Without the family, we are nothing, and in the old days, before white people came, the family was given first consideration by anyone who was about to do anything at all. That is why we got along.[23]

Unfortunately, we have been taught to regard the proliferation of a country's state services as a sign of social and economic progress. The more of them a government provides to its citizens, the higher their perceived standard of living. This notion is consistent with the dogma that all benefits are artificially manufactured, the product of economic development or 'progress' (chapter 39). It is consistent, too, with the modern belief in scientific and technical expertise and professionalism, for the services provided by the state are seen to be superior in these terms to those provided by the family and the community in a vernacular society. In Sweden, according to David Popenoe, the bourgeois family is seen as a major cause of social problems, and in order to destroy it, some Welfare State ideologues are eager to promote alternatives not only to the bourgeois family but to the nuclear family, and to turn over most child rearing to the state.[24]

Even parents in Sweden are apparently succumbing to this propaganda and coming to accept that care is best provided by government-employed professionals. After all, they are scientifically trained to look after children and must therefore be capable of doing so better than their ignorant and amateurish parents.

As people delegate their prerogatives to experts, John McKnight notes, they act less as citizens and more as clients.[25] This is occurring in practically every field of activity—in medicine, in education, and in the care of the elderly—and it is affecting every aspect of social policy. At the same time, normal people are prevented from fulfilling the basic functions for which they were equipped by their evolution, and which *they must fulfil* if they are to maintain the integrity and stability of the families, communities, societies, and ecosystems that make up the wider biosphere.

The state is foreign to society. It is a *gesellschaft*—a special-purpose association—concerned almost exclusively with its own short-term interests and almost invariably oblivious of the real needs of those it has been called on to govern. There is no place for the state or its specialised institutions in a society that seeks to recreate for itself a sustainable existence on a sustainable planet. In its place, we must recreate the extended family and the vernacular community within which we have evolved and that, throughout our evolutionary experience, have been the effective units of whole-maintaining social and ecological behaviour.

61

TRADITIONAL PEOPLE FOLLOW THE WAY

The world mourns and decays,
the land withers and wastes,
the worthiest people are corrupted.

The earth lies ruined beneath the feet of its people,
for they have transgressed the laws,
defied the commandments,
broken the everlasting covenant.
Isaiah 24, 4–5

When the world has the Way,
ambling horses are retired to fertilise fields.
When the world lacks the Way,
war-horses are reared in the suburbs.
Laozi

Man follows the Earth,
Earth follows Heaven,
Heaven follows *dào*,
Dào follows what is natural.
Laozi

Dào is like Dike, the Way, the way of nature—and man's whole religion, his
whole moral effort, is to bring himself into accordance with *dào*.
Jane Ellen Harrison

L IKE THE DEVELOPING embryo in the womb, each life process must follow a critically ordered path of development—its constellation of 'chreods' (chapters 21 and 22)—if it is to achieve its endstate and thereby contribute to maintaining the critical order of the cosmos. Thus, we can talk, as does Rupert Sheldrake, of 'behavioural chreods'[1] and also of 'cultural chreods' in the sense that a society, by means of its specific cultural pattern, is capable of maintaining itself on its path by correcting any diversions from it—so long as they occur within its tolerance range and hence within its natural habitat or 'field' (chapter 49).

The path or 'Way' a society must follow is that which conforms to its traditional law (chapter 5), which the ancient Greeks referred to as Nomos. The Way was also referred to by them as Dike, which meant justice, righteousness, or morality. Jane Harrison tells us that Dike was also 'the Way of the world, the way things happen'.[2]

The Way was also referred to as Themis, which Harrison regards as 'that specialised way for human beings which is sanctioned by the collective conscience.'[3] Themis was also taken to be the Way of the earth and sometimes the Way of the cosmos itself, that which governed the behaviour of the gods. Later, when these concepts were personalised, Themis became the goddess of law and of justice and hence of morality.

The Way was also seen to coincide with Moira, the path of destiny or fate. The gods were subordinated to Moira, as they were to Dike— the two actually coinciding with each other. Thus, for Anaximander, all basic things are attributed to different provinces 'according to what is ordained',[4] thereby providing the basis of the critical order of the natural world—a concept in which, according to F.M. Cornford, 'necessity and right are united'.[5] In Homer, the gods are seen as subordinate to Moira and, indeed, to Dike—cosmic forces that are older than the gods themselves and that are moral. Against fate, and hence against the moral law, the gods can do nothing. As Homer tells us in the *Odyssey*, the gods cannot even save a man whom they love if the 'dread fate of death' is upon him. Herodotus tells us that 'it is impossible even for a god to avoid the fate that is ordained.'[6]

The Way to be followed by all human beings was the same as that which must be followed by society as a whole, by the natural world, by the cosmos, and therefore by the gods themselves. There is thus a unifying law which governs the behaviour of the whole cosmic holarchy. 'Themis in the realm of Zeus', as Pythagoras writes, and Dike in the world below hold the same place and rank as Nomos in the cities of men, so that he who does not justly perform his appointed duty may appear as a violator of the whole order of the universe.[7]

The higher the status of an individual (and hence the greater the *vital force* with which they were endowed—chapter 62), the more important it was that they should rigorously follow the Way. Thus, Odysseus tells us that when a blameless king maintains the Dike,

The black earth bears wheat and barley, and the trees are laden with fruit, and the sheep bring forth and fail not, and the sea gives store of fish—and all out of his good guidance—and the people prosper under him.[8]

The concept of the Way was probably entertained, explicitly or implicitly, by all vernacular societies. Thus, in ancient China *dào* (*tao*) refers at once to the order and to the Way of the cosmos. The term is applied to the daily and yearly 'revolution of the heavens' and of the two powers of light and darkness, day and night, summer and winter, heat and cold.[9] J.J.M. de Groot tells us that *dào*

represents all that is correct, normal, or right (*zhèng* or *duān*) in the universe—it does indeed never deviate from its course. It consequently includes all correct and righteous dealings of men and spirits, which alone promote universal happiness and life.[10]

Dào represents the natural course of things. It was considered, Joseph Needham writes, 'not only as vaguely informing all things but as being the naturalness, the very structure, of particular and individual types of things.'[11] Fung Yu-lan sees *dào* as 'the all-embracing first principle of things.'[12] All living things, including humans, are part of this all-embracing natural order subject to *dào*, which is its governing principle. '*Dào*, as the order of nature,' Fung Yu-lan writes, 'governs their very action.'[13] Humans follow *dào*, or the Way, by behaving *naturally*. In Daoist terms, this means abiding by Laozi's principle of *wú wèi*, for 'when things obey [the Way's] laws,' as Wing-tsit Chan writes, 'all parts of the universe will form a harmonious whole, and the universe will become an integrated organism.'[14]

In ancient Egypt, we learn from Siegfried Morenz that the concept of *ma'at* fulfilled a similar role. *Ma'at* meant 'right order in nature and society as established by the act of creation . . . what is right, what is correct, law, order, justice, and truth'—not only in society but in the cosmos as a whole. Significantly, Re was at once Lord of the cosmos,

Lord of the judgment of the dead, and Lord of *ma'at*. Later, when Osiris came into his own, he also became the Lord of *ma'at*. Although *ma'at* came into being with creation, it still had to be renewed and preserved. It follows that

> Ma'at is . . . not only right order but also the object of human activity. Ma'at is both the task which man sets himself and also, as righteousness, the promise and reward which await him on fulfilling it.[15]

Because ancient Egypt was a centralised kingdom run by a divine king, it was his role in particular to maintain *ma'at* and hence the order of the cosmos. Thus, we read in contemporary texts that 'the sky is at peace, the earth is in joy, for they have heard that (the deceased king) will set right [*ma'at*] in the place of disorder (*isfet*),'[16] and again, Tut-ankh-amun 'drove out disorder (*isfet*) from the Two Lands, and *ma'at* is firmly established in its place—he made lying (*grg*) an abomination, and the land is as it was at the first time.' It was the king's close association with *ma'at* that gave authority to his edicts. What he ordered was necessarily part of *ma'at* that his subjects must follow.

A similar concept existed in Vedic India—referred to as *ṛta*. 'The processes whose perpetual sameness or regular recurrence', writes Maurice Bloomfield, 'give rise to the representation of order, obey *ṛta*—or their occurrence is *ṛta*.'[17] We read in the Vedas that

> 'The rivers flow *ṛta*. . . . According to *ṛta*, the light of the heaven-born morning has come. . . . The year is the path of *ṛta*.' The gods themselves are born of the *ṛta* or in the *ṛta*—they show by their acts that they know, observe, and love the *ṛta*. In man's activity, the *ṛta* manifests itself as the moral law.

Rta also stands for the truth—though in a philosophical context truth is usually *satyá*. Untruth, though it is sometimes *a-satyá*, is usually expressed as *án-ṛta*—hence, as a divergence from *ṛta* or the Way.

The Vedic poet, as Krishna Chaitanya notes, fully realises that, to obtain nature's bounty, humanity must obey *ṛta*,

> For one who lives according to Eternal Law, the winds are full of sweetness, the rivers pour sweets. So may the plants be full of sweetness for us![18]

The great Vedic *Hymn to Earth* clearly expresses the belief in humanity's dependence on the order of the cosmos and in our role in maintaining it by observing the ancient law. In it, the poet expresses their faith in the eternal order and in humanity's duty to preserve it. It is this order that has bound 'rock, soil, stone, and dust' in such a way that 'trees, lords of the forest, stand ever firm.' It is this order that maintains in 'unfailing flow, day and night, the waters that are common to all' and nurtures 'cornfields that nourish quadrupeds and bipeds'. In all this, the poet displays a respect that unites the spiritual and the practical—'Whatever I dig from thee, Earth, may it have quick growth again! O purifier, may we not injure thy vitals or thy heart!'[19]

Later, the concept of *dharma* was also used by the Hindus in the same way. '[. . .] that regularity, that normality of the universe which produces good crops, fat cattle, peace, and contentment', A.M. Hocart writes, 'is expressed by the word *dharma*, which means, etymologically, "support", "upholding".' It describes the way in which animals, people, or things are expected to behave—it is natural law.

> The sun is sometimes identified with *dharma* because it regulates the seasons—sometimes it is considered to be regulated by it. Among the gods, Varuna is the one who lays down ordinances for the universe and so is entitled 'Lord of Right'. The king on his accession becomes to his people as Varuna is to the gods—he is Varuna, so he becomes 'Lord of Right' also.[20]

In Balinese Hinduism, Fred Eiseman writes, *dharma* is seen as

> the organising force that maintains order. [It] is the organisation that governs the universe as a whole, the relationships between various parts of the universe, and actions within the various parts of the universe.[21]

The concept of *dharma* was also taken up by the Buddhists, who brought it to China, where *dharma* of Mahayana Buddhism was identified with *dào*. De Groot describes the Buddhist *dharma* as the universal law that embraces the world in its entirety. 'It exists for the benefit of all beings, for does not its chief manifestation, the light of the world, shine for blessing on all men and all things?'[22]

When a Buddhist Lama sets his prayer-wheel turning, he is performing a ritual that has deep meaning both in terms of *dharma* and *ṛta*. Not only are the prayers printed on it repeated by his audience but, as Jane Harrison notes,

> He finds himself in sympathetic touch with the Wheel of the Universe— he performs the act . . . 'Justice-Wheel-setting-in-motion'. He dare not turn the wheel contrariwise, [lest] that were to upset the whole order of Nature.[23]

In the Persian Avestas, the Way is referred to as *aša* (*asha*), the celestial representative of justice on earth. According to Chantepie de la Saussaye,

Justice is the rule of the world's life, as *aša* is the principle of all well-ordered existence, and the establishment or accomplishment of justice is the end of the evolution of the universe.[24]

In ancient Judaism, the terms used are *mišpat*, which means justice or right judgment, and *ṣedeq*, which also means righteousness or 'right order'. These virtues are attributed to God—but in the words of Father Robert Murray, 'the overarching vision is of human society in harmony with heaven.'[25] This harmony is *šalom* ('shalom'), which means peace but is in reality a wider term standing for harmony between Earth and Heaven—hence, cosmic or moral order or 'the right functioning of all nature as God created it'.[26] As in other ancient societies, the sacral king had a big role to play in the maintenance of *šalom*, which formed the basis of a 'cosmic covenant' or grand settlement established between God and humanity. As Father Murray writes,

> if the king acted according to the divine gift of *ṣedeq*, his Kingdom would be blessed with it in the senses of social justice, victory over enemies, and the fruitfulness of the land, and would enjoy *šalom*.[27]

Traces of this key aspect of ancient Jewish religion are to be found in some of the Psalms, in Isaiah, and more explicitly in 1 Enoch, as Margaret Barker has shown.[28]

Significantly enough, when the Hebrew Bible (the *Tanakh*) was translated into Greek, the *ṣedeq* words, such as *ṣĕdaqah*, were translated by the Greek Dike and its derivatives, such as *dikaios* (δίκαιος) and Dikaiosyne. The same concept was taken up by the early Christians, for whom the term *dikaios* or justice was, through the relationship to Jesus, still imbued with a cosmical dimension. Needless to say, the term gradually lost this aspect of its meaning, especially during the Reformation.

If to follow the Way is to maintain the critical order of the cosmos, then a society can be seen as doing so when its behaviour pattern is whole-maintaining (homeotelic). When, on the contrary, it is whole-disrupting (heterotelic), then a society must be seen as following the anti-Way, that which threatens the order of the cosmos and must thereby give rise to the worst possible discontinuities.

Thus, as Father Murray explains, if the king failed in his sacred duty to uphold *ṣedeq*, the covenant between God and humanity would be broken and a variety of calamities would ensue.

The theme of breach of the 'cosmic covenant', of disorder in nature and society, appears in various forms. It may involve the myth of a rebellion among supernatural beings, or it may picture the land suffering under the curse of drought, or society as the world turned upside down . . .[29]

In the Vedas, as Chaitanya notes, we read that ṛta, though benign, can also be 'stern and fierce' when it comes to transgressions. 'Bṛhaspati rides the fearsome chariot of ṛta for destroying the wicked,' meaning those who violate the eternal laws and hence threaten the critical order of the cosmos.[30] The latter are best seen as following the anti-Way or, in Vedic India, án-ṛta, the opposite to ṛta, and later, among the Buddhists, adharma, the opposite to dharma.

Among the ancient Egyptians, the anti-Way was referred to as isfet. Among the Greeks, it was often called ou themis (οὐ θέμις), the opposite to Themis (which occasionally was used to mean 'social order'[31] and the right custom or path to be followed to achieve such order[32]).

To follow ou themis could not be done with impunity. Among the Greeks, Themis (or Dike) was seen on such occasions as taking on the form of Nemesis, which is seen by Cornford as related to Nomos, in turn related to nemos (νέμος), the sacred grove, which was almost certainly the original place of worship of the Ancient Greeks (chapter 63), as it was of the Celts (and which today is still revered among the Indians and Japanese). Nemesis inhabited such a grove (or nemos). She may originally have been the woodland goddess, identified with Artemis (or Diana) of the woods. She was also a goddess of fertility, closely allied with Tyche (or Fortuna), 'the Lady who . . . brings forth . . . the fruits of the Earth.' However, as Cornford notes,

> . . . she who dispenses good things can withhold them or dispense blights instead of blessings. The awful power which haunts the nemos may blast the profane invader of her sanctuary.[33]

In the earliest times, when nemos was a sacred grove, Nemesis would have wrought vengeance on those who trespassed. Eventually, once the sacred groves fell into disuse, Nemesis would have become the guardian of the law, that is of Nomos and hence of Dike.[34]

Classical mythology abounds in stories of the Earth taking her revenge on those who destroy the natural world. Thus, as Donald Hughes notes,

> Erysichthon, whose name means 'tearer of Earth', cut down a tree inhabited by a dryad, in spite of the tree-spirit's protests. She complained to Mother Earth, who afflicted him with insatiable hunger. Orion boasted that he would kill all the animals in the world. This too was reported to

Mother Earth, who sent a monstrous scorpion to sting him to death. Today they are constellations opposite one another in the sky.[35]

Our modern society has quite clearly set out, systematically, to diverge from the Way. Its overriding goal is economic development or 'progress', the supreme heterotelic enterprise, which can only be achieved by methodically disrupting the critical order of the biosphere so as to replace it with a totally different organisation—that of the technosphere, which derives its resources from the biosphere and consigns to it ever more voluminous and toxic wastes. Technospheric expansion is thereby but another way of looking at biospheric contraction and disintegration, and the pattern of behaviour that must be adopted to achieve this fatal goal is the anti-Way (chapter 65).

FOR TRADITIONAL PEOPLE, TO INCREASE THEIR STOCK OF 'VITAL FORCE' IS TO FOLLOW THE WAY

The [motivation] and final aim of all Bantu effort is . . . to protect or to increase *vital force*—that is the motive and the profound meaning in all their practices. . . . The worst misfortune, [they believe, is] the diminution of this power. Every illness, wound, or disappointment; all suffering, depression, or fatigue; every injustice and every failure—all these are held to be, and spoken of by the Bantu as, a diminution of vital force.

Father Placide Tempels

A vast, old religion which once swayed the earth lingers in unbroken practice there in New Mexico. . . . In the oldest religion, everything was alive, not supernaturally but naturally alive. There were only deeper and deeper streams of life. . . . So rocks were alive, but a mountain had a deeper, vaster life than a rock. . . . For the whole life-effort of man was to get his life into direct contact with the elemental life of the cosmos—mountain-life, cloud-life, thunder-life, air-life, earth-life, sun-life. To come into immediate *felt* contact and so derive energy, power, and a dark sort of joy. This effort into sheer naked contact, without an intermediary or mediator, is the root meaning of religion.

D.H. Lawrence

It is moot whether, without restoring the category of the sacred—the category most thoroughly destroyed by the scientific establishment—we can have an ethics able to cope with the extreme powers which we possess today and constantly increase . . .

Hans Jonas

VERNACULAR PEOPLE follow the Way even in those societies in which the concept has not been clearly articulated. Most vernacular societies have developed another key concept, that of 'vital force', which we can identify with the better-known concept of *the sacred*. F.M. Cornford tells us that, in the classical world, a place was regarded as sacred because of the presence in it of a dangerous power that made it sacrosanct—'"not to be set foot on" . . . by the profane'.[1] Thus, things that were sacred had to be treated with great respect, indeed with trepidation. They were the source of every benefit and also of all misfortunes, for sacred things possessed this dangerous power or 'vital force'. Many traditional societies had their own word for it—*mana*, for instance, among the Melanesians and Polynesians; *orenda* among the Iroquois; and *muntu* among the Bantus (see also glossary).

Émile Durkheim regards vital force as 'the source of all religiosity'. He sees 'the spirits, demons, genii, and gods of every sort' as 'the concrete forms taken by this energy or "potentiality"'.[2] It is partly, at least, because they are endowed with this vital force that they are sacred and have become objects of religious cults. The sun, the moon, and the stars are also worshiped for this reason.

> . . . they have not owed this honour to their intrinsic nature or their distinctive properties but to the fact that they are thought to participate in this force, which alone is able to give things a sacred character, and which is also found in a multitude of other beings, even the smallest.[3]

Adolphe Lods considers that

> the very ancient term which is found in all Semitic languages to express the idea of 'god'—under the various forms of *'el* (Hebrew), *ilu* (Babylonian), *ilah* (Arab)—originally denoted the vague force which is the source of all strength and life . . . [Thus] *harare 'el*, *'erez 'el*, would designate mountains, or a cedar, permeated with *'el*—with divine force.[4]

'Vital force' is seen as powering the whole living world. To acquire it personally is the only sure avenue to success, as it alone improves efficacy or 'potentiality' within the living order of the cosmos. In his seminal work on Bantu philosophy, Father Placide Tempels tells us that, for the Bantu,

> Supreme happiness, the only kind of blessing, is . . . to possess the greatest vital force—the worst misfortune and, in very truth, the only misfortune, is . . . the diminution of this power.[5]

Among the Baluba (a Bantu tribe), vital force is referred to as *muntu*. A powerful man is described as '*muntu mukulumpe*'—a man with a great deal of *muntu*—whereas a man of no social significance is referred to as a '*muntu mutupu*', or one who has but a small amount of *muntu*. A complex vocabulary is used to describe all the changes that can affect someone's stock of *muntu*. All illnesses, depressions, failures in any field of activity are taken to be evidence of a reduction in this vital force and can be avoided only by maintaining a sufficient stock of it. A man with none left at all is known as *mufu*.[6] He has lost his 'potentiality' within the living order of the world, and hence he is as good as dead.

Tempels considers the same to be true of the Bantu in general. 'The . . . final aim of all Bantu effort', Tempels tells us, 'is . . . to protect or to increase vital force.' And, indeed, their customs only make sense if we recognise this as 'the motive and profound meaning in all their practices'.[7] The same is true in Melanesia, so much so that, according to R.H. Codrington, 'All Melanesian religion consists . . . in getting this *mana* for one's self, or getting it used for one's benefit.'[8] Léopold Senghor, the poet, philosopher, and former President of Senegal, considers that the goal of all religious ceremonies, all rituals, and indeed of all artistic endeavour in Africa is but to increase the stock of this vital force.[9] Jamshid Behnam tells us that African painters, sculptors, singers, and dancers believe that to make a work of art is to

> breathe the life force into the tangible form of a mask or a statue so that, in time of need, this life force can be released and blossom again through dance, prayer, or recitation.[10]

Artefacts, however, can only be seen as endowed with vital force, and hence as sacred, if they are made in the correct way. This requires that the necessary rituals are carried out at every stage of their production. Furthermore, the actual materials from which they are made cannot be chosen at random. They must above all be natural. Joseph Epes Brown tells us that, among the North American Indians,

> The natural materials used in the creative activity manifest sacred powers in accord with their particular nature and place of origin—and the completed form itself . . . is seen to manifest its own sacred potency.[11]

Thus, as Brown notes,

> When a vessel is moulded from moist clay, [a] relationship with the creative force of the earth is established, the maker becomes Creator, and the completed vessel is a living being, both alive and containing life. [Sim-

ilarly,] basket-making peoples perceived in their acts of gathering grasses and vegetable dyes, and in the weaving process itself, the ritual recapitulation of the total process of creation. The completed basket is the universe in an image, and in the manufacturing process, the woman actually plays the part of the Creator.[12]

But it is not only the artefacts themselves or the materials out of which they are made that can be endowed with vital force but also the tools used for creating them. These were seen as providing a link between the different realms or levels within the cosmic holarchy—a link between the artist, their society, the natural world, and the world of the gods.

Walter Cline, for instance, writing about the Chaga people of Mount Kilimanjaro, tells us that a 'special power dwells in the smith's hammer, as the chief bearer of all the spiritual force of his profession.'[13] Thus, as Mircea Eliade comments, the hammer, the bellows, and the anvil were seen as 'animate, miraculous objects'—hence, 'they were regarded as capable of operating by their own magico-religious force, unassisted by the smith.'[14]

Vital force is not just accumulated by individuals and their artefacts, however—it is usually seen as permeating the cosmos and concentrating in certain places and beings and, in so doing, forming a pattern of power and hence sanctity. Father Paul Schebesta tells us that for the Mbuti of the Ituri forest in DR Congo, vital force or *megbe*

> is spread everywhere, but its power does not manifest itself everywhere with the same intensity or with the same characteristics. Some animals are richly endowed with it. Humans possess more of some but less of other types of *megbe*. Wise-men are distinguished precisely by the abundance of *megbe* they have accumulated—sorcerers, too, have an abundance.[15]

For the Comanches of the Nevada Desert, according to Ralph Linton, the constituents of the natural world are imbued with different sorts of vital force or 'power'. The greatest is personified by the eagle, the earth, the sky, and the sun. The highest is God. After him come the first fathers, who founded various clans, and next comes the head of the tribe. The living form a similar hierarchical arrangement in accordance with the vital power that they possess, and animals, plants, and minerals are also organised in the same way.[16]

For the Bantu, according to Senghor,

> ... all the forces are organised hierarchically... First come the demigods or *genii*, then the primordial mythical ancestors, then the ordinary ances-

tors, then living men (in order of primogeniture), then animals, plants, and minerals.[17]

It seems that this pattern of power (and hence of *sanctity*) faithfully reflects the essentially holarchical structure (and hence *critical order*) of the cosmos (chapter 42).

In this way, *the distribution of vital force serves to sanctify the cosmic holarchy and hence to preserve it against human depredations.* Significantly, the amount of vital force residing at the different levels of social organisation reflects the extent to which the society is centralised. Thus, in a very decentralised society, individuals and families are endowed with a considerable proportion of the society's vital force. On the other hand, in highly centralised traditional kingdoms, such as ancient Egypt or Benin (now part of Nigeria), the vital force becomes concentrated in the person of the divine king, who is divine precisely for that reason. In such a society, what is more, the welfare of all the inhabitants is regarded as totally dependent on the fulfilment of the important rituals and ceremonies designed to preserve and increase the king's stock of vital force and on the observance of the many tabus surrounding his person.

It is only if we realise this that the practice of killing the king at regular intervals, as described by Sir James Frazer in *The Golden Bough* (1890), can possibly make sense. The king was killed because, for reasons that varied from one society to another, he was no longer seen as being a fit repository for the society's stock of vital force, which if society is to avoid the most terrible calamities, must thereby be transferred to a more appropriate repository.

The relationship between things and beings at different levels within the holarchy of the cosmos is not symmetrical. Vital power is seen as flowing 'downwards' to vitalise and hence sanctify things and beings at the 'lower' levels, though it will only do so if these fulfil their obligations towards the 'higher' levels and hence towards the cosmos as a whole.

It is thus understandable that so many of the rituals and ceremonies of a traditional people—and, indeed, their whole way of life—should be designed to maintain the correct distribution of vital force at each level within the cosmic holarchy. In this way, they can maintain the critical order and stability of the cosmos and thereby follow the Way.

To neglect the performance of these sacred rituals and ceremonies—worse still, to break the sacred laws that govern their performance—is to violate, and thus profane, a *tabu*. This can only lead to a disastrous change in the distribution of vital force within the cosmic holarchy. An act is tabu, according to Roger Caillois, because it disrupts 'the universal order, which is at once that of nature and society' and as a result 'the earth might no longer yield a harvest, livestock might be struck with infertility, the stars might no longer follow their appointed course, death and disease could stalk the land,'[18] (chapter 61).

This all-pervading fear of disrupting the critical order of the cosmos is reflected in the tabus set up in all tribal societies against mixing things that belong to the different classes or spheres into which the cosmos is seen to be arranged. This goes a long way towards explaining food tabus. If it is tabu to eat pork among the Hebrews, this is because the pig, as Mary Douglas notes,

> is put into the class of abominable, unclean creatures, along with the hare, the hyrax, and the camel. The grounds alleged are that these creatures either cleave the hoof or chew the cud but do not do both. In other words, they don't quite make it into the class of ungulates.[19]

To eat water-creatures that do not have fins and scales is also tabu, for they do not fall into natural cosmic categories either. Nor do air creatures that do not fly or hop on the earth and do not have wings and two legs. To eat such creatures can only reduce a person's vital force and simultaneously threaten the critical order of the cosmos. Mixed marriages between people from naturally exogamous social groups are seen in the same light—they threaten the critical order of society and hence that of the cosmos of which it is part.

Among the Igbo of Nigeria, according to Emefie Ikenga-Metuh, 'Offences which disrupt the natural order are called Aru—literally, abominations.' The word Aru, however, also means 'crime against nature'.[20] Such crimes include a number of unnatural acts that defy normal behavioural categories, such as a man having sexual intercourse with his father's wife or with an animal. The birth of twins, and a hen hatching but one chick also fall into this category. These tabu events are Aru because the Igbo believe 'that they transgress the laws guiding the ontological order and will therefore bring disaster to the community.'[21]

The naïve and irresponsible tampering with the inner processes of the natural world by scientists, technologists, and industrialists would be impossible in such a society.

For instance, feeding chickens on their own excrement, cows on offal derived from their fellows, or worse still, as reported in Switzerland, on human placentas acquired from the maternity wards of local hospitals,[22] would undoubtedly be classified as 'crimes against nature' and would be subject to the most stringent tabus. More so still would be the transplanting of human genes into pigs in order to make them fatter, or the transformation of these unfortunate creatures into living factories churning out 'human milk' to be fed to our babies as a substitute for the real human milk that would otherwise be provided by their mothers (see chapter 39).

Built into the cultural pattern of a vernacular society was the knowledge that such sordid practices are violations of the moral laws governing the cosmic order, and that this can only lead to catastrophes on an unimaginable scale.

63

FOR TRADITIONAL PEOPLE, TO SERVE
THEIR GODS IS TO FOLLOW THE WAY

Upon entering those groves, a spirit of awe and reverence came over one.
In the stillness of these mighty woods, man is made aware of the Divine.
Richard St Barbe Baker

There is no better way to please the Buddha than to please
all sentient beings.
Ladakhi saying

[Humanity's] religious behaviour contributes to maintaining
the sanctity of the world.
Mircea Eliade

And God saw everything that He had made
and found it very good.
And He said—This is a beautiful world that I have given you.
Take good care of it—do not ruin it.
Jewish Prayer

And as to love—love God. He is rock, earth, and water, and the beasts,
and stars and the night that contains them.
Robinson Jeffers

THE DEITIES OF VERNACULAR PEOPLE were, above all, the guardians of the critical order of the cosmos. As such, they personified the laws that were seen as governing the cosmos and that people had to observe if they were to assure the preservation of its critical structure. This meant that by observing those laws humanity was also fulfilling its obligations to the appropriate deities. Thus, to follow the Way in Vedic India was to fulfil obligations to Varuna, the god who personified *ṛta*; in ancient Egypt to Re, who personified *ma'at*; in Greece to Themis, once the cosmic force bearing that name came to be represented by the goddess (chapter 61).

The gods also personified the vital force that permeated the living world, reflecting its critical structure and sanctifying it (chapter 62). Jane Harrison notes that originally the gods of the Romans were impersonal and ill-defined, and that, rather than being referred to as *dei* or gods, they were seen as *numina* (the plural of *numen*, which meant divine 'will' or 'power'), suggesting, along with R.R. Marrett, and later Émile Durkheim and Adolphe Lods, that the notion of vital force preceded that of the gods and spirits (chapter 62).[1]

Whether or not this is so, the two concepts are complementary. It is probable that as the gods grew in importance, so did they in turn reinforce the sacred nature of the vital force with which they were imbued. In this way, they sanctified each other as well as the structure of the living world that their organisation faithfully reflected.

The role of the gods of vernacular people in sanctifying and hence in preserving the critical order of society is particularly well documented. 'Ancestor worship' seems to be common to most if not all tribal peoples throughout the world, though the term is misleading, for the ancestors were not 'worshiped' as modern people worship their gods. Their relationship with them was more one of mutual obligations. Thus, rather than pray for favours, tribal people reminded their gods instead that they had fulfilled their obligations towards them and expected them to do likewise. They would even curse their gods if they did not reciprocate. Jomo Kenyatta refers to this relationship as 'communion with the ancestors' (chapter 37).

Thus, the relationship between chthonic or earth-centred peoples and their gods was one of *mutual* obligations. The gods had needs, and their principal need was for the living to fulfil their ritual and ceremonial obligations, observing the laws that the ancestors had enacted *in illo tempore* ('at that time'). For their part, the living—and their families, clans, and tribes—needed the gods to protect them from malnutrition, disease, enemy invasions, and other disasters. In Japan, as Lafcadio Hearn puts it, 'The happiness of the dead depends upon the respectful service rendered them by the living—and the happiness of the living depends upon the fulfilment of pious duty to the dead'—a clear example of *holarchical mutualism* (chapter 46).[2]

Underlying this form of religion is the principle that a dead ancestor (or a deity) remains a member of their family, their community, and their society rather than gravitating to some distant paradise (a concept unknown to chthonic peoples).

In this way, the ancestral gods in these societies are as much part of the society as are the living. As William Robertson Smith pointed out many years ago in a famous passage,

> The circle into which a man was born was not simply a group of kinsfolk and fellow-citizens but embraced also certain divine beings, the gods of the family and of the state, which to the ancient mind were as much a part of the particular community with which they stood connected as the human members of the social circle. The relation between the gods of antiquity and their worshippers was expressed in the language of human relationship, and this language was not taken in a figurative sense but with strict literality. . . . Thus, *a man was born into a fixed relation to certain gods as surely as he was born into relation to his fellow men*—and his religion, that is, the part of conduct which was determined by his relation to the gods, was simply one side of the general scheme of conduct prescribed for him by his position as a member of society. There was no separation between the spheres of religion and of ordinary life. Every social act had a reference to the gods as well as to men, *for the social body was not made up of men only, but of gods and men.*[3]

Significantly, the gods of vernacular people, like their vital force, were seen as faithfully reflecting the particular structure of their society. Thus, Lafcadio Hearn writes of Japan,

> The three forms of the Shintō worship of ancestors are the Domestic Cult, the Communal Cult, and the State Cult—or, in other words, the worship of family ancestors, the worship of clan or tribal ancestors, and the worship of imperial ancestors. The first is the religion of the home; the second is the religion of the local divinity, or tutelar god; the third is the national religion.[4]

Harold E. Driver shows how the differences in the organisation of the gods among native North American societies could be explained in terms of their degree of centralisation (chapter 62),

> There was a strong tendency to arrange gods in a ranked hierarchy in areas where people were ranked in a similar manner, and to ignore such ranking where egalitarianism dominated human societies. Thus, the people of Mesoamerica carefully ranked their gods, while those in the Sub-Arctic Plateau and Great Basin believed in large numbers of spirits of about equal rank. Other areas tended to be intermediate in this respect. Among the Pueblos, where many spiritual personalities were widely enough recognised to be designated as gods, there was little tendency towards ranking, just as there was near equality among human beings.[5]

The people of Alor, as described by Cora Du Bois, have a very loosely organised society. Few constraints are applied at a level higher than that of the family, and the family itself is very weak. The average Alorese is undisciplined and self-indulgent, and has little regard for authority of any kind. Not surprisingly, the Alorese pantheon reflects this disorderly state of affairs. They have a culture hero and a supreme being, but these play a very small part in their thought. Ancestral spirits are more important, but behaviour to them is loose and undisciplined, just as it is towards their parents.

> So slight is the tendency to idealise the parental imago that the effigies by which the Alorese represent the ancestral spirits are made in the most careless and slipshod manner and are used in the most perfunctory way and then forthwith discarded. There is no tendency to give the deity permanent housing or idealised form. The dead are merely pressing and insistent creditors who can enforce their demands through supernatural powers. This is precisely the experience of the child with his parents. Hence, he obeys reluctantly and grudgingly.[6]

The Swazi, on the other hand, have developed a cohesive and hierarchically organised society—and according to Hilda Kuper, their gods are organised in exactly the same way.

> In the ancestral cult, the world of the living is projected into a world of spirits (*emadloti*). Men and women, old and young, aristocrats and commoners continue the patterns of superiority and inferiority established by earthly experiences. Paternal and maternal spirits exercise complementary roles, similar to those operating in daily life on earth; the paternal role reinforces legal and economic obligations; the maternal exercises a

less formalised protective influence. Although the cult is set in a kinship framework, it is extended to the nation through the king, who is regarded as the father of all Swazi. His ancestors are the most powerful of the spirits.[7]

The ancestral gods, and thus the vital force that they personify, *are organised in such a way as to reflect the critical order of the vernacular society*. In this way, the critical structure of society is sanctified and its members impelled (for fear of incurring the most terrible penalties) to preserve it, come what may. By sanctifying the critical order of society, the ancestral gods simultaneously sanctify the natural world of which it is an integral part, and which, as we have seen, is organised along the same basic plan.

Significantly, the original gods of earth-centred or chthonic peoples had animal forms. For instance, among the earliest Greeks, according to Jane Harrison, Zeus Ktesios was once a snake, while

> Zeus Olbios, in local worship, long preserved his bull's head. . . . The Sun God of Crete, in bull-form, wooed the Moon Goddess, herself a cow— their child is a young bull-god, the Minos Bull, the Minotaur.[8]

Because chthonic people made no radical distinction between themselves and other animals, there was no reason in their scheme of things to distinguish between themselves and their gods and the animals and the spirits that represented them, for all were part of the same cosmos. Significantly, among the Ancient Greeks and Romans, the original worshipping place was the sacred grove, known to the Greeks as *temenos* (τέμενος) and to the Romans as *templum* or temple (chapter 61). 'The woods,' as Pliny writes,

> were formerly temples of the deities, and even now simple country-folk dedicate a tall tree to a god with the ritual of olden times—and we adore sacred groves and the very silence that reigns in them no less devoutly than images that gleam in gold and ivory.[9]

Nor could the sacred groves be desecrated with impunity. It was the crime of Agamemnon not just to kill a deer but to do so in a *temenos*. Trees, as Donald Hughes tells us, were sacred to the gods, 'the oak to Zeus, the laurel to Apollo, the willow to Hera, the pine tree (or perhaps an oak) to Pan'.[10]

Robert T. Parsons, writing on the Kono of Nigeria, sums up the nature and function of vernacular religion as

> not only an organisation of human relationships, but it includes also the relationships of people with the earth as a whole, with their own land

and with the unseen world of constructive forces and beings in which they believe. *Religion brings them all into a consistent whole.*[11]

However, chthonic religion dies as society disintegrates. The Olympian gods were the products of this social disintegration. Whereas the behaviour of the original chthonic deities was subjected to the great powers that governed the cosmos (the Moira, or fate, that once also referred to the spatial order of the cosmos—and Dike, or justice, that was responsible for assuring its order in time—chapter 61), the Olympian gods were set above these cosmical powers. Their behaviour—and indeed that of the disintegrating society, whose organisation they reflected—was no longer subject to the constraints that previously served to maintain the order of the cosmos.

Jane Harrison sees the shift from the chthonic to the Olympian gods as a move from the holistic view of society and the cosmos to the individualised or atomised view. 'The Olympian has clear form,' she writes,

> he is the *principium individuationis* incarnate . . . The mystery [or chthonic] god is the life of the whole of things, he can only be felt—as soon as he is thought and individualised, he passes, as Dionysos had to pass, into the thin, rare ether of the Olympian. The Olympians are of conscious thinking, divided, distinct, departmental—the mystery god is the impulse of life through all things, perennial, *indivisible.*[12]

As social disintegration proceeded still further, the Olympian gods ceased to have any relationship with society, for society was no more. The accent was then on the cult of a national god, and eventually on that of the universal God. As society further disintegrated, the only remaining vernacular social grouping was the nuclear family, and predictably, the universal God acquired a wife and a child so that the now truncated pantheon reflected the newly atomised society.

This divine 'trinity' finds its counterpart in the religion of other disintegrated societies. The cult of Isis and Osiris and the baby Horus, for example, developed during the breakdown of ancient Egyptian society during the Ptolemaic age and from there spread throughout the wider Hellenic world. As the role of religion ceases to be social, it serves instead to provide solace to the individual and their nuclear family, beyond which lies but an undifferentiated mass of humanity from which they feel increasingly alienated, as they are from the natural world and from the cosmos. It is then only to the universal God (who, like them, is a social atom, isolated in both time and space) that they feel any duty. As Theodore Roszak puts it, such a god, having become 'infinitely removed from fallen nature, became that cosmic bouillon cube in which all holiness was now to be concentrated for safe keeping'.[13]

The 'revealed' religions of today, such as Christianity, Islam, and modern Judaism, have desanctified society and the natural world, leaving them open to exploitation and destruction. For Nikolai Berdyaev, 'Christianity alone made possible both positive science and technique.' The reason, he argues, is that by destroying the older mythology, it had severed humanity psychologically from the natural world—replacing an earth-centred world-view with an anthropocentric one that exalted humanity above nature (chapter 18).[14] But the same is true of the other revealed religions that developed to satisfy the psychological needs of atomised societies.

As society disintegrates and religion becomes ever more 'otherworldly', as people are severed from nature and, indeed, from the entire biospheric continuum, so their behaviour towards their gods ceases to occur within its correct context—that provided by the wider holarchy of the biosphere, of which they were born to be an integral part. Instead, the society becomes quintessentially disruptive to this holarchy, ceasing to fulfil its true social, ecological, and cosmical role, which leads its members even further along the anti-Way.

PART VI

THE PROBLEM OF MODERN SOCIETY

64

TO MAINTAIN THE WAY, A COMMUNITY MUST BE ABLE TO CORRECT ANY DIVERGENCE FROM IT

Grandfather,
Look at our brokenness.

We know that in all Creation
Only the Human family
Has strayed from the Sacred Way.

We know that we are the ones
Who are divided,
And we are the ones
Who must come back together
To walk in the Sacred Way.

Grandfather,
Sacred One,
Teach us love, compassion, and honour
That we may heal the Earth
And heal each other.
Ojibwe Prayer

The lower doctor heals the illness,
The middle doctor heals the whole person,
The higher doctor heals society.
Sun Sze-mo

Man has lost his way in the jungle of chemistry and engineering and will have to retrace his steps, however painful this may be. He will have to discover where he went wrong and make his peace with nature. In so doing, perhaps he may be able to recapture the rhythm of life and the love of the simple things of life, which will be an ever-unfolding joy to him.
Richard St Barbe Baker

D EVELOPING NATURAL SYSTEMS can only maintain themselves along their developmental path or Way if they can deal effectively with any external or internal challenges that might divert them from it (chapter 21). To do this, they must either secure themselves against such challenges (resistance stability—chapter 19) or, alternatively, correct any diversions from their path or Way (resilience stability), which requires that they interpret the problems caused by such divergences correctly.

Vernacular people in the classical world understood, as Donald Hughes notes, that 'hunger, ill-health, erosion, poverty, and general ruin' were only different forms that the Earth's revenge could take for the mistreatment meted out to her by humanity—punishments for having diverted from the Way in pursuit of the anti-Way or what the ancient Greeks would have called the *ou themis* (chapter 61).[1] The only way to combat these ills, therefore, was to treat the Earth with greater care, which meant to return to the Way of the ancestors, who lived in the Golden Age when such ills were unknown.

Vernacular people invariably interpreted disease in this way. Thus, among the Tukano of Colombia, as Gerardo Reichel-Dolmatoff notes,

> . . . illness is taken to be the consequence of a person's upsetting a certain aspect of the ecological balance. Overhunting is a common cause and so are harvesting activities in which some relatively scarce natural resource has been wasted. The delicate balance existing within the natural environment, between nature and society and within society itself, is bound to affect the whole.

To restore this 'delicate balance',

> . . . the shaman, as a healer of illness, does not so much interfere on the individual level but operates on the level of those supraindividual structures that have been disturbed by the person. To be effective, he has to apply his treatment to the disturbed part of the ecosystem. It might be said, then, that a Tukano shaman does not have individual patients—his task is to cure a *social* malfunctioning.[2]

He does this by reëstablishing the rules that 'will avoid over-hunting, the depletion of certain plant resources, and unchecked population increase'.

Quite clearly then, the shaman is more than a medical practitioner. They are a 'truly powerful force in the control and management of resources',[3] for they can really affect the incidence and severity of diseases over which the modern medical practitioner has no control whatsoever.

Victor Turner shows that among the Ndembu of central Africa, the 'doctor' sees their task in very much the same way. It is

> ... less as curing an *individual* patient than as remedying the ills of a *corporate group*. The sickness of a patient is mainly a sign that 'something is rotten' in the corporate body. The patient will not get better until all the tensions and aggressions in the group's interrelations have been brought to light and exposed to ritual treatment. ... The doctor's task is to tap the various streams of affect associated with these conflicts and with the social and interpersonal disputes in which they are manifested—and to channel them in a socially positive direction. The raw energies of conflict are thus domesticated in the service of the traditional social order.[4]

The philosophy underlying this interpretation of disease and the means of curing it is even more explicit in the case of the Kallawaya healers of the community of Kaata in the Bolivian Andes. They see their community as an integral part of an *ayllu*—conceptualising their mountainous territory as a human body, with communities living on the high ground, the central areas, and in the lowlands. According to Joseph W. Bastien, the head of the *ayllu* is the 'moist *puna* area ...' where herders graze alpacas, llamas, sheep, and pigs; the grasses that grow there are its hair; its eyes are the lakes of Apacheta. Its trunk is formed by the sloping terraced fields of potatoes, oca, and barley.[5]

The Kaata also has a heart and a liver that produce blood and fat and are the 'principles of life and power'. They are circulated by the diviners throughout the community and in particular into the 'earth shrines' by means of rituals and ceremonies in which the sick people 'eat with the mountain'. For the people of Kaata, human health is thereby identified with the integrity of their *ayllu*—it follows that when people, their society, and its environment 'work together to form one body, the bodies of sick individuals become whole' and the sick are restored to health. The body metaphor provides in this way 'a systemic model in which there is an analogy between the human body and the environmental and social bodies.' Diseases are diagnosed as 'signs of disorders between man and his land, or between his vertical *ayllu* and Ayllu Kaata'. The disease is then combated 'not by isolating the individual in a hospital away from his land' but instead by 'gathering the members of his social group in ritual and together feeding all the parts of Ayllu Kaata'.

Bastien sees this as being very much the approach to disease of the people of the Andes in general. For them, disease is an organic, cultural, environmental, and social phenomenon . . . By means of the body metaphor, diviners not only examine but also interrelate the complex networks of environmental factors and social structure with physical distress. This often prevents subsequent illness because action is taken to change social and environmental causes of the sickness.[6]

In this manner, vernacular people correctly diagnose such disorders as the symptoms of social and ecological maladjustments brought about by diverging from the Way and thereby violating the laws of the cosmos and disrupting its critical order—maladjustments that can only be eliminated by correcting the divergence and returning to the Way.

Modern society, on the other hand, interprets problems in terms of cause and effect relationships, on the basis of which a disease is attributed to a discreet event, such as the action of a bacterium, virus, or other pathogen, that must be eliminated—usually by waging chemical warfare against it. To do this, we build factories for manufacturing the chemicals, shops in which to sell them, hospitals in which to administer them, and universities in which to train the chemical engineers, pharmacists, doctors, and other specialists involved. Thus, we put our faith in scientific, technological, and economic development or 'progress'—precisely what our society is organised to provide. This may occasionally serve to cure individual sufferers—it will always serve the interests of corporations and their political allies, *but it will do nothing to reduce the incidence of the disease.*

All the other ever more daunting problems that confront our society today are interpreted in much the same way. Each one is rationalised to appear soluble by the expedients that science, technology, and industry can provide, and hence legitimised in terms of the worldview of modernism. Thus, poverty is seen to be primarily a shortage of material goods and technological devices and of the money required to purchase them. Economic development can solve this problem, since it will enable us to build factories that can manufacture these commodities and provide jobs to enable people to earn the money required to pay for them.

The World Bank and other Multinational Development Banks (MDBs) insist that the object of the destructive economic development that they finance is the eradication of poverty. Thus, in the President of the World Bank's 1987 address to his Board of Governors, he stated that his purpose that day was to

> outline the Bank's strategy for steady advance towards restored global economic growth, for steady progress in the fight against poverty.[7]

Bilateral aid agencies seek to maintain the same fiction. The principal purpose of British foreign aid, we are told, is to meet the basic needs of poor people in the developing countries—which is difficult to reconcile with the fact that about seventy-five per cent of British bilateral aid is 'tied' to the purchase of British goods and services *and thus serves principally to subsidise British exports.*[8]

The rapid degradation of the world's remaining agricultural lands is invariably attributed by governments and international agencies to traditional agricultural techniques. Thus, the United States Agency for International Development (USAID) attributes the rapid deterioration of the 'soil resource base' in arid lands to mismanagement based on the use of 'traditional technology and agricultural practices'[9]—though, in fact, these techniques have been used sustainably for thousands of years. Brooke G. Schoepf also notes how a scientist sent to Zaire (now DR Congo) to work on the UN's Man and the Biosphere Programme saw peasant cultivators as 'enemies of the environment'.[10] On the other hand, corporations operating large plantations were viewed by him as 'progressive in their contributions to development—as forces with whom alliance and accommodation are to be sought'. Margaret Thatcher, in her 1989 address to the United Nations General Assembly, attributed the degradation of agricultural land to what she called 'cut-and-burn' agriculture and recommended action 'to improve agricultural methods—good husbandry which ploughs back nourishment into the soil',[11] a rather rosy view of modern agriculture.

Malnutrition and famine are also attributed to archaic agricultural practices and in particular to low inputs of fertiliser. A report based on a twenty-year study jointly undertaken by the Food and Agricultural Organisation of the United Nations (FAO) and other organisations insists that the amount of food produced in the world is a direct function of fertiliser use, without mentioning the diminishing returns on successive applications of fertiliser experienced wherever farmers have adopted modern agricultural methods. According to the FAO, malnutrition and famine are also due to poverty. People starve because they do not have the money required to buy food—it follows that 'the incomes of the poor and the under-privileged must be increased so that their basic food requirements can be translated into effective demand;'[12] hence more economic development, even though, in spite of the unprecedented economic development of the post-war years, more people than ever before now lack the money to buy food.

The population explosion is also primarily attributed to poverty. Poor people are insecure, which leads them to produce more children, who can be put to work to earn money for their parents. This means that to bring population growth under control requires rapid economic development that will provide them with the money they require to assure their security, assuring in this way 'a demographic transition', as has already occurred in the industrial world. No mention is made of the fact that this transition only occurred in the industrial world once per capita income had reached a much higher level than Third World people can conceivably hope to achieve. Nor is it noted that economic development, by destroying families and communities, annihilating their natural environment, and forcing people off the land and into the slums, is the greatest source of their present insecurity.

The population explosion is seen, above all, to be the result of a shortage of family planning devices—so much so that the World Bank had estimated that to achieve 'a rapid fertility decline goal' in sub-Saharan Africa by the end of the twentieth century, would have meant increasing the amount of money spent on 'family planning' twenty times[13]—an extremely convenient approach to the problem from the point of view of the manufacturers of birth-control pills, condoms, and IUDs.

So it is with all the other problems that confront us, whether it be unemployment, crime, delinquency, drug addiction, alcoholism, pollution, resource depletion, global deforestation, or climate change. Each is interpreted in a way *that rationalises policies we have already decided to apply*—those that make the greatest contribution to economic development and hence best satisfy the requirements of the corporations and other institutions that dominate our society. In other words, instead of interpreting our problems as the inevitable *consequence* of economic development or 'progress'—that anti-evolutionary process that diverts us ever further from the Way—we interpret them instead as evidence that economic development *has not proceeded far or fast enough*; that, in effect, we have not deviated sufficiently from the Way.

This is the essence of the Great Misinterpretation—the ultimate manifestation of modern society's cognitive maladjustment to the industrial world that it has created (chapter 52). It draws us into a self-reinforcing cycle of positive feedback—a vicious cycle, leading to ever greater social and environmental destruction, from which we must waste no time in extracting ourselves if we are to have any future at all on this planet.

MODERN PROGRESS IS ANTI-EVOLUTIONARY
AND IS THE ANTI-WAY

. . . such is my awful Vision.

I see the Four-fold Man, The Humanity in deadly sleep
And its fallen Emanation, The Spectre & its cruel Shadow.
I see the Past, Present, & Future existing all at once
Before me—O Divine Spirit, sustain me on thy wings!
That I may awake Albion from his long & cold repose.
For Bacon & Newton, sheath'd in dismal steel, their terrors hang
Like iron scourges over Albion—Reasonings like vast Serpents
Infold around my limbs, bruising my minute articulations.

I turn my eyes to the Schools & Universities of Europe,
And there behold the Loom of Locke, whose Woof rages dire,
Wash'd by the Water-wheels of Newton—black the cloth,
In heavy wreathes, folds over every Nation—cruel Works
Of many Wheels I view—wheel without wheel, with cogs tyrannic
Moving by compulsion each other—not as those in Eden, which,
Wheel within Wheel, in freedom revolve in harmony & peace.
                    William Blake

We have not stumbled into the arms of Gog and Magog—
            we have *progressed* there.
            Theodore Roszak

Do you think you can take the world and improve it?
            I do not think it can be done.
            The world is sacred.
            You cannot improve it.
If you try to change it, you will ruin it.
If you try to help it, you will lose it.
            Laozi

ACCORDING TO the worldview of modernism and its associated paradigm of science, the destructive changes brought to the biosphere in the name of progress are all part and parcel of the evolutionary process itself. Yet, conveniently, no distinction is made between the process that leads to the development of the world of living things, or the biosphere, and that which leads instead to the development of the industrial world or technosphere.

On the contrary, these two obviously very different and, indeed, conflicting processes are seen as one and the same. If they differ at all, it is only in so far as one type of evolution is seen as *endo*somatic, in that it involves the emergence or modification of innate organs and behaviour —while the other, referred to as technical or *exo*somatic evolution, proceeds largely by the manufacture of new 'organs' or implements outside of the organism.

Sir Peter Medawar makes fun of a student who asks if humans 'might not evolve to possess wings and so make it possible to fly'. 'A foolish question,' he insists, since 'it is obvious that human beings have already acquired some of the capabilities of both birds and fish—capabilities which they owe to their own special style of evolution, the "exosomatic".'[1]

Julian Huxley actually believed that the historical, and particularly the industrial, age have created a heightening of human evolution in psychological and social terms (chapter 18). Even ecologists see things in this way. Erich Jantsch, for instance, tells us that 'industrialisation brought mankind a marked acceleration of evolutionary processes.'[2] He goes even further. For him, 'progress' forms 'a meaningful and integral part of a universal evolution', and he sees humanity as 'an agent of this universal evolution, and even an important one'.[3]

Another ardent supporter of this view is Peter Russell, who invites us to

> sit here and wonder at the whole evolutionary process, which has, step by step, resulted in me and you, in farms, automobiles, and computers, in men walking on the moon, in the Taj Mahal, the Emperor Concerto, and the Theory of Relativity.[4]

For Russell, one of the most powerful tools that modern science makes available to this version of evolution is genetic engineering. This will enable us to create 'completely new species' and, as a result, evolution will no longer have to follow 'the slow process of trial and error, and natural selection'. Instead, new species will be 'consciously designed and created within a matter of months'.[5] Atomic physics, he assures us, will also contribute to our further evolution. It already has, for

> with the advent of particle accelerators, scientists once again became more than just passive observers. They were now able to change some elements into others or even create completely new elements by bombarding the nucleus with atomic particles and thereby changing its structure.[6]

The invention of solar cells, he also insists, 'represents an evolutionary development as significant as that of photosynthesis 3.5 billion years ago'.[7] Moreover, we shall soon be able to influence our evolution by means of our growing ability to colonise space, 'a development as significant as the colonisation of land by the first amphibians 400 million years ago.'[8] Russell is so impressed by all these technological developments that he is led to ask whether 'the rapid acceleration so characteristic of today is heading us towards an evolutionary leap'. Indeed he asks, 'Could we be on the threshold of a leap as significant as the evolution of life from inanimate matter?'[9]

Those who support the notion that economic and technological progress are part and parcel of the evolutionary process usually regard the early stages of evolution as blind and instinctive, while the later stages that we associate with technological progress are seen to be conscious and purposive. This seems to be the standard position of today's mainstream scientists.

Indeed, some of our most brilliant theoretical biologists, among them Julian Huxley and C.H. Waddington, understand 'progress' in this way. For them, 'human evolution', as they refer to it, is the latest phase of evolution, and it is principally the product of the development of *mind*, *consciousness*, and *reason* (chapter 18). Because they considered humanity to be endowed with these three unique attributes, we are free to determine our own evolution—unencumbered, they clearly intimate, by any obligation to subject our 'progressive' activities to any social, ecological, or cosmical constraints (chapter 33).

In the light of the analysis provided in this book, however, what they call 'human evolution' or 'progress' is the very negation of evolution (the biospheric process), and is best referred to as *anti-evolution*. Since evolution can be equated with the Way, serving as it does to maintain the critical order and hence the stability of the biosphere, 'progress' or anti-evolution can be equated with the *anti-Way*—serving to disrupt the critical order of the biosphere and to reduce its stability (chapter 61).

To neo-Darwinists—who see evolution as a blind and random process heading in no particular direction (chapter 26) and hence just as capable of giving rise to a highly elaborate industrial technosphere as to a climax biosphere—the very notion of anti-evolution is meaningless; but this is not so if we view evolution in terms of an ecological or biospheric world-view, in the light of which evolution is seen as a goal-directed process tending towards the increased stability of the biosphere. It then suffices to show that economic development or 'progress' tends in the opposite direction—towards ever greater biospheric instability—to justify regarding it as anti-evolutionary or as corresponding to the anti-Way. Let us see why this must be so.

As biological, ecological, and social systems develop, they become more complex and also more diverse (chapters 24 and 25)—though in ecosystems, complexity and diversity tend to stop increasing shortly before a climax stage is reached. Increasing complexity enables a system to assure its stability in the specific conditions in which it lives, whereas increasing diversity enables it to hold its own in a wide range of conditions, dealing with challenges that it is less likely to encounter in terms of its evolutionary experience.

Biological evolution has led to the development of highly complex forms of life, such as human beings, and also to the most complex ecosystems. It has also given rise to millions of different plant and animal species and countless varieties of these species. Social evolution, likewise, has led to the development of complex social groupings and to a wide diversity of different ethnic groups, each perfectly adapted to the specialised environment in which it developed.

For example, there are at least 130 different tribes in California and more than 830 in Papua New Guinea alone. D.H. Price's *Atlas of World Cultures* (1990) identifies at least 3500 distinct cultural groups described in the ethnographic literature—many now vanished—while the *Ethnologue*, published by the Summer Institute of Linguistics, records around 7000 languages still spoken in the world today; some by only a handful of people.

Together, these remaining ethnic groups constitute what has been referred to as the earth's *ethnosphere*[10]—the rich heritage of cultural diversity that is facing the same threat of extinction from the unrelenting expansion of economic development as is the rest of the earth's biosphere. An indication of this rapid loss of diversity is provided by the linguist Michael Krauss, who estimates that, at present trends, 90 per cent of the world's currently spoken languages will be extinct or terminally moribund by the end of the twenty-first century.[11]

With economic development, the culture of all these ethnic groups is disrupted and their members transformed into a homogeneous mass of alienated people, most of whom today are condemned, before long, to living in the growing slums that will soon accommodate most of humanity. In the meantime, climax forest ecosystems are destroyed and replaced by a series of ever less complex and less diverse systems—secondary forests, then plantations of fast growing exotics, and then pasture; finally, they are paved over to accommodate urban development.

Increasing complexity and diversity that accompany evolution are closely associated with increasing cooperation between the constituents of the biosphere. Indeed, with evolution, competition gives way to cooperation, or what ecologists call mutualism (chapters 44 and 45). However, as the anti-evolutionary process gets under way, and complexity is dramatically reduced as a result, so mutualism gives way to competition. In a human society, the same is true. The cooperation that obtains among the members of an extended family and the vernacular community of which they are part is so great and contributes so much to the quality of their lives (and, indeed, to their survival) that it is best regarded as *social wealth* (chapters 56, 57, and 58). With 'progress', on the other hand, social wealth is rapidly dissipated as social cooperation is replaced by interpersonal competition and aggression. The social wealth lost in this way cannot be compensated for by state services or *economic wealth*, which can only satisfy a small proportion of human needs—and in a largely degraded and disrupting way at that (chapter 47).

As evolution proceeds, there is a reduction in randomness and a corresponding increase in order. This order is preserved by the efforts of the parts towards the maintenance of the larger whole to which they belong (chapter 46).

Thus, as we have already seen, in a climax society education is whole-maintaining to society, to the natural world, and to the cosmos itself—as are settlement patterns, technology, economic activities, religion, and government itself (part v). The efforts of the differentiated parts to maintain the integrity of the whole—outside of which they have no meaning—is complemented by the efforts of the whole to maintain the integrity of its parts (chapter 43), without which it would not survive.

The units of this whole-maintaining activity are the natural social units (*gemeinschaft*) within which human beings evolved—the family, the community, and the society. When these units disintegrate under the impact of economic development or 'progress' they are replaced by corporations and other institutions (*gesellschaft*), whose behaviour is increasingly random and disruptive to the goal of maintaining the critical order of society and of the wider holarchy of the biosphere.

Thus, education no longer serves its basic function of socialising young people so they can become stable and integral members of their families and communities (chapter 59); settlement patterns cease to be designed to reflect social structure and the structure of the cosmos (chapter 55); technology and economic activities in general cease to be embedded 'in social relations' and rapidly spin out of control, eventually becoming the principal agents of social and ecological destruction (chapters 54, 56, and 58). Religion becomes universal and otherworldly and no longer serves to sanctify social structure or the structure of the natural world, leaving them open to exploitation and destruction (chapter 63). Government, instead of being a normal communal function, is fulfilled by the state, an external body that is only preoccupied with its own short-term interests that are necessarily in conflict with both those of the society it is called on to govern and of the natural world (chapter 60).

As evolution proceeds, natural systems also become increasingly self-supporting. Eugene Odum notes that the perfecting of a system's recycling processes is an essential means of increasing self-sufficiency.[12] As ecosystems develop, they are endowed with ever more elaborate methods for recycling materials—this is particularly true of tropical rainforests. A vernacular society, too, becomes increasingly committed to the careful recycling of all materials (chapter 56).

Again, 'progress' or anti-evolution puts this process into reverse. The waste products of one process, rather than serving as the raw material for the next, are simply being released into the environment in the cheapest possible way, without any regard for the pollution and the shortages to which they must inevitably give rise. Worse still, synthetic materials of which the biosphere has had no experience, and cannot recycle without disrupting its vital systems, are released in ever greater amounts, further degrading its critical order.

Societies, as they evolve, also learn to produce for themselves the basic necessities of life. Trade (and hence dependency on external sources of supply as well as on external markets for the sale of their produce) is limited to products that are of *secondary* importance to them. It is only in this way that they can insulate themselves against external changes that could deprive them of their livelihoods (chapter 58).

Once again, with economic development or 'progress', this evolutionary process is also put into reverse, until the world eventually becomes one vast free-trade zone in which all social and ecological imperatives, to which economic activities are normally subjected, are systematically subordinated to the short-term interests of the transnational corporations that control the world market—the most fundamental cause of the social and ecological devastation that is fast making this planet uninhabitable for complex forms of life.

Also, with evolution, living things become increasingly adapted biologically, socially, cognitively, and psychologically to their respective environments, just as societies and ecosystems are to theirs (chapters 50, 51, and 52). As economic development or 'progress' occurs, however, they become, on the contrary, ever less well adapted to their respective environments. The result is an increase in discontinuities of all sorts—crime, delinquency, alcoholism, and drug addiction at the level of the alienated individual; social chaos at the level of society, which is ever less capable of running itself and falls increasingly into the hands of dictatorships (chapter 51); floods, droughts, and epidemics at the level of the ecosystem; and global problems, such as the disruption of our climate and the erosion of the ozone layer, at the level of the biosphere (chapter 19).

Significantly, both Ramón Margalef and Eugene Odum note that the changes brought about by industrial society are unquestionably *reversing ecological succession*. Margalef also points out that our interference with the functioning of ecosystems must return them to a lower and more unstable successional stage[13]—one Odum refers to as a 'disclimax' (a disturbance climax) or an 'anthropogenic subclimax'.[14] This is difficult to reconcile with Tansley's notion of the superiority of the anthropogenic climax over the natural climax (chapter 22)—it is also incompatible with the very notion of economic development or 'progress' as a means of improving human welfare.

Yet today, with the globalisation of 'progress', we are rapidly heading towards a global biospheric disclimax in which modern society will have effectively reversed three thousand million years of evolution to create an impoverished and degraded world that is ever less capable of sustaining complex forms of life. Medawar admits that our hopes have not worked out—'Every folly, every enormity that we look back on with repugnance can find its equivalent in contemporary life.' But still, for him, this does not invalidate the principle of 'progress'. 'There is no need', he writes, 'to be dismayed by the fact that we cannot yet envisage a definitive solution of our problems . . . We can obviously do better than this . . .' In any case, 'it is a bit too early to expect our grander ambitions to be fulfilled.' We must remember that 'human history is only just beginning.' We have known that 'There has always been room for improvement—now we know that there is time for improvement too.'[15]

But is there really time? Is history only just beginning, or is it coming to an end? Is there really any reason to suppose that 'we can do better' if we continue to misinterpret our ever more terrifying problems, as we must do if we insist in continuing to see them in the light of the highly flawed paradigm of science and the worldview of modernism that it so faithfully reflects? The argument put forward in this book is that we can only conceivably do better if, among other things, we set out to reinterpret our problems in the light of a very different worldview—the worldview of ecology—inspired as it must be by the chthonic or earth-centred worldview entertained by our remote ancestors, who knew, as modern society no longer knows, how to live on this planet.

THE GREAT TRANSFORMATION REQUIRES A
RETURN TO THE WORLDVIEW OF ECOLOGY

Every social transformation . . . has rested on a new metaphysical and ideological base—or rather, upon deeper stirrings and intuitions whose rationalised expression takes the form of a new picture of the cosmos and the nature of man.

Lewis Mumford

The quest for a communal reality assumes the shape of a massive salvage operation reaching out in many unlikely directions. I think this is the great adventure of our age and far more humanly valuable than the 'race for space'. . . . For those who respond to the call, what happens within the world of science (though still consequential in public policy) will have less and less existential meaning. The scientists and their many imitators will become for them an arcane priesthood carrying on obscure professional ceremonies and exchanging their 'public knowledge' within the inner sanctum of the state temple.

Theodore Roszak

I believe that this generation will either be the last to exist in any semblance of a civilised world, or it will be the first to have the vision, the bearing, and the greatness to say 'I will have nothing to do with this destruction of life, I will play no part in this devastation of the land, I am destined to live and work for peace, for I am morally responsible for the world of today and the generations of tomorrow.'

Richard St Barbe Baker

Nature always has the last word.

John Stewart Collis

N O AMOUNT of empirical or theoretical evidence is likely to persuade mainstream scientists or other protagonists of the worldview of modernism to accept any of the principles set out in this book. If eventually they are to be accepted, it will not be because they will by then have been 'proved' to be true in the scientific sense of the term, but because the reigning paradigm or canonical knowledge will have changed to such an extent that they will have become consistent with it (chapter 12). Until this occurs, these principles are, in the words of Gunther Stent, 'premature', in that their implications 'cannot be connected by a series of simple logical steps to contemporary canonical or generally accepted knowledge'.[1] In this way, Gleason's 'individualistic' concept of plant association was rejected when ecology was still a holistic discipline, only to be adopted once the subject had been brought into line with the reductionist paradigm of science (chapter 1).

At the same time, no amount of empirical or theoretical 'evidence' as to the untenability of a hypothesis can lead scientists to abandon it if it is part of current wisdom or 'canonical knowledge'. However, once it has ceased to enjoy that status—because of a change in paradigm—then the hypothesis will simply die a natural death. In this way, hypotheses that have achieved the status of 'scientific facts' have, in the space of a few years, been 'completely discredited and committed to oblivion, without ever having been disproved or indeed newly tested'. This is, as Michael Polanyi points out, 'simply because the conceptual framework of science had meanwhile so altered that the facts no longer appeared credible.'[2]

Clearly then, so long as we argue within the accepted 'conceptual framework' or reigning paradigm of the day, we can never dissuade people either to accept a new idea or to abandon an old one. 'Demonstration', Polanyi insists, 'must be supplemented . . . by forms of persuasion which can induce a conversion.'[3] This is the crux of the matter. It is the conceptual framework *itself* that must be changed, and this, as Polanyi suggests, means converting people to a new conceptual framework—a 'Great Reinterpretation' of the fundamental assumptions that underly our view of the world (chapter 15).

For people to accept the kind of principles outlined in this book, it is the reductionist paradigm of science that must be rejected and hence the worldview of modernism that it faithfully reflects; and they must be replaced instead by a holistic and ecological—or biospheric—worldview. Such a conversion or 'generalised paradigm shift' involves *cybernismic reorganisation*—i.e. a profound reärrangement or recombination of the knowledge and values that make up our worldview. It must affect its very metaphysical, ethical, and æsthetic foundations. It must, in fact, involve a change akin to a religious conversion to which—as Thomas Kuhn and Michael Polanyi have noted—a paradigm shift, even one occurring in a purely scientific context, can be realistically compared.

However, we must distinguish between a real religious conversion and a nominal one. All too often a religious conversion is of a very superficial nature—it is largely the terminology used in addressing the world of gods and spirits that changes and little else. A real conversion seems to occur in quite specific conditions, which the psychologist William Sargant compared with those that lead, more stressfully, to a nervous breakdown and also to the brainwashing to which prisoners of war are often subjected in order to make them confess to crimes that they have not committed.[4] It seems probable, too, that the electric shock treatment often given to psychiatric patients fulfils a similar function. This explains why religious conversions are often preceded by physically and mentally exhausting ceremonies, the imbibing of mind-altering preparations, and the inducement of trance-like states, as in the famous Dionysian rites. All this gives rise to a state of mind that may be functionally analogous to a nervous breakdown, a state of heightened suggestibility in which people can assimilate a new worldview.

It may be that the same process occurs—though in a less dramatic way—in new environmental conditions, such as those created by economic development, to which a traditional cultural pattern proves to be unadaptive, causing people to question and eventually to abandon the worldview on which it is based, and with which they and their ancestors have been imbued for centuries or even millennia. Such people pass through a highly stressful, indeed, psychologically intolerable experience, for the human psyche abhors a cultural vacuum, as it does the terrible social disorder and demoralisation to which it must give rise.

Such a situation occurred with the breakdown of paganism (as we refer to the traditional religion or worldview of early Roman society). In the chaos that ensued, there was a frantic search to replace the old worldview with a different one—one that could at least satisfy the psychological requirements of the increasingly atomised and alienated masses that inhabited the growing conurbations of the Roman Empire. Not surprisingly, they turned eastwards for inspiration, to where similar social conditions already existed. Franz Cumont describes the proliferation of eastern cults among the culturally deprived Roman masses. Eastern gods, such as Attis, Adonis, Mithra, Osiris and Isis, all had their devotees. But it was the religion preached by St Paul, the religion of Jesus Christ, that was to prevail.[5]

A.F.C. Wallace seeks to explain the process involved. He sees every person in society as maintaining

> a mental image of the society and its culture, as well as of his own body and its behavioural regularities, in order to act in ways which reduce stress at all levels of the system.[6]

This mental image or model, he refers to as a 'mazeway'. However, when a person under stress receives repeated information indicating

> that his mazeway does not lead to action which reduces the level of stress, he must choose between maintaining his present mazeway and tolerating the stress, or changing the mazeway in an attempt to reduce the stress.

This involves 'changing the total *gestalt* of his image of self, society, and culture, of nature and body, and of ways of action'—in this way, a new culture comes into being. Such a culture is generally referred to as 'millenarian'. They proliferated in Europe during the tenth century—a period of socio-economic change that caused very serious social stresses. Many of the movements that sought to establish new cultural patterns during those troubled times were convinced that the year 1000 A D presaged the end of the world, and they called on their adepts to prepare themselves spiritually for this momentous event.

Such movements are also referred to as 'messianic', in that they are often led by prophets who see themselves as divinely inspired—as a reincarnation of a previous great religious figure, or, in the case of movements of this sort occurring among the Jews, as the Messiah himself. These movements have proliferated throughout the Third World, during the colonial period in particular. Wallace refers to the process giving rise to such cults as 'revitalisation', and defines a 'revitalisation movement' as

> a deliberate, organised, conscious effort by members of a society to construct a more satisfying culture. Revitalisation is thus, from a cultural standpoint, a special kind of culture-change phenomenon—the persons involved in the process of revitalisation must perceive their culture, or some major areas of it, as a system (whether accurately or not); they must feel that this cultural system is unsatisfactory; and they must innovate not merely discrete items but a new cultural system, specifying new relationships as well as, in some cases, new traits.[7]

Wallace considers that both Christianity and Islam, and possibly Buddhism too, originated in revitalisation movements. Indeed, he suggests that all organised religions embody the 'relics' of old revitalisation movements, surviving in routinised form in stabilised cultures.

The increasing failure of all policies based on the worldview of modernism and its derivative paradigms—those of reductionist science and modern economics—to satisfy our most fundamental psychological requirements or indeed solve any of the worsening problems that threaten our very survival on this planet, gives rise to psychological conditions increasingly propitious to the emergence of revitalisation movements. The chances are that such movements will be affected by ecological ideas that are increasingly in the air, and whose relevance is becoming ever more apparent to even the blindest among us. There are signs, too, that such movements are likely to preach a return to the vernacular way of life. Thus, while the rise of Islamic fundamentalism in the Muslim world and of Hindu fundamentalism in India can be seen as an unpleasant trend towards chauvinism, bigotry, and intolerance, it is clearly also a reaction against Western economic imperialism and the disruption of the cultures and traditions of Muslims and Hindus by Western science, technology, and industrial development.

Significantly, too, a considerable proportion of these movements in the Third World have been 'nativistic'—which is to say that they have correctly attributed the ills against which they were reacting to the lifestyle imposed on them by their colonial masters, and preached a return to the Way of their ancestors. Many such movements have been violent and unpleasant, of that there is no doubt. Usually, too, they have been put down with equal violence and unpleasantness, as their ideas were seen as a threat to the established order. However, there is reason to hope that the ecology-based revitalisation movements of the future will seek to achieve their ends in the true nonviolent Gandhian tradition. It could be that Deep Ecology, with its ethical and metaphysical preoccupations, might develop into such a movement. So could the Earth First! movement, whose religious and metaphysical principles, along with those of numerous other similar movements around the world, have been comprehensively collated and described by Bron Taylor.[8]

We cannot afford to wait and see whether such movements will develop into revitalisation cults that are powerful enough to transform our society. Instead, we should work towards their development by helping to create the conditions in which they are likely to emerge. Let us remember that the worldview of ecology is very much that of the vernacular, community-based societies (gemeinschaft), whereas the worldview of modernism is that of industrial society (gesellschaft). We must set out to combat and systematically weaken the main institutions of the industrial system—the state, the corporations, and the science and technology that they use to transform society and the natural world. At the same time, we must do everything to help recreate the stable family and community, and above all the localised and diversified economies based on them, reducing in this way our increasingly universal dependence on a destructive economic system that, in any case, is in decline and may well be close to collapse.

As we multiply our efforts in these directions, so we must create the terrain in which ecological ideas can take root and flourish. May they inspire those who will lead us back to the Way and thereby restore and preserve what still remains of the beautiful world we have been privileged to inherit.

INVOCATION

WE CALL upon the Earth, our planet home, with its beautiful depths and soaring heights, its vitality and abundance of life.

WE CALL upon the mountains, the Cascades and the Olympics, the high green valleys and meadows filled with wild flowers, the snows that never melt, the summits of intense silence.

WE CALL upon the waters that rim the Earth horizon to horizon, that flow in our rivers and streams, that fall upon our gardens and fields.

WE CALL upon the land that grows our food, the nurturing soil, the fertile fields, the abundant gardens and orchards.

WE CALL upon the forests, the great trees reaching strongly to the sky, with the Earth in their roots and the Heavens in their branches, the fir and the pine and the cedar.

WE CALL upon the creatures of the fields and forests and the seas—our brothers and sisters the wolves and deer, the eagle and dove, the great whales and the dolphin, the beautiful orca and salmon, who share our home.

WE CALL upon the Moon and the stars and the Sun, who govern the rhythms and seasons of our lives and remind us that we are part of a great and wondrous universe.

WE CALL upon those who have lived on this Earth, our ancestors and our friends, who dreamed the best for future generations, and upon whose lives our own are raised.

And lastly, WE CALL upon all that we hold most sacred—the presence and power of the Great Spirit of Love and Truth that flows through all the universe—to be with us to . . .

TEACH US AND SHOW US THE WAY.

·Ω·

From a litany composed at the Chinook Learning Center, Whidbey Island, Washington State—now the Whidbey Institute.

APPENDICES

APPENDIX ONE

DOES THE ENTROPY LAW APPLY
TO THE REAL WORLD?

THERE IS A SET OF LAWS that has a privileged status. They are the laws of thermodynamics, in particular the second law, usually referred to as the entropy law.

The term 'entropy' was coined by Rudolph Clausius in 1865. He observed that, within a closed receptacle, heat differences tended to even out. The evening-out continued until total heat uniformity was obtained. This uniformity could thus be regarded as a position of 'equilibrium', at least from the thermodynamic point of view, and he referred to it as 'entropy'.

However, the concept itself is much older. Sadi Carnot, a French engineer, first made use of it in 1827. In trying to understand the workings of a steam engine, he realised that it was exploiting the heat difference between that part of the system which was hot and that which was cold. It was this difference in temperature that enabled it 'to do the work'. The difference tended to even out, however, reducing the system's ability to do the work. In such conditions, energy is said to have been dissipated, which means that it has degraded to a more homogeneous state identified with equilibrium or what Clausius called 'entropy'.

This, in essence, is the entropy law, and it would be quite acceptable if it were applied strictly to the field of thermodynamics. The trouble, however, is that its use has been extended to apply to fields of behaviour that are very distant from thermodynamics, which would appear to most sensible people to be governed by very different laws from those that govern the behaviour of hot air in a closed receptacle or of steam in the boiler of a locomotive.

The entropy law has suffered the fate of many other scientific theories. It has become the object of a cult, worshipped as the key that will unravel the secrets of the universe. The same thing has happened to Claude Shannon and Warren Weaver's 'Information Theory' (appendix 2), which is also perfectly acceptable so long as it is applied to the field of communications, for which it was designed, but has only served to confuse everybody after being hailed as a great scientific discovery that would, among other things, provide a means of measuring biospheric complexity or organisation.

How, then, do we know that the entropy law does not apply to behaviour within the biosphere? To begin with, it is easy to see that it does not. Life probably began on this planet at least three thousand million years ago, and since then—that is, until the beginning of the historical era a few thousand years ago—it has developed in complexity, diversity, and stability. In other words, it has behaved over a sufficient sample of time in a manner diametrically opposed to that in which it should have behaved had it been governed by the entropy law. This is a source of great embarrassment to our scientists. 'How is it possible to understand life', asks Léon Brillouin, 'when the whole world is ruled by such a law as the second principle of thermodynamics, which points toward death and annihilation?'[1] Indeed, either we are all mad and there has not been such a thing as evolution, and the biosphere with its myriad forms of life is an illusion, or else the entropy law does not apply to the behaviour of living things—only to that of inert matter, such as hot air in a closed receptacle or steam in the boiler of a locomotive.

Some of the more thoughtful philosophers of biology, such as Arthur Koestler, seem to realise this,

> . . . the Second Law applies only in the special case of so-called 'closed systems' (such as a gas enclosed in a perfectly isolated container). But no such closed systems exist even in inanimate nature, and whether or not the universe as a whole is a closed system in this sense is anybody's guess. All living organisms, however, are 'open systems', that is to say, they maintain their complex form and functions through continuous exchanges of energies and material with their environment. Instead of 'running down' like a mechanical clock that dissipates its energies through friction, the living organism is constantly 'building up' more complex substances from the substances it feeds on, more complex forms of energies from the energies it absorbs, and more complex patterns of information—perceptions, feelings, thoughts—from the input of its receptor organs.[2]

Brillouin makes the same point. 'Both principles of thermodynamics', he writes, 'apply only to an isolated system, which is contained in an enclosure through which no heat can be transferred, no work can be done, and no matter nor radiation can be exchanged.' The world, on the other hand, is not a closed system.

> It is constantly receiving energy and *negative entropy* from outside—radiant heat from the sun, gravitational energy from the sun and moon (provoking sea tides), cosmic radiation from unknown origin, and so on.

In this way, 'the sentence to "death by confinement" is avoided by living in a world that is not a confined and closed system.' [3]

C.H. Waddington questions the applicability of the entropy law to biospheric processes. He notes that the embryo increases its complexity as it develops, and for this and other reasons he cannot believe that 'any serious embryologists have considered that the second law of thermodynamics can be applied in any simple way to their subject material, in spite of what classical physicists might say.' Indeed, Waddington assures us that the most creative physicists of his day would not have been tempted to impose the entropy law as a rigid dogma of biology. [4]

However, it is not only because the earth receives energy from the sun (and is therefore an open system) that the entropy law does not apply—there are other reasons. After all, other celestial bodies are also open systems. They are all bombarded with energy, 'radiant heat from the sun, gravitational energy from the sun and moon, cosmic radiation, etc.', yet this has not enabled them to develop life as our planet has done.

It is not altogether surprising that other conditions should have to be satisfied, for it is difficult to believe that the development of the biosphere can be explained, as the entropy law implies, simply in terms of energy. This is an old myth that we can refer to as 'energy reductionism'. It originally appears to have come into being as a way of getting round the problems associated with the understanding of matter. The atomic theory of matter was controversial. Thermodynamics was supposed to be based on it. Carnot, however, showed that this science was independent of such a theory—it only involved energy changes. As Stephen Mason points out, this meant that 'Thermodynamics could proceed without a theoretical model of the nature of matter—indeed, it could proceed without the supposition that matter existed objectively' [5]—hence the development of the 'Energetik' school, which taught that the phenomena of nature were explicable in terms of the transformation of energy.

Of course, other writers have told us that everything is number, while atomic reductionists tell us that the world is exclusively made up of atoms. In reality, it is the way these atoms are *organised* that is critical, and there is no reason to believe that atoms have any greater reality than the tables, chairs, dung beetles, or fiddler crabs into which they are organised. It is only possible to maintain these various forms of reductionism if we limit our study to very simple inanimate objects like gases and billiard balls. As soon as we look at the behaviour of complex forms of life in the real world, the illusory character of these theories is quickly revealed. As Brillouin points out,

For inert matter, it suffices to know energy and entropy. For living organisms, we have to introduce the 'food value' of products. Calories contained in coal and calories in wheat and meat do not have the same function. Food value must itself be considered separately for different categories of living organisms. Cellulose is a food for some animals, but others cannot use it. When it comes to vitamins or hormones, new properties of chemical compounds are observed, which cannot be reduced to energy or entropy. All these data remain rather vague, but they all seem to point toward the need for a new leading idea (call it principle or law) in addition to current thermodynamics, before these new classifications can be understood and typical properties of living organisms can be logically connected together.[6]

It is easy to show that if a complex natural system is deprived of any of its basic constituents—energy, information, or any of the basic chemicals of life—it will cease to function properly and will slowly disintegrate, moving in the direction of what we could refer to as 'energy entropy'. Nicholas Georgesçu-Roegen formulated such a law with regard to materials—the Fourth Law of Thermodynamics.[7] We could, of course, go further and subdivide materials entropy into carbon entropy, phosphorous entropy, water entropy, and so on, recognising a different sort of entropy for each of the essential ingredients of living things. All such concepts would be as valid as that of energy entropy, about which people make so much fuss, but they would be equally invalid once all the other conditions favouring biospheric development were satisfied—for, in normal conditions, systems are either able to synthesise their own constituents or derive them from elsewhere in the quantities required.

The availability of these constituents leads to a very strange, indeed, apparently unique phenomenon. Systems tend to organise themselves not in a random or haphazard way—as is suggested by Lotka, Volterra, May, Prigogine, and many others—but in a highly directive way, for randomly produced organisation does not exist in the real world (chapters 2, 26, and 27). What is more, as living things develop, successive thresholds are achieved, which are referred to as 'levels' of organisation. Each time one is achieved, new 'emergent' forms of behaviour appear that display new characteristics. At the higher levels of organisation, behaviour displays those features we associate with life and is governed by a set of laws quite unknown to the physicist and the chemist, whose knowledge is derived from the study of behaviour *at lower levels of organisation*. What is particularly relevant to the thesis of this appendix is that living things are capable of overcoming many of the constraints applying to the behaviour of simpler things. 'Consider a living organism,' writes Brillouin,

> it has special properties which enable it to resist destruction, to heal its wounds, and to cure occasional sickness. This is very strange behaviour, and nothing similar can be observed about inert matter. Is such behaviour an exception to the second principle? It appears so, at least superficially, and we must be prepared to accept a 'life principle' that would allow for some exceptions to the second principle. When life ceases and death occurs, the 'life principle' stops working, and the second principle regains its full power, implying demolition of the living structure. There is no more healing, no more resistance to sickness—the destruction of the former organism goes on unchecked and is completed in a very short time. Thus, the conclusion or question—What about life and the second principle? Is there not in living organisms some power that prevents the action of the second principle?[8]

The notion that living things have some property that distinguishes them from inanimate things is referred to as 'vitalism'. This property was once taken to be of a 'supernatural' nature, as in the case of Aristotle's 'entelechy' or Bergson's *élan vital*. Vitalism is condemned because it implies that the world cannot be understood purely in terms of physics, which our physicists—who want to maintain their dominion over science, indeed over knowledge in general—cannot conceivably accept. But we do not have to appeal to vitalism to show that the second law is irrelevant to an understanding of the real world.

Because of the way living things are *organised*, they are capable of providing themselves with the energy they require to maintain their stability —green plants via photosynthesis, and herbivores by consuming green plants. A physicist might tell us that the sun's energy has been 'dissipated', but the answer to this is 'so what?' As far as the student of the biosphere is concerned, this dissipation is required to power the development of living things and to increase their stability and that of the biosphere.

The case of Georgesçu-Roegen's fourth law is, superficially at least, a stronger one than his case for the second law, since though the world is an open system from the point of view of energy, it is closed from the point of view of materials. But once more, living things can overcome this constraint by developing the means of recycling the materials they require—the waste products of one living process serving as the raw materials for the next (chapter 56).

The question we must now ask ourselves is why our scientists so stubbornly refuse to face both the theoretical and empirical evidence against the applicability of the entropy law to the world of living things? To understand their obstinacy, we must consider what the worldview or paradigm of the physical sciences was in the middle and towards the end of the nineteenth century. In terms of that understanding, the world was seen as an enormous machine, whose components behaved largely like planets and billiard balls. It was just the worldview required to rationalise the trend initiated by the industrial revolution towards materialism, individualism, utilitarianism, and economism—the closely associated values of the industrial age. Science then was largely identified with physics, as indeed it is today. All other sciences were, and still are, considered inferior, so much so that their practitioners are largely preoccupied with raising their status by slavishly imitating the methodology of the physical sciences (chapter 1). If physics was to be the fundamental science governing everything else, then the behaviour of physical things—billiard balls and the like—*must be shown to provide a model for that of living things.*

The trouble was that, in terms of the neo-Newtonian worldview, it failed to do so on two counts. The first and most important problem was that Newtonian time was reversible. It could move backwards or forwards just as a billiard ball can; while in the real world, time is irreversible—we cannot eradicate experience nor restore the past exactly as it once was. As Brillouin puts it,

> One of the most important features about time is its irreversibility. Time flows on, never comes back. When the physicist is confronted with this fact, he is greatly disturbed. All the laws of physics, in their elementary form, are reversible . . . [9]

The Newtonian paradigm also failed to explain the direction of time. Newton formulated laws governing the movement of bodies but did not tell us that they moved in one direction rather than any other. This, again, did not tally with the behaviour of living things.

The entropy law remedied all this. Since energy could only be degraded, it must follow that the time during which its degradation took place is irreversible. As Brillouin notes, 'it is a very strange coincidence that life and the second principle should represent the two most important examples of the impossibility of time's running backward.' [10] All this was just what our physicists were looking for—incontrovertible evidence, as they saw it, that the entropy law underlay the behaviour of living processes. This was further confirmed by the fact that, as in living processes, energy did not move in a random but in a specific direction.

Ludwig Boltzmann's formulation of entropy as a statistical law further confirmed this entropy thesis, since the behaviour of living things was also held to be governed by such laws. Of course, a limitless number of processes can be shown to tend statistically in an irreversible direction. Even a game of snakes and ladders satisfies these conditions, yet nobody suggests that this great nursery game provides a model for life processes. Why the behaviour of gas inside a closed receptacle should provide a better model is not at all clear, but what is clear is the stake our 'aristo-scientists' have in proving that it does.

Another reason why our scientists are so keen to preserve the entropy law, contrary to all the theoretical and empirical evidence, is that *it is easily quantifiable* (chapter 13). This is a critical consideration, for it is a dogma of aristoscience that only a quantifiable proposition can be regarded as scientific. The 'statistical method' is, of course, very convenient. Indeed, if the entropy law can be seen only as a statistical law, then the development of the biosphere over the last three billion years, rather than providing a clear violation of the entropy law, can be interpreted as nothing more than an exception to this law that does not invalidate it. Boltzmann has outdone Imre Lakatos's pre-Einsteinian physicist (chapter 12). Georgeşcu-Roegen realises how unsatisfactory Boltzmann's compromise is. 'According to this new discipline,' he notes,

> a pile of ashes may very well become capable of heating the boiler. Also, a corpse may resuscitate to lead a second life in exactly the reversed order of the first. Only, *the probabilities of such events are fantastically small*.[11]

In other words, once the entropy law is seen to be no more than a statistical law, it tells us nothing about the real world nor about the biological, social, and ecological processes that brought it into being, for these are so statistically improbable as not to be worth considering, and the fact that the laws of thermodynamics are irreconcilable with them is of no importance whatsoever.

A second device for sustaining the entropy law in the face of all the evidence to the contrary is to postulate that though the earth may be an open system, the universe itself is a closed one, which means that life on earth can only develop *at the cost of increasing the entropy of the universe*. The trouble with this argument is that there is no reason whatsoever for supposing that the universe is a closed system. Mark Braham points out that 'A completely closed system is a theoretical construct,' and that 'We have no way of determining whether the universe is closed or not,'[12] while to say that the universe is an open system raises a number of difficult problems. It would mean, for instance, that it is exchanging energy with its environment—but we know nothing about such an environment; if it exists, then it must be part of a wider universe, a 'mega-universe', of which ours is but a sub-system.

'What, then,' Braham asks, 'are the limits to the other [universe], or to the mega-universe, and so on?'[13] Since we are quite incapable of answering such questions, it may be convenient to postulate that the universe is closed. But would this help us very much? As Braham points out,

> To assume closure is to assume a boundary. By definition, a boundary is between something and something else—there must therefore be something on the 'other side'. If we were to speculate meaningfully about this boundary, we would require information about the 'other side', and this would clearly require a leak in the system and hence no closure at all.[14]

But even if we can find a way round this objection—and accept that the system is a closed one and that one day the sun's energy will be entirely dissipated—is this consideration of any practical significance? The terrible problems we face today—the disruption of our climate, the depletion of the ozone layer, the population explosion, social disintegration, deforestation, desertification, the chemical contamination of our groundwater, rivers, seas, and estuaries, and so on—*have not been caused by any reduction in the amount of energy generated by the sun*. To preoccupy ourselves unduly with the possibility that such a reduction may eventually occur *is to divert attention from these immediate problems to an exceedingly long-term one*—for no one suggests that the sun is likely to stop shining in the next few million years or so. It is also to misdirect precious time and energy from problems that can be solved to one about which we can do strictly nothing—for not even our most fanatical technophiles have yet offered to devise a substitute for the sun.

APPENDIX TWO

WHAT IS INFORMATION?

THE TERM 'INFORMATION', in a scientific context, refers to Claude Shannon and Warren Weaver's concept of information developed in 1949. Since then, other theories of information have been proposed, but they seem to constitute little more than minor variations on the original theme. In any case, they do not appear to have earned any general acceptance among scientists. They are listed, together with their most salient features, by Everett Rogers and Lawrence Kincaid.[1]

Shannon was working for the Bell Telephone Laboratories when the two collaborated in developing the theory. Their chief concern was to determine how to maximise the amount of 'information'—not just the number of signs—that could be transmitted via a communication channel with limited capacity. They found it convenient to define information in such a way that it could be measured in terms of Ludwig Boltzmann's mathematical formula for the measurement of entropy (see appendix 1). Information is thereby equated with entropy, with the difference that—whereas entropy is seen as the most probable arrangement of *molecules* in a particular energy state, 'information' is seen as measuring the most probable arrangement of *signs* in a message; probability, in both cases, being equated with randomness in accordance with the Second Law of Thermodynamics, or the entropy law.

It is difficult to understand this notion, unless we realise that, for the communication engineer, randomness (and thus the absence of any organisation or constraints on the arrangement in which the signs appear) is equated with the freedom enjoyed in choosing the message to be sent (and hence the arrangement in which the signs must appear so as to satisfy the engineer's professional requirements). Thus, randomness or entropy is for the engineer the 'ideal' that must be associated with the highest 'information'. To quote Shannon and Weaver, information is highest

> when the probabilities of the various choices are as nearly equal as circumstances permit—when one has as much freedom as possible in making a choice, being as little as possible driven toward some certain choices which have more than their share of probability.[2]

On the other hand, when a 'situation is highly organised, it is not characterised by a large degree of randomness or of choice,' and in these conditions, 'the information (or the entropy) is low.'

The sort of constraints that Shannon and Weaver regard as reducing this freedom of choice (and hence the 'information' content of a message) are linguistic constraints. Each language has a particular structure or organisation, in terms of which we can predict that certain words are more or less likely to follow other words. Thus, 'After the three words "in the event" the probability for "that" as the next word is fairly high and for "elephant" as the next word is very low.'[3] These linguistic constraints reduce the 'information' content of a message by forcing the sender to include signs in their message not because they want to but because it is imposed on them by the structure of the language in which the message is formulated. These signs are regarded as redundant and each language is said to have a quantifiable built-in redundancy—that of the English language being about fifty per cent. Thus, we can say that the higher the organisation (and hence the lower the entropy) the greater must be the constraints, the higher the 'redundancy', and the less the 'information' communicated.

The amount of this 'information' in a message is calculated in terms of the logarithm (base 2) of the number of choices. The result is formulated in terms of 'bits' (the term 'bit' was first suggested by John W. Tukey as an abbreviation for 'binary digit'). When numbers are expressed in the binary system, there are only two digits, zero and one. These may be taken symbolically to represent any two alternative choices. In a situation in which there are only two choices there is said to be one bit of 'information'. The greater the number of free unconstrained choices, the greater the amount of 'information'. If, for instance, there are sixteen choices from among which we are equally free to choose, there are four 'bits' of 'information'.

The greater the freedom enjoyed by the sender in the selection of signs or messages for emission, the greater must be the improbability that a particular sign or message will be sent. To illustrate this, I shall assume that Shannon and Weaver's 'information' takes *meaning* into account. Thus, a message that told us that a horse called Green Crocodile would win a race in which there were sixteen contestants of unknown breeding and with no previous form (all in theory having the same chance of winning) would communicate four 'bits' of information. If we knew something about their breeding and form, and on this basis could classify the horses in accordance with what appeared to be their chances of winning the race, the information communicated would be correspondingly reduced. If one horse were backed down to even money on the theory that it had one chance out of two of winning the race, then a message informing us that it would win would communicate still less information, in fact no more than one 'bit'—the same amount of information as it would communicate were Green Crocodile to have but a single other contestant to deal with rather than fifteen others. The greater the number of 'bits' ascribed to a message the more valuable the information must be. This is clearly a very sensible way of calculating the value of the information communicated to both the bookmaker and the punters.

In reality, it does not quite work this way, since Shannon and Weaver are not concerned with the probability or improbability of a statement being true or false. This is the concern of the epistemologist not the communication engineer. The latter is not even preoccupied with the probability or improbability of a particular statement, nor even of a particular word, but only of particular signs being emitted—regardless of whether these signs make up intelligible words or whether such words make up intelligible sentences. That is to say, the 'information' content of a message, for them, *does not take into account its meaning*. 'Information must not be confused with meaning,' they write, and 'the semantic aspects of communication are irrelevant to the engineering aspects.'[4] This means, as they freely admit, that their use of the term 'information' *is very different from its normal use*.

An essential feature of Shannon and Weaver's theory is that during the emission of a message, its 'information' content is reduced. The reason is that as a message is spelled out along a channel, so does the probability or improbability of specific signs occurring become easier to calculate. Linguistic organisation and thus 'redundancy' are seen to increase, while 'entropy' and 'information' are correspondingly seen to decrease.

Another reason why the amount of information contained in a message must fall as it is spelled out is that communication channels are subject to 'noise' or 'randomness'. Noise, of course, increases uncertainty or improbability. We might think that it would thereby lead to increased rather than decreased 'information'—however, Shannon and Weaver distinguish between the type of uncertainty that is caused by noise (which they regard as *undesirable*) and desirable types of uncertainty, which they identify with 'freedom of choice' and hence with 'information'. The information content of a message is therefore not equal to uncertainty but to 'desirable' uncertainty minus 'undesirable' uncertainty or noise.

That the equations used to measure entropy and 'information' are the same holds great significance for Shannon and Weaver. They point out that for Sir Arthur Stanley Eddington 'the law that entropy always increases—the second law of Thermodynamics—holds, I think, the supreme position among the laws of Nature.' Thus, Shannon and Weaver note, when the engineer meets the concept of entropy in communication theory, he has a right to be rather excited—a right to suspect that one has hold of something that may turn out to be basic and important.[5]

Another aspect of the Theory of Information that makes it so attractive to the scientist is its quantifiability. However, for quantification to be possible, as Michael Apter points out, we must know the exact number of possible messages that could be transmitted at any one time.[6] This may well be possible in the field of communications *but not in the field of behaviour*. It is for this reason, as Anatol Rapoport points out, that

> the modest but, we think, significant applications of information theory to certain psychological experiments owe their success to the fact that in each situation the set in question was strictly defined—a list of syllables to be memorised, associations to be formed, responses selected from, *etc.* There was therefore no difficulty in quantifying the associated 'amounts of information' and relating such accounts to certain aspects of performance.[7]

But, as he also points out, such situations 'appear somewhat trivial'. We can add that *they do not normally occur in the living world*.

In any case, the notion of a passive source of information (whether it displays order or disorder) from which messages are selected by an external agent does not correspond to anything that exists in the world of living things. The natural systems that make up the biosphere are dynamic not static, active not passive (chapter 28); what is more, they are self-regulating, not regulated from the outside (*heterarchically*) by an external agent such as a communication engineer (chapter 43). The source of information and the sender of the message in the world of living things *are part and parcel of the same self-regulating system*.

If, however, we integrate Shannon and Weaver's sender of messages and the source of the messages as part of the same system, it must cease to display entropy—for one of the basic features of entropy is randomness and hence non-purposiveness, whereas the sender of messages acts purposefully since, as we are told, they select for emission those messages that display the minimum redundancy and hence the maximum information content. What is more, if the system is to achieve its goal efficiently, then the information it contains must be organised in the manner most favourable to the achievement of that goal. This we can predict with confidence on the basis of our empirical knowledge of the way patterns of living information or *cybernisms* (brains, genes, genomes, gene pools, *etc.*) are organised in the world of living things.

Another consideration is that the sort of improbability that Shannon and Weaver write about is not a useful concept for understanding the workings of the biosphere. For Shannon and Weaver, improbability is either improbability in relation to the workings of the entropy law—which as we have seen (appendix 1) does not apply to the world of living things—or else it is improbability on the basis of probability theory, which they wrongly take to be the same thing. In the world of living things, improbability, if we are to use this concept, means improbability in relation to a system's model or image of its relationship with its environment (chapter 31). This reflects its own experience, that of its cultural group (if a human animal), and that of its species for the purpose of assuring the system's stability in relation to its environment, and hence of assuring its survival.

Thus, as living things evolve, they develop the capacity to discriminate between an increasing range of different environmental situations, to interpret them correctly, and to react to them adaptively. A very simple organism, such as the *Dionæa* flytrap that so fascinated Darwin, can do one of two things when something lands on its trap—close it, or not; and it does so with the minimum powers of discrimination, since it cannot discriminate between an edible insect and an inedible pebble. At the other end of the scale is a human animal that can handle a vast number of different signals and interpret them correctly and thus has at its disposal an exceptionally large repertoire of adaptive responses. In the language of Shannon and Weaver, we can say that the human animal is capable of handling messages with a high degree of improbability and hence of high information value—thousands of bits of information in contrast to the mere one bit that the *Dionæa* flytrap can handle. The human animal cannot, however, handle each of these messages with equal ease (chapter 25).

The ease with which a living thing can handle messages seems to be a function of their importance or *relevance* to its behaviour pattern and also of the probability—in terms of its own experience and that of its species —that such a message will actually be received. In other words, information in the brain and nervous system is not arranged at random and hence does not display entropy—on the contrary, it is highly organised, as is all information used by natural systems within the biosphere (genetic information being an obvious example).

If information is organised, partly at least, in accordance with the probability of its being required, then systems living in a *protected environment*—in which only *probable* things occur—will need to react adaptively to a correspondingly *limited* range of different environmental situations.

Those that live in a *less protected environment*, however, in which *improbable* things occur, will need to react adaptively to a *wider* range of ever more improbable environmental situations and hence will have to make use of information displaying a greater *diversity* or organised 'redundancy' (chapter 25).

Shannon and Weaver rightly regard a certain amount of 'redundancy' as useful for counteracting the effects of noise. However, they take it to be otherwise undesirable, in that it reduces the information content of a message by reducing the freedom of choice of the sender and hence the variety of messages they can send. But in the world of living things, as already mentioned, organised 'redundancy', or diversity, has a positive value. It increases rather than reduces a message's information content since it determines the system's key ability to adapt to improbable events.

An even more serious criticism of the extension of Shannon and Weaver's concept of information to the world of living things is that information, as I have already indicated, is very much more than improbability. This is also the view of Donald MacKay.

> To dress [improbability] up as a 'definition of information', as some exponents do, seems a most unfortunate obscurantism. Unexpectedness is a measurable *property* or *attribute* of information—not a definition of it.[8]

In the world of living things, a message is not emitted because it is improbable or, for that matter, probable. It is emitted because it is of some relevance to the relationship between the sender and the receiver. However, Shannon and Weaver are not in the least concerned with whether the receiver is interested in receiving a message, let alone whether they can understand it or are likely to believe it. Again, this may make sense in the world of communication engineering but not in the world of living things, where these considerations are critical.

As C.H. Waddington points out, information in the real world largely consists of *instructions* (programs or 'algorithms').[9] Thus, genes combine to provide instructions for protein-synthesis. A gene pool provides instructions for the renewal of a viable population. The brain and central nervous system provide instructions for the proper functioning of an individual's metabolism and day-to-day adaptive relationships with its environment. A culture provides instructions for the coordination of a society's adaptive behaviour pattern.

Such instructions will only be followed by systems that have been designed by their evolution and upbringing to receive, understand, and believe them. This must be true of the transmission of instructions and hence of information in all living processes. What is more, the receiver of a message must also be capable of acting on the information adaptively (chapter 49). The cries of a baby in distress provide an important message to its mother, who is not only disposed to hear them and understand their significance but also to act on them effectively—otherwise, there would be no advantage to be gained from the ability to hear and understand them.

How a message will be interpreted by a natural system is determined by its *relevance to the system's behaviour pattern*. Since the information embodied in a natural system is organised holarchically—from the general to the particular—the importance of a message is determined by its relevance to the most general elements of this cybernismic information. This, in turn, will reflect its relevance to the most important and hence most general phases of the system's behavioural strategy.

As natural systems evolve, they develop the capacity to deal with messages of lesser importance as well. This enables them to develop a more subtle behaviour pattern and thus adapt with greater precision to their specific environment. Nevertheless, the more important messages will remain their primary concern.

The final reason why Shannon and Weaver's theory is inapplicable to the world of living things is that they see the amount of information contained in a message as decreasing as it is being emitted (because of the accumulation of linguistic constraints and noise). In the world of living things, however, the opposite is true—the information content of a message can only increase. It is fairly evident, as Waddington points out, that an adult rabbit running around a field contains a very much greater 'amount of variety' of information than a newly fertilised rabbit's egg. How then, Waddington asks, can we explain such a situation 'in terms of an information theory whose basic tenet is that information cannot be gained?'[10]

That the information content of a natural system increases as it becomes more complex seems clear to a number of writers, who have nevertheless sought to measure a system's complexity in terms of its information content using Shannon and Weaver's concept of information. Thus, S.M. Dancoff and Henry Quastler postulate that the larger the number of different components in a system and hence the greater its 'complexity', the greater must be the amount of information it contains, since the higher must be the improbability of building up such a system by assembling its components in a random manner.[11]

Unfortunately, what Dancoff and Quastler actually measure has nothing in common with the sort of complexity encountered in the biosphere. This cannot be measured by adding up its component parts, because it derives its essential features, above all, from the way these parts are *organised* (chapter 24). For Shannon and Weaver, however, organisation—and hence the constraints associated with it—reduces rather than increases 'information'. Thus, unless increasing complexity is associated with reduced information, and hence the nematode *Ascaris* is taken to contain more information than human beings, Dancoff and Quastler have to ignore the all-important organisational component of complexity.

Significantly, Dancoff and Quastler themselves admit that their work yields but 'crude approximations and vague hypotheses' and that their estimates are 'extremely coarse'. Nevertheless, they insist that this is 'better than no estimate at all'.[12] I do not think this is so. Mathematical calculations based on false premises and making use of inappropriate concepts, by virtue of the impression of great scientific accuracy that they convey, *can only serve to mislead people* and to obscure the real issues at stake.

I have tried to show that the use of the communications concept of information for understanding behaviour in the world of living things cannot be justified on either theoretical or empirical grounds. This is not altogether surprising, *since it was not designed for this purpose*—any more, for that matter, than was the associated concept of entropy (appendix 1). This is Waddington's view. 'Information theory', he points out,

> was developed in connection with a particular type of process and has limitations which make it extremely difficult, if not impossible, to use in many of the biological contexts to which people have been tempted to apply it.[13]

Ramón Margalef makes much the same point. '[. . .] information theory, based on statistical considerations,' he writes, 'is concerned with how data are transmitted—ignoring, however, any human factors involved.'[14] Léon Brillouin, as we have seen (appendix 1), also criticised the extension of this theory to the study of the world of living things.

Yet in spite of these criticisms, all these writers, with the exception of Apter, still explicitly justify its use for this purpose. Waddington, for instance, argues that it allows the concept 'to be clearly expressed', though what I think he really means is 'quantified'.[15] But what, we might ask, is to be gained by quantifying a concept that corresponds to nothing in the world of living things to which it is supposed to apply? *It can only serve to give an air of spurious accuracy* to what is, in effect, little more than a fiction.

Anatol Rapoport's argument for the extension of 'information theory' is that, if it is to 'break out of its original habitat of bandwidths and modulations, a proper beginning must be made, which usually means a modest beginning.'[16] But why not allow Shannon and Weaver's concept of information to remain in its 'original habitat of bandwidths and modulations'? What evidence does Rapoport or anybody else provide for the notion that its use can profitably be extended to other fields for which it was not designed? The answer, I am afraid, is none whatsoever.

On the contrary, the only function that the extension of the theory is likely to serve is to perpetuate the myth that behaviour is mechanistic, passive, atomised, and random, since the theory ascribes precisely such features to the information that governs behaviour. This can only serve to obscure the most important features of the behaviour of living things, which is, on the contrary, dynamic, creative, organised, and purposeful (chapters 28, 29, 26, and 27). Applied to the world of living things, this theory is simply an instrument of scientific obscurantism and mystification.

APPENDIX THREE

A BIOSPHERIC ETHIC

THE BEST KNOWN OBJECTION to a biospheric or 'naturalistic' ethic is a logical one. In his book *A Treatise of Human Nature* (1740), David Hume wrote the now famous passage,

> In every system of morality which I have hitherto met with, I have always remarked that the author proceeds for some time in the ordinary way of reasoning and establishes the being of a god or makes observations concerning human affairs—when of a sudden, I am surprised to find that instead of the usual copulations of propositions, *is* and *is not*, I meet with no proposition that is not connected with an *ought* or an *ought not*. This change is imperceptible—but is, however, of the last consequence. For as this *ought* or *ought not* expresses some new relation or affirmation, 'tis necessary that it should be observed and explained; and at the same time that a reason should be given for what seems altogether inconceivable—how this new relation can be a deduction from others which are entirely different from it.[1]

To argue in this way from 'is' to 'ought' is to be guilty of what G.E. Moore called the 'naturalistic fallacy', which no philosopher or scientist wishes to be accused of. My aim is to show that Hume's argument is invalid. The reason is that although it may well be true that an 'ought' statement cannot be deduced from an 'is' statement, *no one is suggesting that it can.*

In its widest sense, Hume's argument does little more than state the perceived division between knowledge and values, which is still taken to be fundamental to modern science—though many recent epistemologists, among them Karl Popper and Michael Polanyi, have shown that it is illusory, and that there is no such thing as value-free knowledge (chapter 15). This finding is not altogether surprising, since *objective* information (and knowledge is clearly some type of information—appendix 2) plays no role in the strategy of the natural world.

Objective knowledge may be impossible, but as Theodore Roszak notes, the *psychology* of objectivism continues to wield its influence.[2] It leads, above all, to a separation of humanity from the real world of nature, of which we are an integral part and outside of which we are effectively meaningless.

If we cannot entertain objective knowledge, we clearly cannot be motivated by it. It is thus not reason that motivates us but our largely unconscious values—the indelible general instructions that reflect the long-term experience of our species and of our society, and which coordinate those further differentiated instructions that reflect our own short-term experience (chapters 9 and 14).

Human beings are *rationalising* rather than rational animals. We have always cherished values and then sought some authority to rationalise and hence, in our eyes, to legitimise them—so much so that, as Donald Worster puts it, '*ought* has been shaping *is* rather than vice versâ.'[3]

Such a rationalising authority is science, which in the modern world is constantly appealed to in order to legitimise a subjective value. But such an appeal, as A.N. Whitehead puts it, *follows* rather than precedes the *conviction of rightness* that is derived from our emotions and intuitions (chapter 9). In reality, an 'is' proposition is little more than the explicit, seemingly objective and value-free tip of a vast implicit, clearly subjective and value-laden cognitive iceberg. It is this that Michael Polanyi calls a 'conceptual framework' and that Thomas Kuhn refers to (in the very much more restricted field of science) as a 'paradigm' (chapter 12).

It is only in terms of this implicit, subjective, and value-laden worldview that an explicit, apparently objective and value-free proposition has any meaning. What is more, it is only in terms of its ability to fit into a worldview that the validity of a proposition can be established (chapter 12). This is undoubtedly C.H. Waddington's conclusion. 'The validity of Hume's argument', he writes,

> depends entirely on what is the content of the notion conveyed by 'is'. If one conceives of existence as, to put it crudely, Newtonian space-time with some billiard balls flying round in it, then clearly neither 'ought' nor 'owes' nor many other concepts can be logically deduced. But if, to take another extreme, existence is considered as the manifestation of the nature of a beneficent Deity, quite other consequences would follow. In fact, any invocation of 'is', other than as a logical copula, *involves an epistemology—and it is impossible to reduce the relation of 'is' to 'ought' to a matter of pure logic.*[4]

Now, quite clearly, still 'other consequences would follow' when we see Hume's statement in the light of the worldview of modernism, which is clearly reflected in just about all the knowledge imparted today in our universities.

When used to justify the naturalistic ethic, the argument from 'is' to 'ought' is judged to be false by modern thinking, not because it is deemed unverifiable, unfalsifiable, illogical, or meaningless, but because it is *incompatible with the modernist worldview*. In terms of that worldview, an earthly paradise can be achieved with the help of science, technology, and industry, by systematically replacing the natural world—that which has developed as a result of three thousand million years of evolution—with a totally different organisation, the artificial world of human artefacts. This process is known as economic development and is equated with progress (see introduction). This worldview reflects an ethic that is in total opposition to the naturalistic or biospheric ethic—one that we could call the technospheric or 'artificialistic' ethic. This ethic and the worldview that it underlies serve above all to rationalise and hence legitimise the enterprise of economic development to which our society is geared.

It seems clear that the artificialistic ethic is implicit to mainstream science today. Thus, Edward O. Wilson warns against

> the trap of the naturalistic fallacy of ethics which uncritically concludes that 'what is', 'should be'. The 'what is' in human nature is the legacy of a long heritage as hunter-gatherers. Even when we can identify genetically determined behaviour, it cannot be used to justify a continuing practice in present and future societies. As we live in a radically new and changing environment of our own making, such a practice would invite disaster. For example, the tendency under certain conditions to indulge in warfare against competing groups may well be in our genes, having been advantageous to our Neolithic ancestors, but it would be global suicide now.[5]

Implicit in Wilson's warning is the admonition that we 'ought' to adapt to the brave new world that science, technology, and industry are conspiring to create for us—*even if this means behaving in a way that is contrary to our nature as determined by our genes*. This may or may not be possible. However, neither Wilson nor any other writers who preach this 'anti-nature ethic' bother to determine whether it is.

Stephen Boyden has convincingly argued that it is not. As we have seen (chapter 48), he regards the diseases of civilisation, whose incidence increases with per capita GNP (a measure of the extent to which our way of life and environment have diverged from those to which we have been adapted by our evolution), as the symptoms of 'phylogenetic (or evolutionary) maladjustment'. In his view, attempts by our modern society to combat such maladjustments by largely technological means do not constitute adaptations in the true sense of the term, but rather 'pseudoädaptations' (or heterotelic adaptations), whose role it is to mask the symptoms of these maladjustments at the cost of perpetuating them.

The strongest objection to Wilson's argument, however, is that he is, in effect, arguing from 'is *not*' to 'ought'. But why, we might ask, should this be more legitimate than to argue from 'is' to 'ought'? Is the 'ought' logically contained in the 'is not' in a way that it is not contained in the 'is'? Clearly not. Indeed, if a legitimate argument must be one that observes the laws of deductive logic, then Hume, Moore, and Wilson are not arguing legitimately. The artificialistic fallacy violates the laws of deductive logic, just as the naturalistic fallacy does, but its principal failing is quite different. To argue from 'is not' to 'ought' *is to argue for the morality of economic development or 'progress'*—a process that can only occur by disrupting the critical order of the biosphere—whereas to argue from 'is' to 'ought' is to argue for the preservation of the critical order of the biosphere and hence for maximising the welfare of humans and other forms of life—*the only true moral enterprise* (chapter 18).

THE NEED FOR A FEEDBACK PROCESS
LINKING BEHAVIOUR TO EVOLUTION

MAINSTREAM SCIENCE sees evolutionary change as exclusively the result of changes affecting the genes of individual living things. No other processes—neither the development of the embryo into a fœtus, the development of a child into an adult, nor our physiological or behavioural experience—are regarded as affecting the genetic material in any way. These processes are seen as external to evolution and hence unable to play an evolutionary role.

Darwin never said this. For him, natural selection from random mutations (or random variations as he referred to them) was not the only mechanism of evolution—only the principal one. Indeed, towards the end of his life, he actually accepted some of Lamarck's ideas on the inheritance of acquired characteristics, formulating them into his own idea of 'pangenesis' in order to dispose of Fleeming Jenkin's criticism concerning 'blending inheritance'. It was not Darwin but August Weismann who formulated the preposterous dogma that natural selection is the only mechanism of evolution, thereby denying that behaviour could affect evolution through the inheritance of 'acquired characteristics'. This thesis, another of science's gratuitous dogmas, is based on no serious theoretical or ecological considerations. Weismann's main argument for it was that *he* could not conceive of a mechanism whereby acquired characteristics could be translated into the language of the gene, and it was for this reason alone that he insisted—as Paul Wintrebert points out—that all other biologists *had* to agree with him that it did not exist.[1]

It can be argued that Weismann proved his point experimentally—but his experiments were little more than a farce. He cut off the tails of mice, let them breed, repeated the experience on their progeny and went on doing this on five generations of these animals. The fact that a tailless breed of mouse did not arise, he held to be proof that acquired characteristics were not transmitted.[2] However, as Wintrebert notes, Lamarck never suggested that living things passed on *mutilations* to their progeny but only the characteristics that they developed *as a result of their own efforts*. Indeed, the animals, as Arthur Koestler put it, were no more likely to transmit their mutilated tails than a mutilated man is likely to transmit his wooden leg.[3]

Such experiments are, in any case, deeply flawed for another reason. Though the genetic material is indeed plastic or 'fluid' (contrary to what we are told), it is only slightly so. As J.B.S. Haldane noted, it is always possible that such experiments will fail, because the effects of acquired characteristics may not become apparent at a rate that makes them observable, though they may be rapid enough to be significant in geological time.[4]

The basic principle that Weismann formulated (often referred to as the 'Weismann barrier') asserts that genetic information can flow in one direction only—from the germline (or reproductive cells) to the soma (or non-reproductive cells), thus isolating the genome from any changes that might occur to the genes of the soma. There are, however, many reasons why the genetic material in the genome cannot be isolated from the genes of the soma.

To begin with, no life process can maintain its stability without acquiring information concerning its relationship with its environment that allows it to monitor its actions and correct any divergences from the appropriate course on which it is set (homeorhesis—chapter 21). The only possible source of such information being the ongoing physical and behavioural development of the organism—its ontogeny.

Secondly, genetic material is not external to a living system but part of it. The genes do not dictate the development of the embryo, which, as Barry Commoner has shown so convincingly,[5] can only be understood in terms of the interaction between the genetic material and the cytoplasm that forms its environment. Nor, for similar reasons, do the genes dictate evolution.

In addition, as P.P. Grassé points out, if we accept the Weismann–Crick thesis, how do we explain the creation of new genes?[6] The first living thing itself would have been endowed with all the genes that have made possible the evolution of plants and animals in their infinite variety. Since no information can have come from the outside, DNA must have been the unique source of information. This means, surely, attributing miraculous properties to this chemical substance, which is simply not a serious thing to do.

It has always been quite clear to serious students of evolution that there had to be a feedback between behaviour, development (ontogeny), and evolution (phylogeny). In 1896 the American psychologist J.M. Baldwin published the famous article in which he described his principle of 'organic' or 'functional selection'.[7] In adapting to its environment, Baldwin maintained, an organism can affect its congenital characteristics by 'accommodating' them to new environmental conditions. These accommodations, he argued, can eventually become fixed genetically. Forty years later, Richard Goldschmidt suggested that information contained in the physical features of an organism (its phenotype), which are acquired during the course of its life from fertilisation onwards, can, in certain conditions, be 'copied' by the genome and then become fixed genetically as a 'phenocopy'.[8]

C.H. Waddington proposed an analogous process that he referred to as 'genetic assimilation'.[9] He saw organisms as being able to respond to stress by changing their behaviour and sometimes by bringing about corresponding structural changes. To do this, they must be able to defy the pressure on them to resist divergences from their preordained course or constellation of 'chreods' (chapter 21). This can only mean affecting, in some way, the genes that regulate the stability or flexibility of these development pathways or chreods, and eventually—perhaps after a few generations—modifying them. Once this has happened, the altered phenotype can occur with or without the environmental stress, and it would then be said to have been 'assimilated by the genotype'.

At the same time as Waddington developed the theory of genetic assimilation, the Russian theoretical biologist Ivan Schmalhausen worked out a slightly different way in which negative feedback could occur.[10] He referred to it as 'stabilising selection'. Later, Piaget revived Goldschmidt's phenocopy, which he modified considerably. The resulting process is the most interesting, in that it diverges the most from the neo-Darwinian position, as the acquired changes are not seen to be the product of natural selection.[11]

In any case, experiments conducted by John Cairns and others (chapter 26) now seem to have established empirically that information flows in both directions.

The molecular immunologist Edward J. Steele, for example, found himself at the centre of a heated controversy after his studies suggested that certain changes in the genes of the soma of laboratory mice were transferred to those of the germline—thus contradicting Weismann's dogma and providing support for a 'neo-Lamarckian' feedback process in evolution.[12] His findings were later reinforced by work carried out by Corrado Spadafora at the University of Rome.[13]

A further blow to the Weismann barrier is the accumulating evidence of naturally occurring 'horizontal gene transfer' in higher organisms—with viruses, bacteria, and even insects serving as likely intermediaries or 'vectors' for the cross-species 'gene trafficking'; a process, moreover, that provides one of the principal foundations for the transgenic products of the massive and irresponsible biotech industry—products whose proliferation is dramatically increasing the risk of an irreversible ecological catastrophe (chapter 54).[14]

Another rapidly expanding area of research is *epigenetics*, which includes the study of the inheritance of biological traits, the origin of which and mode of transmission lies beyond the genetic code—a form of 'soft inheritance'. Many environmental influences have been shown to reprogram or 'imprint' on an organism's 'epigenome', which affects gene expression. There is mounting evidence that some of these epigenetic variations or 'epialleles' are heritable[15]—representing a process very similar to those proposed by Baldwin, Waddington, and Goldschmidt.

All this means that mainstream scientists no longer have any reasonable argument for opposing the basic principle that development, physiology, and behaviour are integral parts of the evolutionary process, providing it with highly effective feedback processes to ensure that it remains adaptive to changing environmental conditions without sacrificing its stability or continuity (chapter 37).

APPENDIX FIVE

TWO WORLDVIEWS

A few milestones indicating the general course of ideas

THE RISE OF MODERNIST THOUGHT

The Prince (1532) Niccolò Machiavelli
New Instrument of the Sciences (1620) Francis Bacon
Dialogue Concerning the Two Chief World Systems (1632) Galileo Galilei
Meditations on First Philosophy (1641) René Descartes
Leviathan (1651) Thomas Hobbes
Mathematical Principles of Natural Philosophy (1687) Isaac Newton
An Essay Concerning Human Understanding (1690) John Locke
The Man Machine (1747) Julien La Mettrie
The Wealth of Nations (1776) Adam Smith
Principles of Morals and Legislation (1789) Jeremy Bentham
The Course in Positive Philosophy (1842) Auguste Comte
Social Statics (1851) Herbert Spencer
On the Origin of Species (1859) Charles Darwin

THE RENAISSANCE OF ECOLOGICAL THOUGHT

Mutual Aid (1890) Peter Kropotkin
Plant Communities (1895) Eugenius Warming
Science and the Modern World (1925) Alfred North Whitehead
Holism and Evolution (1926) Jan Smuts
Gestalt Psychology (1929) Wolfgang Köhler
Theoretical Biology (1932) Ludwig von Bertalanffy
The Wisdom of the Body (1932) Walter Cannon
Cybernetics (1948) Norbert Wiener
Personal Knowledge (1958) Michael Polanyi
Silent Spring (1962) Rachel Carson
Man's Impact on the Global Environment (1970) Wilson and Matthews
The Limits to Growth (1972) Donella and Dennis Meadows et alia
Gaia—A New Look at Life on Earth (1979) James Lovelock

APPENDIX SIX

TWO WAYS OF SEEING

Gestalt switches, paradigm shifts, and worldviews.

Rabbit?

or duck?[1]

Upright?

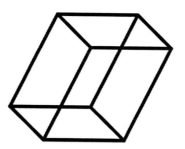

or recumbent?[2]

Blind machine or living organism?
Progress or Promethean enterprise?

REFERENCES

GLOSSARY

A Key to the Way

Italics see entry, (c) compare with entry
* term coined by the author

ANIMISM. The *worldview* common to all *chthonic* societies whereby the world is seen as quintessentially alive, intelligent, possessing initiative, and capable of ordering itself *purposefully* (chapters 38, 32, 28, & 27). Animism was transformed in stages from simple ancestor and nature worship through totemism and polytheism to monotheism; finally being supplanted (in industrial society) by its antithesis—*mechanomorphism*. The term has been variously defined and applied, most notably by Sir Edward Tylor. (c) *vital force, organicism, worldview*

ANOMIE. A broken, *atomised* state of society comprised of individuals alienated from one another due to a lack of shared values and common codes of conduct (chapter 51). Such *demoralised* societies are prone to the rise of dictatorships, *institutional* control, and the doctrine of the *total state*. A concept developed by Émile Durkheim among others. Robert MacIver introduced the related term **anomy** to describe the alienated state-of-mind of the individual within such a society (see *individualism* and chapter 51). An anomic society (*e.g.* an anonymous or mass society) can be contrasted with a *vernacular* society. Anomic, *adj.* (c) *socialisation, pioneer ecosystem, religion, gesellschaft, complexity*

ANTHROPOGENIC CLIMAX. An *ecosystem* that is altered in some manner due to continual human intervention (chapter 22). An artificially engineered ecosystem that is maintained in a *pioneer* stage of ecosystem *development* in order to maximise its productivity—*i.e.* agriculture. The resulting *disclimax* is highly unstable, however, being increasingly prone to discontinuities, such as infestations, epidemics, soil erosion, and so on, which in turn require increasing intervention, resulting in further instability (see *feedback, progress,* and *Great Misinterpretation*). A term originally coined by Arthur Tansley. (c) *disclimax, climax ecosystem*

ANTI-EVOLUTION (AKA 'anti-Way'). See under *biospheric process* and *Way*. (c) *progress, modernism, pioneer ecosystem, traditional, vernacular, climax ecosystem*

ÄSOCIALISED. Absence or failure of the *socialisation* process, resulting in *anomy*. See *socialisation*.

ASSOCIATION (ecological). An ecological *community*. The variety of organisms belonging to an *ecosystem* (as distinct from its geological substrate and atmospheric environment). See *community* and *ecosystem*. (c) *symbiosis*

ASSOCIATION (social). See *community*, *gemeinschaft*, and *gesellschaft*.

ATOM. A discrete, indivisible, and (in some versions) undifferentiated unit existing independently from other units within an equally undifferentiated void or
vacuum. An isolate. (c) *differentiation*. The Greek philosopher Leucippus and his
student Democritus are credited with the original concept, although their
follower Epicurus adjusted their deterministic thesis to accommodate free will.
This ancient Greek concept has been adopted in one form or another by most
disciplines of science. The 'selfish gene' is an example of the atom concept made
to fit biology, the 'engram' an example in neurology, and the 'bit' in *information*
theory—the concept has lost some of its authority in physics, however (chapters
1 & 49).

An atomistic *worldview* is clearly suited to the needs of *quantification* and thus
mathematics—however, it is poorly suited for *qualitative* understanding (see
cognise and chapters 14 & 53). (c) *holon, field, continuum, causality, logical positivism, mechanistic, individualism*

BIOSPHERE. The sphere of influence of living things—the entire world of living things taken together with its geological substrate and atmospheric environment (*i.e.* the lithosphere, hydrosphere, atmosphere, and biota). The general
concept was first proposed in the modern era by James Hutton and also Jean-
Baptiste Lamarck. It was later termed biosphere by Eduard Suess (1875), and the
concept was further elaborated by the Russian geochemist Vladimir Vernadsky
(chapter 35). Similar to LaMont Cole's *ecosphere* and James Lovelock's *Gaia*.
Note that some narrow disciplines, as well as Lovelock himself, tend to use the
term 'biosphere' in the much more limited sense of meaning either the earth's
total **biomass** (both living and dead biological material) or its living **biota** alone.

The biosphere, which herein is taken to encompass *vernacular* societies, must
be distinguished from the *technosphere*, which encompasses *modern* industrial
society, and which expands at the direct expense of the biosphere (see *biospheric
process*). (c) *cosmos, holarchy, continuum, ecosystem, ethnosphere*

BIOSPHERIC ETHIC. A biospheric or 'naturalistic' ethic is a system of internalised values that guides behaviour along the *Way*, in contrast to a *technospheric*
or 'artificialistic' ethic, which directs behaviour along the **anti-Way**. See appendix 3 and *ecological worldview*. (c) *Way, cybernism*

BIOSPHERIC PROCESS (singular). Evolution, where the unit of evolution is
considered to be the *biosphere* as a whole—organisms, populations, and *ecosystems* being but its *differentiated* parts (chapter 37). The antithesis of the biospheric process is the '*technospheric* process' or **anti-evolution**—see *Promethean
enterprise*. (c) *Darwinism, neo-Darwinism, progress, entropy*

The evolutionary process underlying *phylogeny* is considered herein as being
an extension of the same basic process that underlies *ontogeny*. Thus, whether it

be the innate behaviour of *differentiating* cells during *embryogenesis*; the complex instinctual behaviours displayed by these cells acting together as a multicellular unit after birth (chapters 8 & 36); the continued refinement of this behaviour through learning, *socialisation*, and *association*; or the *genetic* and *epigenetic* changes accrued through the transgenerational process of phylogeny—all are considered herein as being expressions of this same basic underlying behavioural process, which in its most general sense can be referred to as the **biospheric process**, the long-term survival strategy of life on earth. (c) *epigenetics, ontogeny, cybernism, unified science*

BIOSPHERIC WORLDVIEW. See *ecological worldview*. (c) *Way*

CAUSALITY (holistic). 'Downward' causation. See *homearchy, purpose, teleology, field*, and next.

CAUSALITY (reductionistic). The notion that events can be explained solely in terms of other events immediately antecedent to them in time and immediately adjacent to them in space. Exclusive (*i.e.* deterministic) faith in this form of causality implies a rejection of the idea of endgoals, *purpose*, or final cause, as well as any kind of non-local, irreducible, indeterminate, or innate cause—the concept having lost some of its authority in physics as a result. See chapter 4 and previous. (c) *teleology, homearchy, field, mechanistic, reductionism*

CHAOS. In Greek mythology, the formless void out of which emerged the *cosmos* (chapter 40). Synonymous with disorder. From the Greek χάος, meaning abyss. (c) *random, entropy, organisation*

CHREOD (AKA creode). The self-correcting *developmental* path along which an organ or tissue proceeds in order to achieve its appropriate endstate (chapter 21)—(c) *ontogeny, succession, climax, stability, Way*. A term coined by C.H. Waddington, along with *epigenetic landscape*, which he used to refer to the total constellation of chreods along which an organism needs to develop. By extension, the path or *Way* of all developing natural processes, including human behaviour, cultural forms, *ecosystems, morphogenesis*, and so on. From the Greek χρή (chre), it needs, and ὁδός (hodos), path or way. (c) *homeorhesis, equifinality, homearchy, field, cybernism, laws*

CHTHONIC RELIGION ('k'thonick' or 'thonick'). The *religion* of the earth or *biosphere*. Chthonic religion could also be referred to as the *worldview* of ecology or the *Way*. It still is the effective religion of many *tribal* and peasant societies that have remained largely outside the orbit of the modern world or *technosphere*.[1] A term adopted, in particular, by Jane Harrison to distinguish the earliest or primal stratum of Greek religion from the later 'Olympian' stratum (chapter 63). Chthonos Χθονός was the Greek god of the soil or earth. *Cosmic* religion. ››

Also, 'chthonic' or '**primal**' peoples and their societies, *adjs.* (c) *animism, vital force, vernacular, ecological worldview, Way*

CLIMAX ECOSYSTEM. An *ecosystem* that has reached maturity. The endstate of the process of ecological *succession*, and the most *stable* state under the existing *biospheric* conditions (chapter 22). (c) *sere, chreod*

A climax stage is characterised by greater *stability, complexity,* and-or *diversity,* more efficient recycling of materials, more extensive integration and *symbiosis,* fewer and less severe discontinuities, and more highly developed internalised controls than are found in a *pioneer* stage. The social equivalent being that of a **climax society** (*e.g.* a *vernacular,* integrated, or stable society), which can only be successfully maintained within a wider climax ecosystem. The behaviour of such a society is maintained by a climax *worldview, e.g.* the *Way* (see *cybernism*). (c) *pioneer ecosystem, vernacular*

COGNISE (AKA cognize). The process of forming **cognitive models**—internalised representations or mental simulations—which are meaningful and functionally adapted to the real needs of the subject but are not necessarily 'literal' or 'precise' in an objective sense (chapter 13). Hence, the process of *developing* subjective, *qualitative,* and *tacit* knowledge or insight by *organising* new data into existing mental models (chapters 14, 15, & 11). A term coined by Roy Rappaport. Related notions found in the literature include 'schemata' and 'frameworks'—however, these fail to emphasise the subjective, qualitative, and dynamic nature of living mental models. See *cybernism, cosmos,* and *tacit.* (c) *information, gestalt, paradigm, worldview*

COMMUNITY (biological). An ecological *association.* The variety of organisms belonging to an *ecosystem* (as distinct from its geological substrate and atmospheric environment). See next. (c) *sere*

COMMUNITY (social). Individuals *naturally* associate together to form larger integrated social units, such as families, forager bands, clans, *tribes,* and so on (see *gemeinschaft* and *complexity*), which can be contrasted with artificial associations or *institutions* that are primarily established and maintained by external means (see *gesellschaft*). See also previous. (c) *vernacular, association*

COMPLEXITY. The intricate, *differentiated* organisation of a living *system* or *holarchy,* as distinguished from the haphazard details of a *mechanically* arranged or *random* system. Complexity should be understood *spatio-temporally* (i.e. as involving complex **processes** in time, not simply complex **structures** in space—see chapter 37).

The greater the *organised* complexity of a particular system, the greater its ability to resist and hence remain immune to **predictable** insults and those that are most likely to occur in terms of its evolutionary experience ('resistance *stability*', chapter 24)—and also the tighter the **integration** of (but the less autonomous) its parts, and the greater its specialisation. Consequently, an overall increase in complexity (as defined herein) results in an overall decrease in *diversity*, and vice versâ (see *cybernism*, however, and below). (c) *diversity, stability*

Nevertheless, at each level of organisation of the *biosphere*, there is a limit to the amount and scale of complexity a system may embody *homeotelically*—beyond this limit it will begin to destabilise, displaying *heterotelic* behaviours. In this situation, order may only be developed further by *associating* these smaller diverse units (or *holons*) together to form a larger *community* or 'complex' at a higher level of organisation. As a result, homogeneous mass societies will tend towards internal randomness and destabilisation (see *total state* and chapter 51), whereas *vernacular* societies are able to maintain their integrity as they enlarge by self-organising their smaller diverse or heterogeneous units from below into larger *differentiated* units or 'complexes' at ever higher levels of organisation—a process of extension and association (*e.g.* diverse individuals associate together into extended families; families into clans; clans into *tribes*; tribes into confederations; and so on—chapter 55), resulting in a stable *holarchy*. See *holarchical mutualism*.

CONTINUUM (biological). The total ordered environment of a living *system* seen as a continuous dynamic *field* of interaction (existing both in space and time—see *spatio-temporal*). The ordered 'external' environment of a living system (its *natural* habitat) is formed by the larger system of which it is part, while its ordered internal 'environment' is formed by the smaller subsystems of which it is composed (chapter 37 and *holon*). This implies that the 'environment', which is usually seen as shaping the *evolutionary process*, is not the inert external stage implied by *Darwinism* but an integral part of a wider living process (chapter 43). Similar ideas have been explored more recently in the field of Developmental Systems Theory (DST).[2] The notion of a continuum and field can be contrasted with that of the vacuum and *atom*. A term adopted by Paul Weiss, among others. See *field*. (c) *holarchy, homearchy*

Also, the related concept that the successful *development* of a child after birth can only occur within a nurturing environment that reflects that under which the species has evolved, and which must therefore be passed down intact (continuously) from one generation to the next. This 'continuum' of child rearing practice has broken-down in modern societies, resulting in widespread social maladjustment and consequent behavioural disorders. A concept formulated by Jean Liedloff.[3] (c) *socialisation, phylogenetic maladjustment, traditional*

COSMOS. The subjectively held view of society, the *biosphere*, and the wider firmament (encompassing the parallel realm of gods and spirits) as seen by *vernacular* peoples. The ordered world or universe—in terms of which the entire *religio*-cultural pattern of vernacular peoples was *organised* (chapters 55, 61, 62, & 63). **Cosmicise**—to be made into a *differentiated* part of the wider cosmic process, and hence to be sanctified, blessed, or endowed with *vital force* (see *cognise*). **Cosmogenesis**—the original act of creation, ritually reënacted in order to cosmicise artefacts, dwellings, ceremonies, people, *etc*. From the Greek κόσμος, meaning order or harmony, as opposed to *chaos*. Cosmic, cosmical, *adjs*. (c) *holarchy of the biosphere, worldview, cybernism, system*

CYBERNETICS. The study of self-regulating and goal-seeking *systems*—in particular, those aspects related to control and communication. A term coined by Norbert Wiener from the Greek κυβερνήτης (cybernetes), steersman. From a cybernetic perspective, a larger entity or system exists wherever parts intercommunicate with one another in such a way that enables them to coordinate their behaviour towards a common, self-determined goal—this self-organising and self-regulating behaviour of *naturally* integrated parts is the principal defining feature of a larger (*ontological*) *whole*. See chapters 2, 20, & 38, *feedback, purpose, field, spatio-temporal, holarchy*, and *system*. (c) *General System Theory, organicism, organisation, cybernism, mechanistic*

*CYBERNISM. The internalised *information* that regulates and coordinates the behaviour and *development* of a living *system*. All *organised* information integrated into a living system that serves to monitor and maintain its *stability* and to fulfil its developmental goals is considered herein as forming a cybernism. The living *biosphere* thus embodies a vast *organisation* of immensely detailed and dynamically integrated information—physical, behavioural, and cybernismic (chapter 37 and appendix 2). (c) *chreod, ontogeny, cognise, information, cybernetics*

   Cybernismic information should be distinguished from the kind of information embodied in the resulting physical features and routine behaviour of a living system (*i.e.* from that of its **behavioural system**). Cybernismic information is that specifically involved in the **coordination** of this development and day-to-day behaviour. It provides an updated model of the living system's relationship with its external and internal environments (*i.e.* with the larger system of which it is part and the smaller systems of which it is composed) together with a dynamic set of instructions allowing it to interpret and strategically plan responses to changing conditions in order to maintain its stability and fulfil its goals (chapter 11). I thus consider a *genome*, a *gene pool*, the mind of living things, the *religio*-cultural pattern of a *vernacular* society, and the very diffuse information that coordinates *ecosystem* regulation as all falling into this category— the biosphere as a *whole* being organised in accordance with (and thus being a living expression of) the dynamic information embodied within this cybernismic *holarchy*.

   Each kind of cybernism employs its own characteristic form of information to encode its relationship with the world—the language of myth in a religio-cultural pattern, for example, or the language of DNA in a genome. Consequently, cybernismic information is both subjective (internalised) and *qualitative* in nature (chapters 15 & 14), determining the way the system 'sees' its world and thus the way it interacts with it. (c) *worldview, paradigm, metaphysics, tacit, gestalt*

The more *complex* a particular cybernismic strategy, the more complex—and thus more **predictable** (as opposed to *random*)—are the conditions it is capable of interpreting and thereby negotiating successfully to maintain overall stability. The more *diversity* a cybernism displays, the greater the range and variety of—and thus more **unpredictable** (random)—conditions it is capable of negotiating. This is in addition to the complexity and diversity that is embodied in the physical features and routine behaviour of a living system (*i.e.* in its behavioural system). In this way, an increase in cybernismic order may offset a relative lack of order or organisation in the rest of the living system, increasing its overall capacity for both complex and diverse adaptive behaviour (involving interpretation, planning, performance, and improvisation).

In certain circumstances, cybernisms may undergo significant reorganisation or **recombination**, such as in the case of a genome during reproduction, or a mind during a religious conversion or during a *paradigm* shift (chapter 66).

From a portmanteau of '*cybernetics*' and '*organism*', specifically distinguishing **living** or biospheric information (which is organised) from the kind of 'information' conceived of by communication engineers (see *information*). **Cybernise, vb.**—to transduce and organise data into a cybernismic medium, such as RNA into DNA (reverse transcription), or written words into thoughts (reading—see *cognise* and *cosmos*).

DARWINISM. Charles Darwin put forward two associated theses. The first, originally referred to as '**transformism**', tells us that living things have slowly evolved from very simple organisms to more and more complex ones (a notion that appears to contradict the 'law of *entropy*'). Darwin also proposed a mechanism for explaining how evolution has occurred. He was impressed by the great store of variations displayed by living things. He took these to be of a purely *random* nature. He was also struck by the competitiveness of living things, as a result of which he saw them as subjected to '**natural selection**' (chapter 2). Those which displayed variations that enabled them to be the victors in the struggle for survival, he described as 'fit'. They would procreate and transmit their characteristics to their progeny so that surviving living things became increasingly 'fit'. This means that evolution, rather than occurring as a result of the efforts of living things—as earlier suggested by Lamarck—was seen instead as stage-managed by the environment, and living things, rather than being seen as dynamic and creative, were instead seen as passive and robotic (chapters 28 & 29). (c) *neo-Darwinism, synthetic theory, sociobiology, mechanomorphism, phylogeny, organisation*

DEMORALISATION (social). The process by which the shared values, outlook, and common codes of conduct that bind a society together are broken down, resulting in the alienation of its members and the subsequent loss of their motivation and resistance to external threats (see *anomie* and chapter 51). Such dis-organised societies are prone to the spread of opportunistic ideologies, ruthless *institutional* controls, and the doctrine of the *total state* (see *individualism* and *tribal societies*). (c) *religion, vernacular, vital force, revitalisation, heterotely, heterarchy*

DEVELOPMENT (biological). *Ontogeny.* Within living *systems* in general, a *succession* of *organised* changes or transformations that proceed sequentially towards an endgoal or *climax*. This must be distinguished from the kind of development characterised by '*progress*', which involves *random* or *heterotelic* change, having no definite endgoal, and imposed by external agents, such as the *state*, NGOs, or corporate *institutions* (*gesellschaft*). See *succession, ontogeny*, and next. (c) *epigenesis, succession, homeorhesis, chreod, Way, spatio-temporal*

DEVELOPMENT (economic). Engineered change as opposed to *natural* development. Colonialism (see *vernacular*).[4] See also *progress* and previous.

DIFFERENTIATION. The *development* of more specific or divergent features from more general or common ones, as demonstrated by the cells of a developing embryo, for example, where new lines of cells are successively 'individuated' through the transformation of common underlying forms—*i.e.* through a process of metamorphosis and *succession*. An increase in the **organised** *complexity* or *diversity* emerging within a larger integrated unit or *whole*. The concept of the differentiation of a whole or *continuum* may be distinguished from that of 'division' within a 'void' or vacuum (see *atom*). (c) *morphogenesis, organisation, qualitative, quantitative*

DISCLIMAX (AKA neo-pioneer stage). A malformation or reversal of ecosystem *development*, resulting in a return to, or persistence of, a *pioneer* stage. (c) *anthropogenic climax, pioneer ecosystem, climax ecosystem*

DIVERSITY. The greater the *organised* diversity of a system, the greater its ability to negotiate and-or recover from **unpredictable** insults and those that are least likely to occur in terms of its evolutionary experience ('resilience *stability*', chapter 25)—and thus the less its integration and specialisation but the more autonomous and adaptable its parts. In reference to a particular unit of organisation, diversity represents one end of the spectrum of the **integration** of *differentiated* parts, while *complexity* represents the other. Nevertheless, the same parts that represent the diversity of a system under one set of conditions may contribute towards its complexity in the face of a different set of challenges (see chapter 25). The term diversity is sometimes used interchangeably with the misnomer 'redundancy'. (c) *complexity, stability*

ECOLOGICAL WORLDVIEW. The *worldview* of 'ecology' is used herein to contrast with the worldview of *modernism*. It is synonymous with a **biospheric**

worldview—in contrast to a **technospheric worldview**. Its *metaphysics* are primarily *holistic* rather than *reductionistic*; *organicist* rather than *mechanomorphic*; and it is principally biocentric rather than simply anthropocentric (or even technocentric) in outlook. Its *epistemology* is primarily *qualitative, tacit,* and personal rather than merely *quantitative,* explicit, and impersonal; and its value system is one that guides behaviour towards the maintenance of the critical order of the *biosphere* rather than simply towards the self-interest of the individual, ego, or 'gene'. Overall, it can be considered to be a continuation of the kind of worldview entertained by *traditional* or *vernacular* peoples, which is most characterised by the *Way. Cosmical* worldview. (c) *biospheric ethic*

ECONOMICS. The term is usually employed to refer to the study of how scarce resources are distributed within human society. I propose a more general use of the term to refer simply to the study of how resources are distributed within any natural *system* (chapter 56). This would require, among other things, distinguishing between the *homeotelic* economy of the *biosphere* and the *heterotelic* economy of the *technosphere, i.e.* between *natural* and unnatural economic behaviour. In natural systems, a homeotelic economy maintains the wider system's *stability* and is thus subject to *homeostasis*—whereas the heterotelic economy of the technosphere is directed towards aggressive, perpetual growth at the expense of the biosphere and is thus more akin to the behaviour of malignant tissue. See *progress* and *market system.*

ECOSPHERE. LaMont Cole's term for the *biosphere.*

ECOSYSTEM. An *association* or *community* of organisms taken together with its geological substrate and atmospheric environment. A term developed by A.R. Clapham and Arthur Tansley. (c) *biosphere*

EMBRYOGENESIS. The origin, formation, and *development* of the embryo. See *epigenesis, morphogenesis, differentiation,* and *ontogeny.*

EMPIRICISM (philosophy). The notion that knowledge can (or ought to be) compiled from observations alone, without regard to theoretical premises, modelling, or interpretation, *i.e.* without prior notions. Contrary to this is the view that knowledge is *developed* by a living *system* through the **detection** of **empirical data** (*i.e.* sensory data), which are then *organised* into an existing model of the system's relationship with its world—the updated model in turn affecting how the system detects and interprets subsequent sensory data (see *cognise, cybernism, paradigm, tacit,* and chapters 10 & 15). (c) *induction, logical positivism*

ENTROPY. In terms of the Second Law of Thermodynamics, the tendency of isolated (or 'closed') systems to move from differentiated states of matter and energy to homogeneous ones ('equilibrium') over time—*i.e.* from order to disorder. There has been a trend, however, of making the 'law of entropy' universal by overextending its application to include everything from living things to the universe itself (see also Newton in chapter 1). Although it may approximately apply to inert materials under certain conditions in the real world, the opposite seems to be the case with *animate* systems, such as the *biosphere* (which appears to be governed by very different *laws*), and to matter in general over the history of the universe—all of which have displayed an increase of order (and hence a decrease of entropy) over the course of time (see *organisation*, *Darwinism*, and appendix 1). A term introduced by Rudolf Clausius for a concept previously defined by Sadi Carnot and later refined by Ludwig Boltzmann and others. Entropy may also be contrasted with *information*. (c) *chaos, random, mechanomorphism, biospheric process*

EPIGENESIS. The term widely adopted to distinguish the modern notion of embryological *development* (by *differentiation*) from the earlier notion of **preformation**. See *embryogenesis, ontogeny,* and *epigenetics.* (c) *epigenetic landscape, spatio-temporal*

EPIGENETIC LANDSCAPE. Those factors outside the *genome* (such as the cytoplasm) that influence the course of embryological *development* after conception (chapter 21). A term coined by C.H. Waddington. (c) *epigenesis, chreod, field*

EPIGENETICS (see also *epigenesis*). The study of the processes underlying biological *development*. A term originally coined by C.H. Waddington but nowadays applied more specifically to the study of developmental *information* originating beyond the *genome*. **Epigenetic inheritance**, for instance, involves the inheritance of biological traits, the origin of which and mode of transmission lies beyond the genetic code (*i.e.* an 'epigenetic code'—programmed, for example, by way of changes made to the histone proteins bonded to the genes of the nucleus, which affect gene expression).

While the *differentiated* physical features of the various cell types that make up an organism are known to be the result of epigenetic changes developed and passed on through *successive* generations of cell during the process of *ontogeny*, there are growing indications to suggest that the evolution of species (*phylogeny*) may also be influenced by epigenetic changes that are passed on between successive generations of organism—the *evolutionary process* would thereby also involve 'epigenotypes', which in turn would affect lower level genetic structures or *genotypes* if maintained over enough generations, thus providing an essential *cybernetic* or adaptive *feedback* process between behaviour, development, and evolution (see appendix 4 and *biospheric process*). (c) *ontogeny, epigenetic landscape*

EPISTEMOLOGY. A theory or study of the nature of knowledge. (c) *metaphysics, ontology*

EQUIFINALITY. The ability of life processes to return to the same (or a very similar) endstate from different starting points (including in *diverse*, uncertain, or unforeseen conditions) and by a variety of means. It is a basic characteristic of living things. (c) *teleology, purpose, homeostasis, homeorhesis, chreod, cybernetics, cybernism*

ETHNOSPHERE. The earth's rich heritage of cultural *diversity*, which faces the same threat of extinction from the unrelenting expansion of economic development as does the earth's biological diversity (chapter 65). A term that has been employed in various ways by a number of authors, including the American philosopher James Feibleman, the Russian anthropologist Leo Gumilëv, and the Canadian anthropologist Wade Davis. (c) *vernacular, biosphere, technosphere*

EUKARYOTES. Plants, animals, and fungi. Specifically, an organism composed of a cell or cells characterised by the presence of a nucleus and organelles. According to **endosymbiotic theory**, eukaryotes have themselves evolved from mutual *associations* of simpler *prokaryotes*—a thesis that challenges a central tenet of *neo-Darwinism* (that life evolves by **competition** between organisms rather than by *mutualism*—chapters 44 & 45). (c) *prokaryotes, symbiosis, Gaia*

EVOLUTION. See *biospheric process* and *phylogeny.*

FEEDBACK. Any activity that in turn affects itself. **Positive feedback** increases the activity (self-reinforcement)—**negative feedback** reduces it (self-correction). Feedback is fundamental to the maintenance and *stability* of all living processes, forming the very basis of self-regulating behaviour. Processes that do not involve feedback are incapable of guiding themselves and are by definition **blind** (see *mechanistic*). The study of such feedback processes (or 'loops') is central to *cybernetics.* (c) *homeostasis, purpose, random*

FIELD (biological). The region of mutual influence and interaction that organises the behaviour and *development* of a natural *system*. The ordered field of a natural system arises from the larger system of which it is an integral part (its *natural* habitat), which together with others comprise a wider *continuum* of mutual influence and interaction (chapter 49). A term adopted by biologists Alexander Gurwitsch, Paul Weiss, C.H. Waddington, and others from the 'field' concept originally developed in physics, representing an alternative to *mechanistic* theories of interaction. Field theory has also been employed in psychology and the social sciences.[5] (c) *continuum, spatio-temporal, epigenetic landscape, holarchy, symbiosis*

A 'field' describes a unit of *organisation* that cannot be reduced to its constituent parts alone, and within which the parts are dynamically ordered and interrelated in some way. For example, there may be a turnover of many generations of individual cells over the lifespan of an organ, but each cell is coordinated by the organ's 'field' in such a way that the correct form and functioning of the organ is maintained throughout ('tissue organisation field theory'[6]). In the same way, a *traditional* society manages to maintain its distinctive cultural pattern despite the continuous turnover of its individual members over the generations —the behaviour of each member being entrained by the larger cultural 'field' that they inhabit, and which outlives them (see *laws, cybernetics, socialisation*, and chapter 37). (c) *homearchy, community, vital force, cybernism*

GAIA. James Lovelock's term for the *biosphere*, adopted at the suggestion of the novelist William Golding. Gaia Γαῖα was the Greek goddess of the earth—(c) *chthonic religion*. Lovelock's Gaia thesis—AKA 'geophysiology', related to Earth System Science (ESS)—sees the earth as a single, unified, self-regulating entity adapting its environment in order to maintain its own *homeostasis* or *stability* in the face of solar, geological, and other externally determined changes (chapter 35). This thesis—along with that of **endosymbiosis** (see *eukaryotes*)—received many important contributions from the American biologist Lynn Margulis. (c) *holarchy of the biosphere, biospheric process, cybernetics*

GEMEINSCHAFT ('guh-mine-shaft'). Ferdinand Tönnies' term for *natural* human *associations*, such as the family, *community*, and *tribe*—as contrasted with *gesellschaft* or artificial associations, such as the *state*, corporations, and NGOs. Herein, used synonymously with the term *vernacular* society. Tönnies' basic categories were further explored by Max Weber, who saw them more as 'ideal types' rather than as real entities (see chapter 1 and *cybernetics*). Note that the term is used both as a noun and adjective (the latter to denote the type of relationships inherent in such associations—see *gesellschaft*), and that the German plural form (gemeinshaften) is not strictly adhered to in English. (c) *institution, tribal societies, community, complexity, climax ecosystem*

GENE POOL. The totality of genes belonging to a population of interrelated individuals. (c) *genome*

GENERAL SYSTEM THEORY (AKA General Systems Theory—GST). A field of study and associated *metaphysics* founded by Ludwig von Bertalanffy that seeks to understand the basic laws or principles applying to *systems* in general. See *unified science, organisation*, and chapter 42. (c) *cybernetics, holism, purpose*

GENOME. The totality of genetic information (in the form of heritable sequences of nucleotides) belonging to an individual organism—its 'genetic code'. (c) *genotype, gene pool, epigenetics*

GENOTYPE. The particular characteristics or 'genetic makeup' of an individual's *genome*. (c) *phenotype*

GESELLSCHAFT ('guh-zell-shaft'). Ferdinand Tönnies' term for artificial special-interest associations, such as those held together by the force of legal **contract** (*e.g.* the state, corporations, and NGOs)—as opposed to *gemeinschaft* or *natural* associations held together by the familial bonds of **custom**. According to Tönnies, members of gemeinschaft are primarily orientated towards (and thus regulated by) group-interest—whereas members of gesellschaft are primarily orientated towards (and thus regulated by) self-interest (chapter 60). From the point of view of the *biospheric process*, where gemeinschaft represents healthy, *differentiated* social tissue, gesellschaft characterises malignant or *heterotelic* growth. Herein, used synonymously with the term *institution*. See *gemeinschaft*. (c) *total state, anomie, pioneer ecosystem, natural*

GESTALT ('gush-talt'). Gestalt psychology (not to be confused with 'Gestalt therapy') noted the tendency of the mind to perceive the whole pattern (or 'gestalt') as distinct from its component parts—the forest from the trees, the melody from the notes, the face from the features—and how the same arrangement of parts may be perceived in different and mutually exclusive ways (the result of a **gestalt switch** or 'shift'—see *paradigm*, chapter 15, and appendix 6). A particular instance or way of seeing. (c) *worldview, cybernism, cognise, whole, field, holism, organicism*

GREAT MISINTERPRETATION, THE. The way of seeing and interpreting things characterised by *modernism*, which rationalises the transformation or 'economic development' of the living *biosphere* into a lifeless *technosphere* (*i.e.* of the organic into the inorganic)—see *Promethean enterprise*. Consequently, using the problems caused by economic development as a rationale for pursuing further economic development to try to solve them, thereby exacerbating the original problems used to justify the modernist project in the first place (chapter 64)—a classic example of positive *feedback* or 'vicious cycle', which leads to an ever increasing divergence from the *Way*. (c) *Great Reinterpretation, Great Transformation, ecological worldview, progress*

GREAT REINTERPRETATION, THE. The corollary of the *Great Misinterpretation*. A return to the *Way* through the reädoption of an *ecological worldview*. (c) *Great Transformation*

GREAT TRANSFORMATION, THE. The title of Karl Polanyi's 1944 work in which he describes the social and economic transformation of the previous agrarian order, through various stages, into the modern industrial order. (Polanyi reserves the designation 'Great' for a specific stage within this more general process.) Herein, the term has been adopted to refer to the corollary *stabilising* process characterised by an organic (*homeotelic*) transformation of the modern industrial order into a post-industrial *biospheric* order—a return to the

Way (chapter 66). (c) *Great Reinterpretation, Great Misinterpretation, vernacular, Promethean enterprise*

* HETERARCHY. From the Greek ἕτερος (heteros), different, and ἀρχός (archos), leader or ruler. I use the term to mean the control of the parts of a *system* by an agent that is alien or external to it, just as people are controlled by corporations and state *institutions* as opposed to the families, communities, and the extended society of which they are the innate and *homeotelic* constituents (chapter 43). Äsystemic regulation. (c) *homearchy, heterotely, hierarchy*

    Note that the term originally meant 'rule by an alien'. In the 1940s, however, the American cybernetician Warren S. McCulloch used the term in quite a different sense, to refer to the anomalous or paradoxical logic seemingly embodied in self-referencing neural circuits. Herein, the term is defined closer to its original meaning.

* HETEROTELY ('hetter-otteh-lee'). From the Greek ἕτερος (heteros), different, and τέλος (telos), end or goal. Äsystemic behaviour—abnormal or misdirected behaviour, which, although it may at least partly satisfy the requirements of the *individual*, does not satisfy those of the larger *system* of which it is part (*i.e.* of the *holarchy of the biosphere*), and which, if sustained for long enough, will reduce the *stability* and integrity of the wider *whole* and ultimately that of its individual parts (see chapter 47 and *holarchical mutualism*). Behaviour that follows the **anti-Way**. Heterotelic ('hetter-oh-tellick') *adj.* (c) *homeotely, Way, random, phylogenetic maladjustment, tolerance range*

HIERARCHY. In the natural and formal sciences, the term is generally used to refer to *information* arranged into classes and ordered with respect to its level, scope, precedence, and so on (*e.g.* taxonomy—see *qualitative*). In the humanities and social sciences, on the other hand, the term is often used to refer to a system of top–down authority or social ranking. Much confusion arises from this. Herein, the term is used closer to the former meaning and may be substituted, in many instances, by the term *holarchy* (see chapter 42).

    Note, however, that a holarchy is an actual entity or domain, which is itself composed of nested *associations* of smaller subunits or sub-domains (see *homearchy* and *complexity*)—a 'hierarchy', on the other hand, generally refers either to an arrangement of levels of classification and scope, such as that displayed within a holarchy, or to the ranking of controlling parts that exist separately from the entities they are assigned to control, such as military officers appointed to command various divisions of troops—the officer is clearly not composed of these troops but rather commands them from without (see *heterarchy*). It must be borne in mind, however, that in *vernacular* societies, leaders are themselves integral parts of the wider social body and consequently subject to its homearchic constraints, unlike their modern counterparts, who remain largely impervious to social reproach. From the Greek ἱερός (hieros), *sacred*, and ἀρχός (archos), leader or ruler—the order of the sacred (see *vital force*), or the rule of 'hierarchs' (high priests).

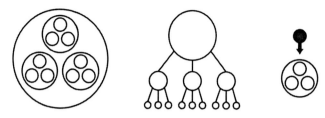

From left to right—*holarchy, hierarchy, heterarchy*

*HOLARCHICAL MUTUALISM. The mutual relationship between a natural *system* and the larger natural system of which it is an integral part. Both must contribute to the maintenance and integrity of the other in order to maintain their own *stability*. A necessary condition for the maintenance of the wider *holarchy of the biosphere* (chapter 46). Holarchical mutualism is but another way of stating the principle that both *homeotely* and *homearchy* are prerequisites of *homeostasis*. It thereby lays emphasis on part–whole (local–global) relationships, rather than exclusively on one or the other aspect (see *holon*). The common good —*unus pro omnibus, omnes pro uno* ('All for one and one for all'—motto of the Swiss Confederation). (c) *holarchy, symbiosis, eukaryotes*

HOLARCHY. The total *differentiated* structure of a self-generating *system* or life-form. The larger elements of a holarchy being formed from nested *associations* of smaller modular elements or *holons*. See *complexity*.

The more general (or common) features of the holarchy contribute to the maintenance and integrity of the more particular (or divergent) features, and vice versâ, thus ensuring their mutual *stability* (see *holarchical mutualism*)—or if this is not possible, with priority given to the maintenance of the more general or critical features (chapter 45).

A holarchy exists in time as well as space, forming a total dynamic life-cycle or *continuum*, consisting of longer term processes composed of sub-units of shorter term processes (see *field* and chapter 37). (c) *spatio-temporal, succession, differentiation, organisation*

It is only by seeing living things in the context of the wider holarchy or *whole* to which they belong that their function or *purpose* may be determined—a *reductionist* approach, on the other hand, is necessarily blind to such a perspective and must therefore deny purpose *per se* (chapters 1 & 2). The original term was coined by Arthur Koestler. See *hierarchy* and *complexity*. (c) *whole, continuum, system, homearchy, holism*

HOLARCHY OF THE BIOSPHERE. The total *differentiated* and self-organised structure of the *biosphere* (existing both in space and time), which herein is taken to encompass *vernacular* societies. See *holarchy* and *spatio-temporal*. Synonymous with *cosmic* holarchy, which encompasses the ordered universe. The holarchy of the biosphere embodies a vast *organisation* of immensely detailed and dynamically integrated life forms and life processes, representing the de facto preëxisting order on this planet, and which seeks to maintain itself and ensure its stability and continuity in the face of external challenges, such as that currently posed by the unrelenting growth of the *technosphere*. (c) *biospheric process, holon, continuum, cosmos*

HOLISM. The tendency found in nature to form integrated *wholes* (organisms, bodies, entities, *systems*) from the self-organisation and *differentiation* of constituent parts. From this, the notion that *natural* systems are not determined by their component parts alone (*reductionism*) but must also be determined by the influence of the larger four-dimensional or *spatio-temporal* system of which they form an integral part—(c) *field, homearchy, purpose*. Holism has its roots in the ideas of 'ganzheit' (wholeness), mereology (part–whole logic), *gestalt*, and *organism* developed by such thinkers as Johann von Goethe, Edmund Husserl, Christian von Ehrenfels, Max Wertheimer, Frederic Clements, and Alfred North Whitehead among others. A term coined by Jan Smuts. **Holistic** *adj*. See also *holon*. (c) *organicism, mechanomorphism, holarchy, symbiosis*

HOLON. A sub-unit of a *holarchy*, being itself both a *whole* composed of further sub-units and simultaneously a sub-unit of a larger whole. A term coined by Arthur Koestler that distinguishes an entity integrated as part of a larger *continuum* or whole from a purely *atomistic* entity or one isolated from all others in a **vacuum** (chapter 42). The holon concept thus embodies aspects of atomism (*reductionism* and *causality*) with aspects of *holism* (*organicism* and *teleology*) laying emphasis on part–whole (local–global) relationships. Holonic *adj*. (c) *holarchical mutualism, holarchy, field*

    Whereas the atomic concept extends the idea of the homogeneous, indivisible, and isolated particle up to the level of the largest entities (rendering them easily *quantifiable*), the holistic concept extends the idea of a highly *organised* and *differentiated* whole down to the level of the smallest entities (exhibiting rich and distinctive *qualities*).

*HOMEARCHY. From the Greek ὅμοιος (homeos), same, and ἀρχός (archos), leader or ruler. Used herein to refer to the regulation of natural *systems* by the *holarchy* of systems of which they are an integral part. For instance, the regulation of people (much of which is likely to be internalised and hence subconscious—chapter 23) by the *natural* supraïndividual units to which they belong (*gemeinschaft*), such as individuals by their families, families by their *communities*, communities or populations by their *ecosystems*, *etc*. Innate or systemic regulation. Not to be confused with the term 'homōarchy'. See *heterarchy, field, chreod*, and *teleology*. (c) *holarchy* › › ›

Whereas *homeotely* is the maintenance of the *whole* by the parts, homearchy is the regulation of the parts by the whole. Thus, homearchy may be understood as holistic *causation* (also referred to as 'downward causation' by Donald Campbell and others—see *purpose*), as opposed to reductionistic causation—the whole thereby coordinating the *stability* and end-goals (and thus predictability) of its constituent parts (chapter 43). (c) *homeotely, purpose, cybernetics, laws, Way*

HOMEORHESIS. *Homeostasis* applied to a *developing* system—one seeking to maintain itself along its *chreods* or *epigenetic landscape* or (in the case of a human society) along the *Way*, and to correct diversions from it caused by internal or external challenges (chapters 20 & 65). A term coined by C.H. Waddington from the Greek ὅμοιος (homeos), same, and ῥέος (rheos), stream. Maintaining a stable course or trajectory. (c) *Way, chreod, succession, sere, cybernism, spatio-temporal*

The term has also been adopted by ecologists to refer to the way in which natural *systems* maintain their overall *stability* through adaptation (rather than stasis) within their *tolerance range* (chapter 48)—i.e. to the 'balance of nature', which is dynamic (see *stability* and chapter 41).

HOMEOSTASIS. The ability of a system to return to its previous state after a disturbance or, in the case of a living *system*, the reduction of discontinuities, and thus stress, to a minimum in the face of internal or external challenges. Living things can only achieve this within their *tolerance range*. It is essential to the thesis of this book that a living system can only properly maintain its own homeostasis by also maintaining that of the *holarchy* of larger systems of which it is part. In other words, both *homeotely* and *homearchy* are preconditions for homeostasis (see *holarchical mutualism*). The term was coined by the physiologist Walter Cannon from the Greek ὅμοιος (homeos), same, and στάσις (stasis), standing (see *homeorhesis* and chapter 20). Allostasis. (c) *Way, stability, equifinality, homearchy, cybernetics, feedback, teleology*

*HOMEOTELY ('hommy-otteh-lee'). From the Greek ὅμοιος (homeos), same, and τέλος (telos), end or goal. Systemic behaviour—that which serves to maintain the critical order of the *whole* or, more precisely, of the wider living *continuum* or *holarchy of the biosphere* (chapter 46)—i.e. that which follows the *Way*. Such behaviour can be cooperative, in that it serves at the same time the immediate interests of the constituent parts—*holarchical mutualism*. It can also be competitive, serving the critical interests of the whole but to the detriment of some of its less well *differentiated* or less adaptive parts, which may fall victim to such competition (chapters 44 & 45).

There is an optimum degree of **homeotelic order** that is appropriate at each level of the holarchy of the biosphere—inappropriately strict order giving rise to instability, as will inappropriately loose order (chapter 40). See *tolerance range* and *complexity*. ›››

Whereas *homearchy* is the regulation of the parts by the whole, homeotely is the maintenance of the whole by the parts. Homeotelic ('hommy-oh-tellick') *adj.* (c) *heterotely, homearchy, symbiosis, Way*

INDIVIDUALISM. The *atom* concept applied to a society or *community*. The individual is thus regarded as the unit or atom of social behaviour, rather than as being an integral member of a *natural* social unit or *holon* (*e.g.* of a family, hunting band, tribe, *etc.—gemeinschaft*), with self-interest and competitive behaviour regarded as the prime ethic rather than group-interest and cooperative behaviour (see *gesellschaft, pioneer society*, and chapters 45, 51, *&* 60). Individualism is a trait characteristic of societies in which the natural units have already largely disintegrated, resulting in a **mass society**, which in turn provides the conditions for ruthless institutional controls and the doctrine of the *total state* (see *anomie*)—the very antithesis of *vernacular* society and, ironically, of the ideals of individualism itself. Egoism. (c) *heterotely, demoralisation, complexity, religion*

INDUCTION. *Empiricists* entertained the notion that knowledge may only be validly acquired by accumulating individual observations of specific phenomena and noting any apparent cause and effect relationships between them without seeking to apply any theoretical considerations—**deduction** being the corollary process of predicting observations from existing knowledge built up through induction. It is a premise of this book that induction (and thereby deduction) cannot occur successfully without also relying on theoretical modelling—and thus interpretation—as an integral part of the process, which necessarily limits the validity of the empiricists' approach, as it is inescapably dependent on subjective values and preconceptions (chapter 10). Furthermore, due to the accumulated experience acquired by living things during their evolution—inherited by successive generations in the form of generalised instinctual and cultural knowledge—it is deduction from highly *organised* (and thus *qualitative*) models that is the principal, and indeed the most valid, method of acquiring knowledge within the *biosphere*; knowledge that is further refined and adapted during the ongoing learning experience of each successive generation of the organism (see chapters 8 *&* 15, *cybernism, cognise, information, tacit*, and *epigenetics*). (c) *empiricism, logical positivism, causality, paradigm, ontology, unified science*

INEFFABLE. Knowledge that cannot easily be expressed, if at all. See *tacit*.

INFORMATION. There is a fundamental difference between information found in the world of living things (*biospheric* information, which is *organised*—see *cybernism*) and the kind of 'information' conceived of by engineers and mainstream scientists for the development of communications technology, rendering mainstream information theory a flawed and misleading model when applied to the living world (see appendix 2 and *organisation*). ›››

Biospheric information—including that embodied in the culture and mythology of *vernacular* societies—is adapted by the *evolutionary process* to fit in with the wider *holarchy of the biosphere*; this being its primary *epistemological* criterion for validation (see *induction*). Technospheric 'information', on the other hand, fails such validation, receiving its justification from altogether alien criteria (see *mechanomorphism* and chapters 14 & 15, for example). (c) *heterotely, empiricism, cybernism, tacit*

INSTITUTION. Herein, used in the sense of something established by decree—more specifically in reference to artificially engineered associations (bureaucracies, corporations, NGOs, *etc.*) and their attendant practices and professions, which are primarily established and maintained by the force of law and other external (*heterarchic*) means (see *gesellschaft* and *gemeinschaft*). In the social sciences, however, the term is generally used in relation to any association or social custom without regard to the manner of its formation or maintenance.

For Ivan Illich, the 'institutional process' of professional services[7] contrasts sharply with the 'vernacular domain' of self-generated and self-regulating endeavours,[8] which the former seeks to colonise and enclose (see *vernacular* and *Promethean enterprise*). Illich also identifies 'shadow work'—unpaid labour (*e.g.* 'self-service') that directly serves the needs and interests of the 'institutional process' rather than those of the 'vernacular domain'. (c) *community, association, technosphere, market system*

INTUITION. See *tacit*.

LAWS (biospheric). Used herein to refer to innate or systemic (*homearchic*) constraints that order the behaviour of natural *systems*, as opposed to artificial 'laws', which are imposed *heterarchically* by external agents (chapter 5). The concept of systemic 'constraints' ordering life processes was most notably adopted by C.H. Waddington—see *chreod* and *field*. Similar ideas have been discussed in the social sciences—in the school of 'structural functionalism', for example—which see people as being embedded in (and thus constrained by) larger cultural or 'socioëconomic' structures. However, these ideas do not distinguish between *biospheric* structures and processes, which are homearchic (and thus systemic), and *technospheric* ones, which are heterarchic (and thus äsystemic) to *natural* systems. Systemic constraints constitute neither absolute nor negligible forces, but ones which must be observed in order to maintain *homeostasis* (chapters 40 & 43). (c) *Way, cybernism, organisation, tolerance range, stability*

LINGUISTIC PHILOSOPHY (AKA Oxford philosophy, ordinary language philosophy). A school of thought that tended to reduce philosophical problems (*metaphysics*) down to misunderstandings of language alone, and proffered the hope, thereby, that metaphysical theorising could be dismissed altogether as nonsensical (chapters 10 & 14). It is perhaps most closely associated with the

Oxford scholars Gilbert Ryle and J.L. Austin, who helped bring it to prominence in the 1940s and '50s—it had fallen out of favour by the 1960s, however, along with the closely related schools of *logical positivism* and **emotivism**. (c) *empiricism*

LOGICAL POSITIVISM. One of the more hardened schools of *reductionist* thought, ascending to prominence in the 1930s and '40s but losing much of its favour in academic circles by the '50s and '60s. Its underlying tenets, however, very closely reflect those of the *paradigm* of science and the *worldview* of *modernism* that permeate most of our modern *institutions*. Famously criticised by Karl Popper, Michael Polanyi, and Thomas Kuhn among others (see chapter 12). (c) *reductionism, empiricism, modernism, linguistic philosophy*

MARKET SYSTEM (AKA 'market economy'). The *modern* market system, which is *heterotelic* to the *biosphere*, must be distinguished from the *traditional* markets, fairs, and other forms of customary exchange that have always been a feature of *vernacular* societies, and which are *homeotelic* to the biosphere (chapters 58, 57, 56, & 39). The modern market system seeks to colonise and enclose all areas of vernacular life in order to **commoditise** (*i.e.* to free from all *homearchic* constraints and attachments) its land, people, natural resources, and day-to-day activities— thus mobilising them towards its own xenobiotic ends. The market system thus represents a highly efficient colonial mechanism for maximising the plundering and exploitation of host populations. (c) *economics, Promethean enterprise, progress, gemeinschaft, institution, technosphere, total state*

MECHANISM (philosophy). See *mechanomorphism*.

MECHANISTIC. Reduced to the operation of discrete and independent parts or *atoms* interacting blindly and passively with one another and having no intrinsic connection or common *purpose*. From 'mechanism'—see *mechanomorphism*. (c) *atom, causality, random, reductionism, cybernetics*

MECHANOMORPHISM (AKA 'mechanism'). The notion that living things and other natural phenomena have the form or qualities of a machine, *i.e.* blind, inert, composed of isolated or *atomised* parts, *etc*. An idea put forward in particular by Galileo, Descartes, Hobbes, La Mettrie, and Laplace, with its roots in ancient Greek philosophy (chapter 38). See *organicism*. (c) *mechanistic, causality, reductionism, holism, animism, field*

METAPHYSICS. A theory of the underlying nature of reality—of knowing (*epistemology*), being (*ontology*), and values (**axiology**). The fundamental assumptions of a *worldview*. Philosophy. The term is also employed in a derogatory sense to imply 'abstract nonsense' or 'supernaturalism'; or it may simply be used to refer to purely non-material or mental phenomena in contrast to 'physical' phenomena (chapter 6). Its normal philosophical meaning is applied herein. (c) *world-view, paradigm, cybernism, tacit*

MODEL (mental). See *cognise* and *cybernism*. (c) *paradigm, tacit, worldview, unified science*

MODERNISM. The underlying *worldview* shared by most scientists and other people of influence in our modern industrial society, as contrasted with that held by most *traditional* peoples outside the orbit of the modern world. The underlying worldview common to traditional or *vernacular* peoples is referred to herein as the *Way*, which reflects the values of the *biosphere*, in contrast to modernism, which can be identified with the 'anti-Way', and which reflects the values of the *technosphere* (see *worldview* and chapter 65). One of the most radical expressions of modernism today can perhaps be found in the so-called 'transhumanist' movement, which seeks to transform humanity itself into a technological artefact. In the humanities, the term is used to refer to a particular (but somewhat related) movement in the arts.

It is argued in this book that despite the fact that many of the facets of the worldview of modernism have come under attack and lost favour in some academic circles, it nonetheless remains the reigning orthodoxy engaged in rationalising modern society (AKA **modernity**), forming the de facto doctrine underpinning economic development or *'progress'* and the **modernist** project in general. See *Promethean enterprise*. **Modernise**, vb. (c) *Great Misinterpretation, reductionism, logical positivism, mechanomorphism, individualism, Darwinism, causality, ecological worldview, Way*

MORPHOGENESIS. The origin and *development* of an organism's physical features. See *differentiation, embryogenesis*, and *ontogeny*. (c) *phylogeny*

MUTUALISM. See *symbiosis* and *holarchical mutualism*.

NATURAL. There is a certain tendency to characterise all things that exist as being 'natural' by definition. Thus, the *technosphere* might be considered, in this respect, as being just as 'natural' as the *biosphere* (chapter 65). If the term is to have any meaning, however, a sensible distinction must be drawn between **natural** and **unnatural**, as there is between **healthy** and **unhealthy** (see *whole*).

It should be clear that there is an essential difference between those things that are created as integral and whole-maintaining (*homeotelic*) parts of the self-generating process of the biosphere, and those products and activities of human origin that are in direct conflict with them, resulting in a disruption of the *biospheric process* (*heterotely*). See von Bertalanffy in chapter 1, and *Way*.

NEGATIVE FEEDBACK. See *feedback*.

NEO-DARWINISM. A later variant of *Darwinism* developed, in particular, by August Weismann in Germany and William Bateson in Britain towards the end of the nineteenth century. It differed from Darwinism in that it took on board Mendel's genetic theories, with which Darwin was not acquainted. This enabled Darwin's followers to answer a particularly embarrassing objection to his theory —that, put forward by Fleeming Jenkin, of 'blending inheritance'—which had reduced the credibility of Darwinism.

Neo-Darwinism was in many respects a hardening of Darwinism. For instance, whereas Darwin saw selection from random variations as just one of the means of evolution, they insisted it was the 'only' one. Neo-Darwinism slowly went out of favour in the 1920s and 1930s, until it was again revived in a slightly different form (see *synthetic theory* and appendix 4). (c) *Darwinism*

ONTOGENY (AKA ontogenesis—not to be confused with *ontology*). The origin and *development* of an individual organism—more specifically, of a fertilised egg into its adult form. The term is used herein to include *morphogenesis* as well as the individual's instinctive behaviour after birth, their *socialisation* in early life, and their continued learning during adulthood, encompassing behavioural (and thus also physical) development throughout the whole course of life. Ontogeny is often contrasted with *phylogeny*—however, I take ontogeny to be an essential part of phylogeny, which may be considered to be a continuation of the same underlying behavioural process (see *biospheric process*, *epigenetics*, and chapter 37). (c) *embryogenesis*, *sere*, *chreod*, *succession*

ONTOLOGY (not to be confused with *ontogeny*). A theory or study of the essential nature of things—the nature of being. The term '**ontological**' (real in essence) may be contrasted with '**nominal**' (in name only—see 'nominal realism' in chapter 14 and *linguistic philosophy*)—as is 'metaphysical' with 'methodological' ('in essence' or 'in practice'). Philisophical debates often rage around the question of whether something or other exists in reality (realism, essentialism, *etc.*), or only in the mind of the beholder (idealism, constructionism), or some combination of these two basic positions (*e.g.* perspectivism, functionalism)— each faithfully reflecting the partisan's underlying *worldview* (chapter 12). (c) *metaphysics*, *epistemology*, *paradigm*, *induction*

ORGANICISM. The thesis that living things are, above all, living *organisations*— or natural *systems*—which by their very nature must behave differently to inanimate things or machines, being *ontologically* distinct from them. It is particularly associated with members of the Theoretical Biology Club of Cambridge University, such as Joseph Needham, Conrad Waddington, and Joseph Woodger, who were influenced by Alfred North Whitehead's 'organic theory'—and also with the theoretical biologists associated with the Vienna 'Vivarium', such as Paul Weiss and Ludwig von Bertalanffy.[9] It is an alternative to both *mechanomorphism* and *vitalism* (see chapter 38). (c) *holism*

ORGANISATION. Arranged, coordinated, and integrated into a functioning *whole*. Matter or *information* that is organised (and hence *differentiated*) can be said to be in an antithetical state to that which is *random*, distinguishing a living *system* from inert matter (*e.g.* a machine). By derivation—organ, organelle, organism, *etc.* Organic, organismic, *adjs.* (c) *differentiation, complexity, hierarchy, holarchy, field, cosmos, chaos, entropy, mechanistic*

Alexander Bogdanov's 'tektology', Alfred North Whitehead's 'organic theory', Jan Smuts's *holism*, Norbert Weiner's *cybernetics*, and Ludwig von Bertalanffy's *General System Theory* represent some of the attempts that have been made to develop a general theory and *metaphysics* of organisation or wholeness. It could also be argued that *Darwinism* provides reductionist science with a theory of 'organisation' (chapter 45)—however, its *mechanistic* principles are *ontologically* incompatible with the very notion of organisation or wholeness. See *unified science* and *organicism*. (c) *entropy*

It is argued in this book that the preëxisting organisation of the natural world is largely ignored or even denied by *reductionist* science so as to justify its wholesale reärrangement. If the preëxisting order of the natural world were to be properly acknowledged, however, human behaviour would, by implication, have to be subject to natural *laws* rather than arbitrary artificial laws (chapter 5), thereby impeding the wholesale destruction of society and the natural world, and bringing to an end the *modernist* project (see *worldview* and appendix 3). (c) *laws, homearchy, homeotely, Way*

PARADIGM. Used herein to refer to a theory or model developed by likeminded scholars to explain a particular set of phenomena within their field of study, and which faithfully reflects their *worldview*. A particular way of seeing and interpreting things ('hermeneutic'). Similar to Michael Polanyi's notion of a 'framework' or 'interpretative framework', under which he describes both 'conceptual' and 'cultural' forms (see chapter 12 and *worldview*).

According to Thomas Kuhn, 'normal science' proceeds by seeking out (largely unconsciously) confirming instances of the reigning paradigm while strenuously contorting or simply laying aside unaccountable discrepancies. 'Revolutionary science', on the other hand, occurs when an insurmountable body of discrepancies precipitates a crisis of faith in the reigning paradigm. This 'crisis' eventually leads to a conversion of faith to a new paradigm, incompatible with the old (a **paradigm shift**—see *gestalt*), that enables its adherents to perceive the same body of findings in such a way that resolves the former crisis. Henceforth, 'normal science' is quietly resumed within the confines of the new paradigm. This was contrary to Karl Popper's view, for instance, that inadequate theories were (or rather ought to be) rejected rationally through a rigorous process of critical scrutiny and falsification (chapter 12). Polanyi also differed, arguing that a change of 'paradigm' may involve an informed choice based on a reasoned comparison of the alternatives, rather than being merely an arbitrary or relativistic shift of position as Kuhn had implied. See *tacit*. (c) *cybernism, cognise, worldview*

PHENOTYPE. The particular features expressed by an individual organism, including its anatomy, physiology, and behavioural pattern. (c) *genotype*

PHYLOGENETIC MALADJUSTMENT. An organism attempting to negotiate environmental conditions that its evolutionary history has not equipped it for, resulting in maladjustment—an example might be malnourishment caused by a diet lacking the vital nutrients found in its ancestors' diet. Such maladjustments may be physical, physiological, social, and psychological. A term proposed by Stephen Boyden (chapter 48). (c) *phylogeny, continuum, sociobiology*

PHYLOGENY (AKA phylogenesis). The evolutionary *development* of a species. I argue in this book that evolution can only be understood properly if we take the *biosphere* as a whole—rather than an individual species, let alone individual organisms—as the unit of evolution. For this reason, evolution may be referred to as the *biospheric process* (chapter 37). (c) *ontogeny*

PIONEER ECOSYSTEM. The 'embryonic' stage of a *developing* ecosystem prior to achieving maturation or *climax* (chapter 22). A climax *ecosystem* will revert back to a pioneer (*i.e.* 'neo-pioneer') stage after a major disturbance, such as that caused by a volcanic eruption, severe storm, wildfire, or industrial development scheme, and hence will attempt to regenerate a new climax stage—*i.e.* to heal itself as best it can under the given circumstances (**resilience** *stability*). (c) *disclimax, anthropogenic climax, succession*

A pioneer stage is marked by less stability, *complexity* and-or *diversity*, higher material productivity, greater competition, larger discontinuities, and more reliance on crude controls (such as infestations, epidemics, mass starvation, overkill, *etc.*) than are found in a climax stage. The social equivalent being that of a (neo-)**pioneer society** (*e.g.* an *anomic*, disintegrated, or unstable society), which, if sustained for long, will disrupt the wider ecosystem, further driving it into a degraded neo-pioneer stage. The behaviour of such a society is perpetuated by a (neo-)**pioneer** *worldview, e.g. modernism.* (c) *anomie, feedback, climax ecosystem*

PROGRESS (modern). The term has become synonymous with **economic development** and thus with industrial society or the 'developed' world. One of the underlying assumptions of this kind of progress is the belief in the benefit of continual, overriding change (chapter 19). It thus represents the antithesis of *stability* and hence of a *traditional* society. Another related assumption is the belief in the benefit of continual growth and thus the lack of *climax* or maturity —Gross National Product (GNP) being but a measure of the extent to which our way of life and environment have diverged from those to which we have been adapted by our evolution (*i.e.* of *technospheric* progress and thus *biospheric* **regress** or **anti-evolution**). (c) *pioneer ecosystem, market system, biospheric process*

To a certain extent, the more that disruptive or *heterotelic* processes spread in a society, the more its GNP may grow in response to dealing with the symptoms (chapters 4 & 47)—however, once a society's critical *tolerance ranges* have been breached by these accumulating maladjustments, as with any other unstable *system*, it is condemned to rapid decline and eventual collapse. Such sustained disruption must necessarily spread destabilisation further, to every domain of the biospheric and technospheric systems—*i.e.* to the personal, social, economic, ideological, (geo-)political, institutional, technological, ecological, and climatic realms (chapters 47–53 & part vi). See *Promethean enterprise* and *pioneer ecosystem*. (c) *homeostasis*

PROKARYOTES. The simplest forms of cellular life, such as bacteria, which are characterised by the lack of a nucleus and organelles. See *eukaryotes*.

PROMETHEAN ENTERPRISE. An expression denoting humanity's attempt to conquer and control nature and the tragic long-term consequences thereof.

It has become customary to refer to the *modernist* project of systematically transforming the living *biosphere* into a lifeless *technosphere* as 'progress'. The alternative term 'Promethean enterprise' has been employed by Ivan Illich in reference to the engineering or *institutionalisation* of all human endeavour, along with the mobilisation of all natural resources, in an effort to 'wage war' against the perceived ills and challenges of life (chapters 39 & 65)—a process that can only succeed within very narrow limits; going beyond which inevitably leads to 'counterproductivity', ever diminishing returns, and ultimately to tragic failure—(c) *tolerance range*. Illich termed the thinking underlying this fatal enterprise as the **Promethean fallacy**.[10] (c) *Great Misinterpretation, gesellschaft, total state, Great Transformation, vernacular*

PUNCTUATED EQUILIBRIUM. The observation that the fossil record is characterised by long periods of *stability* punctuated by short periods of dramatic and rapid evolutionary change. A point made by palæontologists Stephen J. Gould, Niles Eldredge, and Steven Stanley, which calls into question the conventional *neo-Darwinian* view of continuous and gradual evolutionary change (chapter 19). Interestingly, Darwin himself would likely have agreed with Gould and his colleagues, noting that '. . . the periods during which species have undergone modification, though long as measured by years, have probably been short in comparison with the periods during which they retained the same form.'[11] (c) *stability*

PURPOSE. An aim, endgoal, function, or meaning. To know the purpose of something is to know how it relates to the larger *whole* of which it is part (see chapter 31)—a whole that exists both in space and in time (see *spatio-temporal*). By ignoring this larger four-dimensional context (*i.e.* the higher levels of *organisation*), a *reductionist* approach is unable to consider ends or purpose (chapter 40). Purpose, in this sense, represents order in time (*i.e.* in an organised living **process**) and hence *stability* and predictability. Seen another way, purpose to the part is *causality* from the whole—*i.e.* holistic or so-called 'downward' causation (see *homearchy, field,* and chapters 40 *&* 43). The study of purpose is central to both *cybernetics* and *General System Theory.* See *teleology.* (c) *feedback, mechanistic*

QUALITATIVE. Relating to quality or kind, *i.e.* species, types, forms. Related together and thus *organised.* Classifiable. (c) *quantitative, holon, continuum, organicism, gestalt, hierarchy*

QUANTITATIVE. Relating to quantity or amount, *i.e.* number, divisions, partitions. Divided up and thus countable. Divisible. (c) *qualitative, atom, reductionism*

RANDOM. Not ordered or *organised* in relation to any other thing, wider context, or *whole.* Not meaningful. Lacking *purpose.* Unpredictable. *Chaos,* disorder, disintegration, noise, *entropy, heterotely.* The *mechanical* systems of the *technosphere*—*i.e.* institutions *(gesellschaft)* and the technologies characteristic of them —are random in respect of the *biosphere,* as they are not organised as integral, *homeotelic* parts of the wider *biospheric process.* As a result, they can only act indifferently or, as is more likely the case, heterotelically towards it, increasing disorder and contributing towards the disintegration of the biosphere. (c) *entropy, heterotely, tolerance range, homeotely, teleology, feedback*

REDUCTIONISM. The notion that all phenomena may be solely explained or reduced to the aggregate action of their constituent parts without reference to the way in which those parts are *organised* to form a *whole* (chapter 1)—that is, explaining higher level phenomena exclusively in terms of lower levels. Classical or analytical science. Reductionist *adj.* (philosophy); reductionistic *adj.* (quality). (c) *holism, mechanomorphism, atom, causality, holon, purpose, hierarchy, gestalt*

RELIGION. Religio-cultural pattern. The pattern of dominant beliefs, values, customs, rituals, *etc.* that regulate general behaviour within a society. Some confusion has arisen over the term, which is often employed more specifically to refer to beliefs involving supernatural beings or deities operating beyond natural *laws*—a usage that ignores nontheistic forms of *animism,* Buddhism, Jainism, and Daoism, for example, as well as ignoring the wider cultural pattern of which 'religion' is often an indistinguishable part. The term is used here in its anthropological sense—hence why 'materialism' may be said to be the religion of **modernity,** deriving from a *metaphysical* belief in *mechanomorphism* and expressing the values of *individualism* and the rituals and customs of mass consumerism, *etc.*—see introduction and chapter 39. (c) *cybernism, worldview, Way, vital force, revitalisation, modernism*

REVITALISATION (cultural). The process whereby new cultural forms are spontaneously generated in a society undergoing cultural breakdown or *demoralisation.* Such cultural innovations are also referred to as 'messianic', as they are often led by prophetic figures who have themselves undergone a process of personal breakdown and transformation (chapter 66). Revitalisation movements tend to flourish in societies undergoing prolonged disruption from external agents, such as from an overbearing *state* or an alien culture whose values cannot be successfully assimilated by **acculturation**. Such movements provide the demoralised population with a coherent vision of themselves and their relationship with the world, along with a clear goal structure and associated set of values (see *cybernism*), that restores morale and provides a basic blueprint for the *development* of a new cultural pattern. The phenomenon was most notably explored by the anthropologist A.F.C. Wallace,[12] who argued that the origins of many religious and ideological systems can be found in these revitalisation movements. See *demoralisation*. (c) *religion, vital force, vernacular, technosphere, total state, anomie, punctuated equilibrium*

SACREDNESS. A notion found in all *traditional* societies that conveys authority, value, and validity to things. The divinely ordained order of the world that must not be violated, reflecting a society's *worldview*. See *vital force, tabu, Way,* and *whole.*

SERE. A unit of *succession*. The particular series of *communities* or 'seral phases' a specific ecosystem exhibits as it proceeds through succession towards *climax* (chapter 22). (c) *ontogeny, spatio-temporal*

SOCIALISATION. Social *differentiation*. The process by which a child internalises the specific knowledge, skills, and values required for it to function as an integral member of the particular society and culture in which it is raised. The failure of the socialisation process leads to *anomy*. Socialisation is considered herein as being an integral part of *ontogeny* and as being synonymous with **education** (as opposed to mere schooling[13]—chapter 59). The alternative term **enculturation** is generally found in anthropology. (c) *epigenesis, succession, continuum, field, homearchy, phylogenetic maladjustment*

SOCIOBIOLOGY. This is seen as a field of study, though it is in reality a school of thought or, even more so, a movement among theoretical biologists (chapter 45). It sees society as having a primarily biological basis. However, it is a biology that is fundamentally *mechanistic* and *reductionistic,* and that faithfully reflects the *paradigm* of mainstream science in its most basic form. Closely related to **evolutionary psychology.** (c) *phylogenetic maladjustment, neo-Darwinism, synthetic theory, Darwinism*

SPATIO-TEMPORAL. Relating to both space and time, *e.g.* space-time *continuum.* **Four-dimensional.** Used herein with regard to the dynamic nature of living processes, which can only be properly understood if they are considered as existing in time as much as in space (chapter 37). ›››

A purely spatial perspective only takes into account static structure, whereas a spatio-temporal perspective takes into account the whole dynamic process of *development*. Things are thus considered as having a history, rather than as having appeared fully-formed out of nowhere; as having a future, rather than as having no direction or *purpose*; and as having a context, rather than as having no existence or meaning beyond themselves. (c) *field, continuum, epigenesis, chreod, succession, holism, holarchy, atom, mechanomorphism*

STABILITY. This must not be mistaken for stasis. Stability in the natural world is dynamic (see *spatio-temporal*). A stable *system* is one whose behaviour is marked by the smallest possible discontinuities (chapter 48). Such a system will, by the same token, seek to preserve the more general features of its critical order by adapting its more particular features. This stability can only be maintained within its *tolerance range*. As a system becomes more stable and integrated, so it becomes correspondingly more **sustainable** and thus more **predictable**. (See chapters 19, 20, & 21) (c) *punctuated equilibrium*

Resistance stability enables a system to withstand a disturbing influence, while **resilience stability** enables it to recover from a disturbance (*i.e.* to heal itself—see also *complexity* and *diversity*). (c) *homeostasis, homeorhesis, homeotely, homearchy, holarchical mutualism, traditional*

STATE, THE. See *total state*.

SUCCESSION (ecological). The **sequential** *development* of a *pioneer ecosystem* as it proceeds towards a *climax* stage. All life processes must undergo proper sequential development if they are to maintain their *stability* and fulfil their goals—whether it be in the case of a pioneer ecosystem, a developing *embryo*, the cognitive development and *socialisation* of a child, or the long-term development of the *biospheric process* itself (chapter 22 & 37). This does not mean that the whole process is predetermined in a precise way, for at each stage there may be a large number of possible variations of a basic behavioural response, of which only one or more are likely to be adopted under given conditions (see *equifinality* and *cybernism*). Nonetheless, succession must always follow an appropriate sequence or series of transformations (*sere*), and at an appropriate rate, if it is to successfully achieve its endgoals. Equally, all stages of the development of a life process must be coordinated with those of the larger *system* of which it is part and of the smaller systems of which it is composed. See *homeorhesis*. (c) *ontogeny, development, sere, chreod, climax, spatio-temporal, differentiation*

SYMBIOSIS. Organisms living under the influence of one another, thereby forming a *continuum*, resulting in their coädaptation and-or coëvolution (chapters 44 & 45). There are usually considered to be four kinds of symbiotic relationship—**parasitism**, whereby one party in the relationship clearly benefits at the expense of the others; **mutualism**, whereby all parties benefit from the relationship; **ämensalism**, whereby one party in the relationship exerts a harmful influence on the others but remains unaffected itself; and **commensalism**, whereby one party in the relationship benefits while the others remain relatively unaffected. Note how these definitions are made only with regard to the other parts and not to the wider *whole*, of which they are integral members (see *holarchical mutualism*, *homeotely*). A fifth relationship whereby all parties ultimately suffer (**synnecrosis**) can be regarded as a critical disorder rather than as a symbiosis (*e.g.* cancer—see *heterotely*). (c) *association, field, eukaryotes*

SYNTHETIC THEORY OF EVOLUTION (AKA 'modern evolutionary synthesis'). Biologists tended to lose interest in *neo-Darwinism* in the 1920s and '30s. It was revived by Julian Huxley, Theodosius Dobzhansky, George Gaylord Simpson, Ernst Mayr, and others in the early 1940s. This still later variant of *Darwinism* took into account population genetics, which had been developed in the meantime, and also sought to express the theory in more *quantitative* terms, making it correspondingly more respectable in scientific circles. This meant defining the 'fit'—until then a vague term—as those who best succeeded in proliferating their genes (see chapter 18). (c) *Darwinism, neo-Darwinism, sociobiology*

SYSTEM (natural). *Natural* or 'behavioural' systems must be distinguished from the *mechanistic* systems built by engineers, which are only superficially similar. Natural systems include cells, organisms, non-human animal societies, human *vernacular* societies, ecosystems, and the *biosphere* itself. The generalities of the structure and function of all these natural systems are taken to be the same, which justifies the use of the term—defined by Paul Weiss as a complex unit in space and time, whose subunits cooperate to preserve its integral structure and behaviour and tend to restore them after non-destructive disturbances (see *cybernetics*, *General System Theory*, and chapter 42). (c) *holarchy, whole, cosmos, continuum, holon, teleology, atom, entropy*

SYSTEMS THEORY. See *General System Theory* (GST).

TABU (AKA tapu, taboo). A word found throughout the Pacific islands, denoting *sacredness*—hence, to violate a tabu is to profane and thus upset the critical or sacred order of the *cosmos*, resulting in tragic consequences or divine retribution. See *vital force*, *Way*, and *whole*.

TACIT. Knowledge or intelligence that is primarily implicit or *ineffable* (and therefore internalised), in contrast to that which is explicit or expressible (*i.e.* 'articulate' or externalised). A term adopted, in particular, by Michael Polanyi (see chapter 9). (c) *cognise, cybernism*

According to Polanyi, scientific knowledge, far from being acquired through objective or impersonal means, involves instead the passionate commitment of the scientist to a core of 'personal' knowledge and belief, primarily acquired through intuitive and imaginative insight (or 'indwelling')—a process more akin to art or craft than to a dispassionate and detached research. Such informal and unspoken skills and knowledge, moreover, can only be passed on intact through an intimate process of mentoring from the master of the science to their pupil —*i.e.* via a direct transmission of living *tradition*—the much lauded 'scientific method' performing the supplementary role of precision tool in the employ of the scientist's own body of 'personal knowledge'. The scientist necessarily knows more than they can tell and believes more than they can prove, being in reality an intimate participant in the world rather than a mythical 'detached observer'. Similarly, as knowledge is by nature personal, facts and values cannot truly be separated from each other nor the sciences from the humanities. However, this did not lead Polanyi to the conclusion that knowledge is simply relativistic in nature, as other *epistemologists* had argued (idealism). Rather, he maintained that the knower is capable of moving towards a truer understanding of the real world through a personal and passionate commitment to its existence (realism). See chapters 15, 16, *&* 17, and *paradigm*. (c) *metaphysics, continuum*

TECHNOSPHERE. The fabricated or **surrogate world** of human industrial artefacts and *institutions*, as contrasted with the **real world** of living things and *vernacular* communities (*i.e.* the *biosphere*). The artificial growth and development of the technosphere is achieved directly at the expense of the *natural* growth and *development* of the biosphere. As the former expands ('**progress**'), the latter necessarily goes into contraction (**regress**), breaking-down into increasingly degraded and disintegrated parts (see *pioneer ecosystem*). (c) *total state, ethnosphere*

The *heterotelic* technologies of the technosphere must be distinguished from the *homeotelic* technologies of vernacular *communities*, which are adapted to the wider biosphere as well as to the real needs of the community and the families and individuals that compose it (see chapter 54).

As *animism*, in one form or another, was the principle *worldview* of the biosphere, so *mechanomorphism* has become the de facto worldview of the technosphere. (c) *gemeinschaft, gesellschaft, progress*

The term arose in the 1960s and was later employed by Max Nicholson, who contrasted '. . . the ancient biosphere or realm of all living things', with 'the new impersonal "technosphere" of flows of energy through man-made structures, devices, and economic or social channels'.[14] An earlier term, 'cyborg', was proposed by Manfred Clynes to refer to the resulting hybrid of human beings grown dependent on these technospheric artefacts. Its more evangelical advocates see this process developing along 'transhumanist' lines, whereby human beings are themselves transformed into predominantly technological artefacts.[15] This book argues that the further this process of technospheric colonisation continues, the more disruptive (*heterotelic*) are its effects on living systems— individuals, societies, *ecosystems*, and the biosphere itself—leading to increasing instability and ultimately to collapse. A further term, 'anthroposphere' (along with the related 'anthropocene'), has also been employed but fails to address the critical distinction between industrial and vernacular forms of human society. See *Promethean enterprise* and *vernacular*.

TELEOLOGY. Aristotle's 'final cause', as distinguished from antecedent or 'initial' cause (see *causality*). A goal, aim, end, function, *purpose*, or directive. 'Downward causation' (see *homearchy*). As with reductionistic causality, an exclusive faith in teleology can prove equally deterministic (see *holon*). Teleology may be internalised (homearchic), as in the case of an **organism**, or externalised (*heterarchic*), as in the case of a **mechanism** or machine (*e.g.* an *institution*—see next and *system*).

Some of the objection to teleological explanations of life seems to have arisen from the widespread notion that it implies some kind of 'conscious design', 'supernatural cause', or non-linear view of time (see next and chapter 2). From the Greek τέλος (telos), end-goal, and λογια (logia), discourse—the study of goals, plans, design, purpose, *etc.* (c) *teleonomy, purpose, homearchy, equifinality, spatio-temporal, random*

TELEONOMY. A term used instead of *teleology* by adherents of *reductionism*— 'The conception of "teleology" has been associated with that of a final aim of life, implying metaphysical or religious beliefs. To avoid this, recent authors have used the word "teleonomy" to describe the directional character of living activities . . . But words of this sort confuse many people and one is enough, let us keep to "teleology".'—J.Z. Young.[16] See previous.

TEMPORAL. Relating to time. See *spatio-temporal*.

TOLERANCE RANGE (AKA 'limits of tolerance'). The degree of disturbance, discontinuity, or stress that a living process may tolerate while maintaining its overall *stability* (chapter 48). Beyond this tolerance range living processes begin to destabilise, resulting in maladjusted behaviour and, if sustained, increasing degradation and disintegration, ultimately ending in collapse. Stable *systems* can thereby tolerate a certain amount of environmental change, so long as it is neither too radical nor too rapid for them to adapt to *homeotelically*. Interestingly, the English word 'evil' derives from the Germanic 'ubils', over, in the sense of 'going over due limits'.[17] (c) *homeorhesis, homeostasis, homeotely, heterotely, phylogenetic maladjustment, whole*

TOTAL STATE, THE. Totalitarianism. The doctrine that state *institutions* (and other related bodies—*gesellschaft*) are the sole units of society and that citizens are merely wards of the state. Benito Mussolini defined 'fascism' in similar terms. Whatever the nuances of the various forms of totalitarianism, they generally result from the breakdown of *traditional* forms of social organisation (*gemeinschaft*) and the subsequent rise of mass society. The resulting *anomie* provides a breeding ground for despotism and ruthless institutional control, and the consequent mobilisation of all human and natural resources towards those *het-erotelic* ends (chapters 41 & 65)—a process perhaps most thoroughly examined by William Kornhauser.[18] (c) *Promethean enterprise, technosphere, individualism, market system, demoralisation, vernacular*

TRADITIONAL. Perennial. Surviving the test of time and hence adaptive, sustainable, *stable*, alive. In particular, indicating societies and their features that contribute most successfully to the maintenance of their stability and long-term viability within the *biosphere* and hence that succeed in being handed-down to successive generations. Tradition therefore represents a society's long-term be-havioural strategy, without which it cannot survive for long. The same under-lying process is evident at the biological level, where stable *genetic* information is passed on intact from one generation to the next (chapter 37). Regeneration, renewal, rebirth, reënactment, continuity, heredity—in contrast to **modernity** or *anti-evolution* (see *modernism* and *vernacular*). (c) *tribal societies, gemeinschaft, continuum, field, homeostasis, homeorhesis, Way*

TRIBAL SOCIETIES. Stateless societies—organised solely by means of familial associations, social custom, status, ritual, lore, mores, *etc.* (*i.e.* by living *tradition*, which is internalised—see *homearchy*). With the introduction of Westernised systems of 'law' and 'education', living **custom** is replaced by legal **contract**, and all other cultural patterns are supplanted by externalised surrogates. In this manner, the traditional society is systematically extinguished and its land and people mobilised into the *state* and *market* systems (see *vernacular* and chapters 60 & 59). (c) *gemeinschaft, animism, vital force, total state, market system*

TROPHIC STRUCTURE. Food web or 'cycle' (chapters 20 & 56).

UNIFIED SCIENCE. An approach to knowledge that attempts to study the world in unity (*i.e.* as a *whole*) rather than in disconnected compartments of study (chapter 42). Holistic science. A study of the underlying behaviour com-mon to all natural *systems*, which aims at developing a general theory or model of behaviour—and thus an improved methodology of knowledge—to better understand and hence better coordinate adaptive behaviour within the *biosphere* (chapters 6 & 35). See *General System Theory, organisation*, and *Way*. A term orig-inally employed (somewhat differently) by members of the Vienna Circle of *logical positivists*, such as Rudolf Carnap and Otto Neurath. (c) *cybernism, tacit, cognise, epistemology, holon, atom*

VERNACULAR. From the Latin 'vernāculus', homegrown—hence, something that arises spontaneously or *naturally* from a local culture; domestic, native, indigenous. The term is usually applied to a social group's local dialect or ar-chitecture. Ivan Illich extended the use of the term to refer to all features of a society's culture that have not been acquired through professional services and thus from external agents, such as the church, *state*, or corporate institution (chapter 60).[19] Similarly, I apply the term to societies and their features that are self-organising and self-governing (*i.e.* internalised or systemic—see *homearchy*), rather than those that are managed by external agents (see *heterarchy* and *institution*). As used herein, a 'vernacular society' is synonymous with a *traditional* or *stable* society (*i.e.* a *climax* society). (c) *complexity*

Of the 186 distinct societies profiled in the Standard Cross-Cultural Sample (SCCS), approximately eighty per cent are purely stateless societies.[20] Such vernacular societies (*gemeinschaft*) have sustained their order, stability, vital needs, and traditions for countless generations without recourse to state institutions (*gesellschaft*). Stateless societies have been the normal and most widespread form of human society in history, controlling the majority of the earth's surface right until the rapid expansion of industrial society over the past one hundred years or so[21]—in many areas this destruction has only occurred within living memory. Nonetheless, in a few places, self-governing stateless societies still remain largely intact, although they live under the constant threat of destruction from industrial states attempting to claim both their lands and people.

Such state-based societies arise and grow primarily by colonising, enclosing, and subsequently breaking-up existing vernacular cultures in order to exploit their land (for resources) and people (for labour)—a process known as 'development' or, more accurately, ethnocide (see chapter 58, *Promethean enterprise*, and *tribal societies*).

The commonplace languages, customs, and rituals of vernacular societies are often highly *complex* in comparison to those of modern state-based societies. In this respect, industrial state-based societies have exchanged social complexity (**social wealth**—*i.e.* vernacular life, artisan skills, *biospheric* integrity) for technical and institutional sophistication (**economic wealth**—*i.e.* institutional life, industrial technologies, *technospheric* development—chapters 58 & 65)—that is to say, internalised, systemic *development* has been exchanged for externalised, äsystemic 'development'; the local *economy* for the global; and homearchic coordination for heterarchic controls. (c) *climax ecosystem, pioneer ecosystem, socialisation, anomie, market system*

It is important to note that it is not being suggested herein that societies literally 'go back' to those of the past, but rather that any society, of whatever variety, must follow the same general underlying biospheric *laws* and *homeotelic* behaviour pattern found in common with all vernacular societies if it is to provide a truly sustainable and fulfilling way of life for its members—that is, in order to survive in the long term, a society must follow the *Way*. By following the **anti-Way**, as is our modern industrial society, it will instead be condemned to the increasing disruption of its critical *natural* processes and hence to increasing destabilisation, disintegration, and eventual collapse. See *progress* and *Way*. (c) *ethnosphere, total state, technosphere*

VITAL FORCE (AKA life force, 'breath', 'power', 'virtue'). The notion that the natural world is endowed with a generative principle or vital quality, and that such vitality may become diminished, intensified, or transferred in various ways, beings, objects, places, and situations. It is to the extent that these possess 'vital force' that they are valued and respected and thus considered *sacred*, blessed, or hallowed—or if they reduce 'vital force', are considered profane, cursed, or unholy. This was an essential part of the belief systems of *vernacular* peoples and *chthonic* peoples in particular. It still is among many vernacular societies that have remained largely outside the orbit of the modern world, employing their own particular terminology to describe its various features—*e.g.* for Melanesians, 'vital force' or blessedness is **mana**; for Māori, **mauri**; Iroquois, **orenda**; Bantus, **muntu**; Arabs, **baraka**; Hindus, **prāṇa**; Chinese, **qì** (chi 氣) and **dé** (te 德); Anglo-Saxons, 'luck' and **mæġen** ('my-en').[22] I attempt to demonstrate in this book that the organisation of this 'vital force' or sacredness throughout the world, as seen by vernacular peoples, directly reflects their understanding of the critical order of the *cosmos* and hence the behavioural pattern or *Way* that they must follow in order to maintain it (see chapter 62, *Way*, and *whole*). (c) *tabu, field, animism*

VITALISM. The notion that life processes cannot be explained without reference to some element or principle distinct from ordinary matter, such as the 'entelechia' of Aristotle, the 'entelechy' of Driesch, or the 'élan vital' of Bergson (chapter 38). The alternatives to vitalism are seen to be *mechanomorphism* (AKA 'mechanism') and *organicism*.

WAY, THE. A term found in use around the world to refer to that which is divinely ordained or fated; the *natural* order of things or *cosmic law*; the way in which natural *systems* behave and *develop* when not interfered with by external (*heterarchic*) agents. Those things that follow 'the Way' are said to be endowed with *vital force*, virtue, holiness (see *whole*), *sacredness* (*tabu*), and so on.

  Ma'at in ancient Egypt, **ṛta** in the Indian Vedas, **aša** (asha) in the Persian Avestas, **dharma** in Buddhism, **Themis** in ancient Greece, and **dào** (tao 道) in China all reflect a closely related concept fundamental to the *worldview* of these *traditional* peoples—the belief that human society must also follow the Way, remaining in harmony with the wider cosmos on which it depends for its survival or invite certain calamity by neglecting or even deliberately straying from the Way (*i.e.* following the **anti-Way** or **isfet, án-ṛta, druj, adharma, ou themis** respectively—see chapter 61 and *Promethean enterprise*).

  It is argued herein that this common underlying behaviour pattern or 'primordial tradition' represents the basic blueprint required by all societies in order for them to maintain their long-term viability within the *biosphere* and to ensure the fulfilment and well-being of their members—a way that has been abandoned by modern industrial society in exchange for unsustainable short-term gains. (c) *homeostasis, homeorhesis, homeotely, chreod, laws, tolerance range, chthonic religion, modernism*

WHOLE. An integrated and self-organised body or entity. A natural *system*. The totality of a living thing (seen *spatio-temporally*) as distinct from either its general or particular features (chapter 37). A *holarchy*. By derivation—hale, heal, healthy, holy, hallow, wholesome; synonymous with *sacred*, bound, integrated, coherent, harmonious, unified, *organised*, etc. Interestingly, the English word 'good' derives from the Germanic 'godo', united, in the sense of 'fitting together'.[23]

Those things that uphold the wholeness of the *cosmos* (*i.e.* its critical order) were regarded by *traditional* peoples as being sacred ('holy') and thus blessed ('healthy'), hence increasing *vital force* (virtue and vitality)—whereas those things that disrupt wholeness were regarded as being profane (unholy) and thus cursed (unhealthy), hence reducing virtue and vitality (see *Way*, *vital force*, and chapter 62). (c) *holarchy, holon, holism, gestalt, organicism, continuum, system, cosmos, homeotely, heterotely*

WORLDVIEW. A way of seeing the world. A belief system. The body of underlying assumptions that form the basis of how an individual or social group interprets and thereby perceives their world—and thus, ultimately, how they interact with it. **Weltanschauung** (German). **Cosmovisión** (Spanish). See *cybernism*. (c) *gestalt, paradigm, metaphysics, cosmos, cognise*

In general terms, the *modern* worldview—the worldview of the *technosphere* derived from a *metaphysics* of *mechanomorphism*—sees the earth as merely a jumble of raw materials to be exploited for personal gain. Whereas the older worldview—the worldview of the *biosphere* born of a metaphysics of *animism*—sees the earth as a vast *sacred* being or divine order to be protected and maintained at all cost (chapter 16). Each worldview thereby rationalises the opposite attitude and thus opposite behaviour towards the natural world (see chapters 53 & 54, for example, and Aldo Leopold's 'land ethic' in chapter 18). (c) *modernism, ecological worldview, gesellschaft, gemeinschaft, vital force, Way*

·Ω·

BIBLIOGRAPHY

List of sources

Names are ordered without regard to the particles de, St, van, *and* von

Ackoff, Russell L., 1963, 'General system theory and systems research: Contrasting conceptions of systems science', *General Systems Yearbook*, Vol. 8.

Adams, C.C., 1913, *Guide to the Study of Animal Ecology*, Macmillan, New York.

Adams, Patricia, and Solomon, Lawrence, 1985, *In the Name of Progress: The Underside of Foreign Aid*, Energy Probe Research Foundation, Toronto.

Akpala, Agwu, 1972, 'Problems of initiating industrial labour in preindustrial community', *Cahiers d'Études Africaines*, Spring.

Allee, W.C., Emerson, W.C.E.A., Park, O., Park, T., and Schmidt, K.P., 1949 *Principles of Animal Ecology*, Philadelphia, W.B. Saunders.

Altieri, Miguel A., 1985, *Agroecology: The Scientific Basis of Alternative Agriculture*, Division of Biological Control, University of California, Berkeley.

——1991, 'Traditional farming in Latin America', *The Ecologist*, Vol. 21, No. 2, March.

Apffel-Marglin, Frédérique, ed., 1998, *The Spirit of Regeneration: Andean Culture Confronting Western Notions of Development*, Zed Books, London.

Apter, Michael J., 1966, *Cybernetics and Development*, Pergamon Press, Oxford.

Armelagos, George, and McArdle, Alan, 1976, 'The Role of culture in the control of infectious diseases', *The Ecologist*, Vol. 6, No. 5, June.

Armstrong, W.E., 1924, 'Rossel Island money: A unique monetary system', *The Economic Journal*, 34.

Asch, S.E., 1955, 'Opinions and social pressure', *Scientific American*, November.

Ashby, W. Ross, 1957, *An Introduction to Cybernetics*, Chapman & Hall, London.

Atlan, Henri, 1979, *Entre le Cristal et la Fumée: Essai sur L'Organisation du Vivant*, Editions du Seuil, Paris.

Audy, J. Ralph, 'Measurement and diagnosis of health', in Shepard and McKinley, eds., 1971, *Environ/Mental*.

Augros, Robert, and Stanciu, George, 1987, *The New Biology: Discovering the Wisdom in Nature*, New Science Library, Boston, Massachusetts.

—— ——'Competition and the enculturation of science', in Combs, ed., 1992, *Cooperation*.

Augustine, 'On free will', in John H.S. Burleigh, ed., 1953, *Augustine: Earlier Writings*, Westminster John Knox Press, Kentucky.

Ayala, F.J., and Dobzhansky, Theodosius, eds., 1974, *Studies in the Philosophy of Biology: Reduction and Related Problems*, University of California Press, Los Angeles.

Baillie, Jonathan E.M., Hilton-Taylor, Craig, and Stuart, Simon N., 2004, *IUCN Red List of Threatened Species: A Global Species Assessment*, IUCN, Cambridge.

Bajaj, Jatinder, 'Francis Bacon, the first philosopher of modern science: A non-western view', in Nandy, ed., 1988, *Science, Hegemony and Violence*.

Bakeless, John, 1977, 'Our land as it was', *The Ecologist*, Vol. 7, No. 7, (originally published in the *Smithsonian*, January 1972).

Baker, Richard St Barbe, 1950, 'New Earth Charter', in *Occasional Paper: Man and Nature*, The Council for the Church and Countryside, London.

——1956, *Land of Tane: Threat of Erosion*, Lutterworth Press, London.

——1989, *Man of the Trees: Selected Writings of Richard St Barbe Baker*, ed. Karen Gridley, Ecology Action, California.

Baldwin, J.M., 1896, 'A new factor in evolution', *American Naturalist*, 30.

Baltimore, David, 'Limiting science: A biologist's perspective', in Daedalus, 1978, *Daedalus.*

Banfield, Edward C., 1958, *The Moral Basis of a Backward Society*, The Free Press, New York.

Banks, Joseph, 1963, *The Endeavour Journal of Joseph Banks, 1768–1771*, Vol. 2, Angus & Robertson, Sydney.

Barbour, Ian G., 1971, *Issues in Science and Religion*, Harper & Row, New York.

Barbour, M.G., Burk, J.H., and Pitts, W.D., 1980, *Terrestrial Plant Ecology*, Benjamin/Cummings, San Francisco.

Barker, Jonathan, ed., 1984, *The Politics of Agriculture in Tropical Africa*, Sage Publications, London.

Barker, Margaret, 1988, *The Lost Prophet: The Book of Enoch and its Influence on Christianity*, SPCK, London.

Barnes, Nick, 'Conflicts over biodiversity', in Peter B. Sloep and Andrew Blowers, eds., 1996, *Environmental Problems as Conflicts of Interest*, Arnold, London.

Bartlett, Frederic C., 1977, *Remembering: A Study in Experimental and Social Psychology*, Cambridge University Press, Cambridge.

Baskin, Yvonne, ed., 1997, *The Work of Nature: How the Diversity of Life Sustains Us*, The Scientific Committee on Problems of the Environment (SCOPE), Island Press, Washington.

Bastien, Joseph W., 'Metaphorical relations between sickness, society and land in a Qollahuaya ritual', in Joseph W. Bastien and John Donahue, eds., 1981, 'Health in the Andes', Monograph 12, *American Anthropological Association Bulletin.*

Beer, Gavin de, 1958, *Embryos and Ancestors*, Clarendon Press, Oxford.

Beer, Stafford, 1960, 'Below the twilight arch: A mythology of systems', *General Systems Yearbook*, Vol. 5.

Begon, Michael, Harper, John L., and Townsend, Colin R., 1990, *Ecology*, Blackwell, Oxford.

Behnam, Jamshid, (Bihnām, Ǧamšīd), 1977, *An Introduction of the Art of Black Africa*, (*Introduction à l'art de l'Afrique noire: catalogue*), Soroush Press, Tehran.

Bender, Tom, 'Appropriate Technology', in Lane deMoll, ed., 1977, *Rainbook: Resources for Appropriate Technology*, Schocken Books, New York.

Bentham, Jeremy, 1823 (original edition 1789), *An Introduction to the Principles of Morals and Legislation*, Vol. 1, Pickering, London.

Berdyaev, Nikolai Aleksandrovich, 1949, *The Meaning of History*, Geoffrey Bles, London.

Bergson, Henri, 1981, (original edition 1911), *L'Évolution Créatice*, ('Creative Evolution'), Presses Universitaires de France, Paris.

Berman, Morris, 1981, *The Reenchantment of the World*, Cornell University Press, Ithaca.

Bernal, J.D., 1969, *The World, The Flesh & The Devil: An Inquiry Into the Future of the Three Enemies of the Rational Soul*, Indiana University Press, Bloomington.

Bernard, Claude, 1878, *Leçons sur les Phénomènes de la Vie communs aux Animaux et aux Végétaux*, Vol. 1, ed. A. Dastre, Cours de Physiologie Générale du Muséum d'Histoire Naturelle, Paris.

Bernardin de Saint-Pierre, Jacques-Henri, 1808 (original edition 1784), *Studies of Nature*, trans. H. Hunter, Abraham Small, Philadelphia.

Bernier, François, 1941 (original edition 1670), *Voyages de François Bernier: Contenant la Description des États du Grand Mogul, de l'Hindoustan, du Royaume de Kachemire*, Paul Marret, Amsterdam (1699 edition, trans. Archibald Constable, London).

Berry, Wendell, 1970, *The Hidden Wound*, Houghton Mifflin, Boston.

——1987, *Home Economics*, North Point Press, San Francisco.

Bertalanffy, Ludwig von, 1952, *Problems of Life: An Evaluation of Modern Biological Thought*, Vol. 1, John Wiley, New York.

——1962 (original edition 1933), *Modern Theories of Development: An Introduction to Theoretical Biology*, trans. J.H. Woodger, Harper Torchbook, New York.

——1967, *Robots, Men, and Minds: Psychology in the Modern World*, George Braziller, New York.

——'Chance or law?', in Koestler and Smythies, eds., 1972, *Beyond Reductionism*.

——1973, *General System Theory: Foundations, Development, Applications*, Allen Lane, London.

Beversluis, Joel Diederik, ed., 1993, *A Sourcebook for the Community of Religions*, Council for a Parliament of the World's Religions, Chicago.

Birch, L.C., 1957, 'The meanings of competition', *The American Naturalist*, Vol. 91.

Blake, William, 1979, *Blake: Complete Writings*, ed. Geoffrey Keynes, Oxford University Press, Oxford.

Blyth, Reginald Horace, 1950, *Haiku: Volume 1: Eastern Culture*, Hokuseidō, Tokyo.

Bodenheimer, F.S., 'The concept of biotic organization in synecology', in Bodenheimer, ed., 1957, *Studies in Biology and its History*, Biological Studies Publishers, Jerusalem.

Bodley, John H., 2008, *Victims of Progress*, 5th Edition, AltaMira Press, Plymouth.

Bohannan, Paul, 1955, 'Some principles of exchange and investment among the Tiv', *American Anthropologist*, 57.

——ed., 1967, *Law and Warfare: Studies in the Anthropology of Conflict*, Natural History Press, New York.

——'The impact of money on an African subsistence economy', in Dalton, ed., 1967, *Tribal and Peasant Economies*.

——and Dalton, George, 1962, *Markets in Africa*, ('Eight Subsistence Economies in Transition'), Northwestern University Press.

Bonner, John Tyler, 1958, *The Evolution of Development: Three Special Lectures Given at University College, London*, Cambridge University Press, London.

Botkin, Daniel B., 1990, *Discordant Harmonies*, Oxford University Press, New York.

Boucher, D.H., ed., 1985, *The Biology of Mutualism: Ecology and Evolution*, Croom Helm, London.

——'The idea of mutualism, past and future', in Boucher, ed., 1985, *The Biology of Mutualism*.

——James, S., and Keeler, K.H., 1982, 'The ecology of mutualism', *Annual Review of Ecology and Systematics*.

——and Risch, S., 1976, 'What ecologists look for', *Bulletin of the Ecological Society of America*, 57, Issue 3.

Bowles, B.D., 'Underdevelopment in agriculture in colonial Kenya: Some ecological and dietary aspects', in Ogot, ed., 1979, *Ecology and History in East Africa*.

Boyden, Stephen, 1973, 'Evolution and health', *The Ecologist*, Vol. 3, No. 8.

Braham, Mark, 1973, 'A general theory of organization', *General Systems Yearbook*, Vol. 18.

Branigin, William, 1989, 'Hurricane Hugo haunts Virgin Islands', *Washington Post*, 31st October.

Bridges, Bryn, 1971, 'Environmental genetic hazards: The impossible problem?', *The Ecologist*, Vol. 1, No. 12, June.

Brillouin, L., 'Life, thermodynamics, and cybernetics', in Buckley, ed., 1968, *Modern Systems Research for the Behavioral Scientist*.

Broad, Charlie Dunbar, 1959, *Scientific Thought*, Littlefield Adams, New Jersey.

Brown, Harold I., 1979, *Perception, Theory and Commitment: The New Philosophy of Science*, University of Chicago Press, Chicago.

Brown, Joseph Epes, 2007, *The Spiritual Legacy of the American Indian: Commemorative Edition with Letters While Living with Black Elk*, World Wisdom, Indiana.

Brown, Lester R., and Wolf, Edward C., 1985, *Reversing Africa's Decline*, Worldwatch Institute.

Buckle, Henry Thomas, 1862, *History of Civilization in England*, Vol. 1, Appleton, New York.

Buckley, Walter, ed., 1968, *Modern Systems Research for the Behavioral Scientist: A Sourcebook*, Aldine, Chicago.

Bunyard, Peter, and Goldsmith, Edward, eds., 1988, *Gaia: The Thesis, the Mechanism and the Implications*, Wadebridge Ecological Centre, Wadebridge.

Burckhardt, Titus, 1967, *Sacred Art in East and West: Its Principles and Methods*, trans. Lord Northbourne, Perennial Books, London.

——1995, *Chartres: And the Birth of the Cathedral*, Golgonooza Press, Ipswich.

Caillois, Roger, 1950, *L'Homme et le Sacré*, Gallimard, Paris.

Cairns, J., Overbaugh, J., and Miller, S., 1988, 'The origin of mutants', *Nature*, Vol. 335.

Calow, Peter, 1976, *Biological Machines: A Cybernetic Approach to Life*, Edward Arnold, London.

Cameron, William Bruce, 1963, *Informal Sociology: A Casual Introduction to Sociological Thinking*, Random House, New York.

Cannon, Walter, 1932, *The Wisdom of the Body*, Norton, New York.

Carnap, Rudolf, 1936, 'Testability and meaning', *Philosophy of Science*, Issue 3.

Carson, Rachel, 1962, *Silent Spring*, Houghton Mifflin, Boston.

Cattel, R.B., Cohen, J., and Travers, R.M.W., eds., 1937, *Human Affairs: An Exposition of What Science Can Do for Man*, Macmillan, London.

Cavalieri, Liebe F., 1976, 'New strains of life—or death', *New York Times Magazine*, 22nd August.

Chaitanya, Krishna, 1972, *The Physics and Chemistry of Freedom*, Somaiya Publications, Bombay.

——1975, *The Biology of Freedom*, Somaiya Publications, Bombay.

——1976, *The Psychology of Freedom*, Somaiya Publications, Bombay.

——1983, 'A profounder ecology: The Hindu view of man and nature', *The Ecologist*, Vol. 13, No. 4.

Chan, Wing-tsit, ed., 1963, *A Source Book in Chinese Philosophy*, Princeton University Press, Princeton.

Chaney, William A., 1970, *The Cult of Kingship in Anglo-Saxon England: The Transition from Paganism to Christianity*, Manchester University Press, Manchester.

Clark, J., and Yiangou, A., 1990, 'The generative order of life: Jane Clark and Alison Yiangou talk to Professor Brian Goodwin of the Open University', *Beshara Magazine*, Issue 12, Autumn–Winter.

Clark, Mary E., 2002, *In Search of Human Nature*, Routledge, London.

Clastres, Pierre, 1974, *La Société contre L'État*, Les Editions de Minuit, Paris.

——1989 (see also original French edition, 1974), *Society against the State: Essays in Political Anthropology*, ('The Leader as Servant and the Humane Uses of Power among the Indians of the Americas'), trans. Robert Hurley and Abe Stein, Zone Books, New York.

Clements, Frederic E., 1916, *Plant Succession: An Analysis of the Development of Vegetation*, Carnegie Institution, Washington.

Cloward, Richard A., and Ohlin, Lloyd E., 1961, *Delinquency and Opportunity: A Theory of Delinquent Gangs*, Free Press of Glencoe, New York.

Clwyd, Ann, 1991, 'Famine (sub-Saharan Africa)', *Hansard*, HMSO, London, 30th January.

Codrington, Robert Henry, 1891, *The Melanesians: Studies in their Anthropology and Folklore*, Clarendon, Oxford.

Cohen, Mark N., 1989, *Health and the Rise of Civilization*, Yale University Press, New Haven.

Cohn, D'Vera, and Morin, Rich, 2008, *American Mobility: Who Moves? Who Stays Put? Where's Home?*, Pew Research Center, Washington.

Coleman, James S., 1967, *The Adolescent Society: The Social Life of the Teenager and its Impact on Education*, The Free Press of Glencoe, New York.

——1990, *Equality and Achievement in Education*, Westview Press, Boulder.

Collis, John Stewart, 1950, *The Triumph of the Tree*, Jonathan Cape, London.

Combs, Allan, ed., 1992, *Cooperation: Beyond the Age of Competition*, Gordon and Breach, Philadelphia.

Commoner, Barry, 1964, 'DNA and the chemistry of inheritance', *American Scientist*, Vol. 52.

Connell, J.H., 1980, 'Diversity and the coevolution of competition, or the ghost of competition past', *Oikos*, 35.

Connor, John, 2002, *The Australian Frontier Wars: 1788–1838*, University of New South Wales, Sydney.

Coomaraswamy, Ananda, 1983, *Symbolism of Indian Architecture*, The Historical Research Documentation Centre, Jaipur.

——1997, *The Door in the Sky: Coomaraswamy on Myth and Meaning*, Princeton University Press, Princeton.

Cornford, F.M., 1957 (original edition 1912), *From Religion to Philosophy: A Study in the Origins of Western Speculation*, Harper Brothers, New York.

Craik, Kenneth, 1967 (original edition 1943), *The Nature of Explanation*, Cambridge University Press, London.

Crawford, Michael, and Crawford, Sheilagh, 1972, *What We Eat Today: The Food Manipulators vs. the People*, Stein and Day, New York.

Crick, Francis, 1966, *Of Molecules and Men*, University of Washington Press, Seattle.

Cuénot, Lucien, 1941, *Invention et Finalité en Biologie*, Flammarion, Paris.

Culliton, Barbara J., 'Science's restive public', in Daedalus, 1978, *Daedalus*.

Cummings, Edward Estlin, 1954, 'voices to voices, lip to lip', in *100 Selected Poems*, Grove Press, New York.

Cumont, Franz, 1956, *Oriental Religions in Roman Paganism*, Dover Publications, New York.

Curtis, J.T., 1959, *The Vegetation of Wisconsin: An Ordination of Plant Communities*, University of Wisconsin Press, Madison.

Daedalus, 1978, *Daedalus: Journal of the American Academy of Arts and Sciences*, Vol. 107, American Academy of Arts and Sciences, Harvard.

Dalrymple, Theodore, 1991, 'Nasty, British and Short', *Spectator*, London, 21st September.

Dalton, George, 1961, 'Economic theory and primitive society', *American Anthropologist*, Vol. 63.

——ed., 1967, *Tribal and Peasant Economies: Readings in Economic Anthropology*, University of Texas Press, Austin.

——'Primitive money', in Dalton, ed., 1967, *Tribal and Peasant Economies*.

——ed., 1971, *Economic Development and Social Change: The Modernization of Village Communities*, The Natural History Press, New York.

Daly, Herman E., and Cobb, John B., 1989, *For the Common Good: Redirecting the Economy Towards Community, the Environment, and a Sustainable Future*, Beacon Press, Boston.

Damon, Albert, 1974, 'Human ecology in the Solomon Islands: Biomedical observations among four tribal societies', *Human Ecology*, Vol. 2, No. 3, July.

Dancoff, S.M., and Quastler, H., 'The Information content and error rate of living things', in Quastler, ed., 1953, *Essays on the Use of Information Theory in Biology*.

Darwin, Charles, 1871, *The Descent of Man, and Selection in Relation to Sex*, Vol. 1, Appleton, New York.

——1872 (original edition, *On the Origin of Species*, 1859), *The Origin of Species: By Means of Natural Selection: Or the Preservation of Favoured Races in the Struggle for Life*, 6th Edition, Odhams Press, London.

——'Autobiographical sketch', in Francis Darwin, 1888, *The Life and Letters of Charles Darwin*.

——1909 (original edition 1839), *Diary of The Voyage of the Beagle*, P.F. Collier, New York.

——1987, *Charles Darwin's Natural Selection: Being the Second Part of his Big Species Book Written from 1856 to 1858*, Cambridge University Press, Cambridge.

Darwin, Francis, ed., 1888, *The Life and Letters of Charles Darwin: Including an Autobiographical Chapter*, Vol. 2, John Murray, London.

——ed., 1896 (original edition 1887), *The Life and Letters of Charles Darwin*, Vol. 1, John Murray, London.

——and Seward, A.C., eds., 1903, *More Letters of Charles Darwin: A Record of His Works in a Series of hitherto Unpublished Letters*, Vol. 1, John Murray, London.

Davis, Wade, 2001, *Light at the Edge of the World: A Journey through the Realm of Vanishing Cultures*, Bloomsbury, London.

Dawkins, Richard, 1989, *The Selfish Gene*, Oxford University Press, Oxford.

Day, W.R., 1929, 'Environment and disease: A discussion on the parasitism of armillaria mellea', *Forestry*, Vol. 3, No. 2.

Derman, William, 'USAID in the Sahel: Development and poverty', in Barker, ed., 1984, *The Politics of Agriculture in Tropical Africa*.

Dewes, Te Kapungs, 'The case for oral arts', in Michael King, ed., 1975, *Te Ao Hurihuri: The World Moves On: Aspects of Maoritanga*, Hicks Smith, Wellington.

Diamond, Stanley, 1974, *In Search of the Primitive: A Critique of Civilization*, Transaction Books, New Brunswick.

Dobben, W.H. van, and Lowe-McConnell, R., eds., 1975, *Unifying Concepts in Ecology: Report of the Plenary Sessions of the First International Congress of Ecology, the Hague, September 1974*, Funk, The Hague.

Dobzhansky, Theodosius, 'Chance and creativity in evolution', in Ayala and Dobzhansky, eds., 1974, *Studies in the Philosophy of Biology*.

Dogra, Bharat, 1983, 'Traditional agriculture in India: High yields and no waste', *The Ecologist*, Vol. 13, No. 2.

DoT, 1989, *Roads for Prosperity*, Department of Transport, HMSO, London.

Douglas, Mary, 'Lele economy compared with the Bushong: A study of economic backwardness', in Bohannan and Dalton, 1962, *Markets in Africa*.

——'Primitive rationing: A study in controlled exchange', in Firth, ed., 1970, *Themes in Economic Anthropology*.

Drack, Manfred, and Apfalter, Wilfried, 2007, 'Is Paul Weiss' and Ludwig von Bertalanffy's system thinking still valid today?', *Systems Research and Behavioral Science*, Vol. 24, No. 5.

Driesch, Hans, 1908, *The Science and Philosophy of the Organism: The Gifford Lectures Delivered before the University of Aberdeen in the Year 1907 and 1908*, Black, London.

Driver, Harold E., 1961, *Indians of North America*, University of Chicago Press, Chicago.

Drucker, Philip, 1963, *Indians of the Northwest Coast*, Natural History Press, New York.

Du Bois, Cora, 'The Alorese', in Kardiner et alia, 1945, *The Psychological Frontiers of Society*.

Dubos, René, 1967, *Man Adapting: His Limitations and Potentialities*, Yale University Press, New Haven.

——1970, 'Will man adapt to megalopolis?', *The Ecologist*, Vol. 1, No. 4.

Dunbar, Robin I.M., 1996, *Grooming, Gossip, and the Evolution of Language*, Harvard University Press, Cambridge, Massachusetts.

Durkheim, Émile, 1964 (original edition 1915), *The Elementary Forms of the Religious Life: A Study in Religious Sociology*, George Allen & Unwin, London.

——1966 (original edition 1897), *Suicide: A Study in Sociology*, Routledge and Kegan Paul, London.

——and Mauss, Marcel, 1963, *Primitive Classification*, trans. Rodney Needham, University of Chicago Press, Chicago.

Ecologist, The, 1991, 'The UN Food and Agricultural Organization: Promoting world hunger', *The Ecologist*, Special Issue, Vol. 21, No. 2.

Economist, The, 1970, 'When the lights go out', *The Economist*, 12th December.

Edwards, Rob, 1996, 'Swiss cows fed on human placentas', *New Scientist*, No. 2029.

Egerton, Frank, 1973, 'Changing concepts of the balance of nature', *Quarterly Review of Biology*, Vol. 48.

Eibl-Eibesfeldt, Irenäus, 1961, 'The fighting behavior of animals', *Scientific American*, December.

Eiseman, Fred B., 1989, *Bali: Sekala and Niskala: Essays on Religion, Ritual, and Art*, Vol. 1, ed. David Pickell, Periplus Editions, Berkeley.

Eliade, Mircea, 1959, *The Sacred and the Profane: The Nature of Religion*, Harcourt and Brace, New York.

——1971 (original edition 1949), *The Myth of the Eternal Return: or Cosmos and History*, Princeton University, Princeton.

Eliot, Thomas Stearns, 1939, *The Idea of a Christian Society*, Harcourt, Brace & Co., New York.

Elton, Charles S., 1930, *Animal Ecology and Evolution*, Clarendon Press, Oxford.

Emmet, Dorothy Mary, 1953, *The Nature of Metaphysical Thinking*, Macmillan, London.

Empedocles, in Arthur Fairbanks, trans., 1898, 'Empedocles, Fragments: Book II, *333*', in *The First Philosophers of Greece: An Edition and Translation of the Remaining Fragments of the Pre-Socratic Philosophers . . .*, Kegan Paul & Co., London.

Epstein, S.S., 1978, *The Politics of Cancer*, Sierra Club, San Francisco.

Evans, E.P., 1906, *The Criminal Prosecution and Capital Punishment of Animals: The Lost History of Europe's Animal Trials*, Heinemann, London.

Fantz, Robert L., 1961, 'The origin of form perception', *Scientific American*, May.

FAO (Food and Agriculture Organization of the United Nations), 1981, *Agriculture: Towards 2000*, FAO Social and Economic Development Series, No. 27, Rome.

Farley, Reynolds, and Haaga, John, eds., 2005, *The American People: Census 2000*, Russell Sage Foundation, New York.

Faulkner, Harold U., 1951, *The Decline of Laissez Faire, 1897–1917*, Farrar & Rinehart, New York.

Feinberg, Gerald, 1967, 'Ordinary matter', *Scientific American*, 216, No. 5.

Fernando, Ranjit, ed., 1991, *The Unanimous Tradition: Essays on the Essential Unity of All Religions*, Sri Lanka Institute of Traditional Studies, Colombo.

Fernea, Robert A., 1970, *Shaykh and Effendi: Changing Patterns of Authority Among the El Shabana of Southern Iraq*, Harvard University Press, Cambridge, Massachusetts.

Firth, Raymond, ed., 1970, *Themes in Economic Anthropology*, Tavistock, London.

Fischler, Claude, 1990, *L'Homnivore: Le Goût, la Cuisine et le Corps*, Odile Jacob, Paris.

Fisk, E.K., ed., 1978, *The Adaptation of Traditional Agriculture: Socio-economic Problems of Urbanisation*, Development Studies Centre Monograph, No. 11, Australian National University, Canberra.

Flew, Anthony, 1968, *Evolutionary Ethics*, Macmillan, London.

Forrester, Jay W., 1971, 'Alternatives to catastrophe: Understanding the counterintuitive behaviour of social systems', Part 1, *The Ecologist*, Vol. 1, No. 14, August.

Forster, E.M., 'Art for arts sake', in E.M. Forster, 1951, *Two Cheers for Democracy*, Harcourt, Brace, & World, New York.

Fox, Warwick, 1984, 'Deep ecology: A new philosophy of our time?', *The Ecologist*, Vol. 14, No. 5.

Frankl, Viktor E., 'Reductionism and nihilism', in Koestler and Smythies, eds., 1972, *Beyond Reductionism*.

Frazer, James George, 1935, *Creation and Evolution in Primitive Cosmogonies, and Other Pieces*, Macmillan & Co., London.

Freud, Sigmund, 1961 (original edition 1930), *Civilization and its Discontents*, trans. James Strachey, Norton, New York.

Fromm, Erich, 1974, *The Revolution of Hope: Toward a Humanized Technology*, Harper & Row, New York.

Fuller, R. Buckminster, 1971, *Nine Chains to the Moon*, Doubleday, New York.

Fuller, Robert W., and Putnam, Peter, 1966, 'On the origin of order in behavior', *General Systems Yearbook*, Vol. 11.

Fustel de Coulanges, Numa Denis, 1927 (original edition 1864), *La Cité Antique: Étude sur le Culte, le Droit, les Institutions de la Grèce et de Rome*, Hachette, Paris.

Galbraith, J.K., 1967, *The New Industrial State*, Houghton Mifflin, Boston.

Gandhi, M.K., 1967, *The Gospel of Swadeshi*, Bharatiya Vidya Bhavan, Bombay.

Geertz, Clifford, 1976, *The Religion of Java*, University of Chicago Press, Chicago.

Geist, Valerius, 1974, 'About natural man and environmental design', in International Cultural Foundation, *Science and Absolute Values*, Vol. 1.

George, Chief Dan, 'My Very Good Dear Friends', in Waubageshig, ed., 1970, *The Only Good Indian: Essays by Canadian Indians*, New Press, Toronto.

Georgescu-Roegen, Nicholas, 1971, *The Entropy Law and the Economic Process*, Harvard University Press, Cambridge, Massachusetts.

——1972, 'Economics and entropy', *The Ecologist*, Vol. 2, No. 7.

Gerard, Ralph W., 'Hierarchy, entitation and levels', in Whyte, Wilson, and Wilson, eds., 1969, *Hierarchical Structures*.

Ghent, William J., 1902, *Our Benevolent Feudalism*, Macmillan, New York.

Gleason, H.A., 1917, 'The structure and development of the plant association', *Bulletin of the Torrey Botanical Club*, 44.

——1926, 'The individualistic concept of the plant association', *Bulletin of the Torrey Botanical Club*, 53.

Goethe, 1996, *Goethe on Science*, ed. Jeremy Naydler, Floris Books, Edinburgh.

Goldschmidt, Richard, 1935, 'Gen und ausseneigenschaft', Parts I & II, *Zeitschrift für Induktive Abstammungs und Verebungiehre*, 69.

Goldsmith, Edward, 1978, *The Stable Society: Towards a Social Cybernetics*, Wadebridge Press, Cornwall.

——1980, 'Under control?: Do the laws regulating pesticide use in Britain really protect our health and environment?', *The Ecologist*, Vol. 10, No. 3.

——'Development as colonialism', in Mander, Jerry, and Goldsmith, Edward, eds., 1996, *The Case Against the Global Economy: And For a Turn Toward the Local*, Sierra Club Books, San Francisco.

——2008, *An Ethnographic Study of The Comores: Fieldwork Conducted During a Month Spent on Mayotte and Grand Comore, 1971*, privately published, London.

——Allen, Robert, Allaby, Michael, Davoll, John, and Lawrence, Sam, 1972, *A Blueprint for Survival*, special issue, *The Ecologist*, Vol. 2, No. 1.

——and Hildyard, Nicholas, 1984, *The Social and Environmental Effects of Large Dams*, Vol. 1, Wadebridge Ecological Centre, Cornwall.

Goldsmith, Maurice, 1976, 'Nuclear fission and war', *New Scientist*, 17th June.

Gould, Nicholas, 1974, 'William Cobbett: Cottage economist', *The Ecologist*, Vol. 4, No. 4.

Graham, Frank Jr., 1980, 'The witch-hunt of Rachel Carson', *The Ecologist*, Vol. 10, No. 3.

Granit, Ragnar, 1966, *Charles Scott Sherrington: An Appraisal*, Thomas Nelson, London.

——1974, 'Adaptability of the nervous system and its relation to chance, purposiveness, and causality', in International Cultural Foundation, *Science and Absolute Values*, Vol. 2.

——1977, *The Purposive Brain*, MIT Press, Cambridge, Massachusetts.

Grassé, P.P., 1973, *L'Évolution du Vivant: Matériaux pour une Nouvelle Théorie Transformiste*, Albin Michel, Paris.

——1977 (see also original French edition, 1973), *Evolution of Living Organisms: Evidence for a New Theory of Transformation*, Academic Press, New York.

Grene, Marjorie, 'Hierarchy: One word, how many concepts?', in Whyte, Wilson, and Wilson, eds., 1969, *Hierarchical Structures*.

Grey, George, 1841, *Journals of Two Expeditions of Discovery in North-West and Western Australia, During the Years 1837, 38, and 39 . . .* , 2 Vols., T. & W. Boone, London.

Grinewald, Jacques, 'Sketch for a history of the idea of the biosphere', in Bunyard and Goldsmith, eds., 1988, *Gaia*.

Grönbech, Vilhelm, 1932, *The Culture of the Teutons*, Vol. 1, trans. William Worster, Oxford University Press, Oxford.

Haan, J.A. Bierens de, 1946, *Animal Psychology: Its Nature and its Problems*, Hutchinson's University Library, London.

Haeckel, Ernst, 1903, *Histoire de la Création des Êtres Organisés D'Après les Lois Naturelles*, Librarie C. Reinwald, Paris.

Hall, A.D., and Fagen, R.E., 1956, 'Definition of system', *General Systems Year Book*, Vol. 1.

Hall, B.G., 1990, 'Spontaneous point mutations that occur more often when advantageous than when neutral', *Genetics*, Vol. 126, No. 1.

Hall, Ross Hume, 1976, 'Beware of those fabricated foods', *Executive Health*, Vol. 12, No. 7, April.

Hamburger, V., 1935, 'Regeneration', *Encyclopædia Britannica*, Vol. 19, London.

Harding, Thomas G., 'Adaptation and stability', in Sahlins and Elman, eds., 1960, *Evolution and Culture*, University of Michigan Press.

Harlow, H.F., 'The evolution of learning', in Roe and Simpson, eds., 1958, *Behavior and Evolution*.

Harrison, Jane, 1927, *Themis: A Study of the Social Origins of Greek Religion*, Cambridge University Press, Cambridge.

——1928, *Myths of Greece and Rome*, Doubleday, New York.

Head, Henry, 1920, *Studies in Neurology*, Vol. 2, Oxford University Press, Oxford.

Hearn, Lafcadio, 1904, *Japan: An Attempt at Interpretation*, Macmillan, New York.

Heatwole, H., and Levins, R., 1972, 'Trophic structure stability and faunal change during recolonization', *Ecology*, 53.

Hebb, D.O., 1949, *The Organization of Behavior: A Neuropsychological Theory*, John Wiley, New York.

Heckman, Charles W., 1984, 'Telling them what they want to hear', *The Ecologist*, Vol. 14, No. 4.

Heim, A.W., 1954, *The Appraisal of Intelligence*, Methuen, London.

Helms, Mary W., 1993, *Craft and the Kingly Ideal: Art, Trade, and Power*, University of Texas Press, Austin.

Herrick, C. Judson, 1961, *The Evolution of Human Nature*, Harper & Brothers, New York.

Hildebrand, Martín von, 1981, 'An Amazonian tribe's view of cosmology', in Bunyard and Goldsmith, eds., *Gaia*.

Hildyard, Nicholas, 1976, 'How an ideal city works', *The Ecologist*, Vol. 6, No. 9.

——1977, 'Building for collapse', *The Ecologist*, Vol. 7, No. 2.

——1978, 'There's more to food than eating', *The Ecologist*, Vol. 8, No. 5.

Hingston, R.W.G., 1928, *Problems of Instinct and Intelligence*, Edward Arnold, London.

Ho, Mae-Wan, 2003, *Living with the Fluid Genome*, ISIS, London.

Hobbes, Thomas, 2002 (original edition 1651), *Leviathan*, Broadview Press, Ontario.

Hobbs, Mel, 1965, 'Mohole Phase 2 on schedule; cost now up to $100 million', *World Oil*, Vol. 161, Gulf Publishing Company, Housten.

Hocart, A.M., 1936, *Kings and Councillors: An Essay in the Comparative Anatomy of Human Society*, Paul Barbey, Cairo.

Hodges, Lucy, 1981, 'More police mean more crime', *The Times*, 7th September.

Hodgkin, Robin A., 1983, *Playing and Exploring: Education through the Discovery of Order*, Methuen, London.

Holbrook, Bruce, 1981, *The Stone Monkey: An Alternative, Chinese-Scientific, Reality*, William Morrow, New York.

Holling, C.S., 'Resilience and stability of ecosystems', in Jantsch and Waddington, eds., 1976, *Evolution and consciousness*.

Hope, Kempe R., 1996, *Development in the Third World: From Policy Failure to Policy Reform*, Sharpe, New York.

Hopkins, Edward Washburn, 1901, *India Old and New: With a Memorial Address*, Scribner, New York.

Horowitz, Norman H., 1956, 'The Gene', *Scientific American*, October.

Hoy, Don R., 1961, *Agricultural Land Use of Guadeloupe*, National Academies, Washington.

Huber, Peter B., 'Organizing production and producing organization: The sociology of traditional agriculture', in Fisk, ed., 1978, *The Adaptation of Traditional Agriculture*.

Hughes, J. Donald, 1981, 'Early Greek and Roman environmentalists', *The Ecologist*, Vol. 11, No. 1.

——1983, 'Gaia: An ancient view of the planet', *The Ecologist*, Vol. 13, No. 2–3.

Hull, C.L., 1952 (original edition 1927), *A Behavior System: An Introduction to Behavior Theory*, Yale University Press, New Haven.

Hume, David, 1888 (original edition 1740), *A Treatise of Human Nature*, (*Being an Attempt to Introduce the Experimental Method of Reasoning into Moral Subjects: And Dialogues Concerning Natural Religion*), ed. L.A. Selby-Bigge, Clarendon Press, Oxford.

Hungerford, T.A.G., ed., 1956, *Australian Signpost: An Anthology*, Cheshire, Melbourne.

Hutton, James, 1788, 'Theory of the Earth: Or, an investigation of the laws observable in the composition, dissolution and restoration of land upon the globe', *Transactions of the Royal Society of Edinburgh*, 1, Part 2.

Huxley, Julian S., 1953, *Evolution in Action*, (based on the Patten Foundation Lectures delivered at Indiana University in 1951), Harper Bros, New York.

Huxley, T.H., 'The struggle for existence in human society', in T.H. Huxley, 1894, *Collected Essays, Vol. 9: Evolution and Ethics*, Macmillan, London.

——and Huxley, Julian S., 1947, *Evolution and Ethics: 1893–1943*, The Pilot Press, London.

IAITPTF (International Alliance of Indigenous and Tribal Peoples of the Tropical Forests), and IWGIA (International Work Group for Indigenous Affairs), 1996, *Indigenous Peoples, Forests, and Biodiversity: Indigenous Peoples and the Global Environmental Agenda*, IAITPTF, London, IWGIA, Copenhagen.

IIPS, 2000, *India National Family Health Survey 1998–99*, The International Institute for Population Sciences, Mumbai.

Illich, Ivan, 1979 (original edition 1971), *Deschooling Society*, Penguin Books, Middlesex.

——1981, *Shadow Work*, Marion Boyars, London.

Inhelder, Bärbel, Discussion after Piaget and Inhelder, 'The gaps in empiricism', in Koestler and Smythies, eds., 1972, *Beyond Reductionism*.

International Cultural Foundation, 1974, *Science and Absolute Values: Proceedings of the Third International Conference on the Unity of the Sciences, November 21–24, 1974, London, United Kingdom*, 2 Vols., International Cultural Foundation, New York.

Jacob, François, 1998, *Of Flies, Mice, and Men*, Harvard University Press, Cambridge, Massachusetts.

Jantsch, Erich, 1975, *Design for Evolution: Self-Organization and Planning in the Life of Human Systems*, Braziller, New York.

——'Evolution: Self-realization through self-transcendence', in Jantsch and Waddington, eds., 1976, *Evolution and Consciousness*.

——1980a, *The Self-Organizing Universe: Scientific and Human Implications of the Emerging Paradigm of Evolution*, Pergamon Press, Oxford.

——1980b, 'The unifying paradigm behind autopoiesis, dissipative structures, hyper and ultracycles', in Milan Zelený, ed., *Autopoiesis, Dissipative Structures and Spontaneous Social Orders*, Westview Press, Boulder.

——and Waddington, Conrad H., eds., 1976, *Evolution and Consciousness: Our Human Systems in Transition*, Addison–Wesley, Reading, Massachusetts.

Janzen, D.H., 'The natural history of mutualisms', in Boucher, ed., 1985, *The Biology of Mutualism*.

Jaulin, Robert, 1971, 'Ethnocide: The theory and practice of cultural murder', trans. Robert Allen, *The Ecologist*, Vol. 1, No. 18, Dec.

Jeffers, Robinson, 1959, *The Selected Poetry of Robinson Jeffers*, Random House, New York.

Johnson, C.G., 1963, 'The aerial migration of insects', *Scientific American*, December.

Johnson, D.G., 'Increasing availability of food for the world's poor', in Kevin M. Cahill, ed., 1982, *Famine*, Orbis Books, New York.

Jonas, Hans, 1958, *The Gnostic Religion: The Message of the Alien God and the Beginnings of Christianity*, Beacon Press, Boston.

——1985, *The Imperative of Responsibility: In Search of an Ethics for the Technological Age*, University of Chicago Press, Chicago.

Jonas, Steven, Goldsteen, Raymond L., and Goldsteen, Karen, 2007, *An Introduction to the U.S. Health Care System*, Springer Publishing Company, New York.

Jones, Alwyn, 1983, 'Beyond industrial society: Towards balance and harmony', *The Ecologist*, Vol. 13, No. 4.

Jones, W.H.S., 1946, 'Philosophy and medicine in ancient Greece', *Bulletin of the History of Medicine*, Supplement 8, Baltimore.

Jung, Carl Gustav, 1968, *Analytical Psychology: Its Theory and Practice: The Tavistock Lectures*, Pantheon Books, New York

Jurion, F., and Henry, J., 1967, *Can Primitive Farming be Modernised?*, INEAC, Brussels.

Kaberry, Phyllis Mary, 1939, *Aboriginal Women: Sacred and Profane*, Routledge and Kegan Paul, London.

Kalmus, H., ed., 1967, *Regulation and Control of Living Systems*, John Wiley, New York.

Kardiner, A., Linton, R., Du Bois, C.A., and Withers, C., 1945, *The Psychological Frontiers of Society*, Columbia University Press, New York.

Katz, S.H., and Young, M.V., 1976, 'Biological and social aspects of breastfeeding', (Paper presented at the 1976 meeting of the American Association for the Advancement of Science), reproduced in *The Ecologist Quarterly*, Spring 1978.

Keay, Douglas, 1987, 'AIDS, education, and the Year 2000!', *Women's Own*, 31st October.

Kennedy, William S., 1924, *The Real John Burroughs: Personal Recollection and Friendly Estimate*, Funk & Wagnalls, New York.

Kenyatta, Jomo, 1979, *Facing Mount Kenya: The Traditional Life of the Gikuyu*, Heinemann, London.

Keynes, John Maynard, 1933, 'National self-sufficiency', *The Yale Review*, Vol. 22, No. 4.

Kiev, Ari, ed., 1967, *Magic, Faith, and Healing: Studies in Primitive Psychiatry Today*, The Free Press, New York.

King, F.H., 1911, *Farmers of Forty Centuries: Or, Permanent Agriculture in China, Korea and Japan*, King, Madison.

Kline, Morris, 1972, *Mathematics in Western Culture*, Penguin, Harmondsworth.

Knight, Charles, 1859, *Knowledge is Power: A View of the Productive Forces of Modern Society and the Results of Labour, Capital, and Skill*, John Murray, London

Koestler, Arthur, 1967, *The Ghost in the Machine*, Hutchinson, London.

——'Beyond atomism and holism: The concept of the holon', in Koestler and Smythies, eds., 1972, *Beyond Reductionism*.

——1976, *The Act of Creation*, Hutchinson, London.

——1978, *Janus: A Summing Up*, Hutchinson, London.

——et alia, 1950, *The God that Failed: Six Studies in Communism*, ed. Richard Crossman, Hamish Hamilton, London.

——and Smythies, J.R., eds., 1972 (original edition 1969), *Beyond Reductionism: The Alpbach Symposium 1968: New Perspectives in the Life Sciences*, Hutchinson, London.

Köhler, Wolfgang, 1947 (original edition 1929), *Gestalt Psychology: An Introduction to New Concepts in Modern Psychology*, Liveright Publications, New York.

Kornhauser, William, 1998 (original edition 1959), *The Politics of Mass Society*, Routledge, New York.

Korten, David C., 1994, 'Sustainable livelihoods: Redefining the global social crisis', *Earth Ethics*, Vol. 6, No. 1, Fall.

Kothari, Manu L., and Mehta, Lopa A., 'Violence in modern medicine', in Nandy, ed., 1988, *Science, Hegemony and Violence*.

Koyré, Alexandre, 1965, *Newtonian Studies*, University of Chicago Press, Chicago.

Kraemer, Hendrik, 1938, *The Christian Message in a Non-Christian World*, Edinburgh House Press, London.

Krauss, M., 1992, 'The world's languages in crisis', *Language*, Vol. 68, No. 2.

Krige, Eileen Jensen, 1936, *The Social System of the Zulus*, Longman Green, London.

Kropotkin, Peter, 1907 (original edition 1890), *Mutual Aid: A Factor in Evolution*, Heinemann, London.

——1924, *Ethics: Origin and Development*, trans. Louis S. Friedland & Joseph R. Piroshnikoff, Dial Press, New York.

Kuhn, Thomas S., 1970 (original edition 1962), *The Structure of Scientific Revolutions*, 2nd Edition, University of Chicago Press, Chicago.

——'Logic of discovery or psychology of research?', in Lakatos and Musgrave, eds., 1979, *Criticism and the Growth of Knowledge*.

Kuper, Hilda, 1963, *The Swazi: A South African Kingdom*, Holt, Rinehart and Winston, New York.

Kurzweil, Ray, 2005, *The Singularity is Near: When Humans Transcend Biology*, Viking Press, New York.

La Barre, Weston, 1954, *The Human Animal*, University of Chicago Press, Chicago.

LaChapelle, Dolores, 1988, *Sacred Land, Sacred Sex: Rapture of the Deep: Concerning Deep Ecology and Celebrating Life*, Finn Hill Arts, Colorado.

Lakatos, Imre, 'Falsification and the methodology of scientific research programmes', in Lakatos and Musgrave, eds., 1979, *Criticism and the Growth of Knowledge*.

——and Musgrave, Alan, eds., 1979 (original edition 1970), *Criticism and the Growth of Knowledge*, (Volume 4 of the Proceedings of the International Colloquium in the Philosophy of Science), Cambridge University Press, London.

Laozi, 1972, *Lao Tzu, Tao Te King*, trans. Gia-Fu Feng and Jane English, Vintage, New York.

——1974, *The Simple Way of Lao Tsze: An Analysis of the Tao Têh Canon*, trans. Shrine of Wisdom, Surrey.

——1988, *Tao Te Ching*, trans. Stephen Mitchell, HarperCollins, New York.

——1989, *Lao-tzu: Te-tao Ching: A New Translation Based on the Recently Discovered Ma-wang-tui Texts*, trans. Robert G. Henricks, Ballantine, New York.

Lashley, Karl S., 1958, 'Persistent problems in the evolution of mind', *Quarterly Review of Biology*, 24.

——1960, 'The problem of serial order in behavior', in *The Neuropsychology of Lashley: Selected Papers of K.S. Lashley*, McGraw–Hill, New York.

Latouche, Serge, 1998, *L'autre Afrique: Entre don et Marché*, Albin Michel, Paris.

Le Corbusier, 1931, *Towards a New Architecture*, J. Rodker, London.

Ledeen, Michael A., 2003, *The War Against the Terror Masters*, St. Martin's Griffin, New York.

Leder, Philip, 'The genetic basis of antibody diversity', in Philip Leder, David A. Clayton, and Edward Rubenstein, eds., 1994, *Scientific American Introduction to Molecular Medicine*, Scientific American, New York.

Lee, Richard B., '!Kung Bushman subsistence: An input–output analysis', in Vayda, ed., 1969, *Environment and Cultural Behavior*.

——and DeVore, Irven, eds., 1968, *Man the Hunter*, Aldine Publishing Co., Chicago.

Leggett, Jeremy, 1992, 'Global warming: The worst case', *Bulletin of the Atomic Scientists*, Vol. 48, No. 5.

Leopold, Aldo, 1953, *A Sand County Almanac: And Sketches Here and There*, Oxford University Press, Oxford.

——1992, *The River of the Mother of God: And Other Essays*, eds. S.L. Flader and J.B. Callicott, University of Wisconsin Press, Madison.

Lévi-Strauss, Claude, 1992, *Tristes Tropiques*, Penguin Books, London.

Lewis, C.S., 1962 (original edition 1943), *The Abolition of Man*, Geoffrey Bles, London.

Lewis, Oscar, 1966, *La vida: A Puerto Rican family in the Culture of Poverty: San Juan and New York*, Random House, New York.

Lichnerowicz, A., Perroux, F., and Gadoffre, G., eds., 1976, *Structure et Dynamique des Systèmes*, Maloine, Doin, Paris.

Liedloff, Jean, 1989a (original 1975), *The Continuum Concept*, ('*A Rediscovery of Man's Natural Capacity for Happiness: From the Critical First Months of Life*'), Arkana, London.

——1989b, 'The importance of the in-arms phase', *Mothering*, Winter.

Linton, Ralph, 'The Comanche', in Kardiner et alia, 1945, *The Psychological Frontiers of Society*.

Locke, John, 1801 (original edition 1690), *An Essay Concerning Human Understanding: With Thoughts on the Conduct of the Understanding*, Vol. 1, Mundell, Edinburgh.

——1821, *Two Treatises on Government*, Butler, London.

Lods, Adolphe, 1932, *Israel: From its Beginnings to the Middle of the Eighth Century*, trans. S.H. Hooke, Routledge and Kegan Paul, London.

Loeb, Jacques, 1916, *The Organism as a Whole: From a Physicochemical Viewpoint*, Putnam's Sons, New York.

Lorenz, Konrad, 1943, 'Die angeborenen Formen möglicher Erfahrung', *Zeitschrift für Tierpsychologie*, 5.

——1997, *Natural Science of the Human Species: An Introduction to Comparative Behaviorial Research: The Russian Manuscript (1944–1948)*, ed. Agnes von Cranach, trans. Robert D. Martin, MIT Press, Massachusetts.

Los Angeles Times, 2000, 'U.S. weighed A-blast on Moon in 1950s', 18th May.

Lovelock, J.E., 1979, *Gaia: A New Look at Life on Earth*, Oxford University Press, Oxford.

——1985, 'Are we destabilising world climate? The lessons of geophysiology', *The Ecologist*, Vol. 15, No. 1.

——'Gaia: A model for planetary and cellular dynamics', in Thompson, ed., 1987, *Gaia*.

——'The Gaia Hypothesis', in Bunyard and Goldsmith, eds., 1988, *Gaia*.

——1991, *Healing Gaia: The Practical Science of Planetary Medicine*, Gaia Books, London.

——2000, *The Ages of Gaia: A Biography of Our Living Earth*, Oxford University Press, New York.

Lowie, Robert H., 1920, *Primitive Society*, Liveright, New York.

Lumsden, C.J., and Wilson, E.O., 1981, *Genes, Mind, and Culture: The Coevolutionary Process*, Harvard University Press, London.

Lux, Kenneth, 1990, *Adam Smith's Mistake: How a Moral Philosopher Invented Economics and Ended Morality*, Shambhala, Boston.

Lyons, John, 1981, *Language, Meaning, and Context*, Fontana, London.

MacIver, Robert, 1964, *The Ramparts We Guard*, Macmillan, New York.

MacKay, Donald, 'Communication and meaning: A functional approach', in Northrop and Livingstone, eds., 1964, *Cross-cultural Understanding*.

Mackewen, Douglas, 1989, *Tribalism in History: The Contribution of Ancient and Modern Tribal Cultures*, Cupra/Volturna, Hythe.

Macko, D., and Mesarović, M.D., 'Foundations for a scientific theory of hierarchical systems', in Whyte, Wilson, and Wilson, eds., 1969, *Hierarchical Structures*.

Maine, Henry Sumner, 1906 (original edition 1861), *Ancient Law: Its Connection with the Early History of Society and its Relation to Modern Ideas*, 10th Edition, John Murray, London.

Malinowski, Bronislaw, 'Anthropology as the basis of social science', in Cattel, Cohen, and Travers, eds., 1937, *Human Affairs*.

——1961 (original edition 1922), *Argonauts of the Western Pacific: An Account of Native Enterprise and Adventure in the Archipelagoes of Melanesian New Guinea*, E.P. Dutton, New York.

Mann, R.B., 1990, 'Time Running Out: The urgent need for tree-planting in Africa', *The Ecologist*, Vol. 20, No. 2.

Margalef, Ramón, 1958, 'Information theory in ecology', *General Systems Yearbook*, Vol. 3.

——1963, 'On certain unifying principles in ecology', *The American Naturalist*, Nov–Dec, No. 897.

——'Diversity, stability and maturity in natural ecosystems', in Dobben and Lowe-McConnell, eds., 1975, *Unifying Concepts in Ecology*.

Marsh, George Perkins, 1864, *Man and Nature: Or, Physical Geography as Modified by Human Action*, Sampson Low, London.

Martin, Gary, and Kats, Vladimir, 2003, *Families and Work in Transition in 12 Countries, 1980–2001*, Monthly Labor Review, September.

Mason, Stephen F., 1956, *Main Currents of Scientific Thought: A History of the Sciences*, Routledge and Kegan Paul, London.

Masterman, Margaret, 'The nature of the paradigm', in Lakatos and Musgrave, eds., 1979, *Criticism and the Growth of Knowledge*.

Mathes, J.C., and Gray, Donald H., 1975, 'The Engineer as social radical', *The Ecologist*, Vol. 5., No. 4.

Mauss, Marcel, 1954, *The Gift: Forms and Functions of Exchange in Archaic Societies*, Cohen and West, London.

May, Robert M., 1974, *Stability and Complexity in Model Ecosystems*, Princeton University Press, Princeton.

McCully, Patrick, 1991, 'The case against climate aid', *The Ecologist*, Vol. 21, No. 6.

McDougall, William, 1938, *The Riddle of Life: A Survey of Theories*, Methuen, London.

——1999 (original edition 1896), *A Textbook of Psychology*, Discovery, New Delhi.

McEwan, P.J.M., and Sutcliffe, R.B., 1967, *The Study of Africa*, Methuen, London.

McIntosh, Robert P., 1975, 'H.A. Gleason, "individualistic ecologist" 1882–1975: His contribution to ecological theory', *Bulletin of the Torrey Botanical Club*, Vol. 102.

——'The background and some current problems of theoretical ecology', in Saarinen, ed., 1982, *Conceptual Issues in Ecology*.

McKinney, H.L., 1966, 'Alfred Russel Wallace and the discovery of natural selection', *Journal of the History of Medicine and Allied Sciences*, 21.

McKnight, John, 1978, 'The politics of medicine', *The Ecologist*, Vol. 8, No. 4.

McNaughton, S.J., 1979, 'Grazing as an optimization process: Grass-ungulate relationships in the Serengeti', *The American Naturalist*, 113.

McNeill, W.H., 1976, *Plagues and Peoples*, Anchor Press–Doubleday, New York.

Mead, Margaret, 'Our educational emphases in primitive perspective', in Middleton, ed., 1970, *From Child to Adult*.

Meadows, Donella, Meadows, Dennis, Randers, Jørgen, and Behrens, William W. (III), 1972, *The Limits to Growth*, Earth Island, London.

Medawar, P.B., 1969, *Induction and Intuition in Scientific Thought*, American Philosophical Society, Philadelphia.

——1974, *The Hope of Progress: A Scientist Looks at Problems in Philosophy, Literature and Science*, Wildwood House, London.

——1982, *Pluto's Republic*, Oxford University Press, Oxford.

——and Medawar, J.S., 1977, *The Life Science: Current Ideas of Biology*, Wildwood House, London.

Merrell, David J., 1981, *Ecological Genetics*, Longman, London.

——and Underhill, J.C., 1956, 'Selection for DDT resistance in inbred laboratory and wild stocks of Drosophila melanogaster', *Journal of Economic Entomology*, 49.

Merton, Robert, 1951, *Social Theory and Social Structure: Toward the Clarification of Theory and Research*, The Free Press of Glencoe, New York.

Metuh, Emefie Ikenga, 1981, *God and Man in African Religion: A Case Study of the Igbo of Nigeria*, Geoffrey Chapman, London.

Middleton, John, ed., 1970, *From Child to Adult: Studies in the Anthropology of Education*, The Natural History Press, New York.

Midgley, Mary, 1992, *Science as Salvation: A Modern Myth and Its Meaning*, Routledge, London.

Monod, Jacques, 1970, *Le Hasard et la Nécessité: Essai sur la Philosophie Naturelle de la Biologie Moderne*, Seuil, Paris.

——1972 (see also original French edition, 1970), *Chance and Necessity: An Essay on the Natural Philosophy of Modern Biology*, Vintage, New York.

——Discussion following Pierre Delattre, 'Langage interdisciplinaire et théorie des systèmes', in Lichnerowicz, Perroux, and Gadoffre, eds., 1976, *Structure et Dynamique des Systèmes*.

——and Jacob, François, 1961, 'General conclusions: Teleonomic mechanisms in cellular metabolism, growth, and differentiation', *Cold Spring Harbor Symposia on Quantitative Biology*, Vol. 26, Cold Spring Harbor Laboratory Press, New York.

Mooney, Patrick Roy, 1979, *Seeds of the Earth: A Private and Public Resource*, Inter Pares, Ottawa.

Moore, Barrington, 1920, 'The scope of ecology', (Presidential address delivered before the St Louis meeting of the Ecological Society of America, 31st December 1919).

Morenz, Siegfried, 1973, *Egyptian Religion*, trans. Ann E. Keep, Methuen, London.

Morgan, Lewis H., 1877, *Ancient Society: Or, Researches in the Lines of Human Progress from Savagery, through Barbarism to Civilization*, H. Holt, New York.

Morin, Edgar, 1977, *La Méthode, Vol. 1: La Nature de la Nature*, Seuil, Paris.

——1980, 'Au-delà du déterminisme: Le dialogue de l'ordre et du désordre (Sur le déterminisme)', *Le Débat*, No. 6, November.

Muller, Herbert J., 1956, *Science and Criticism: The Humanistic Tradition in Contemporary Thought*, George Braziller, New York.

Mumford, Lewis, 1972, *The Transformations of Man*, Harper, New York.

Murdock, George P., 'Waging baseball on Truk', in George P. Murdock, 1965, *Culture and Society: Twenty-Four Essays*, University of Pittsburgh, Pennsylvania.

——and White, Douglas R., 1969, 'Standard cross-cultural sample', *Ethnology*, 8.

Murray, Robert, 1991, 'The biblical vocabulary of justice', lecture at a summer school for Jewish and Christian lay people reading Amos together (unpublished notes).

——1992, *The Cosmic Covenant: Biblical Themes of Justice, Peace and the Integrity of Creation*, Sheed & Ward, London.

Nandy, Ashis, 1983, 'The pathology of objectivity', *The Ecologist*, Vol. 13, No. 6.

——1987, *Traditions, Tyranny and Utopia: Essays in the Politics of Awareness*, Oxford University Press, New Delhi.

——ed., 1988, *Science, Hegemony and Violence: A Requiem for Modernity*, Oxford University Press, New Delhi.

Napton, Lewis K., and Heizer, Robert F., 1970, 'Analysis of human coprolites from archaeological contexts with primary reference to Lovelock Cave, Nevada', *University of California Archaeological Research Facility Contributions* 10 (2), Berkeley.

National Academy of Sciences, 1991, *Policy Implications of Greenhouse Warming*, ('Mitigation, Adaptation, and the Science Base'), National Academy Press, Washington, D.C.

National Geographic, 1989, *National Geographic*, Vol. 175, National Geographic Society, Washington, D.C.

Ndaw, Alassane, 1983, *La Pensée Africaine: Recherches sur les Fondements de la Pensée Négro-Africaine*, Les Nouvelles Editions Africaines, Dakar.

Necker, Louis Albert, 1832, 'Observations on some remarkable optical phænomena seen in Switzerland: And on an optical phænomenon which occurs on viewing a figure of a crystal or geometrical solid', *The London and Edinburgh Philosophical Magazine and Journal of Science*, Vol. 1, No. 5, November, London.

Needham, Joseph, 1936, *Order and Life*, MIT Press, Cambridge, Massachusetts.

——1956, *Science and Civilization in China*, Vol. 2, *History of Scientific Thought*, Cambridge University Press, Cambridge.

——1969, *The Grand Titration: Science and Society in East and West*, George Allen and Unwin, London.

Nelkin, Dorothy, 'Threats and promises: Negotiating the control of research', in Daedalus, 1978, *Daedalus*.

Nicholson, Max, 1970, *The Environmental Revolution: A Guide for the New Masters of the World*, Hodder & Stoughton, London.

Nisbet, Robert, 1966, *The Sociological Tradition*, Heinemann Educational Books, London.

Noël, Émile, ed., 1979, *Le Darwinisme Aujourd'hui*, Le Seuil, Paris.

Norberg-Hodge, Helena, 1991, *Ancient Futures: Learning from Ladakh*, Sierra Club Books, San Francisco.

Northrop, F.S.C., and Livingston, Helen H., eds., 1964, *Cross-cultural Understanding: Epistemology in Anthropology*, Harper and Row, New York.

Oatley, Keith, 1978, *Perceptions and Representations: The Theoretical Bases of Brain Research and Psychology*, Methuen, London.

Odum, Eugene P., 1953, *Fundamentals of Ecology*, W.B. Saunders, Philadelphia.

——'The strategy of ecosystem development', in Shepard and McKinley, eds., 1971, *Environ/Mental*.

——1975, *Ecology: The Link Between the Natural and the Social Sciences*, Holt, Rinehart, and Winston, New York.

——1983, *Basic Ecology*, Saunders College Publishing, Philadelphia.

——1989, *Ecology and Our Endangered Life-Support Systems*, Sinauer Associates, Massachusetts.

OED, 1989, *Oxford English Dictionary*, 2nd Edition, Clarendon Press, Oxford.

Ogot, Bethwell A., ed., 1979, *Ecology and History in East Africa: Proceedings of the 1975 Conference of the Historical Association of Kenya*, Kenya Literature Bureau, Nairobi.

Opler, Marvin K., 1967, *Culture and Social Psychiatry*, Atherton Press, New York.

Orians, G.H., 'Diversity, stability and maturity in natural ecosystems', in Dobben and Lowe-McConnell, eds., 1975, *Unifying Concepts in Ecology*.

Ortega y Gasset, José, 'History as a system', in Raymond Klibansky and H.J. Paton, eds., 1936, *Philosophy and History: Essays Presented to Ernst Cassirer*, Clarendon Press, Oxford.

Ospovat, Dov, 1981, *The Development of Darwin's Theory: Natural History, Natural Theology, and Natural Selection, 1838–1859*, Cambridge University Press, Cambridge.

Overend Prior, Jennifer, and Gerard, Maureen R., 2007, *Family Involvement in Early Childhood Education: Research into Practice*, Thomson, New York.

Owen, D.F., and Wiegert, R.G., 1981, 'Mutualism between grasses and grazers: An evolutionary hypothesis', *Oikos*, 36.

Oyama, Susan, Griffiths, Paul E., and Gray, Russell D., eds., 2001, *Cycles of Contingency: Developmental Systems and Evolution*, MIT Press, Cambridge, Massachusetts.

Pantin, C.F.A., 1968, *The Relations Between the Sciences*, eds. A.M. Pantin and W.H.Thorpe, Cambridge University Press, Cambridge.

Park, Mungo, 1984 (original edition 1799), *Travels in the Interior of Africa: Performed Under the Direction and Patronage of the African Association, in the Years 1795, 1796, and 1797*, Folio Society, London.

Parsons, Robert T., 1964, *Religion in an African Society: A Study of the Religion of the Kono People of Sierra Leone in its Social Environment: With Special Reference to the Function of Religion in that Society*, E.J. Brill, Leiden.

Passmore, John, 1978, *Science and its Critics*, Duckworth, London.

Patai, Raphael, 1947, *Man and Temple: In Ancient Jewish Myth and Ritual*, Thomas Nelson, London.

Pattee, Howard H., 1970, 'The Problem of Biological Hierarchy', in C.H. Waddington, ed., *Towards a Theoretical Biology 3: Drafts*, Edinburgh University Press, Edinburgh.

——ed., 1973, *Hierarchy Theory: The Challenge of Complex Systems*, George Braziller, New York.

Patten, B.C., and Odum, E.P., 1981, 'The cybernetic nature of ecosystems', *American Naturalist*, 118.

Pavlov, Ivan P., 1927, *Conditioned Reflexes: An Investigation of the Physiological Activity of the Cerebral Cortex*, trans. G.V. Anrep, Oxford University Press, London.

Payer, Cheryl, 1982, *The World Bank: A Critical Analysis*, Monthly Review Press, New York.

——1991, *Lent and Lost: Foreign Credit and Third World Development*, Zed Books, London.

Peerenboom, R.P., 1991, 'Beyond naturalism: A reconstruction of Daoist environmental ethics', *Environmental Ethics*, Vol. 13, Spring.

Pennisi, Elizabeth, 1997, 'Haeckel's embryos: Fraud rediscovered', *Science*, 5th September.

Perrin, Noel, 1979, *Giving Up the Gun: Japan's Reversion to the Sword, 1543–1879*, Shambhala, Boulder.

Piaget, Jean, 1967, *Biologie et Connaissance: Essai sur les Relations entre les Régulations Organiques et les Processus Cognitifs*, Gallimard, Paris.

——1968, *The Child's Conception of the World*, Adams & Co., Littlefield, New Jersey.

——1974 (see also French edition, 1967), *Biology and Knowledge: An Essay on the Relations Between Organic Regulations and Cognitive Processes*, University of Chicago Press, Chicago.

——1980, *Adaptation and Intelligence: Organic Selection and Phenocopy*, University of Chicago Press, Chicago.

——and Inhelder, Bärbel, 'The gaps in empiricism', in Koestler and Smythies, eds., 1972, *Beyond Reductionism*.

Pimentel, David, 'Genetic diversity and stability in parasite–host systems', in Bryan Shorrocks, ed., 1982, *Evolutionary Ecology: The 23rd Symposium of the British Ecological Society, Leeds, 1982*, Blackwell, Oxford.

Pirie, N.W., 1969, 'Gardyloo', *The Listener*, 82.

Pittendrigh, Colin, 'Adaptation, natural selection, and behavior', in Roe and Simpson, eds., 1958, *Behavior and Evolution*.

Planck, Max, 1949, *A Scientific Autobiography and Other Papers*, Philosophical Library, New York.

Plato, *Laws*, Book 5.

Polanyi, Karl, 1957 (original edition 1944), *The Great Transformation: The Political and Economic Origins of Our Time*, Beacon Press, Boston.

——1968, *Primitive, Archaic and Modern Economics: Essays of Karl Polanyi*, ed. George Dalton, Anchor Books, New York.

Polanyi, Michael, 1978 (original edition 1958), *Personal Knowledge: Towards a Post-Critical Philosophy*, Routledge and Kegan Paul, London.

Police Journal, The, 1991, 'Police Superintendent's Conference', *The Police Journal*, Vol. 64, London.

Pollard, Nigel, 1981, 'The Gezira scheme: A study in failure', *The Ecologist*, Vol. 11, No. 1.

Pólya, George, 1954, *Mathematics and Plausible Reasoning: Volume 1: Induction and Analogy in Mathematics*, Princeton University Press, Princeton.

Popenoe, David, 1991, 'Family decline in the Swedish welfare state', *The Public Interest*, 102, Winter.

Popper, Karl, 1963, *Conjectures and Refutations: The Growth of Scientific Knowledge*, Routledge and Kegan Paul, London.

——1973, *Objective Knowledge: An Evolutionary Approach*, Clarendon Press, Oxford.

——1983 (original German edition 1935), *The Logic of Scientific Discovery*, Hutchinson, London.

——and Eccles, John C., 1977, *The Self and Its Brain*, Springer International.

Post, Laurens van der, 1977, *The Lost World of the Kalahari*, Harcourt Brace Jovanovich, London.

Price, Henry H., 1973 (original edition 1932), *Perception*, Methuen, New York.

Price, Peter W., 'Alternative paradigms in community ecology', in P.W. Price, C.N. Slobodchikoff, and W.S. Gaud, eds., 1984, *A New Ecology*, Northern Arizona University.

Price, Weston A., 1939, *Nutrition and Physical Degeneration: A Comparison of Primitive and Modern Diets and their Effects*, Harper & Brothers, New York.

Prigogine, Ilya, and Stengers, Isabelle, 1979, *La Nouvelle Alliance: Métamorphose de la Science*, Gallimard, Paris.

Prior, I.A., Welby, T.J., Ostbye, T., Salmond, C.E., and Stokes, Y.M., 1987, 'Migration and gout: The Tokelau Island migrant study', *British Medical Journal*, 295, August.

Putman, R.J., and Wratten, S.D., 1984, *Principles of Ecology*, Croom Helm, Beckenham, Kent.

Quastler, H., ed., 1953, *Essays on the Use of Information Theory in Biology*, University of Illinois Press, Urbana.

Radcliffe-Brown, A.R., 1965, *Structure and Function in Primitive Society: Essays and Addresses*, Cohen and West, London.

Ramnath, Madhu, 1988, 'Predicting the monsoon: Modern science versus traditional wisdom', *The Ecologist*, Vol. 18, No. 6.

Ramsay, W.R., and Broadhurst, Anne, 1968, 'The non-randomness of attempts at random responses: Relationships with personality variables and psychiatric disorder', *British Journal of Psychology*, Vol. 59, August.

Randall, John H., 1940, *The Making of the Modern Mind*, Houghton Mifflin, Boston.

Rapoport, Anatol, 1956, 'The promise and pitfalls of information theory', *Behavioral Science*, 1.

Rappaport, Roy A., 1967a, *Pigs for the Ancestors: Ritual in the Ecology of a New Guinea People*, Yale University Press, New Haven.

——1967b, 'Ritual regulation of environmental relations among a New Guinea people', *Ethnology*, Vol. 6.

——'Maladaptation in social systems', in J. Friedman and M.J. Rowlands, eds., 1978, *The Evolution of Social Systems: Proceedings of a Meeting of the Research Seminar in Archaeology and Related Subjects, Held at the Institute of Archaeology, London University*, University of Pittsburgh Press, Pittsburgh.

——1979, *Ecology, Meaning, and Religion*, North Atlantic Books, Richmond, California.

Raum, O.F., 'Some aspects of indigenous education among the Chaga', in Middleton, ed., 1970, *From Child to Adult*.

Ravetz, Jerome R., 1971, *Scientific Knowledge and its Social Problems*, Oxford University Press, Oxford.

Read, Margaret H., 'Education in Africa: Its pattern and role in social change', in Middleton, ed., 1970, *From Child to Adult*.

Reichel-Dolmatoff, Gerardo, 1977, 'Cosmology as ecological analysis: A view from the rainforest', *The Ecologist*, Vol. 7, No. 1.

——1978, 'The Loom of Life: A Kogi principle of integration', *Journal of Latin American Lore*, Vol. 4, No. 1.

Reinheimer, Hermann, 1931, *Synthetic Biology and the Moral Universe*, Rider, London.

Resurgence, 1969, 'Editorial', *Resurgence*, Vol. 2, No. 10.

Richards, Eric J., 2006, 'Inherited epigenetic variation: Revisiting soft inheritance', *Nature Reviews: Genetics*, 7.

Ricklefs, R.E., 1973, *Ecology*, Nelson, London.

Ricqlès, Armand de, 'Darwinisme, paléontologie et anatomie comparée', in Noël, ed., 1979, *Le Darwinisme Aujourd'hui*.

Riedl, Rupert, 1978, *Order in Living Organisms: A Systems Analysis of Evolution*, John Wiley, New York.

Rifkin, Jeremy, and Perlas, Nicanor, 1983, *Algeny: A New Word—A New World*, The Viking Press, New York.

Roberts, Elizabeth, and Amidon, Elias, eds., 1991, *Earth Prayers: 365 Prayers, Poems, and Invocations from Around the World*, (originaly presented to the Sixth Assembly of the World Council of Churches), HarperCollins, New York.

Robertson Smith, W., 1914, *Lectures on the Religion of the Semites*, Adams and Charles Black, London.

Roe, Anne, and Simpson, George Gaylord, eds., 1958, *Behavior and Evolution*, Yale University Press, New Haven.

Rogers, Everett M., and Kincaid, D. Lawrence, 1981, *Communications Networks: Toward a New Paradigm for Research*, Collier Macmillan, London.

Roht-Arriaza, Naomi, 1992, *UNCED Undermined: Why Free Trade Won't Save the Planet*, Greenpeace International, Amsterdam.

Rolt, L.T.C., 1947, *High Horse Riderless*, George Allen & Unwin, London.

Rose, Walter, 1942, *Good Neighbours*, Cambridge University Press, Cambridge.

Roszak, Theodore, 1969, *The Making of a Counter Culture: Reflections on the Technocratic Society and its Youthful Opposition*, Anchor Books, New York.

——1972, *Where the Wasteland Ends: Politics and Transcendence in Postindustrial Society*, Faber and Faber, London.

Roux, W., 1891, *Der Kampf der Teile im Organismus*, ('The Struggle of the Parts in the Organism'), Engelmann, Leipzig.

Rummel, Rudolph J., 1975, *Understanding Conflict and War, Volume 1: The Dynamic Psychological Field*, John Wiley, New York.

——1997, Interview, *The Freeman: Ideas on Liberty*, 47.

Ruse, Michael, 1985, *Sociobiology: Sense or Nonsense?*, Reidel, Holland.

Russell, Bertrand, 1959, *My Philosophical Development*, Allen & Unwin, London.

——1976 (original edition 1917), *A Free Man's Worship, and Other Essays*, Unwin Paperbacks, London.

Russell, Peter, 1982, *The Awakening Earth: The Global Brain*, Routledge and Kegan Paul, London.

Ryle, Gilbert, 1949, *The Concept of Mind*, Hutchinson's University Library, London.

Saarinen, Esa, ed., 1982, *Conceptual Issues in Ecology*, Reidel, Dordrecht, Holland.

Sagan, Carl, 1995, *Cosmos*, Abacus, London.

Sagan, Dorion, and Margulis, Lynn, 1983, 'The Gaian perspective of ecology', *The Ecologist*, Vol. 13, No. 5.

Sahlins, Marshall, 'Political Power and the Economy in Primitive Society', in Gertrude E. Dole and Robert L. Carneiro, 1960, *Essays in the Science of Culture*, Crowell, New York.

——'Tribal economics', in Dalton, ed., 1971, *Economic Development and Social Change*.

——1972, *Stone Age Economics*, Aldine de Gruyter, New York.

Salaman, Redcliffe N., 1949, *The History and Social Influence of the Potato: With a Chapter on Industrial Uses by W.G. Burton*, Cambridge University Press, Cambridge.

Salati, E., and Vose, P.B., 1984, 'Amazon Basin: A system in equilibrium', *Science*, 225.

Sampson, R. Neil, 1981, *Farmland or Wasteland: A Time to Choose: Overcoming the Threat to America's Farm and Food Future*, Rodale Press, Pennsylvania.

Sancton, Andrew, 1985, *Governing the Island of Montreal: Language Differences and Metropolitan Politics*, University of California Press, Berkeley.

Sargant, William, 1957, *The Battle for the Mind: A Physiology of Conversion and Brain-Washing*, Heinemann, London.

Schebesta, Paul, 1940, *Les Pygmées*, Gallimard, Paris.

Schillp, P.A., 1959, ed., *Albert Einstein: Philosopher Scientist*, Harper and Row, New York.

Schoepf, Brooke Grundfest, 'Man and biosphere in Zaire', in Barker, ed., 1984, *The Politics of Agriculture in Tropical Africa*.

Schubert-Soldern, Rainer, 1962, *Mechanism and Vitalism: Philosophical Aspects of Biology*, Burns & Oates, London.

Schumacher, E.F., 1966, 'Industrialisation through intermediate technology', *Resurgence*, Vol. 1, No. 2.

Schweitzer, Albert, 1949, *Out of My Life and Thought: An Autobiography*, Holt, New York.

Scott, James C., 1978, 'The subsistence ethic', *The New Ecologist*, Vol. 8, No. 3.

Selye, Hans, 1984, *The Stress of Life*, McGraw–Hill, New York.

Senghor, Léopold, Preface, in Ndaw, 1983, *La Pensée Africaine*.

Seton, Ernest Thompson, 1922, *Wild Animals I Have Known: Being the Personal Histories of Lobo, Silverspot, Raggylug, Bingo, the Springfield Fox, the Pacing Mustang, Wully, and Redruff*, Scribner, New York.

Shannon, Claude E., and Weaver, Warren, 1962 (original edition 1949), *The Mathematical Theory of Communication*, University of Illinois Press, Urbana.

Shaw, George Bernard, 1972, *The Bodley Head Bernard Shaw: Collected Plays with Their Prefaces*, Vol. 5, Bodley Head, London.

Sheldrake, Rupert, 1988, *The Presence of the Past: Morphic Resonance and the Habits of Nature*, Collins, London.

Shepard, Paul, and McKinley, Daniel, eds., 1971, *Environ/Mental: Essays on the Planet as a Home*, Houghton Mifflin, Boston.

Sherrington, Charles, 1940, *Man on his Nature*, (The Gifford Lectures, 1937–8), Cambridge University Press, Cambridge.

——1947 (original edition 1906), *The Integrative Action of the Nervous System*, Cambridge University Press, Cambridge.

Simberloff, D.S., 'A succession of paradigms in ecology: Essentialism to materialism and probabilism', in Saarinen, ed., 1982, *Conceptual Issues in Ecology*.

——and Wilson, E.O.L., 1969, 'Experimental zoogeography of islands: The colonization of empty islands', *Ecology*, 50.

Simon, Julian L., 1996, *The Ultimate Resource 2*, Princeton University Press, Chichester.

Simpson, George Gaylord, 1950, *The Meaning of Evolution: A Study of the History of Life and of its Significance for Man*, Oxford University Press, London.

Singh, Rev. J.A.L., and Zing, Robert M., 1942, *Wolf Children and Feral Man*, Harper and Bros, New York.

Sinnott, Edmund W., 1961, *Cell and Psyche: The Biology of Purpose*, Harper and Row, New York.

——1962, *Matter, Mind and Man: The Biology of Human Nature*, Atheneum, New York.

Skolimowski, Henryk, 'Problems of rationality in biology', in Ayala and Dobzhansky, 1974, *Studies in the Philosophy of Biology*.

——1983, *Technology and Human Destiny*, University of Madras, Madras.

Smuts, Jan C., 1926, *Holism and Evolution*, Macmillan, New York.

Sonnenschein, C., and Soto, A.M., 1999, *The Society of Cells: Cancer and Control of Cell Proliferation*, Springer Verlag, New York.

Spadafora, C., et alia, 2006, 'Generation of biologically active retro-genes upon interaction of mouse spermatozoa with exogenous DNA', *Molecular Reproduction and Development*, 73.

Spencer, Herbert, 1871 (original edition 1851), *Social Statics: Or the Conditions Essential to Human Happiness Specified, and the First of them Developed*, Appleton, New York.

Sperry, Roger W., 1985, *Science & Moral Priority: Merging Mind, Brain, and Human Values*, Praeger, New York.

Sprigge, T.L.S., 'Definition of a moral judgment', in Wallace and Walker, eds., 1970, *The Definition of Morality*.

Stanner, W.E.H., 'The Dreaming', in Hungerford, ed., 1956, *Australian Signpost*.

Steele, Edward J., Lindley, Robyn A., and Blanden, Robert V., 1998, *Lamarck's Signature: How Retrogenes are Changing Darwin's Natural Selection Paradigm*, Allen & Unwin, Sydney.

Stent, Gunther, 1978, *Paradoxes of Progress*, W.H. Freeman, San Francisco.

Stirling, Paul, 1965, *Turkish Village*, John Wiley, New York.

Stokes, David R., and Wilson, Nicholas, 2006, *Small Businesss Management and Entrepreneurship*, Thompson Learning, London.

Suess, Eduard, 1875, *Die Entstehung der Alpen*, W. Braumuller, Vienna.

Sumich, James L., and Morrissey, John F., 2004, *Introduction to the Biology of Marine Life*, Jones & Bartlett Learning, Sudbury.

Tainter, Joseph, 1988, *The Collapse of Complex Societies*, Cambridge University Press, Cambridge.

Tansley, Arthur, 1935, 'The use and abuse of vegetational concepts and terms', *Ecology*, 16, July.

Taylor, Bron, 1991, 'The religion and politics of Earth First!', *The Ecologist*, Vol. 21, No. 6.

——ed., 2005, *Encyclopedia of Religion and Nature*, 2 Vols., Continuum, New York.

Teilhard de Chardin, Pierre, 1999 (original edition 1955), *The Human Phenomenon: A New Edition and Translation of Le Phénomène Humain*, trans. Sarah Appleton-Weber, Sussex Academic Press, Brighton.

Tempels, Placide, 1969 (original French edition, 1948), *Bantu Philosophy*, Présence Africaine, Paris.

Tenner, Edward, 1996, *Why Things Bite Back: New Technology and the Revenge Effect*, Fourth Estate, London.

Thatcher, Margaret, 1989, Speech on the global environment to the United Nations General Assembly, New York, 8th November, typescript only, The Prime Minister's Office, London.

Thompson, D'Arcy Wentworth, 1992 (original edition 1917), *On Growth and Form*, abridged edition, ed. John Tyler Bonner, Cambridge University Press, Cambridge.

Thompson, William Irwin, ed., 1987, *Gaia: A Way of Knowing: Political Implications as a New Biology*, Lindisfarne Press, Hudson, New York.

Thorpe, W.H., 1965, *Science, Man, and Morals*, ('Based upon the Fremantle lectures delivered in Balliol College, Oxford, Trinity term, 1963'), Methuen & Co., London.

——1969, 'Why the brain is more than a mere computer', *The Times*, London, 25th January.

——1972a, Discussion after Waddington, 'The theory of evolution today', in Koestler and Smythies, *Beyond Reductionism*.

——1972b, Discussion after Bertalanffy, 'Chance or law?', in Koestler and Smythies, eds., *Beyond Reductionism*.

Tinbergen, N., 1951, *The Study of Instinct*, The Clarendon Press, Oxford.

Tisdall, Simon, 1991, 'America loses moral values', *The Guardian*, 2nd May.

Tocqueville, Alexis de, 2004 (original edition 1835), *Democracy in America*, trans. Arthur Goldhammer, Penguin Putnam, New York.

Todd, J.E., and Whitworth, A., 1974, *Adult Dental Health in Scotland, 1972*, HMSO, London.

Tolman, E.C., 1932, *Purposive Behavior in Animals and Men*, The Century Co., New York.

Tönnies, Ferdinand, 1955 (original German edition 1887), *Community and Association*, ('Gemeinschaft und Gesellschaft'), Routledge and Kegan Paul, London.

Toynbee, Arnold J., 1935, *A Study of History*, Vol. 1, Oxford University Press, London.

Trivers, R.L., Foreword, in Richard Dawkins, 1976 (original edition), *The Selfish Gene*, Oxford University Press, Oxford.

Turner, Victor, 'An Ndembu doctor in practice', in Kiev, ed., 1967, *Magic, Faith, and Healing*.

Unknown artist, 1892, 'Kaninchen und Ente', ('Rabbit and Duck'), *Fliegende Blätter*, 23rd October, Munich.

US Department of Health, Education, and Welfare, Office of Education, (J.S. Coleman), 1966, *Equality of Educational Opportunity*, Washington, D.C.

Valente, Judith, 'Hate winter? Here's a scientist's answer: Blow up the moon', in Jane Berentson, ed., 1985, *Dressing for Dinner in the Naked City, and other Tales from the Wall Street Journal's Middle Column*, Hyperion, New York.

Vandermeer, John, 1980, 'Indirect mutualism: Variations on a theme by Stephen Levine', *The American Naturalist*, Vol. 116, No. 3.

Vayda, Andrew P., 'Maori warfare', in Bohannan, ed., 1967, *Law and Warfare*.

——ed., 1969, *Environment and Cultural Behavior: Ecological Studies in Cultural Anthropology*, American Museum of Natural History, New York.

Vernadsky, V.I., 1945, 'The biosphere and the noösphere', *American Scientist*, 33.

Visvanathan, Shiv, 'Atomic physics: The career of an imagination', in Nandy, ed., 1988, *Science, Hegemony and Violence*.

Vitousek, P.M., Ehrlich, P.R., Ehrlich, A.H., and Matson, P.A., 1986, 'Human appropriation of the products of photosynthesis', *BioScience*, Vol. 36, No. 6.

Wach, Joachim, 1944, *Sociology of Religion*, Vol. 1, University of Chicago Press, Chicago.

Waddington, C.H., 1960, *The Ethical Animal*, University of Chicago Press, Chicago.

——ed., 1969, *Towards a Theoretical Biology*, 3 Vols., Edinburgh University Press, Edinburgh.

——'The basic ideas of biology', in Waddington, ed., 1969, *Towards a Theoretical Biology*.

——'The theory of evolution today', in Koestler and Smythies, eds., 1972, *Beyond Reductionism*.

——1975, *The Evolution of an Evolutionist*, Edinburgh University Press, Edinburgh.

——'Concluding remarks', in Jantsch and Waddington, 1976, *Evolution and Consciousness*.

——1977, *Tools for Thought: How to Understand and Apply the Latest Scientific Techniques of Problem Solving*, Basic Books, New York.

Walker, Ranginui, 1987, *Nga Tau Tohetohe: Years of Anger: A Selection of 'Korero' Columns from the New Zealand Listener*, ed. Jacqueline Amoamo, Penguin, New Zealand.

Wallace, A.F.C., 1956, 'Revitalization movements: Some theoretical considerations for their comparative study', *American Anthropologist*, Vol. 58, April.

——1963, *Culture and Personality*, Random House, New York.

——2003, *Revitalizations and Mazeways: Essays on Culture Change, Volume 1*, ed. Robert S. Grumet, University of Nebraska Press, Lincoln.

Wallace, G., and Walker, A.D.M., eds., 1970, *The Definition of Morality*, Methuen, London.

Wanniski, Jude, 1991, 'Macroeconomics: The enemy within', *The Wall Street Journal*, 27th June.

Washburn, S.L., and Lancaster, C.S., 'The evolution of hunting', in Lee and DeVore, eds., 1968, *Man the Hunter*.

Wasserman, Harvey, and Solomon, Norman, 1982, *Killing Our Own: The Disaster of America's Experience with Atomic Radiation*, Delacorte Press, New York.

Watkins, John, 'Against "normal science"', in Lakatos and Musgrave, 1979, *Criticism and the Growth of Knowledge*.

Watson, John B., 1925, *Behaviourism*, Kegan Paul Trench Trubner, London.

Weismann, August, 1889, *Essays upon Heredity and Kindred Biological Problems*, eds. E.B. Poulton, S. Schönland, and A.E. Shipley, Clarendon Press, Oxford.

Weiss, Paul, 1971, *Hierarchically Organized Systems in Theory and Practice*, Hafner, New York.

——1972a, 'The living system: Determinism stratified', in Koestler and Smythies, eds., *Beyond Reductionism*.

——1972b, Discussion after presentation of his paper 'The living system', in Koestler and Smythies, eds., *Beyond Reductionism*.

——1972c, Discussion after Waddington, 'The theory of evolution today', in Koestler and Smythies, eds., *Beyond Reductionism*.

——1973, *The Science of Life: The Living System—A System for Living*, Futura Publishing Co., New York.

Wheeler, J. A., 'From relativity to mutability', in J. Mehra, ed., 1973, *The Physicist's Conception of Nature*, Reidel, Dordrecht.

Wheeler, Robert Eric Mortimer, 1959, *Early India and Pakistan: To Ashoka*, A. Praeger, New York.

White, Lynn, 1979, 'The ecology of our science', *Science*, Vol. 80, No. 1.

Whitehead, Alfred North, 1927, *Symbolism: Its Meaning and Effect*, ('Page-Barbour' Lectures, University of Virginia), Macmillan, New York.

——1932, *Science and the Modern World*, (Lowell Lectures, 1925), Cambridge University Press.

Whittaker, R.H., 1967, 'Gradient analysis of vegetation', *Biological Reviews*, 42.

Whitten Jr., N.E., 1978, 'Ecological imagery and cultural adaptability: The Canelos Quichua of Eastern Ecuador', *American Anthropologist*, Vol. 80, No. 4, December.

Whorf, Benjamin Lee, 1956, *Language, Thought, and Reality: Selected Writings*, ed. John B. Carroll, MIT Press, Cambridge, Massachusetts.

Whyte, Lancelot Law, Wilson, Albert G., Wilson, Donna, eds., 1969, *Hierarchical Structures: Proceedings of the Symposium Held November 18–19, 1968 at Douglas Advanced Research Laboratories, Huntington Beach, California*, American Elsevier, New York.

Wilson, Carroll, and Matthews, W.H., 1970, *Man's Impact on the Global Environment: Report of the Study of Critical Environmental Problems (SCEP)*, MIT Press, Cambridge, Massachusetts.

Wilson, Edward O., 1975, *Sociobiology: The New Synthesis*, Harvard University Press, Cambridge, Massachusetts.

——1976, 'Sociobiology: A new approach to understanding the basis of human nature', *New Scientist*, 13th May.

Wilsson, Lars, 1968, *My Beaver Colony*, Doubleday, New York.

Wintrebert, P., 1963, *Le Développement du Vivant par Lui-même*, Vol. 1, Masson et Cie, Paris.

Wittgenstein, Ludwig, 1921, *Logisch-philosophische Abhandlung*, ('Tractatus Logico-Philosophicus'), Unesma, Leipzig.

Woodburn, James, 'An introduction to Hadza ecology', in Lee and DeVore, eds., 1968, *Man the Hunter*.

Woodger, J.H., 1967 (original edition 1929), *Biological Principles: A Critical Study*, Routledge and Kegan Paul, London.

Wordsworth, William, 'Prospectus to The Recluse', in Roger Sharrock, ed., 1958, *Selected Poems of William Wordsworth*, Heinemann, Oxford.

World Bank, 1981, *Accelerated Development in Sub-Saharan Agriculture: An Agenda for Action*, (A K A 'Berg Report'), Washington, D.C.

——1987, *1987 Annual Meetings of the Boards of Governors: Summary Proceedings*, Washington, D.C.

Worster, Donald, 1994 (original edition 1977), *Nature's Economy: A History of Ecological Ideas*, 2nd Edition, Cambridge University Press, New York.

Wurmstedt, Robert, 1977, 'The American underclass', *Time Magazine*, 29th August.

WWAP, 2003, *The World Water Development Report 1: Water for People, Water for Life*, United Nations World Water Assessment Programme, UNESCO, Paris.

Wynn Davies, Patricia, 1994, 'Howard gives ground on the roots of crime', *The Indepenedent*, London, 27th April.

Wynne-Edwards, V.C., 1962, *Animal Dispersion in Relation to Social Behaviour*, Oliver Boyd, Edinburgh.

——1964, 'Population control in animals', *Scientific American*, 211, August.

Yellowlees, W.W., 1979, 'Ill fares the land: The James MacKenzie lecture, 1978', *Journal of the Royal College of General Practitioners*, 29.

Yoffee, Norman, and Cowgill, George L., eds., 1988, *The Collapse of Ancient States and Civilizations*, University of Arizona Press, Tucson.

Zuckerman, S., 1932, *The Social Life of Monkeys and Apes*, Kegan Paul Trench Trubner, London.

——Address to the UN Conference on the Environment, Stockholm, June 1972.

OTHER WORKS MENTIONED IN THE TEXT

Æneid by Virgil, p. 156
An Essay on the Principle of Population by Thomas Malthus (1798), p. 270
Atlas of World Cultures by D.H. Price (1990), p. 420
Avestas (Iranian sacred texts), p. 389
Chaga Childhood by O.F. Raum (1940), p. 371
Cybernetics by Norbert Wiener (1948), p. 461
Dialogue Concerning the Two Chief World Systems by Galileo Galilei (1632), p. 461
Enoch (Book of), p. 390
Ethnologue by the Summer Institute of Linguistics, p. 420
Études de la Nature by Bernardin de Saint-Pierre (1784), p. 247
Hymn to Earth (Vedas), p. 388
Isaiah (Book of), p. 385, 390
Meditations on First Philosophy by René Descartes (1641), p. 461
Midrash Tanhuma (Rabbinic texts), p. 343
Novum Organum by Francis Bacon (1620), p. 82, 461
Origin and Development of the Moral Ideas by Edvard Westermarck (1906), p. 196
Philosophiæ Naturalis Principia Mathematica by Isaac Newton (1687), p. 461
Plant Communities by Eugenius Warming (1895), p. 461
Psalms (Book of), p. 390
Rigveda (Vedas), p. 341
Tanakh (Hebrew Bible), p. 390
The Course in Positive Philosophy by Auguste Comte (1842), p. 461
The Day America Told the Truth by James Pattison & Peter Kim (1991), p. 312
The Golden Bough by James Frazer (1890), p. 397
The New Atlantis by Francis Bacon (1627), p. 331
The Odyssey by Homer, pp. 386–7
The Prince by Niccolò Machiavelli (1532), p. 461
The Wealth of Nations by Adam Smith (1776), p. 87, 461
Theoretical Biology by Ludwig von Bertalanffy (1932), p. 461
Traité de L'Homme Machine by Julien La Mettrie (1747), p. 220, 461
Traité de Mécanique Analytique by Joseph Louis Lagrange (1788), p. 70, 220
Traité de Mécanique Céleste by Pierre-Simon Laplace (1799), p. 70, 220
Travels in the Moghul Empire by François Bernier (1670), p. 230
Vedas (Hindu texts), p. 388, 391
Works and Days by Hesiod, p. 326
Worlds in Collision by Immanuel Velikovsky (1950), p. 91

* For a list of *journals* mentioned in the text, see the Subject Index, p. 560

NOTES

Bibliographical references

Letters refer to opening quotations
*Indicates a direct translation

INTRODUCTION
1. Baillie et alia 2004, pp. 41–2
2. Vitousek et alia 1986, pp. 368–73
3. *see* DoT 1989
4. Leggett 1992, pp. 28–33
5. Banks 1963, entry 15th May 1770

CHAPTER 1
a. Muller 1956, p. 107
b. Woodger, *cit.* Bertalanffy 1962, p. 63
c. Polanyi 1978, p. 57
d. Goodwin, *cit.* Clark & Yiangou 1990
1. Adams 1913, pp. 5–6
2. Simberloff *in* Saarinen 1982, p. 73
3. Bodenheimer *in* Bodenheimer 1957, pp. 75–90
4. Pirie 1969, p. 331
5. Barbour 1971, p. 52
6. Passmore 1978, p. 53
7. Rutherford, *cit.* Passmore 1978, p. 53
8. Crick 1966, p. 10
9. Koyré 1965, p. 23
10. Tansley, *cit.* Worster 1994, p. 301
11. Gleason 1926, pp. 7–26
12. Gleason 1917, pp. 463–81
13. Gleason, *cit.* Barbour et alia 1980, p. 22
14. McIntosh 1975, p. 253
15. Colinvaux, *cit.* McIntosh *in* Saarinen 1982, p. 15
16. Curtis 1959, p. 510
17. Whittaker 1967, pp. 207–64
18. Köhler 1947, p. 29
19. Bertalanffy 1967, p. 62
20. Passmore 1978, p. 53
21. Odum 1983, p. 7
22. Thorpe, *cit.* Chaitanya 1972, p. 200

CHAPTER 2
a. Medawar & Medawar 1977, p. 11
b. von Brücke, *cit.* Granit 1966, p. 54
c. Thompson 1992, p. 5
d. Lovelock 2000, p. 32
e. Lovelock 1979, p. 12

1. Granit 1977, p. 7
2. Fuller & Putnam 1966, pp. 99–112
3. Granit 1977, pp. 18–19
4. Lovelock *in* Thompson 1987, pp. 90–1
5. Gerard, *cit.* Herrick 1961, p. 351
6. Huxley 1953, p. 7
7. Simpson 1950, p. 52
8. Calow 1976, pp. 13–14
9. Merrell 1981, p. 18
10. Pittendrigh *in* Roe & Simpson 1958, p. 393
11. Calow 1976, pp. 13–14
12. Atlan 1979, p. 21*
13. Grassé 1973, p. 216*

CHAPTER 3
a. Oatley 1978, p. 227
b. White 1979, pp. 72–6
1. Driesch 1908, pp. 59–63
2. Apter 1966, p. 41
3. Weiss 1973, p. 75
4. Odum 1989, p. 31
5. Zuckerman 1932, pp. 215–47
6. Clark 2002, pp. 84–7
7. Oatley 1978, p. 158
8. Chaitanya 1976, p. 214

CHAPTER 4
a. Pasteur, *cit.* Selye 1984, p. 301*
b. Woodger 1967, p. 441
c. Herrick, *cit.* Chaitanya 1972, p. 38
1. Marsh 1864, pp. 108–9
2. Dubos 1967, pp. 163–95
3. Lynn Margulis, personal communication
4. Dubos 1967, pp. 163–95
5. Pasteur, *cit.* Selye 1984, p. 301
6. Day 1929, p. 95
7. Sumich & Morrissey 2004, p. 211

CHAPTER 5
a. Wheeler (in Mehra) 1973, pp. 202–47
b. Aquinas, *cit.* Fernando 1991, p. 220
c. Cornford 1957, p. 14
d. Richard St Barbe Baker, unpublished papers

e. Odum 1983, p. 2
1. Ashby 1957, p. 130
2. Boyle, *cit.* Mason 1956, p. 136
3. Prigogine & Stengers 1979, p. 193
4. Prigogine & Stengers 1979, p. 64
5. Morin 1980, p. 105

CHAPTER 6
a. Durkheim & Mauss 1963, p. 43
b. Whitehead 1932, p. 245
c. Kuhn 1970, p. 5
1. Shelford, *cit.* Saarinen 1982, p. 74
2. Tansley 1935, pp. 299–303
3. Odum 1953, pp. 192–3
4. Eugene Odum, personal communication
5. Moore 1920, pp. 4–5
6. Woodger 1967, p. 22
7. Ackoff 1963, pp. 117–22
8. Craik, *cit.* Granit 1977, p. 19
9. Ackoff 1963, pp. 117–22
10. Whitehead 1932, p. 129
11. Georgesçu-Roegen 1972, pp. 13–18
12. Daly & Cobb 1989, p. 37
13. Dobzhansky *in* Ayala & Dobzhansky 1974, p. 310
14. *see* Roux 1891

CHAPTER 7
a. Empedocles (*in* Fairbanks) 1898, p. 199
b. Wordsworth 1958, p. 32
c. Roszak 1972, p. 161
1. Heller, *cit.* Worster 1994, p. 89
2. Thoreau, *cit.* Heller, *cit.* Worster 1994, p. 78
3. Tillich, *cit.* Chaitanya 1972, p. 29
4. Darwin 1896, p. 285
5. Trivers 1976 (*in* Dawkins), p. vi
6. Ruse 1985, pp. 204–6
7. Wilson 1975, pp. 562–4
8. Waddington 1975, p. 36
9. Lorenz 1997, pp. 12–19
10. Piaget, *cit.* Skolimowski *in* Ayala & Dobzhansky 1974, p. 221

CHAPTER 8
a. Locke 1801, p. 9
b. Medawar 1969, p. 26
c. Liedloff 1989b, pp. 17–19
1. Fantz 1961, pp. 66–72

2. *see* Tinbergen 1951
3. Fantz 1961, pp. 66–72
4. *see* Wilsson 1968

CHAPTER 9
a. Wittgenstein 1921, final sentence *
b. Laozi 1988, c. 1
c. Polanyi 1978, p. 130
d. Pólya 1954, p. 76
e. Zhuangzi 1974, p. 16
1. Polanyi 1978, p. 88
2. Koestler 1967, p. 287
3. Frankl *in* Koestler & Smythies 1972, p. 331
4. Polanyi 1978, p. 56
5. Tempels 1969, p. 120
6. von Humboldt, *cit.* Worster 1994, p. 136
7. Blyth 1950, p. 198
8. Fox 1984, pp. 194–200
9. Cobbett, *cit.* Gould 1974, p. 137
10. Weiss, *cit.* Chaitanya 1972, p. 30
11. Jeffers 1959, p. 594

CHAPTER 10
a. Ryle 1949, p. 58
b. Koestler 1967, p. 13
c. Feinberg 1967, pp. 126–34
d. Ackoff 1963, pp. 117–22
1. *see* Hume 1888 in general, & p. 157
2. Ryle 1949, p. 50
3. Watson, *cit.* Koestler 1967, p. 15
4. Tolman 1932, p. 2
5. Watson, *cit.* Koestler 1978, pp. 166–7
6. Lundberg, *cit.* Herrick 1961, p. 19
7. Watson, *cit.* Koestler 1978, p. 168
8. Hume 1888, p. 104
9. Hume 1888, p. 138
10. Popper 1983, c. 1.1
11. Polanyi 1978, p. 168
12. Popper 1973, p. 258
13. *see* Hodges 1981
14. Popper 1973, p. 259
15. Darwin, *cit.* Medawar 1982, p. 80
16. Darwin *in* Darwin & Seward 1903, p. 195
17. Medawar 1982, p. 88
18. Polanyi 1978, p. 167
19. Thorpe 1969, p. 9

CHAPTER 11

a. Weiss 1973, p. 37
b. Wallace 1956, p. 266
c. Rappaport 1979, p. 101
1. Horowitz 1956, pp. 78–90
2. Oatley 1978, p. 135
3. Head 1920, p. 669
4. Lashley 1960, pp. 511–15
5. Bartlett 1977, p. 197 & p. 213
6. Herrick 1961, p. 302 & pp. 403–4
7. Craik 1967, p. 61
8. Polanyi 1978, p. 74

CHAPTER 12

a. Planck 1949, pp. 33–4
b. Brown 1979, p. 151
c. Polanyi 1978, p. 271
1. Ravetz 1971, p. 150
2. Brown 1979, p. 23
3. Carnap 1936, pp. 419–71
4. Popper 1963, pp. 34–5
5. Koestler *in* Koestler et alia 1950, p. 60
6. Popper 1963, p. 256 & p. 37
7. Medawar 1982, p. 107
8. Popper, *cit.* Kuhn *in* Lakatos & Musgrave 1979, p. 14
9. Waddington 1977, pp. 121–2
10. Lakatos *in* Lakatos & Musgrave 1979, p. 119
11. Lakatos *in* Lakatos & Musgrave 1979, p. 132
12. Lakatos *in* Lakatos & Musgrave 1979, p. 179
13. Kuhn *in* Lakatos & Musgrave 1979, pp. 6–7
14. Watkins *in* Lakatos & Musgrave 1979, p. 27
15. Polanyi 1978, pp. 150–1
16. Wallace 1963, p. 161
17. Evans-Pritchard, *cit.* Polanyi 1978, p. 289
18. Polanyi 1978, p. 289
19. Polanyi 1978, p. 291
20. Polanyi 1978, p. 291
21. Polanyi 1978, p. 291
22. Evans-Pritchard, *cit.* Polanyi 1978, p. 287
23. Lakatos *in* Lakatos & Musgrave 1979, adapted from pp. 100–1
24. Polanyi 1978, p. 291
25. Polanyi 1978, p. 294

CHAPTER 13

a. Goethe 1996, p. 68
b. *see* Wanniski 1991
c. Gerard *in* Whyte et alia 1969, p. 219
d. Cameron 1963, p. 13
e. *see* Cummings 1954
1. Descates, *cit.* Randall 1940, pp. 241–2
2. Kline 1972, p. 217
3. Pantin 1968, p. 18
4. Weiss 1972b, *in* Koestler & Smythies, p. 48
5. Woodger 1967, p. 3
6. Singer, *cit.* Kothari & Mehta *in* Nandy 1988, p. 184
7. Orians *in* Dobben & Lowe-McConnell 1975, pp. 139–50
8. Merrell 1981, p. 422
9. Masterman *in* Lakatos & Musgrave 1979, pp. 59–89
10. Margalef *in* Dobben & Lowe-McConnell 1975, p. 151
11. Waddington *in* Koestler & Smythies 1972, p. 360
12. Putman & Wratten 1984, p. 11 & p. 79
13. O'Neill, *cit.* McIntosh *in* Saarinen 1982, p. 34
14. Putman & Wratten 1984, p. 69
15. McIntosh *in* Saarinen 1982, pp. 1–62
16. Polanyi 1978, c. 5
17. Robert Mann, personal communication

CHAPTER 14

a. Payer 1991, p. 25
b. Patten & Odum 1981, pp. 886–95
1. Nicholson, *cit.* Putman & Wratten 1984, pp. 224–5
2. Putman & Wratten 1984, p. 103
3. Putman & Wratten 1984, p. 104
4. Piaget 1968, pp. 61–87
5. Rappaport 1979, p. 98
6. Reichel-Dolmatoff 1977, pp. 4–11
7. Whitten 1978, pp. 836–59

CHAPTER 15

a. Ngawai, *cit.* Dewes (*in* King) 1975, pp. 58–9
1. Rappaport 1979, pp. 97–8
2. Bacon, *cit.* Bajaj *in* Nandy 1988, p. 44
3. Farrington, *cit.* Bajaj *in* Nandy 1988, p. 45

4. Worster 1994, p. 30
5. Nandy 1987, p. 118
6. Izutsu, *cit.* Nandy 1987, p. 118
7. Herrick 1961, adapted from pp. 334–5
8. Oatley 1978, p. 166
9. Asch 1955, pp. 31–5
10. Kuhn 1970, p. 118
11. Popper 1973, p. 109
12. Polanyi 1978, p. 295
13. Popper 1973, pp. 154–9
14. Whorf 1956, p. 58
15. Spengler, *cit.* Rifkin & Perlas 1983, p. 107

CHAPTER 16

a. Bernard, *cit.* Evans 1906, p. 245
b. Hume 1888, p. 415
c. Fromm 1974, p. 42
d. Berry 1970, p. 118
1. Darwin 1896, pp. 209–10
2. Worster 1994, p. 315
3. Polanyi 1978, p. 134
4. Carson 1962, p. 297
5. Bean, *cit.* Graham 1980, pp. 75–7
6. *see* Meadows & Meadows 1972
7. *see* Zuckerman 1972
8. Brown 1979, p. 162
9. Sagan 1995, p. 110
10. Koestler 1967, pp. 267–312
11. Freud, *cit.* Nandy 1983, p. 202
12. Nandy 1983, p. 202
13. Bettelheim, *cit.* Nandy 1983, p. 206
14. Césaire, *cit.* Nandy 1983, p. 206
15. Jungk, *cit.* Visvanathan *in* Nandy 1988, p. 131
16. Polanyi 1978, p. 134

CHAPTER 17

a. Augustine 1953, p. 115
b. Resurgence 1969, p. 8
c. Whitehead 1932, p. 20
d. Polanyi 1978, p. 266
1. Augustine, *cit.* Polanyi 1978, p. 266
2. Polanyi 1978, p. 266 & p. 286
3. Polanyi 1978, p. 312
4. Polanyi 1978, p. 266
5. Popper 1983, p. 38
6. Whitehead 1932, p. 23
7. Waddington 1975, p. 1
8. Kuhn 1970, pp. 136–7
9. Passmore 1978, p. 57

CHAPTER 18

a. Kropotkin 1924, p. 45
b. Radcliffe-Brown 1965, p. 130
c. Leopold 1953, pp. 224–5
1. Cornford 1957, p. 13
2. Hesiod, *cit.* Cornford 1957, p. 5
3. Cornford 1957, p. 6
4. Flew 1968, p. 59
5. Sprigge *in* Wallace & Walker 1970, p. 145
6. Lyons 1981, pp. 109–10
7. Huxley (T.H.) *in* Huxley & Huxley 1947, p. 82
8. Simpson, *cit.* Waddington 1960, p. 177
9. Jonas 1958, p. 250
10. Jonas 1958, p. 264
11. Monod, 1970, p. 220
12. Huxley (J.) *in* Huxley & Huxley 1947, p. 133
13. Needham 1969, pp. 144–5
14. Monod 1970, p. 220
15. Simpson 1950, p. 347
16. Simpson 1950, p. 308
17. Simpson 1950, p. 347
18. *see* Wynne-Edwards 1962
19. Simpson 1950, p. 306 & p. 345
20. Monod 1970, p. 220[*]
21. Huxley (J.) *in* Huxley & Huxley 1947, p. 126
22. Leopold 1953, p. viii
23. Gerard, *cit.* Worster 1994, p. 336

CHAPTER 19

a. Botkin 1990, p. 62
b. Marsh 1864, p. 27
c. Thorpe 1972b *in* Koestler & Smythies, p. 77
1. Darwin *in* Darwin 1888, p. 346
2. Simpson 1950, p. 212
3. Dobzhansky *in* Ayala & Dobzhansky 1974, p. 324
4. Thorpe 1972a *in* Koestler & Smythies, p. 393
5. Weiss 1972b *in* Koestler & Smythies, p. 46
6. Weiss 1972b *in* Koestler & Smythies, p. 46
7. Dobzhansky *in* Ayala & Dobzhansky 1974, pp. 322–4
8. Monod 1970, p. 159[*]

9. Waddington *in* Koestler & Smythies 1972, pp. 369–73
10. Monod 1970, p. 159
11. Bridges 1971, pp. 19–24
12. Dawkins 1989, pp. 17–18
13. Stanner *in* Hungerford 1956, p. 62
14. Odum 1983, p. 52
15. Orians *in* Dobben & Lowe-McConnell 1975, pp. 139–50
16. Holling *in* Jantsch & Waddington 1976, p. 81
17. Waddington *in* Jantsch & Waddington 1976, p. 246
18. Holling *in* Jantsch & Waddington 1976, p. 91

CHAPTER 20
a. Bernard 1878, p. 121*
b. Cannon 1932, p. 24
c. Audy *in* Shepard & McKinley 1971, p. 142
1. Bernard 1878, p. 113*
2. Frédéricq, *cit.* Cannon 1932, p. 21
3. Cannon 1932, p. 22
4. Cannon 1932, p. 22
5. Cannon 1932, p. 24
6. Cannon 1932, p. 23
7. Cannon 1932, p. 24
8. Cannon 1932, p. 25
9. Patten & Odum 1981, pp. 886–95
10. Rappaport 1967a, pp. 3–4
11. Reichel-Dolmatoff 1977, pp. 4–11
12. Harding (*in* Sahlins & Elman) 1960, p. 54
13. Patten & Odum 1981, pp. 886–95
14. Putman & Wratten 1984, p. 212
15. Patten & Odum 1981, pp. 886–95
16. Odum 1983, p. 46
17. Odum (H.), *cit.* Odum 1983, p. 49
18. Simberloff & Wilson 1969, pp. 278–90
19. Heatwole & Levins 1972, pp. 531–4
20. Putman & Wratten 1984, pp. 343–4
21. Weiss 1973, p. 52
22. Sagan & Margulis 1983, pp. 160–7
23. Lovelock 1979, p. 10

CHAPTER 21
a. Piaget 1974, p. 24
b. Waddington *in* Koestler & Smythies 1972, p. 366
1. Waddington 1975, p. 286
2. Orians *in* Dobben & Lowe-McConnell 1975, pp. 139–50

CHAPTER 22
a. Putman & Wratten 1984, p. 97
b. Odum 1983, p. 466
c. Inhelder *in* Koestler & Smythies 1972, p. 149
1. Piaget 1967, p. 36*
2. Piaget & Inhelder *in* Koestler & Smythies 1972, p. 145
3. Riedl 1978, p. 80 & pp. 104–5
4. Piaget & Inhelder *in* Koestler & Smythies 1972, p. 145
5. *see* Clements 1916
6. Worster 1994, p. 211
7. Gleason, *cit.* McIntosh 1975, p. 255
8. Tansley, *cit.* Worster 1994, pp. 240–2
9. Malin, *cit.* Worster 1994, p. 243
10. Malin, *cit.* Worster 1994, p. 243
11. Ricklefs 1973, p. 726
12. Putman & Wratten 1984, p. 97
13. Ricklefs 1973, p. 729
14. Putman & Wratten 1984, p. 100
15. Putman & Wratten 1984, p. 103
16. Putman & Wratten 1984, p. 101
17. Putman & Wratten 1984, pp. 102–3
18. Putman & Wratten 1984, pp. 103–4
19. Odum 1983, pp. 442–6 & p. 459
20. Odum 1975, p. 151
21. Odum 1975, p. 151
22. Odum 1975, pp. 150–1

CHAPTER 23
a. Rappaport 1967b, pp. 17–30
b. Reichel-Dolmatoff 1977, p. 7
1. Wynne-Edwards 1964, pp. 68–74
2. Wynne-Edwards 1964, pp. 68–74
3. Wynne-Edwards 1964, pp. 68–74
4. Mackewen 1989, pp. 8–16
5. Reichel-Dolmatoff 1977, pp. 4–11
6. Reichel-Dolmatoff 1977, pp. 4–11

CHAPTER 24
a. May 1974, p. 39
b. Weiss 1972a *in* Koestler & Smythies, p. 8
1. May 1974, pp. 37–78
2. Prigogine & Stengers 1979, pp. 178–9 & pp. 294–6*

3. May 1974, p. 49
4. May 1974, p. 173
5. May 1974, pp. 173–4

CHAPTER 25
a. Pimentel 1984, pp. 295–311
b. Altieri 1985, p. 106
1. Mooney 1979, p. 12
2. Merrell & Underhill 1956, pp. 300–6
3. Waddington 1975, p. 69
4. Jurion & Henry 1967, p. 45
5. Scott 1978, pp. 75–6
6. Altieri 1991, p. 94

CHAPTER 26
a. Russell 1976, p. 10
b. Medawar in Medawar & Medawar 1977, p. 167
c. Grassé 1973, p. 181*
1. Monod 1972, pp. 112–13
2. Huxley 1953, p. 39
3. Ramsay & Broadhurst 1968, pp. 299–304
4. Beer 1960, p. 13
5. Darwin 1872, p. 144
6. Waddington in Koestler & Smythies 1972, p. 370
7. Ho 2003, pp. 61–2, & Cairns et alia 1988, pp. 142–5
8. Ho 2003, pp. 61–2, & Hall 1990, pp. 5–16
9. Riedl 1978, p. 69
10. Waddington, cit. Koestler 1978, p. 173
11. Eden, cit. Waddington in Waddington 1969, Vol. 1, p. 111
12. Bernal 1969, p. 66
13. Berry 1987, pp. 3–4

CHAPTER 27
a. Simpson 1950, p. 101 & p. 179
b. Muller 1956, p. 109
1. Sherrington 1940, p. 104
2. Sherrington 1940, p. 98
3. Sherrington 1940, p. 98
4. Beer 1958, p. 16
5. Haan 1946, p. 50
6. Oatley 1978, p. 166
7. Stent, cit. Chaitanya 1975, p. 105
8. Monod, cit. Stent, cit. Chaitanya 1975, p. 105

CHAPTER 28
a. Tempels 1969, p. 51
b. Bertalanffy 1973, p. 106
c. Koestler 1976, p. 447 & p. 448
1. von Hoist, cit. Bertalanffy 1973, p. 106
2. Lorenz 1943, p. 252
3. Granit 1974, pp. 1372–87
4. Linton in Kardiner et alia 1945, pp. 47–100
5. Hardy, cit. Koestler 1967, p. 105

CHAPTER 29
a. Darwin 1909, p. 421
b. Herrick 1961, p. 60
1. Merrell 1981, p. 90
2. Merrell 1981, p. 89
3. Fisher, cit. Chaitanya 1975, p. 90
4. Bertalanffy in Koestler & Smythies 1972, p. 66
5. Woodger, cit. Reinheimer 1931, p. 84
6. Leder (in Leder et alia) 1994, p. 83
7. Ohno, cit. Grassé 1977, pp. 217–18

CHAPTER 30
a. McDougall 1999, p. 195
b. Price 1973, p. 179
c. Schweitzer, cit. Carson 1962, dedication
1. Johnson 1963, pp. 132–8
2. Kalmus 1967, p. 157
3. see Pavlov 1927
4. Hull 1952, p. 350
5. Young, cit. Dawkins 1989, p. 55
6. Dixon & Webb, cit. Thorpe 1965, p. 45
7. Dixon & Webb, cit. Thorpe 1965, p. 45
8. Waddington in Koestler & Smythies 1972, p. 381
9. Grassé 1973, p. 180
10. Ramnath 1988, pp. 223–4
11. Ramnath 1988, pp. 223–4

CHAPTER 31
a. Bentham 1823, p. 1
b. Oatley 1978, p. 116
1. Sherrington 1947, p. 7
2. Herrick 1961, pp. 253–4
3. Skinner, cit. Koestler 1978, p. 169
4. Skinner, cit. Koestler 1978, p. 169
5. Skinner, cit. Koestler 1978, p. 169

6. Skinner, *cit.* Koestler 1978, p. 169
7. Polanyi 1978, p. 371
8. Oatley 1978, p. 116
9. Herrick 1961, p. 358
10. Krechevsky, *cit.* Herrick 1961, pp. 358–9
11. Ellis, *cit.* Darwin 1909, p. 431
12. Lashley 1958, pp. 28–42
13. Knight 1859, p. 101

CHAPTER 32
a. Salt, *cit.* Kennedy 1924, p. 181
b. Harlow *in* Roe & Simpson 1958, p. 288
1. Herrick 1961, p. 364
2. Ashis Nandy, personal communication
3. Binet & Simon, *cit.* Chaitanya 1976, p. 230
4. Heim 1954, p. 29
5. Harlow, *cit.* Roe & Simpson 1958, pp. 269–90
6. Harlow, *cit.* Roe & Simpson 1958, pp. 269–90
7. Hingston 1928, p. 287
8. Hingston 1928, p. 283
9. Hingston 1928, pp. 283–4
10. Hingston 1928, p. 198
11. Hingston 1928, p. 284
12. Hingston 1928, p. 284
13. Hingston 1928, p. 285
14. Cuénot, *cit.* Piaget 1967, p. 66*
15. Piaget 1967, p. 66
16. Sherrington 1940, pp. 92–4
17. Ramón-y-Cajal, *cit.* Sherrington 1940, p. 108
18. Darwin 1872, p. 185

CHAPTER 33
a. Medawar *in* Medawar & Medawar 1977, p. 171
b. Thorpe 1965, p. 62
1. Jantsch 1980a, p. 308
2. Jantsch 1980a, p. 307
3. Jantsch 1980a, p. 307
4. Jantsch 1980a, p. 292 & p. 164
5. Herrick 1961, p. 289
6. Thorpe 1965, pp. 96–9
7. Huxley, *cit.* Thorpe 1965, pp. 62–3
8. Teilhard de Chardin 1999, pp. 216–17

CHAPTER 34
a. Patai 1947, p. 8
b. Harrison 1927, p. 533
c. Darwin 1871, p. 101
d. Seton 1922, p. 12
1. Patai 1947, p. 11
2. Frazer 1935, p. 16
3. Campbell, *cit.* Frazer 1935, p. 16
4. Sternberg, *cit.* Frazer 1935, p. 16
5. Cornford 1957, p. 78
6. Warren, *cit.* Frazer 1935, p. 17
7. Frazer 1935, p. 18
8. Darwin 1909, pp. 219–46
9. Darwin 1871, p. 193

CHAPTER 35
a. Russell 1959, p. 269
b. Tempels 1969, p. 120
c. Lovelock 1979, p. 9
1. Hughes 1983, pp. 54–60
2. Plato, *cit.* Hughes 1983, pp. 54–60
3. Hughes 1983, pp. 54–60
4. Morgan, *cit.* Worster 1994, p. 38
5. Leopold 1992, p. 95
6. Dobzhansky, *cit.* Thorpe 1965, p. 12
7. Monod & Jacob 1961, pp. 389–401
8. Jacob 1998, p. 109
9. Ricqlès *in* Noël 1979, pp. 65–6*
10. *see* Hutton 1788
11. Suess 1875, p. 159
12. *see* Vernadsky 1945
13. Lamarck, *cit.* Grinewald *in* Bunyard & Goldsmith 1988, pp. 1–12
14. Suess, *cit.* Grinewald *in* Bunyard & Goldsmith 1988, pp. 1–12
15. Vernadsky, *cit.* Jacques Grinewald, personal communication
16. Lovelock 1985, p. 52
17. Lovelock 1979, p. 10
18. Lovelock *in* Thompson 1987, p. 87
19. Lovelock *in* Thompson 1987, p. 87
20. Sagan & Margulis 1983, pp. 160–7
21. Lovelock 1979, p. 10
22. Lovelock 1979, p. 11

CHAPTER 36
a. Broad 1959, p. 409
b. Broad 1959, p. 406
c. Huxley (J.) *in* Huxley & Huxley 1947, p. 182
d. Bertalanffy 1952, p. 134

1. Woodger 1967, p. 300
2. Whorf 1956, pp. 57–64 & p. 213
3. Eliade 1959, pp. 73–4
4. Eliade 1959, p. 31
5. Gesell, *cit.* Sinnott 1961, pp. 62–4
6. Bergson, *cit.* Sinnott 1962, p. 37
7. Lumsden & Wilson 1981, p. 242
8. Sinnott 1961, p. 60
9. Sinnott 1961, p. 60

CHAPTER 37
a. Bethe, *cit.* Wach 1944, p. 68
b. Jung 1968, p. 143
c. Emmet 1953, p. 163
d. Liedloff 1989a, p. 38
1. Haeckel 1903, pp. 204–29
2. Pennisi 1997, p. 1435
3. MacLean, *cit.* Koestler 1967, pp. 277–8
4. Kenyatta 1979, p. 232
5. Hearn 1904, p. 38
6. Radcliffe-Brown 1965, p. 166
7. *see* Eliade 1959, c. 2
8. *see* Stanner 1956

CHAPTER 38
a. Fuller 1971, p. 18
b. Woodger 1967, p. 436
c. George (*in* Waubageshig) 1970, p. 184
1. Roszak 1972, p. 143
2. Berman 1981, p. 16
3. La Barre 1954, p. 283
4. Calow 1976, pp. 5–7
5. Woodger 1967, p. 264 & p. 441
6. Woodger 1967, p. 270
7. Woodger 1967, pp. 229–30
8. Polanyi 1978, p. 142
9. Worster 1994, p. 40
10. More, *cit.* Worster 1994, p. 42
11. Goethe, *cit.* Heller, *cit.* Worster 1994, p. 82
12. Wordsworth, *cit.* Stallknecht, *cit.* Worster 1994, p. 82
13. Driesch 1908, pp. 59–63
14. Driesch, *cit.* Sheldrake 1988, p. 82
15. Bergson 1981, p. 98
16. Bergson 1981, p. 42
17. Waddington 1960, p. 99
18. Schubert-Soldern 1962, p. 109
19. Needham 1936, p. 117

20. Lovelock 1988, p. 35
21. Lovelock 1991, p. 31

CHAPTER 39
a. Locke 1821, p. 223
b. Baker 1989, p. 38
c. John Aspinall, personal communication
d. Hopkins 1901, p. 231
1. Goldsmith & Hildyard 1984, pp. 135–66
2. Johnson (*in* Cahill) 1982, p. 106
3. Castle, *cit.* Sampson 1981, p. 82
4. *see* Simon 1996 in general, & p. 129
5. Medawar 1974, p. 133
6. Ward, *cit.* Worster 1994, p. 175
7. Bakeless 1977, pp. 247–9
8. World Food Programme, *cit.* Clwyd 1991, c. 997
9. Lee *in* Vayda 1969, pp. 47–79
10. Woodburn *in* Lee & DeVore 1968, p. 52
11. Park 1984, p. 5
12. Poncet & Brévedent, *cit.* Crawford, *cit.* Pollard 1981, pp. 21–31
13. Bowles *in* Ogot 1979, pp. 195–215
14. Bernier 1941, p. 437
15. Grey 1841, Vol. 2, p. 262
16. Post 1977, p. 276
17. Ch'ien-lung, *cit.* Toynbee 1935, p. 161
18. Crawford & Crawford 1972, p. 164
19. Katz & Young 1976, pp. 75–86
20. Katz & Young 1976, pp. 75–86
21. Salati & Vose 1984, pp. 129–38
22. Lovelock 1991, p. 183
23. Wilson & Matthews 1970, pp. 123–6
24. Drucker 1963, p. 3
25. National Academy of Sciences 1991, pp. 57–63
26. National Academy of Sciences 1991, pp. 442–57

CHAPTER 40
a. Riedl 1978, p. 1
b. Riedl 1978, p. 280 & p. 1
c. Radcliffe-Brown 1965, p. 167
d. Needham 1956, p. 581
e. Needham 1956, p. 558
1. Eliade 1971, pp. 55–6
2. Loeb 1916, p. 167 & pp. 153–4

3. Pittendrigh *in* Roe & Simpson 1958, p. 394
4. Bertalanffy 1962, p. 9
5. Weiss 1973, p. 25
6. Morin 1977, p. 78*

CHAPTER 41

a. Lovelock 1979, p. 10
b. Kraemer 1938, p. 151
c. Rolt 1947, p. 167
1. Jones 1946, pp. 1–10
2. Egerton 1973, p. 333
3. Forbes, *cit.* McIntosh *in* Saarinen 1982, p. 12
4. Allee et alia 1949, p. 728
5. Wallace, *cit.* McKinney 1966, pp. 345–6
6. Elton 1930, p. 17
7. Bernardin de Saint-Pierre 1808, p. 214
8. Passmore 1978, p. 65
9. Ortega y Gasset (*in* Klibansky & Paton) 1936, p. 313
10. Goldsmith 1978, pp. 108–9
11. *see* Goldsmith 2008

CHAPTER 42

a. LaChapelle 1988, p. 112
b. Pattee *in* Waddington 1969, Vol. 3, p. 120
c. Koestler *in* Koestler & Smythies 1972, p. 197
1. Hall & Fagen 1956, pp. 18–28
2. Koestler *in* Koestler & Smythies 1972, p. 197
3. Jantsch 1980b, p. 86
4. *see* Jantsch *in* Jantsch & Waddington 1976
5. Monod *in* Lichnerowicz et alia 1976, p. 34*
6. Bertalanffy 1973, p. 33, p. 38, & p. 55
7. Weiss 1971, p. 14
8. Bertalanffy 1973, p. 87
9. Bertalanffy 1962, pp. 184–5
10. Bertalanffy 1962, pp. 185–7
11. Odum 1983, pp. 3–4
12. Weiss, *cit.* Ayala & Dobzhansky 1974, p. 78
13. Koestler 1978, pp. 23–56
14. *see* Begon et alia 1990
15. *see* Whyte et alia 1969
16. *see* Pattee 1973

17. Macko & Mesarović *in* Whyte et alia 1969, p. 29
18. Grene *in* Whyte et alia 1969, p. 56
19. Koestler 1978, p. 34

CHAPTER 43

a. Whitehead 1927, p. 79
b. Whitman, *cit.* McDougall 1938, p. 151
1. Woodger 1967, p. 295
2. Patten & Odum 1981, pp. 886–95
3. Weiss 1973, p. 82
4. *see* Bernard 1878
5. *see* Sperry 1985
6. Popper & Eccles 1977, pp. 14–21
7. Weiss 1973, p. 52
8. Weiss 1972a, & Weiss 1972c *in* Koestler & Smythies, pp. 28–32 & pp. 379–80
9. Nisbet 1966, pp. 107–8
10. Chan 1963, p. 136

CHAPTER 44

a. Kropotkin 1907, p. 6
b. Whitehead 1932, p. 257
c. Odum 1983, p. 183
1. Worster 1994, p. 37
2. White, *cit.* Worster 1994, p. 7
3. Darwin, *cit.* Worster 1994, p. 156
4. Darwin, *cit.* Ospovat, p. 24.
5. Ospovat 1981, pp. 60–85
6. Warming, *cit.* Worster 1994, pp. 199–200
7. Pound, *cit.* Boucher 1985, p. 15
8. Worster 1994, pp. 326–9
9. Boucher & Risch, *cit.* Vandermeer 1980, pp. 441–8
10. Boucher & Risch 1976, p. 8
11. Boucher *in* Boucher 1985, pp. 5–6
12. Boucher et alia 1982, pp. 315–47
13. McNaughton 1979, pp. 691–703
14. Owen & Wiegert 1981, pp. 376–8
15. Mattson & Addy, *cit.* Owen & Wiegert, pp. 376–8
16. Boucher *in* Boucher 1985, p. 22
17. Janzen *in* Boucher 1985, p. 40
18. Boucher *in* Boucher 1985, p. 22

CHAPTER 45

a. Darwin 1987, p. 175
b. Huxley 1894, p. 200
c. Rockefeller, *cit.* Ghent 1902, p. 29

d. Shaw 1972, p. 316
e. Simberloff, *cit.* Augros & Stanciu 1987, pp. 89–90
1. Spencer 1871, pp. 352–4
2. Darwin 1872, p. 142
3. Kropotkin 1907, pp. 5–6
4. Boucher & Risch 1976, p. 9
5. Ricklefs 1973, p. 708
6. Putman & Wratten 1984, c. 6
7. Dawkins 1989, p. 131
8. Birch 1957, pp. 5–18
9. Merrell 1981, p. 425
10. Connell 1980, pp. 131–8
11. Price (*in* Price et alia) 1984, p. 354
12. Kormondy, Messenger, *cit.* Augros & Stanciu *in* Combs 1992, p. 126
13. Augros & Stanciu 1987, p. 158 & p. 93
14. Shaw, *cit.* Eibl-Eibesfeldt 1961, p. 116
15. Eibl-Eibesfeldt 1961, p. 119
16. Connor 2002, p. 3
17. Vayda *in* Bohannan 1967, p. 367
18. Murdock 1965, pp. 291–4
19. Hildyard 1976, pp. 320–6
20. Engels, *cit.* Worster 1994, p. 148

CHAPTER 46
a. Linnaeus, *cit.* Worster 1994, p. 38
b. Smuts 1926, p. 79
1. Cuénot 1941, pp. 240–1
2. Radcliffe-Brown 1965, p. 181
3. Bertalanffy 1962, p. 12
4. Ungerer, *cit.* Bertalanffy 1962, p. 12
5. Radcliffe-Brown 1965, p. 181, *see also* pp. 178–187
6. Radcliffe-Brown 1965, p. 186
7. Baskin 1997, pp. 28–38
8. Barnes (*in* Sloep & Blowers) 1996, p. 228
9. Putman & Wratten 1984, pp. 268–9
10. Odum 1983, p. 5
11. Monod 1972, pp. 85–6
12. Weiss, *cit.* Polanyi 1978, p. 338

CHAPTER 47
a. Ledeen 2003, pp. 212–3
b. Geertz 1976, p. 281
1. Boyden 1973, pp. 304–9
2. *see* Todd & Whitworth 1974
3. *see* Price 1939
4. Jonas et alia 2007, p. 265

CHAPTER 48
a. Odum 1983, pp. 222–3
b. Lovelock 1985, p. 53
c. Collis 1950, p. 127
1. McIntosh *in* Saarinen 1982, pp. 21–2
2. Odum 1983, p. 225 & p. 240
3. Washburn & Lancaster *in* Lee & DeVore 1968, p. 293
4. Wes Jackson, personal communication
5. Boyden 1973, pp. 304–9

CHAPTER 49
a. Driesch, *cit.* Bonner 1958, p. 59
b. Temples 1969, p. 103
c. Norberg-Hodge 1991, p. 73
1. Weiss 1972a *in* Koestler & Smythies, p. 36
2. Einstein, *cit.* Schillp 1959, p. 257
3. Ashmore, *cit.* Chaitanya 1972, p. 127
4. Weiss 1972a *in* Koestler & Smythies, p. 5
5. Waddington, *cit.* Chaitanya 1975, p. 207
6. Hamburger 1935, p. 67
7. Weiss 1972a *in* Koestler & Smythies, p. 38
8. Rapoport 1956, p. 307
9. Weiss 1973, p. 10
10. Waddington *in* Waddington 1969, Vol. 1, p. 30
11. Waddington 1960, p. 28
12. Waddington *in* Waddington 1969, Vol. 1, p. 30
13. *see* Liedloff 1989a
14. *see* Singh & Zing 1942
15. *see* Hodgkin 1983 in general, & p. 26

CHAPTER 50
a. Cohen 1989, p. 32
b. Yellowlees 1979, pp. 7–21
1. *see* Epstein 1978
2. Damon 1974, pp. 191–215
3. Prior et alia 1987, pp. 457–61
4. *see* Price 1939
5. *see* Cohen 1989
6. Katz & Young 1976, pp. 75–86
7. Midgley 1992, p. 20 & pp. 25–6

CHAPTER 51

a. Howard, *cit.* Wynn Davies 1994
b. Eliot 1939, p. 19
c. *see* Wurmstedt 1977
1. Banfield 1958, pp. 62–6
2. Seligman, *cit.* Lux 1990, p. 195
3. MacIver 1964, p. 84
4. Farley & Haaga 2005, p. 218
5. Martin & Kats 2003, pp. 3–31
6. Overend Prior & Gerard 2007, pp. 198–202
7. *see* Hebb 1949
8. Dalrymple 1991, pp. 9–10
9. Dalrymple 1991, pp. 9–10
10. Dalrymple 1991, pp. 9–10
11. Lewis 1966, Introduction
12. Latouche 1998, p. 99*
13. Latouche 1998, p. 99*
14. Latouche 1998, p. 99*
15. Latouche 1998, p. 105*
16. Dickey, *cit.* Lux 1990, p. 107
17. Pattison & Kim, *cit.* Tisdall 1991, p. 10
18. Sancton 1985, p. 109
19. *see* Economist 1970
20. *see* Branigin 1989
21. Police Journal 1991, p. 2
22. *see* Cloward & Ohlin 1961
23. Merton 1951, pp. 142–3
24. Durkheim 1966, p. 208

CHAPTER 52

a. Freud 1961, p. 44
b. Hall 1976, p. 5
c. Forster (*in* Forster) 1951, p. 91
1. Hall 1976, p. 5
2. Forrester 1971, pp. 4–9

CHAPTER 53

a. Monod 1972, pp. 172–3
b. Rolt 1947, p. 164
c. Koyré 1965, p. 23
d. Eliade 1959, p. 44
1. Frankl *in* Koestler & Smythies 1972, p. 400
2. Frankl *in* Koestler & Smythies 1972, pp. 398–9
3. Monod 1972, p. 31 & p. 180
4. Stent 1978, p. 127

CHAPTER 54

a. Polanyi 1957, p. 33
b. Skolimowski 1983, p. 22
c. Bender (*in* deMoll) 1977, p. 1
d. Paul Blau, personal communication
e. Lewis 1946, p. 42
f. National Geographic 1989, p. 766
1. Cornford 1957, p. 167
2. Reichel-Dolmatoff 1977, pp. 4–11
3. Reichel-Dolmatoff 1977, pp. 4–11
4. Douglas *in* Bohannan & Dalton 1962, pp. 211–33
5. de Garine, *cit.* Fischler 1990, p. 50
6. *see* Perrin 1979
7. Jean Liedloff, personal communication
8. Skolimowski 1983, pp. 14–15
9. Fernea 1970, p. 152
10. Voelcker, *cit.* Dogra 1983, pp. 84–5
11. Mollison, *cit.* Dogra 1983, p. 85
12. Mann 1990, pp. 48–53
13. Payer 1982, pp. 218–19
14. World Bank 1981, p. 35 & p. 12
15. Sharp, *cit.* Wallace 2003, pp. 100–3
16. Sachs, *cit.* McCully 1991, p. 249
17. Keyes, *cit.* Mathes & Gray 1975, pp. 119–25
18. Mathes & Gray 1975, pp. 119–25
19. McCully 1991, p. 249
20. Ravetz 1971, p. 63
21. Goldsmith 1976, pp. 646–7
22. Medawar 1974, p. 135
23. Nelkin *in* Daedalus 1978, pp. 191–210
24. Wasserman & Solomon 1982, pp. 208–12
25. Shapiro et alia, *cit.* Roszak 1972, pp. 239–40
26. Baltimore *in* Daedalus 1978, pp. 37–45
27. Chargaff, *cit.* Culliton *in* Daedalus 1978, pp. 147–56
28. *see* Cavalieri 1976
29. *see* Tenner 1996
30. Hobbs 1965, p. 129
31. *see* Los Angeles Times 2000
32. Valente (*in* Berentson) 1985 p. 316 & p. 315

CHAPTER 55

a. Le Corbusier 1931, p. 95
b. Burckhardt 1967, p. 39

c. trad. *in* Walker 1987, p. 147
1. *see* Plato
2. Stanner *in* Hungerford 1956, p. 58
3. *see* Yoffee & Cowgill 1988, and *see also* Tainter 1988
4. Wheeler 1959, pp. 112–13
5. Armelagos & McArdle 1976, pp. 179–82
6. Napton & Heizer 1970, pp. 87–129
7. *see* McNeill 1976 in general, & p. 62 & p. 69
8. Dubos 1970, pp. 12–15
9. Rapoport 1978, pp. 269–79
10. Krige 1936, pp. 39–53
11. Jaulin 1971, pp. 12–15
12. Stirling 1965, p. 26
13. McEwan & Sutcliffe 1967, pp. 42–3
14. Geist 1974, pp. 331–50
15. Dunbar 1996, pp. 69–77
16. Jaulin 1971, pp. 12–15
17. Lévi-Strauss 1992, pp. 220–1
18. Hildyard 1977, pp. 46–54
19. Blake, *cit.* Hildyard 1977, pp. 46–54
20. Mumford, *cit.* Dubos 1970, pp. 12–15
21. Katherine Goldsmith, personal communication
22. Coomaraswamy 1983, p. 8
23. Eliade 1959, p. 31
24. Plutarch, *cit.* Cornford 1957, p. 53
25. Coomaraswamy 1997, pp. 205–6
26. Coomaraswamy 1997, p. 208
27. Eiseman 1989, p. 5
28. Reichel-Dolmatoff 1978, pp. 5–27
29. Patai 1947, p. 116
30. Patai 1947, p. 114
31. Burckhardt 1995, p. 17
32. Burckhardt 1995, p. 19
33. Burckhardt 1995, p. 12

CHAPTER 56
a. Gossen, *cit.* Daly & Cobb 1989, p. 89
b. Morgan, *cit.* Faulkner 1951, p. 374
c. Polanyi 1957, p. 46
d. Daly & Cobb 1989, p. 164
1. Dalton 1961, pp. 5–6
2. Gerard *in* Whyte et alia 1969, p. 224
3. Gerard *in* Whyte et alia 1969, p. 224
4. Anaximander, *cit.* Cornford 1957, p. 8
5. Cornford 1957, p. 10
6. Nicholas Hildyard, personal communication

7. Hildebrand *in* Bunyard & Goldsmith 1988, pp. 186–236
8. WWAP 2003, pp. 10–11
9. King 1911, p. 48
10. Polanyi 1957, p. 46
11. Polanyi 1957, p. 46
12. Sahlins *in* Dalton 1971, pp. 43–61
13. Jean Liedloff, personal communication
14. Park, *cit.* Burton, *cit.* Polanyi *in* Polanyi 1968, p. 227
15. Sahlins 1960, pp. 390–416
16. Thurnwald, *cit.* Polanyi 1968, p. 21
17. Sahlins *in* Dalton 1971, pp. 43–61
18. Akpala 1972, pp. 291–301
19. Huber *in* Fisk 1978, pp. 158–79
20. Huber *in* Fisk 1978, p. 174
21. Kaberry 1939, p. 33
22. *see* Goldsmith 2008
23. Malinowski *in* Cattel et alia 1937, p. 232
24. Malinowski 1961, p. 167
25. Polanyi 1957, p. 57

CHAPTER 57
a. Bohannan *in* Dalton 1967, p. 135
b. Dalton *in* Dalton 1967, p. 255
c. IAITPTF & IWGIA 1996, p. 66
1. Armstrong 1924, pp. 423–9
2. *see* Mauss 1954
3. Malinowski 1961, pp. 81–104
4. Dalton 1967, p. 277
5. Douglas *in* Firth 1970, pp. 119–47

CHAPTER 58
a. Schweitzer 1949, p. 149
b. Gandhi 1967, p. 46
c. Gandhi 1967, p. 47
d. Keynes 1933, pp. 755–69
e. Daly & Cobb 1989, p. 234
1. Odum *in* Shepard & McKinley 1971, pp. 5–24
2. Malinowski 1961, p. 175
3. Polanyi 1957, p. 50
4. Rose 1942, pp. 51–5
5. Gandhi 1967, p. 1
6. Sunderlal Bahuguna, personal communication
7. Bohannan 1955, p. 60
8. Deuteronomy (King James Bible), 23:20

9. Sahlins 1972, p. 198
10. Korten 1994, pp. 8–13
11. Polanyi 1957, p. 43
12. Polanyi 1957, p. 72
13. Polanyi 1957, p. 160
14. Salaman 1949, p. 293
15. Hoy 1961, p. 9
16. Roht-Arriaza 1992, p. 7
17. Lux 1990, pp. 104–7
18. IIPS 2000, pp. 17–19
19. Adams & Solomon 1985, pp. 18–19
20. Schumacher 1966, pp. 8–13
21. see Gandhi 1967
22. Stokes & Wilson 2006, p. 81

CHAPTER 59
a. Mead in Middleton 1970, p. 1
b. Illich 1979, p. 35 & p. 44
1. U.S. Dept. of Health 1966
2. Coleman 1990, pp. 121–4
3. Raum in Middleton 1970, p. 93
4. Waddington 1975, pp. 285–286
5. Read in Middleton 1970, p. 275
6. Coleman 1967, p. 3 & p. 9

CHAPTER 60
a. Rummel 1997, pp. 396–403
b. Buckle 1862, p. 449
c. Galbraith 1967, p. 296
d. Jones 1983, p. 142
e. Tocqueville 2004, p. 67
1. Thatcher, cit. Keay 1987, p. 10
2. Hobbes 2002, p. 98 & p. 96
3. see Maine 1906 in general, &
    pp. 172–4
4. Maine 1906, pp. 373–4
5. Fustel de Coulanges 1927, p. 194*
6. see Morgan 1877
7. Lods 1932, p. 392
8. see Cohn & Morin 2008
9. see Tönnies 1955
10. Pappenheim, cit. Jones 1983,
     pp. 141–7
11. Rappaport (in Friedman &
     Rowlands) 1978, pp. 49–73
12. Goldsmith 1980, pp. 102–9
13. see Ecologist 1991
14. Heckman 1984, pp. 153–5
15. Clastres 1989, p. 200
16. Lowie 1920, pp. 358–9
17. Tylor, cit. Diamond 1974, p. 136

18. see Opler 1967
19. Diamond 1974, p. 142
20. Clastres 1974, p. 174, and Clastre
     1989, p. 205
21. Banfield 1958, pp. 83–92
22. Banfield 1958, pp. 155–6
23. Diamond 1974, p. 145
24. Popenoe 1991, pp. 65–77
25. McKnight 1978, pp. 112–14

CHAPTER 61
a. from the original Hebrew *
b. Laozi 1989, c. 46
c. Laozi 1972, adapted from c. 25
d. Harrison 1927, p. 527
1. Sheldrake 1988, pp. 150–4 & p. 243
2. Harrison 1927, p. 517
3. Harrison 1927, pp. 517–19 & p. 482
4. Anaximander, cit. Cornford
    1957, p. 8
5. Cornford 1957, p. 12
6. Homer, Herodotus, cit. Cornford
    1957, pp. 12–13
7. Pythagoras, cit. Iamblichus, cit.
    Cornford 1957, p. 54
8. Homer, cit. Harrison 1927, p. 532
9. de Groot, cit. Cornford 1957, p. 174
10. de Groot, cit. Cornford 1957, p. 174
11. Needham 1956, p. 45
12. Yu-lan, cit. Peerenboom 1991, p. 4
13. Yu-lan, cit. Peerenboom 1991, p. 5
14. Chan, cit. Peerenboom 1991, p. 5
15. Morenz 1973, p. 113
16. Morenz 1973, p. 114
17. Bloomfield, cit. Cornford 1957,
     p. 175 & p. 175
18. Chaitanya 1983, pp. 127–35
19. Chaitanya 1983, pp. 127–35
20. Hocart 1936, p. 139
21. Eiseman 1989, p. 12
22. de Groot, cit. Cornford 1957, p. 174
23. Harrison 1927, p. 526
24. Chantepie de la Saussaye, cit.
     Cornford 1957, p. 176
25. Murray 1991, p. 1
26. Murray 1991, p. 1
27. Murray 1991, p. 1
28. see Barker 1988
29. Murray 1992, p. xxii
30. Chaitanya 1983, pp. 127–35
31. Harrison 1927, pp. 533–4

32. Harrison 1927, p. xxi
33. Cornford 1957, p. 33
34. Cornford 1957, p. 33
35. Hughes 1983, pp. 54–60

CHAPTER 62
a. Tempels 1969, p. 175 & p. 46
b. Lawrence, cit. LaChapelle 1988, p. 116
c. Jonas 1985, p. 23
1. Cornford 1957, p. 32
2. Durkheim 1964, pp. 199–200
3. Durkheim 1964, p. 199
4. Lods 1932, p. 250
5. Tempels 1969, p. 46
6. Tempels 1969, p. 101 & p. 46
7. Tempels 1969, p. 175
8. Senghor in Ndaw 1983, p. 32
9. Codrington 1891, p. 119
10. Behnam 1977, p. 21
11. Brown 2007, pp. 2–3
12. Brown 2007, pp. 58–9
13. Cline, cit. Helms 1993, p. 21
14. Eliade, cit. Helms 1993, p. 21
15. Schebesta 1940, p. 64*
16. Linton in Kardiner et alia 1945, p. 63
17. Senghor in Ndaw 1983, p. 32*
18. Caillois 1950, p. 24*
19. Douglas, cit. Hildyard 1978, pp. 166–8
20. Metuh 1981, p. 57
21. Metuh 1981, p. 57
22. see Edwards 1996

CHAPTER 63
a. Baker 1989, p. 71
b. trad., cit. Helena Norberg-Hodge, personal communication
c. Eliade 1959, p. 99
d. trad. in Beversluis 1993, p. 153
e. Jeffers 1959, p. 640
1. Harrison 1928, p. 5
2. Hearn 1904, p. 37
3. Robertson Smith 1914, p. 29 & p. 30
4. Hearn 1904, p. 27
5. Driver 1961, p. 515
6. Du Bois in Kardiner et alia 1945, p. 167
7. Kuper 1963, p. 58
8. Harrison 1927, pp. 447–9

9. Pliny the Elder, cit. Hughes 1981, p. 13
10. Hughes 1981, p. 13
11. Parsons 1964, p. 176
12. Harrison 1927, p. 476
13. Roszak 1972, p. 127
14. Berdyaev 1949, p. 117

CHAPTER 64
a. trad. in Roberts & Amidon 1991, p. 95
b. Holbrook 1981, adapted from p. 336
c. see Baker 1956
1. Hughes 1983, pp. 54–60
2. Reichel-Dolmatoff 1977, pp. 4–11
3. Reichel-Dolmatoff 1977, pp. 4–11
4. Turner in Kiev 1967, pp. 230–63
5. Bastien (in Bastien & Donahue) 1981, pp. 19–37
6. Bastien (in Bastien & Donahue) 1981, pp. 19–37
7. World Bank 1987, p. 14
8. Hope 1996, p. 60
9. Derman in Barker 1984, p. 88
10. Schoepf in Barker 1984, p. 285
11. see Thatcher 1989
12. F.A.O. 1981, p. v
13. see Brown & Wolf 1985

CHAPTER 65
a. Blake 1979, pp. 635–6
b. Roszak 1972, p. xix
c. Laozi 1972, adapted from c. 29
1. Medawar & Medawar 1977, p. 171
2. Jantsch 1980a, p. 279
3. Jantsch 1975, p. xvi
4. Russell 1982, p. 38
5. Russell 1982, p. 59
6. Russell 1982, p. 60
7. Russell 1982, p. 60
8. Russell 1982, p. 61
9. Russell 1982, p. 62
10. see Davis 2001
11. Krauss 1992, pp. 4–10
12. Odum 1983, pp. 215–20
13. Margalef 1963, pp. 371–2
14. Odum 1983, p. 473
15. Medawar 1974, pp. 126–7

CHAPTER 66
a. Mumford 1972, p. 179
b. Roszak 1972, p. 262

c. *see* Baker 1950

d. Collis 1950, p. 254

1. Stent 1978, pp. 95–113

2. Polanyi 1978, p. 293

3. Polanyi 1978, p. 151

4. *see* Sargant 1957

5. Cumont 1956, pp. 20–72

6. Wallace 1956, pp. 264–81

7. Wallace 1956, pp. 264–81

8. Taylor 1991, pp. 258–66, and *see* Taylor 2005

APPENDIX 1

1. Brillouin *in* Buckley 1968, p. 147

2. Koestler 1967, p. 198

3. Brillouin *in* Buckley 1968, p. 149 & p. 152

4. Waddington *in* Jantsch & Waddington 1976, p. 244

5. Mason 1956, p. 404

6. Brillouin *in* Buckley 1968, p. 155

7. Georgesçu-Roegen 1971, p. 138

8. Brillouin *in* Buckley 1968, p. 147

9. Brillouin *in* Buckley 1968, p. 150

10. Brillouin *in* Buckley 1968, p. 150

11. Georgesçu-Roegen 1971, p. 7

12. Braham 1973, p. 21

13. Braham 1973, p. 21

14. Braham 1973, p. 21

APPENDIX 2

1. Rogers & Kincaid 1981, pp. 34–5

2. Shannon & Weaver 1962, p. 106 & p. 103

3. Shannon & Weaver 1962, p. 102

4. Shannon & Weaver 1962, p. 99

5. Shannon & Weaver 1962, p. 103

6. Apter 1966, p. 80

7. Rapoport 1956, p. 306

8. MacKay *in* Northrop & Livingstone 1964, p. 173

9. Waddington 1975, p. 216

10. Waddington 1975, p. 215

11. Dancoff & Quastler *in* Quastler 1953, pp. 263–73

12. Dancoff & Quastler *in* Quastler 1953, p. 263 & p. 270

13. Waddington 1975, p. 214

14. Margalef 1958, pp. 36–71

15. Waddington 1975, p. 214

16. Rapoport 1956, p. 307

APPENDIX 3

1. Hume 1888, p. 469

2. Roszak 1969, pp. 205–38

3. Worster 1994, p. 336

4. Waddington 1960, p. 54

5. Wilson 1976, p. 345

APPENDIX 4

1. *see* Wintrebert 1963

2. Weismann 1889, pp. 431–4

3. Koestler 1978, p. 197

4. Haldane, *cit.* Koestler 1978, p. 198

5. Commoner 1964, pp. 365–88

6. Grassé 1977, pp. 217–18

7. Baldwin 1896, pp. 441–51 & pp. 536–53

8. Goldschmidt 1935, pp. 38–131

9. Waddington 1975, pp. 59–92 & p. 33

10. Schmalhausen, *cit.* Waddington 1975, p. 75 & p. 96

11. *see* Piaget 1980

12. *see* Steele et alia 1998, & Ho 2003, pp. 64–7

13. Spadafora et alia 2006, pp. 1239–46

14. Ho 2003, pp. 55–6 & pp. 70–119

15. Richards 2006, pp. 395–401

APPENDIX 6

1. Unknown artist 1892, p. 17

2. Necker 1832, adapted from p. 336

GLOSSARY

1. *see* Apffel-Marglin 1998

2. *see* Oyama et alia 2001

3. *see* Liedloff 1989a

4. *see* Goldsmith (*in* Mander & Goldsmith) 1996, c. 22

5. *see* Rummel 1975

6. *see* Sonnenschein & Soto 1999

7. *see* Illich 1979

8. *see* Illich 1981

9. Drack & Apfalter 2007, pp. 537–46

10. Illich 1979, pp. 105–16

11. Darwin 1872, p. 470

12. *see* Wallace 2003

13. *see* Illich 1979

14. Nicholson 1970, p. 325

15. *see* Kurzweil 2005

16. Young, *cit.* OED 1989, 'teleonomy'

17. OED 1989, 'evil'

18. *see* Kornhauser 1998

19. *see* Illich 1981

20. Murdock & White 1969, pp. 329–69

21. Bodley 2008, pp. 1–2

22. Grönbech 1932, pp. 127–74 &
    Chaney 1970, pp. 12–17, and p. 55

23. OED 1989, 'good'

NAME INDEX

SUBJECT INDEX

Bold digits refer to major entries
Italic digits refer to Glossary entries
Page–ranges may indicate either
continuous or multiple entries

The Subject Index has been organised
taxonomically:

» for named entries, see under: *deities,
diseases, governments, groups, journals,
NGOs, peoples, places, pollution, religions,
species, verse,* and *worldviews*
» for theories and philosophies named
after their originators (*e.g.* Cartesian,
Copernican, Newtonian), see also
Name Index
» for related subjects, see under:
*agriculture, anomie, biosphere, culture,
Darwinism, economics, ecosystems,
families, genetics, knowledge, science,
technology, Way, etc.*
» for the most general subjects, see the
Contents and Glossary

Lightning Source UK Ltd.
Milton Keynes UK
UKOW01f0850130916

282876UK00001B/23/P